Advances in Manufacturing Technology – XXII

Proceedings of the 6th International Conference on Manufacturing Research (ICMR2008)

Brunel University, UK

9th - 11th September 2008

Edited by
Professor Kai Cheng, Dr. Harris Makatsoris and Professor David Harrison

Volume II

About the Editors

Professor Kai Cheng holds the chair professorship in Manufacturing Systems at Brunel University. His current research interests focus on micro manufacturing, design of precision machines and instruments, and digital manufacturing and enterprise technologies. Professor Cheng has published over 160 papers in learned international journals and referred conferences, authored/edited 5 books and contributed 6 book chapters. Professor Cheng is a fellow of the IET and a member of the IMechE and Euspen. He is the head of the Advanced Manufacturing and Enterprise Engineering (AMEE) Department which incldes 9 academics and over 30 research assistants and PhD students. The department is currently working on a number of research projects funded by the EPSRC, EU Programs, KTP Programs, DTI, and the industry. Professor Cheng is the European editor of the International Journal of Advanced Manufacturing Technology and a member of the editorial board of the International Journal of Machine Tools and Manufacture.

Dr Harris Makatsoris is the research coordinator for the Advanced Manufacturing and Enterprise Engineering (AMEE) subject area and Lecturer in manufacturing and engineering systems at Brunel University. He is the co-founder and co-director of the Brunel UIRC "The London Institute for Enterprise Performance, Sustainability and Systems". He is also Honorary Research Fellow at the Chemical Engineering Department of Imperial College and a member of Brunel's Centre for the Analysis of Risk and Optimisation Modelling Applications (CARISMA). He leads an interdisciplinary research team comprising engineers, and physicists undertaking research in bottom up computational nanotechnology, evolvable process design, manufacturing and enterprise systems and robotics. His research is currently funded by the EPSRC research council. His research interests include artificial intelligence, multi-scaled materials modelling, computer aided engineering, control, automation and robotics. He is a Chartered Engineer and a Member of IMechE. He has a first degree in Mechanical Engineering from Imperial College London. He also holds a PhD in Computer Aided Systems Engineering from the Mechanical Engineering department of Imperial College. Following completion of his PhD he worked as a Research Associate for three years in the same department. During that time he led a research team in a £6m EU project relating to the development of a pioneering distributed optimisation and control system for ASIC manufacturing and employed evolutionary programming optimisation technology. He has eleven years overall work experience in academic R&D and also in commercial software product development in the area of artificial intelligence, systems modelling, optimisation and control. He has established a university spin out Software Company in the UK in which he is still the Technical Director. He was also involved in the set up of a semiconductor wafer recycling company based in Germany. In addition he is the non executive director in a European IT services company. He has authored 35 papers in journal publications, peer-reviewed conferences and book chapters and one book.

Professor David Harrison is currently Head of Design within the School of Engineering and Design, and his research interests are in sustainable design and printed electronics. Over the past decade he has lead a number of research projects inspired by the goals of environmentally sensitive design. These projects include the application of offset lithographic printing to the manufacture of electronics. New manufacturing processes arising from this project have been successfully patented and licensed. He has also worked on the development of the concept of "Active Disassembly", where by features are designed into products to permit them to disassemble at end of product life, facilitating recycling. He is a Director of a spin out company, Active Fasteners, set up to commercialise this work. Other recent projects supervised include work on ecological footprinting of products, eco innovation, and tools to calculate ecologically optimum product lifetimes.

Preface

The Consortium of UK University Manufacturing Engineering Heads (COMEH)

The Consortium is an independent body and was established at a meeting held at Loughborough University on 17 February 1978. Its main aim is to promote manufacturing engineering education, training, and research. To achieve this the Consortium maintains a close liaison with those Government Departments and other bodies concerned with the initial/continuing education and training of professional engineers, while also responding to appropriate consultative and discussion documents and other initiatives. It organizes and supports national manufacturing engineering education research conferences and symposia. COMEH is represented on the Engineering Professors' Council (EPC). The Consortium consists of heads of those university departments or sections whose first priority is to manufacturing engineering and who have a direct responsibility for running honours degree courses in the field of manufacturing engineering. Currently there are about seventy members of COMEH.

COMEH decided in 1984 that a national forum was needed in which the latest research work in the field of manufacturing engineering and manufacturing management could be disseminated and discussed. The result of this initiative was that an annual series of these national conferences on manufacturing research (NCMR) was started, the first NCMR being held at the University of Nottingham in 1985. The first ICMR (ICMR 2003) built upon the NCMR series of conferences and was held at the University of Strathclyde in 2003. The subsequent NCMR/ICMR conferences have been held as follows:

1986	Napier
1987	Nottingham
1988	Sheffield
1989	Huddersfield
1990	Strathclyde
1991	Hatfield
1992	University of Central England
1993	Bath
1994	Loughborough
1995	De Montfort
1996	Bath
1997	Glasgow Caledonian
1998	Derby
1999	Bath
2000	University of East London
2001	Cardiff
2002	Leeds Metropolitan
ICMR 2003	Strathclyde
ICMR 2004	Sheffield Hallam
ICMR 2005	Cranfield
ICMR 2006	Liverpool John Moores
ICMR 2007	De Montfort
ICMR 2008	Brunel

Table of Contents

Session - Advanced Manufacturing Technologies

Session - Advanced Manufacturing Systems

Session - Extended Manufacturing Enterprises: Systems and Tools

Session - Micro/Nano and Precision Manufacturing

Volume II

Session - Product-Service Systems (PSS)

Session - Design and Manufacturing Simulations

Session - E-Manufacture

Session - Manufacturing Supply Chains

Session - Cost Engineering

Session - Computer Aided Engineering (CAE)

Session - Product Life Cycle Management

Product-Service Systems (PSS)

The 6th International Conference on Manufacturing Research (ICMR08)
Brunel University, UK, 9-11th September 2008

STANDARDIZATION WITHIN THE SERVICE CREATION PROCESS IN VALUE GENERATING NETWORKS

H. Meier, R. Krings, U. Kaiser

Chair of Production Systems, Ruhr-University Bochum

Abstract

One of the most important arguments for the successful disposal of industrial product service systems (ips²) is the higher availability of production machines for the customer guaranteed by the machine manufacturer. Machines are constructed with the focus on sustainable design to enable service technicians to reduce machine downtimes to a minimum. Beside methods existing for the design process of hardware components as one part of industrial product service systems, methods for the configuration and implementation of product accompanying services have to be developed to fulfill the customer's demands best possible considering his specific boundary conditions. To reduce complexity within service creation processes and assure continuous information flow throughout the whole service provision, a service creation framework is needed.

Keywords: industrial product service system, process simulation, service creation system.

1.0   Introduction

The manufacturing industry is undergoing a paradigm shift throughout the last couple of years. As was customary to concentrate mostly on producing and selling material goods for instance machines or production plants, today's business is strongly influenced by product accompanying services as the immaterial part of industrial product service systems. Justified by the focus on customer use, these product accompanying services like maintenance, teleservice or spare part provision are constantly gaining importance in business today. [1] Especially services of the utilization phase are important for the availability of the plant and the satisfaction of the customer. On the one hand a lot of companies are enabled to keep or even strengthen their position on the global market by the provision of services. On the other hand also the opening of new fields of business gets into companies focus. [2] Beside individual solutions in production plants, customers need services that empower them to run these plants with the optimum level of performance over the whole plant lifecycle [3]. Therefore products have to be designed as systems with a high level of sustainability. With existing methods and procedures within the creation process of material goods customer individual solutions can be included in the products. According to the rising importance of industrial services, the industry is forced to improve the development and commercialization of the latter. Regarding that the immanent characteristics of services strongly differ from those of products, methods and procedures have to be found to advance the standardization of service design and provision. [4] An approach to optimize the availability of industrial plants by a standardized workflow with product accompanying services was developed by the Chair of Production Systems. Therefore the concept of a service process library (SPL) was set up within the joined project Ogemo.net (Optimum Business Models for Product Service Systems in Cooperative Time Value Networks), which enables participants of value generating networks to decrease the complexity of service creation processes. It also reduces the sources of error in service provision especially for services which influence the availability. While the service process library can be used in several tasks of a holistic lifecycle-oriented business model [5], the greatest benefit in many value generating networks is caused by faster processes in unscheduled breakdowns of the plant.

2.0   Requirements for the Service Process Library

In general every member of a network knows his own processes. But most of the processes regarding an industrial product service system are provided by a network of several companies. With this in mind there is the question on how to adjust the own as well as the unknown foreign process parts to gain an efficient and effective over-all process. The solution defined by the three exemplary value generating networks of the project considers all inputs and requirements for a SPL, intending the reduction of sources of error and the increase of process speed. Each network consists of one system supplier, one original equipment manufacturer (OEM) and one user respectively the customer. For an optimum provision of service in a manufacturing network, information flow in every part of the service process has to be assured. Continuous information flow inside a company is necessary to enable fast and efficient processes. Interfaces between different departments cause a loss of information which in many cases leads to an expensive waste of plant production time. Looking at manufacturing networks this problem gets worse because information flow over company borders is more difficult and the amount of time to search for missing information is even higher. Providing the users with a framework that assures information flow within service processes inside a company and over company borders can be defined as the first requirement for the SPL. This framework can be given by reference processes consisting of process modules – as placeholder for detailed process models – connected by fixed input and output information providing the continuous information flow. A sample for the connection of the process outputs (indexed with "O") with the inputs of the next process module (indexed with "I") is shown in figure 1. The aim is to create no output information that is not needed in one of the latter process modules but also not to have a lack of information in a later process module that could have been easily generated in an earlier step. In an optimum over-all process there are only 1:1 connections between all process modules.

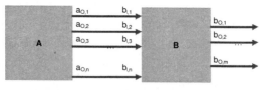

$$(a_{O,1}, a_{O,2}, a_{O,3}, ..., a_{O,n}) = (b_{I,1}, b_{I,2}, b_{I,3}, ..., b_{I,n})$$

Fig. 1.   Module in- and output connection in a reference process

STANDARDIZATION WITHIN THE SERVICE CREATION PROCESS IN VALUE GENERATING NETWORKS

If there are major changes during the life cycle of a plant, the offered services have to change, too. For example, if the warranty of a plant provided by the OEM has expired, service could change from a full service contract including spare part exchange to a simple plant repair or spare part delivery by order. To execute such changes of services, within the SPL exchanges of service processes have to be possible by keeping relevant data like customer or plant specific information. This second requirement shows the necessity of a database structured solution, which enables users to store additional data into a service process. A software tool is needed comprehending process visualization and the data storage. Another important aspect of any cross-company activity is data security. Company specific information about times or costs stored as additional information in a process for instance used for cost calculation, must not be available for other companies in the network. The required information for a continuous process flow over company borders has to be separated from company specific information. This segregation of data implies the third requirement for the SPL in form of a two layer structure (Fig. 2).

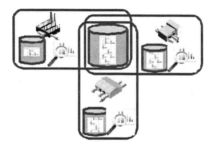

Fig. 2.   Two layer structured database usage.

On the first layer companies have to have the possibilities to create or store their own processes including all necessary data to calculate their costs and the availability of their resources. Furthermore the second layer is used to define the information that is needed or can be provided at process interfaces. With growing service offers of companies, the aspired solution in form of the SPL presupposes a sustainable design as the fourth requirement, whereas company's service offer grows by time. New markets are opened offering new services or offering actual provision of services in other countries as the ongoing trend of globalization shows. [6] Therefore the SPL needs to be expandable; additional and alternative process modules for instance for factoring or delivery in reference to different countries with differing customs regulations have to be storable and exchangeable.

3.0   Industrial Services in the Lifecycle

To set up the SPL, significant services already provided in each network were needed. The actual situation in the provision process had to be analyzed and optimized to build up reference processes as best practice examples for further use as frameworks in the SPL. To find adequate processes for the SPL, a survey was set up within the joined project about actual service provision and service usage. Overall 86 industrial services could have been identified and clustered into four phases along the product lifecycle. Additionaly, the amount of services in the particular phase is given in figure 3.

**STANDARDIZATION WITHIN THE SERVICE CREATION PROCESS IN VALUE GENERATING
NETWORKS**

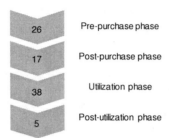

26	Pre-purchase phase
17	Post-purchase phase
38	Utilization phase
5	Post-utilization phase

Fig. 3.   Distribution of common services in the product lifecycle.

- Pre-purchase phase: In this phase the customer is searching for a product accompanying service which fits his particular demands. Common services in this stage are problem analysis, all kind of planning operations, cost calculations, feasibility studies and further more.
- Post-purchase phase: After the customer, the later user of the plant, has signed the contract, the selected OEM starts his manufacturing processes. Typical services of this phase are software engineering or education of the operating workers. At the end of this stage the plant is delivered, mounted and implemented.
- Utilization phase: During the usage of the plant the whole network from supplier to user is bound together in order to maintain the availability. Widely offered services are spare part delivery, preventive maintenance and repair. For this purpose there are three business models in which the responsibility for the output of the plant is different.
- Post-utilization phase: The end of a plant lifecycle can be set back by modernization measures but in the follow up phase a company wants to get rid of the used plant. When there is no one to trade-in and overhaul it, the plant has to be scrapped and recycled. In this phase often not network members but third party specialists are called in.

With most services provided throughout the utilization phase, those were pointed out for the following analysis in the networks of the joined research project and the integration into the SPL.The customer in the first network is running two interlinked molding presses. If malfunctions appear in one part of the press, the whole production plant is affected and 50% of the companies' productivity will be missing. For plants with this complexity the information flow among the user and the OEM is distinctive. Very long time cooperation between user and OEM is characteristic because of the long time usage of molding presses. The situation in the second network is similar. Seamless rolled steel is produced on different sized plants. Since plant downtime in the second network is caused mostly because of failure of standard components, a stronger integration of the supplier into the service process exists. Due to the continuous workload in both networks, the displacement of the production during a plant downtime to another plant is not possible. This causes the importance of maintaining services because high plant availability is required by the customers to run their production in an efficient way. Looking at the seven classified types of industrial services defined within the scope of the collaborative research project SFB Transregio 29, three types of services were found to be of special interest for the industrial partners. These seven types of services are: [7]

1.   planning services
2.   counseling services
3.   training services
4.   logistic services
5.   function creating services

STANDARDIZATION WITHIN THE SERVICE CREATION PROCESS IN VALUE GENERATING NETWORKS

6.   function maintaining services

7.   optimizing services

4.0   Reference Processes and Module Design

With the focus on the customer use and his demand for an optimum performance and a high availability of his plants over the whole lifecycle, logistic, function maintaining and optimizing services were pointed out to be the most important types of services providing the customer with high plant availability during the utilization phase. Beside maintenance and plant modernization an unexpected plant malfunction was chosen to be one of the most significant scenarios for further analysis and optimization. In the following, this scenario will be used to explain the use of the SPL exemplarily. Within the scenario of an unexpected plant malfunction, the user is interested in a fast repair of the plant which can be provided with short reaction times by the own maintenance department or by service technicians of the OEM or the system supplier. Fault investigation and repair are also included in this scenario as well as hotline services and spare part delivery services. After defining the scenario, the actual processes in each network were recorded and needed to be visualized. Fulfilling the defined requirements for the SPL, the process modeling method of the event-driven process chain consisting of functions, events, information flow and process responsible organizational units as a part of the software ARIS was chosen. [Figure 4]

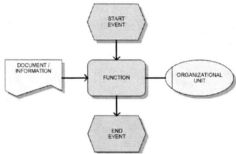

Fig. 4.   Event-driven process chain objects in ARIS.

The three processes of the different networks displayed the same scenario solved in differint ways corresponding to the network individual boundary conditions. To generate processes that fulfill all requirements for the integration into the SPL, reference processes had to be found consisting of process modules as a framework for new process design. The comparison of the recorded network processes resulted in one reference process shown in Fig. 5.

The coding of the three network process for the unexpected plant malfunction is to interpret as following:

A   fault investigation

(A)   further problem

B   fault investigation with OEM/supplier

C   spare part needed

STANDARDIZATION WITHIN THE SERVICE CREATION PROCESS IN VALUE GENERATING NETWORKS

535

D   spare part OEM

E   spare part supplier

F   repair OEM

G   repair supplier

H   assembly

I   accounting

X   delivery

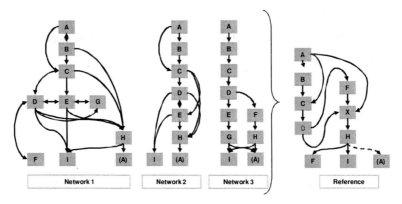

Fig. 5   Compilation of network processes to one reference process.

As shown in figure 3 the reference process is build up with a certain level of aggregation. Similar modules like the fault investigation are adapted to the reference process. Modules with different process owners like fault investigation with the OEM or the supplier, are compiled to one process owner neutral module to offer a leaner process for module redesign. When the network is up to design a new service process, the framework given by a reference process can be used as a guideline. First of all the process owners of the single modules have to be defined to fill the modules with necessary information and to create the module output as input for further modules. [Figure 6]

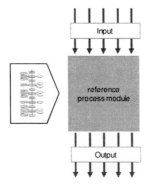

Fig. 6.   In- and output definition by process owner data.

STANDARDIZATION WITHIN THE SERVICE CREATION PROCESS IN VALUE GENERATING NETWORKS

Determining module output and input in this stage of the design reduces problems within the service process due to missing information or data. Using the two layer structure allows the provision of the module input and output by the process owner to other involved companies without uncovering details and internal information of his process.

5.0   Future Prospects

With this methods the three value generating networks aim to reduce their process costs and increase the customers' satisfaction. For this terms especially the fast reaction to unscheduled breakdowns of the plant is an important criterion.

An upcoming problem to be solved in the joined project is the implementation of the described concept into a software solution including the described two layer structure. First steps of this concept were initiated by using ARIS. The final solution should be open to different process modeling methods which are adaptable to the existing software tools used in the industry. Still in the phase of conception, a server-client structure is needed to integrate the network members into the process design procedure by using the two layer structure. The main focus here is the definition of so called visibility lines in the server-client structure. All network members need to gain access to all information about the module input and output, the module interfaces and the reference process frameworks. Access to critical company specific data must be denied.

6.0   Conclusion

Presently the service development is suffering from a lack of adequate tools and methods for improving the standardization of the service processes. Being in line with the approach of the Chair of Production Systems originated in the joint project Ogemo.net, first steps have been created for a structured way to design processes according to the reference process restrictions. By enabling networks to work with this method, on the one hand the provision of customer individual solutions can be advanced. On the other hand the modules offer support for the service creation. Especially in time-critical services of the plant utilization phase a saving of time and money can be achieved.

Acknowledgement

The approaches and concepts described are contents of the joined project "Optimum Business Models for Product Service Systems in Cooperative Time Value Networks" (Ogemo.net). The project is financially supported by the German Federal Ministry of Education and Research (BMBF) within the framework of "Forschung für die Produktion von morgen" and supervised by the project executing organization Karlsruhe, field of production (PTKA-PFT).

References

[1]   Arai, T., Shimomura, Y., 2005, Service CAD System - Evaluation and Quantification; Annals of the CIRP, Vol. 54/1, pp 463-466.

[2]   Bullinger, H.-J., Entwicklung innovativer Dienstleistungen, in: Bullinger, H.-J. (Hrsg.), 1999, Dienstleistungen – Innovation für Wachstum und Beschäftigung, Gabler Verlag Wiesbaden, ISBN-Nr. 3-409-11466-1.

[3]   Aurich, J. C., Fuchs, C., 2004, An Approach to Life Cycle Oriented Technical Service Design; Annals of the CIRP, Vol. 53/1, pp 151-154.

[4]   Luczak, H., Gill, C., Sander, B., The Design and Development of Industrial Service Work, in: Spath, D., Fähnrich, K.-P. (Hrsg.), 2007, Advances in Services Innovations, Springer Berlin Heidelberg New York, ISBN-Nr. 10 3-540-29858-4.

[5]   Meier, H., Kaiser, U., Krings, R., Service as enabler for lifecycle-oriented business models. Proceeding of the 15th CIRP Conference on Life Cycle Engineering, Sydney, Australia, 2008.

[6]   Kreibich, R., Internationalisierung und Globalisierung von Dienstleistungen, in: Bullinger, H.-J. (Hrsg.), 1995, Dienstleistung der Zukunft, Gabler Verlag Wiesbaden, ISBN-Nr. 3-409-88196-4.

[7]   Kortmann, D., 2007, Dienstleistungsgestaltung innerhalb hybrider Leistungsbündel, Schriftenreihe des Lehrstuhls für Produktionssysteme, Shaker Verlag Aachen, ISBN-Nr. 978-3-8322-6622-6.

The 6th International Conference on Manufacturing Research (ICMR08)
Brunel University, UK, 9-11th September 2008

DIFFERENCES IN FORECASTING APPROACHES BETWEEN PRODUCT FIRMS AND PRODUCT-SERVICE SYSTEMS (PSS)

Dr Rebecca De Coster

School of Engineering and Design, Brunel University r.decoster@brunel.ac.uk

Abstract

This paper examines the forecasting implications for Product-Service Systems (PSS) applications in manufacturing firms. The approach taken is to identify the scope of operations for PSS applications by identifying all the activities associated with the total cost of ownership (TCO). The paper then develops a revenue model for manufacturing firms providing PSS applications. The revenue model identifies three generic revenue streams that provide the basis for discussion on the differences in forecasting approaches between product firms and Product-Service Systems (PSS) in manufacturing firms.

The forecasting approaches are different due to the nature of customer involvement in the service aspect of PSS applications. This necessitates an understanding of the customer service experience and the factors affecting this such as the service profit chain which links profitability, customer loyalty and service value to employee satisfaction, capability and productivity.

The forecasting approaches identified raises forecasting challenges for each of the three generic revenue sources. These challenges vary from the difficulty in obtaining the service user's viewpoint through to difficulties in determining market acceptance of PSS applications.

Keywords: forecasting, total cost of ownership, Product-Service Systems (PSS), revenue model.

1.0   Introduction

As technology becomes more common, competition may shift away from technology to other areas [1]. One alternative approach is the scenario where equipment is leased rather than purchased – either by service providers or end users. This approach is known as the Product-Service Systems (PSS) where the focus changes to providing utility to consumers through the use of services rather than products [2]. The PSS enables equipment providers to have a much closer relationship with the users of their equipment. This knowledge can provide a firm with competitive intelligence that should enable the firm to maintain a competitive advantage [1].

The difficulty with a move to PSS is that the timescales in which the forecasts can be proved to be valid are lengthy. This may cause forecasting difficulties in terms of market research amongst the service end users [3] but also organisational forecasting problems [4] amongst the equipment/service providers who are unused to this business approach. Resistance to adopting new financial forecasts is likely to occur until such a time that field trials enable forecasts to be evaluated [4].

2.0   The Scope Of Operations For PSS Applications

The scope of operations for PSS applications will be examined by identifying all the activities associated with the total cost of ownership (TCO) as shown in Fig 1. This represents the users' perspective for owning and using equipment and enables identification of the total expenditure on equipment over the lifetime of a purchase. For a user of traditional electronic consumer product the majority of cost is at the initial purchase with little necessity to spend money on upgrades or maintenance, for example, TVs or Hi-Fis. For consumers, the Internet era has led to a world where devices are increasingly connected to other devices or access networks. Upgrades are sought by consumers so that additional uses of the product are supported – these form an important source or revenue for businesses.

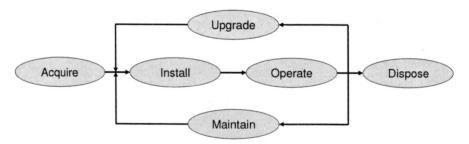

Fig. 1.   The activities associated with total cost of ownership (TCO).

**DIFFERENCES IN FORECASTING APPROACHES BETWEEN PRODUCT FIRMS AND
PRODUCT-SERVICE SYSTEMS (PSS)**

2.1 Provision of Operations for PSS Applications

Having established the scope of activities this paper will now examine the implications to the manufacturing firm which is supplying equipment for PSS applications. At a generic level a manufacturing firm supplying equipment for PSS applications will be incurring costs in order to provide the necessary functions for the TCO activities (shown in Fig. 1). The main cost elements comprise: capital investment; manufacturing activities; logistics activities and customer lifecycle support. Thus, the expenditure on these activities is a mixture of traditional product based activities plus the associated support activities for PSS applications. Forecasting approaches will need to account for both of these types of activities otherwise the planning process will neglect resourcing the support activities. For example, marketing activities are required by manufacturing firms providing PSS applications to promote and support the launching of upgrades and new product features [5].

The additional expenditure on services for the provision of PSS applications has the benefit that manufacturing firms will be working more closely with their end users and hence, get greater insights to their needs [6]. This can become the basis for competitive advantage as markets become global companies look to differentiate themselves from their competitors (to avoid losing market share or having to reduce prices and hence, margins). The ability to differentiate from competitors can only be based on greater market knowledge [7].

2.2 Organisational Implications

Competitive advantage based on core competencies has become a recognised part of strategic thinking [8] and [9]. Within Nokia *the generic strategy decisions to determine whether new products fall within the core or context competencies of the firm are subject to continuous evaluation*" [10]. The development of the necessary competences (technological or otherwise) of a firm involves accessing external knowledge as well as relying on internal knowledge building activities.

Establishing business relationships with external partners is increasingly necessary to meet market requirements; however, business processes are context dependent [11] which makes it more challenging to provide PSS applications using business partnerships. A review of the ability of organizations to innovate and successfully achieve technological and organizational change [12] highlighted the complexity involved of knowledge transfer across organisations.

3.0 Key Components of the Revenue Model for PSS Firms

The revenue model describes the main ways in which a firm will generate its revenues. The revenue model for a manufacturing firm which is supplying equipment for PSS applications identifies three generic sources of revenue as shown in Fig. 2:

1. PSS contracts established between the manufacturing firm and the user of the equipment. In this case the users subscribe to a service and pay a negotiated fee to receive the service.

2. Product sales which may be for existing or new products for which assessing market potential is critical to get the greatest return on investment (ROI) for the development costs.

3. Bespoke (or custom development) of products or consulting services. Manufacturing firms may also provide turnkey solutions to meet the required functionality of the end users.

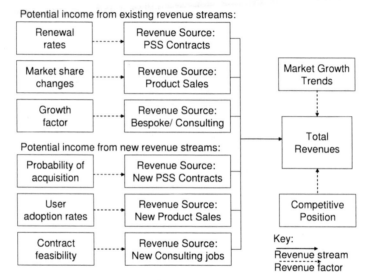

Fig. 2.   The revenue model for PSS firms

Each of the generic revenue sources will have different factors affecting the forecasting of future demand. Further, different forecasting methods are required to develop estimates as discussed in the next section.

4.0   Key Components of The Revenue Model for PSS Firms

The revenue model for a manufacturing firm which is supplying equipment for PSS applications (shown in Fig. 2) comprises three generic revenue sources. Forecasts will need to be established for each of the three generic revenue sources for the firm as summarised in Table 1 and discussed in the following sections.

Table I: Typology of Forecasting Challenges for PSS Applications

Revenue Source for PSS Applications		Forecasting Challenges
PSS Contract Revenues	Renewals	• Customer oriented perspective required internally • Measurement of the customer service experience
	New contracts	• Service benchmarking • Establishing the service profit chain
Product Sale Revenues	Established products	• Determining market growth trends • Estimating market share (based on competitive environment)
	New products	• Diffusion and market acceptance • Competitive pricing strategies
	New firms	• Segmenting demand • Price sensitivity
Bespoke/ Consultancy Revenues	Turnkey Solutions	• Historical analogy requires identifying previous deployment with similar growth patterns • Market acceptance may delay predicted take-up • Brand acceptance (for market share) is difficult to assess
	Extensions / Upgrades	• Cross-impact analysis requires identifying relationship between future upgrades and initial acquisitions

The forecasting approaches for PSS contracts are different to those usually used by manufacturing firms due to the nature of customer involvement in the service aspect of PSS applications. This necessitates an understanding of the customer service experience and the factors affecting this such as the service profit chain which links profitability, customer loyalty and service value to employee satisfaction, capability and productivity [13].

Other factors are common ones which affect all the revenue streams in the revenue model. For established manufacturing firms the development of forecasts requires establishing market growth trends and the firm's market share. Market share is dependent on a firm's competitive position and that of its products. The basis for competitive advantage will often change during the product lifecycle particularly when dominant design or technological regimes become established. Faster renewal of resources and products is achieved which is necessary to counter changes of markets, competitors and technological advancements.

4.1 PSS Contract Forecasts

Forecasting whether or not existing contracts will be renewed requires a very customer oriented perspective on behalf of the manufacturing firm who need to be very aware of the important factors for their users. The forecasting approach requires an analysis of customer satisfaction. This is necessitated by the increased customer expectations of quality in terms of the market requirements and the benchmark established by competitors including an efficient customer response [13].

Benchmarking metrics for products aimed at consumers (looking to satisfy individual needs) will have different factors than for innovations aimed at businesses that are looking for value-add [14]. Retention of existing contracts will need to consider the decision makers in the organizations who will be going through a decision making process which *"is made up of action-taking steps indicating how to make a decision"* [15].

DIFFERENCES IN FORECASTING APPROACHES BETWEEN PRODUCT FIRMS AND PRODUCT-SERVICE SYSTEMS (PSS)

Development of a qualitative reasoning model for financial forecasting for contract renewals can be based around a hierarchical model which identifies the main decision making components [16].

Forecasts for winning new PSS contracts will also be required. The competitive environment has been shown to have a significant influence on innovation adoption [17]. The forecasting challenges are establishing service benchmarking and the service profit chain [13] and [18].

4.2   Product Sales Forecasts

Forecasts for product sales could potentially make use of statistical methods (e.g. extrapolating historical data), however, *"organizations are shown to rely on judgemental methods far more than statistical"* [19]. For well established successful firms the monitoring of market share is crucial as that determines their earning potential in a given market place. Growing market share requires not only having a superior offering compared to competitors but also the anticipated user benefits need to be weighed against switching costs. Firms are under pressure to deploy applications quickly to gain advantages over competitors by being early to market. Following market deployment firms then obtain customer feedback to optimize the solution to provide what is really wanted for that scenario.

Any technology-based firm needs to not only develop the technological capability to provide technologically sophisticated products for the current innovation or technology, but also for the next innovation or technology. The greater challenge is to forecast product sales for new products. The disruptive nature of new technologies may potentially impact business structures, operations and their interaction with customers. Technological developments can cause erosion of a firm's technological lead thus; the management of technological innovation requires more than the successful innovation – there is the need for an ongoing stream of successive innovations.

The commercialization of new products requires forecasts to justify resources however; these forecasts can be problematic particularly when new markets are involved [20]. Four perspectives highlighted by [21] are the firm's strategy, company business (and the impact of new products), customers and competition and lastly, the technology perspective. The technology trajectory (the path a technology follows over time), will vary depending on a number of factors including diffusion [22] and the potential for performance improvements.

The successful commercialisation of products encompassing new technologies in the Internet era requires a high level of market sensing [6]. This refers to the ability of firms to anticipate the desires of customers and trends in markets. Product forecasts in the case of product substitution can be based on market sizes for the product that is being replaced [23]. New product failure can be due to a lack of competitive advantage – there needs to be sufficient "meaningful product uniqueness" [24]. Techniques used in practice were investigated during a study funded by the PDMA and were found to comprise: customer/ market research; jury of executive opinion; sales force composite method; looks-like analysis; trend line analysis; moving average and scenario analysis [20].

The hardest forecasts are forecasting product sales by new firms where there is a lack of established customer base or market presence. The risks are greater for new technology ventures because they have more dimensions of novelty than other new ventures. The technology trajectory (the path a technology follows over time), will vary depending on a number of factors including diffusion [22] and potential for performance improvements. Early work on factors affecting new product forecasting accuracy by new firms highlighted two sets of antecedent factors: firstly, the firm's founder and the use of marketing research data sources and methods and secondly, environmental factors [25].

4.3   Bespoke/ Consultancy Forecasts

Forecasts for bespoke or consultancy or custom work (such as turnkey solutions [26]) are likely to require a broader view of potential market value [27] and may utilize techniques of strategic foresight [28]. The ratio between product and service components in PSS applications varies [29] and is likely to have a higher service ratio for custom work [30]. Historical analogy may provide a basis for establishing forecasts providing that firms can identify a previous occurrence which is likely to have a comparable growth pattern.

Market acceptance may require identifying a lead customer with whom the technological solution is tested [31], and the accompanying issues of system integration resolved. However, PSS applications face internal and external barriers to uptake [32]. The competitive basis which may be a differentiation strategy based on relative product performance or some additional firm attributes, for example, brand. Forecasts for extensions/ upgrades can be based on cross-impact analysis whereby initial purchases are correlated to the likelihood of future upgrades.

5.0   Conclusion

The environmental pressures on manufacturers are increasing and this may drive a move towards PSS applications. The field of PSS literature is new and tools and techniques are not yet well established. This paper contributes by proposing methods and analytical models to better understand the issues of forecasting PSS applications. This paper reviews three generic revenue sources for PSS applications. The generic revenue source of PSS contracts uses literature from the field of service management which emphasizes the service user's perspective. It is argued here that customer satisfaction will be a key factor which determines the renewal rates of existing contracts. The generic revenue source of product sales contrasts the forecasting challenges for existing products vs. new products or even new firms where market sensing is a key attribute for firms. The generic revenue source of bespoke/ consulting work recognizes that historical analogy may provide a basis for identifying likely deployment patterns for a new technology against which contract feasibility must be assessed.

The present article, however, argues that a revenue model for PSS applications involves a combination of the three generic revenue sources each involving different forecasting approaches and challenges. Forecasts are the start of the planning process in firms and hence, drive the decision making concerning resources and equipment allocation. The recognition of forecasting approaches for PSS applications is still unclear and the aim is that this paper raises discussion of the approaches and associated issues.

References

[1] AD Lemos and AC Porto. Technological forecasting techniques and competitive intelligence: tools for improving the innovation process. *Journal of Industrial Management & Data Systems* 98 (7) pp. 330 – 337. 1998.

[2] OK Mont. Clarifying the concept of product–service system. *Journal of Cleaner Production* 10 pp. 237–245. 2002.

[3] P McBurney; S Parsons and J Green. Forecasting market demand for new telecommunications services: an introduction. *Journal of Telematics and Informatics* 19 (3) pp. 225-249. 2002.

[4] NR Sanders. Managing the forecasting function. *Journal of Industrial Management & Data Systems* 95 (4) pp. 12 – 18. 1995.

[5] JM Thölke; E Jan Hultink and H S J Robben . Launching new product features: a multiple case examination. *Journal of Product Innovation Management* 18 (1) pp. 3-14. 2001.

[6] JC Anderson and JA Narus. Business market management, Prentice-Hall, New Jersey. 1999.

[7] E Bigne. Competitive positioning and market orientation: two interrelated constructs. European Journal of Innovation Management (3) 4, pp. 190-198, 2000.

[8] SD Hunt SD. A general theory of competition: resources, competences, productivity, economic growth. Sage Publications. 1999.

[9] H Chesborough and R Rosenbloom. The dual-edged role of the business model in leveraging corporate technology investment cited in LM Branscomb and P Auerswald Taking technical risks MIT Press. 2001.

[10] Y Choi; K Kim and C Kim. An enterprise architecture framework for collaboration of virtual enterprise chains. *The International Journal of Advanced Manufacturing Technology.* 35 (11-12), pp. 1065-1078. 2008.

[11] M Gilbert and M Cordey-Hayes. Understanding the process of knowledge transfer to achieve successful technological innovation. *Technovation*, 16 (6), pp. 301-315. 1996.

[12] K Dittrich and G Duysters. Networking as a Means to Strategy Change: The Case of Open Innovation in Mobile Telephony. *Journal of Product Innovation Management*, 24 (6), pp. 510-521. 2007.

[13] JL Heskett; TO Jones; GW Loveman; WE Sasser Jr and LA Schlesinger. Putting the Service-Profit Chain to Work. Harvard Business Review, Mar/Apr94, Vol. 72 Issue 2, pp. 164-170.

[14] RL Day and PA Herbig. How the diffusion of industrial innovations is different from new retail products. *Industrial Marketing Management.* 1990.

[15] PC Nutt. Investigating the Success of Decision Making Processes. Journal of Management Studies 45 (2) pp. 425–455. 2008.

[16] Kesh and Raja. Development of a qualitative reasoning model for financial forecasting. *Information Management & Computer Security* 13 (2), pp. 167-179. 2005.

[17] RT Frambach; HG Barkema; B Nooteboom and M Wedel. Adoption of a service innovation in the business market: an empirical test of supply-side variables. *Journal of Business Research* 41, pp. 161–174. 1998.

[18] A Harrison, and R Van Hoek. International logistics: a supply chain approach. Financial Times/ Prentice Hall. 2001.

[19] NR Sanders. Managing the forecasting function. Journal of Industrial Management & Data Systems 95 (4) pp. 12 – 18. 1995.

[20] KB Kahn. An Exploratory Investigation of New Product Forecasting Practices. Journal of Product Innovation Management 19 (2), pp. 133–143. 2002.

[21] P Suomala and I Jokioinen. The patterns of success in product development: a case study. Journal of Innovation Management (6) 4, pp. 213- 227. 2003.

[22] R Kemp; J Schot and R Hoogma R. Regime shifts to sustainability through processes of niche formation: the approach of strategic niche management. *Technology Analysis and Strategic Management* 10 (2) pp.175-186. 1998.

[23] BC Twiss. Forecasting market size and market growth rates for new products. *Journal of Product Innovation Management*, (1) 1, pp. 19-29. 1984.

[24] G Stevens; J Burley and R Divine. Creativity + business discipline = higher profits faster from new product development - An MBTI(R) Research Compendium. *The Journal of Product Innovation Management* 16 (5) pp. 455-468. 1999.

[25] WB Gartner and RJ Thomas. Factors Affecting New Product Forecasting Accuracy in New Firms. *Journal of Product Innovation Management* 10 (1), pp. 35–52. 1993.

[26] N Morelli. Developing new product service systems (PSS): methodologies and operational tools. *Journal of Cleaner Production* (14) 17, pp. 1495 – 1501. 2006.

[27] A Tukker. Eight types of product–service system: eight ways to sustainability? Experiences from SusProNet. *Business Strategy and the Environment* (13) 4, pp. 246 – 260. 2004.

DIFFERENCES IN FORECASTING APPROACHES BETWEEN PRODUCT FIRMS AND PRODUCT-SERVICE SYSTEMS (PSS)

[28] K Cuhls. From forecasting to foresight processes - new participative foresight activities in Germany. *Journal of Forecasting* 22 (2-3) pp 93-111. 2003.

[29] N Morelli Designing product/service systems: a methodological exploration. *Design Issues* (18) 3, pp. 3-17. 2002.

[30] JC Aurich; C Fuchs and C Wagenknecht. Life cycle oriented design of technical product-service systems. Journal of Cleaner Production (14) 17, pp.1480-1494. 2006.

[31] N Franke; E von Hippel and M Schreier. Finding commercially attractive user innovations: a test of lead-user theory. *Journal of Product Innovation Management* 23 (4) pp. 299-389. 2006.

[32] OK Mont. Drivers and barriers for shifting towards more service-oriented businesses: Analysis of the PSS field and contributions from Sweden. *The Journal of Sustainable Product Design* (2) 3-4, pp. 89-103. 2002.

DIFFERENCES IN FORECASTING APPROACHES BETWEEN PRODUCT FIRMS AND PRODUCT-SERVICE SYSTEMS (PSS)

PRODUCT SERVICE SYSTEMS IN THE AUTOMOTIVE INDUSTRY: AN ALTERNATIVE BUSINESS MODEL FOR A SUSTAINABLE SATISFACTION SYSTEM

Carlo Vezzoli *[sections 2.0, 4.1 and 5.0]*, Fabrizio Ceschin *[sections 1.0, 3.0 and 4.2]*

Politecnico di Milano, INDACO Department, Research unit Design and system Innovation for Sustainability (DIS), via Durando 38/A, 20158 Milan, Italy

Abstract

The paper presents the intermediate results of an on-going research project called Vehicle Design Summit (VDS), run by an international Consortium of Universities coordinated by the MIT of Boston. The project aims at designing and prototyping an eco-efficient vehicle as well as defining an innovative and sustainable business model to introduce and diffuse it into the mobility sector. In this framework the paper explores the potential contribution that PSSs can have in moving beyond incremental technological improvements towards system innovation in the automotive industry. This is outlined presenting and discussing an alternative business model, characterized by: an approach to mobility as the scope of design; an innovative stakeholders network; a shift from selling products to selling results; a change in product ownership; and a consequent change in vehicle design.

Keywords: PSS, system innovation, design, sustainability, automotive industry, sustainable mobility.

1.0   Sustainable Mobility and the Vehicle Design Summit Consortium

Awareness of the environmental and social problems linked with mobility continues to grow. As a matter of fact it is a shared opinion that in the transition towards sustainable consumption and production patterns *mobility* is one of the priority area in which intervene to drastically reduce the use of resources per "unit of satisfaction" [1]-[2]. Several studies indicates four main unsustainable issues to focus on [4]-[5]: an high dependence on fossil resources and a consequent high level of environmental pollutant and damaging emissions; an increase in congestion levels; a lack in equity of access to mobility; and a still un-safety of transport, with high levels of injured people and fatalities. Mobility is deeply embedded in all aspects of life, and covers a wide range of activities (from people to goods transport), kinds of use (private and professional), and means of transport. In this sense it is obvious that mobility is characterized by a complex production and consumption chain involving different actors: private producers of vehicles, energy supplier, infrastructure building companies, private and public transport service companies, insurance companies, political authorities and users. Given the complexity of the socio-technical system it is clear that there is a broad-spectrum of strategies that can be adopted to steer mobility towards more sustainable solutions, that generally speaking go from the increase of access to (environmentally sustainable) transportation means for low-income communities, to the drastic reduction of inefficient use of private vehicles in industrialized countries, to the promotion of more sustainable collective modes of transport, to the improvement of the sustainability performance of all modes of transport [3]-[4].

Within the complexity of the mobility domain and within the broad-range of the potential interventions, the focus of the work is on people transport, and specifically on proposing innovative and sustainable Product Service System (PSS) solutions based on the use of cars. A narrow field of action that however could potentially bring to significant environmental and social improvements, if considered that currently cars collectively represent the largest single source of global air pollution, accounting for 30% of industrialized country emissions and 17% of CO_2 emissions [5].

In this perspective the paper presents the intermediate results of an on-going research project denominated Vehicle Design Summit (VDS), run by an international Consortium of universities coordinated by the Massachusetts Institute of Technology (MIT) of Boston. The Consortium's goal is to design and realize a low environmental impact vehicle as well as the definition of the conditions for its introduction into the market through innovative and sustainable "mobility offers". The final aim is to influence and re-orient the whole automotive sector towards the adoption of radically more sustainable *offer* modalities and consequent *production* strategies. Each university has got a team of students working on a technical, strategic or organizational task of the project. The role of Politecnico di Milano team[1] is to design an innovative and eco-efficient business model, as well as a transition path to introduce and diffuse this model into the market. The assumed hypothesis is that incremental technological improvements in the automotive industry is a necessary but not sufficient condition to reach radical environmental impact reduction, and that (product service) system innovations are needed. For this reason a system design approach has been adopted, integrating products and services as well as the related socio-economic stakeholders and the user, with the aim of fulfilling specific demands of satisfaction. In other words the approach focuses on designing the system of actors and the related interactions and partnerships, in order to make eco-efficient the delivered "mobility offer".

In this framework the first part of the text analysis why (product-service) system design approach may be considered an opportunity to develop new business strategies, to compete and generate value and social quality, and at the same time decreasing the total amount of resources consumption and emitted pollutants. The argumentation will then focus on the sustainability problems associated with the automotive industry. Finally, the text will present and discuss the elaborated hypothesis for an alternative business model for a sustainable automotive industry.

2.0   Designing Sustainable Product Service Systems

By most design researchers a more significant ambit in which to act to promote radical changes for sustainable consumption, is the widening possibilities for innovation beyond the product, towards innovation of the system

---

[1] The team is made up by the students Lorenzo Davoli, Francesca Fiocchi and Jun Lin, coordinated by Carlo Vezzoli and Fabrizio Ceschin (research unit Design and system Innovation for Sustainability, INDACO dept., Politecnico di Milano).

as an integrated mix of products and services that together lead to the satisfaction of a given demand for well-being [6]-[7]-[8]. In this sense PSS are shifting the centre of business from the design and sale of (physical) products alone to the offer of product and service systems that are together able to satisfy a particular demand. So when we talk about (product-service) system innovation, it is meant an innovation that involves all the different socio-economic stakeholders in this "satisfaction system". Furthermore, it is a shared opinion that these innovations could lead "to a system minimization of resources, as a consequence of innovative stakeholder interactions and related converging economic interests" [9]. Thus eco-efficient system innovation derives from a new convergence of interest between the different stakeholders: innovation not only at a product (or semi-finished) level, but above all as new forms of interaction/partnership between different stakeholders, belonging to a particular value chain, or "value constellation". In other terms, the research interest in this innovation model relies on the fact that it can raise system eco-efficiency through innovative stakeholders' interactions.

To understand in general terms why system innovation and innovative stakeholder interaction could be more eco-efficient compared to traditional product sales/design let's take as example the traditional offer of a washing machine. In this case the producer of the washing machine (but also of the detergent and the electricity) has an interest in reducing material and energy consumption during the production phase. On the contrary, he has no direct economic interest either in limiting consumption during use, or in reducing divestment impact and valorising the resulting waste. Sometimes the producer is even interested in selling products with a short life span, with the only aim of accelerating replacement. In other words it can be observed that the fragmentation of stakeholders in the various phases of a product's life cycle (in the traditional economic framework of industrialized countries), means that the eco-efficiency of the life cycle system usually does not coincide with the economic interests of the individual constituent stakeholders.

At this point proper questions are: which could be the incentives for companies to enhance the system eco-efficiency? In this sense innovative elements can be found in the stakeholder interactions and configuration that could be trans-phasal innovations (involving different phases of a product's life cycle), or trans-cyclic innovations (involving different product's life cycle in a satisfaction system)[10]. Without going into details, two helpful strategies are: a stakeholder integration (extension of control of a single actor in different life cycle phases different products and services within one satisfactory system); and an extension of the stakeholders interactions in time (more stakeholders extend their interaction within a given product life cycle or within PSS life cycles).

Thus eco-efficient system innovation derives from a new convergence of interest between the different stakeholders: innovation not only at a product (or semi-finished) level, but above all at configuration level, i.e. when setting up new forms of partnership/interaction between different stakeholders in a "satisfaction system". In this sense a (product service) system approach can "lead to a system minimisation of resources, as a consequence of innovative stakeholder's interactions and related converging economic interests". System innovation can be seen as a strategic innovation [11], a possible choice for companies to separate resource consumption from its traditional connection with profit and standard of living improvements; to find new profit centres, to compete and generate value and social quality while decreasing (directly or indirectly), total resource consumption. In other words, system innovation is potentially a win-win solution: winning for the producers/providers, the users and the environment.

The introduction of (product service) system innovation for eco-efficiency into design has led researchers to work on defining new skills of a more strategic nature, that aim at system eco-efficiency through the

PSS IN THE AUTOMOTIVE INDUSTRY: AN ALTERNATIVE BUSINESS MODEL FOR A SUSTAINABLE SATISFACTION SYSTEM

stakeholders' strategic convergence of interests, and are coherent with the "satisfaction-based", "multi-life-cycle" perspective. In synthesis, the main characteristics of the system design for eco-efficiency approach are: a *satisfactory approach* (*demand-satisfaction design*); a *stakeholder interaction approach* (*stakeholder's configuration design*); and a *system eco-efficiency approach* (*ecoefficient-oriented design*). In this perspective design activity should focus on [10]:

1) developing environmentally sustainable products and services together;
2) promoting and facilitating new configurations (partnership/interaction) between different stakeholders, to find innovative solutions able to lead to a convergence of economic, social and environmental interests;
3) promoting and facilitating new sustainable locally-based and network-structured initiatives/enterprises;
4) facilitating a participatory design process among all the stakeholders.

Nevertheless it has to be underlined that not every (product service) system innovation is eco-efficient [10]-[11], and therefore it is of key importance to adopt appropriate methods and tools, when designing new systems (with the potentialities to be radically sustainable), that would steer it towards a sustainable solution. For this reason, in terms of the development of new systems it is expedient to operate and adopt appropriate criteria and guidelines. The first design methods and tools that have been recently developed as outcomes of some European projects of the 5th Framework Programme, are PROSECCO (Product & Service Co-Design process), HiCS (Highly Costumerized Solutions) [12], and MEPSS (Method for PSS development) [11].

3.0   Sustainability and the Traditional Business Model in the Automotive Industry

The automotive industry is characterized by a business model in which vehicle manufacturers represent the pivotal actor, directing both component suppliers and the distribution and retailing system [13]; and their primarily source of profits is the sale of new vehicles. Within this model, vehicle producers, in order to increase profit margins, have adopted a strategy of mass production, that brought to high volume output and

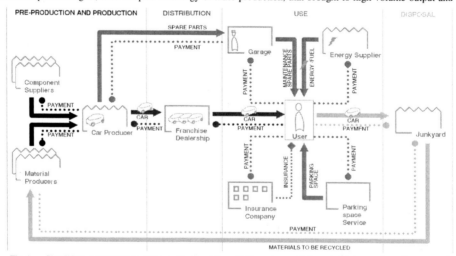

Fig. 1.   Simplified stakeholders system map visualizing all the actors and the related interactions (in terms of material, informational and financial flows), of the traditional business model in the automotive system.

**PSS IN THE AUTOMOTIVE INDUSTRY: AN ALTERNATIVE BUSINESS MODEL FOR A
SUSTAINABLE SATISFACTION SYSTEM**

high volume of sales to global market [14]. The main reason is that some of the production technologies necessary in the manufacture processes are high capital intensive, and therefore companies have to sell greater number of cars in order to recover the initial investments. In this sense there is an high break-even point that act as a barrier for the entry of new competitors into the market and moreover encourages the establishment of even larger global operation [15], and conservative design attitude. This is why is often less costly for a vehicle manufacturer to overproduce and oversupply newly produced cars than to cut back on manufacturing capacity [14]. In synthesis all these elements brought to a situation characterized by the presence of large centralized and conservative mass producers aimed at selling the higher amount of vehicles to global markets. From an economical point of view, return to capital are low, typically below 5% and often negative with periodic crisis [13]. The reason is that the overproduction lead companies to offer incentives in order to create increased demand, and therefore as result we have a continuous discounting of the price of new cars, and a consequent reducing in profit margins. What it has to be underlined is that vehicle producers earn their profits mainly from the cars sale and the spare parts sale, but they do not catch most of the earnings associated with the use of the vehicle. In fact, how illustrated in fig. 1, the automotive system of production and consumption is characterized by a variety of stakeholders, and the profit generated by cars in use go mainly to fuel companies, independent garages and insurance companies [16].

In the automotive production and consumption system, in terms of environmental sustainability, the main impact along the vehicle life cycle are [17]:

- in the use phase, cause of the several pollutants present in the emissions of the vast majority of cars (exhaust fumes from cars represent the biggest source of air pollution in half the world cities [18]);
- in the pre-production and production phases, cause of: high levels of energy, water and non-renewable materials (and the related emissions) used in the manufacturing processes; and cause of the use of some specific production processes like painting and metal finishing;
- in the distribution phase, cause of the logistic and distribution system required for global market sales;
- in the disposal phase, cause of the high waste flow at the end of cars' life (in the European Community end-of-life vehicles are responsible of between eight and nine millions tones of waste each year [19]).

In relation to these environmental impacts, it has to be underlined that there is a fragmentation of actors in the various phases of a product's life cycle (fig. 1), and this makes the eco-efficiency of the life cycle system not coincident with the economic interests of the individual stakeholders. To better understand this concept let's take in consideration the car producer. Of course it has the interest in reducing the amount of energy and material used in the production phase, with a convergence between economic interest and resources optimization. On the contrary, as it has been described before, the vehicle producer has got also the interest in selling the greater amount of vehicle (and therefore to accelerate its replacement), and a no direct interest in reducing consumption in use. In this sense the economic interest does not coincide with a resources minimization. In the same way fuel companies are economical interested in selling how much fuel they can, and garages have a direct interest in selling the higher quantity of spare parts. In other words, the biggest environmental problems do not appear within one given phase, when related to a single stakeholder (e.g. vehicle manufacturer). In terms of eco-efficiency, more problems arise in the so called "phase's transaction", during the sale or disposal of products (e.g. the sale of vehicles or the sale of fuel). Here can occur indifference towards reducing resources consumption; or even worse an interest to increase consumption of resources.

PSS IN THE AUTOMOTIVE INDUSTRY: AN ALTERNATIVE BUSINESS MODEL FOR A SUSTAINABLE SATISFACTION SYSTEM

In conclusion it is possible to say that the automotive sector is characterized by a stakeholders fragmentation along the life cycle phases (fig. 1), and the consequence is that the economic interest of each single actor does not coincide with an interest in optimize the resources use on a system level. For this reason vehicle producers are not directly interested in design and realize high efficient, long lasting, reusable and recyclable cars; and fuel companies are not directly interested in having in the market low-consumption vehicles.

4.0   Hypothesis of Alternative Business Model for a Sustainable Satisfaction System

The definition of an alternative business model is based, as previously mentioned, on a system design approach, integrating products, services, the related socio-economic stakeholders and the user, in order to fulfill a given demand of satisfaction. The aim is to design the interactions and partnerships between the various actors in order to make eco-efficient the delivered offer of "mobility".

4.1   Characteristics of the Alternative Business Model

The first characteristic of the alternative business model (fig. 2), is that the car is produced by small-scale and locally-based manufacturers. In this sense the idea is to take up the already elaborated micro-factory retailing (MFR) concept [13]-[20], and to use it as starting point for the business model development. As it has been argued [13]-[20], the MFR approach can potentially facilitate the adoption of eco-efficient PSSs via aspects such as the unification of the commerce and manufacturing function, and the proximity of manufacturing and servicing sites to users. But differently from the MFR concept, small manufacturers do not operate alone. In fact it has been imagined a partnership between them, an energy supplier and an insurance company. The generated partnership keeps the ownership of the vehicle and offers a service of "access to mobility" (e.g. car sharing). This service is supported by the local administration (which provides facilitations such as parking spaces and vehicles' recharging spaces), and is in collaboration with the local public transport company (in order to facilitate inter-modality of transport). A series of garages displaced on the territory and in agreement with the partnership, will provide the needed maintenance. The payment of the service is per "unit of satisfaction", and so in this case per kilometers covered; it includes the use of the vehicle, the needed energy supply, the insurance, the maintenance, as well as free parking space and access to public transport. Moreover the partnership will deal with the vehicles' upgrading and take-back service.

Four main innovative characteristics can be identified:

- *an innovative stakeholders network,* including actors like energy supplier, insurance company, local administration and public transport company, which usually works autonomously within the supply chain; in this way the stakeholders' fragmentation along the life cycle phases, and the related indifference in system resources optimization (present in the traditional business model), are avoided.
- *a shift from selling products to selling results,* meaning that it is not the vehicle and the fuel that are sold, but what it is offered is a service of "access to mobility". Users do not pay for the vehicle, the fuel, the spare parts, etc, but they pay per unit of "satisfaction".
- *a change in product ownership,* in the sense that, differently from the traditional sale models, the partnership providing the PSS solution keeps the ownership of all the products that are part of the

solutions (vehicle, fuel, etc.). As a consequence the relationship between the producer and the user does not end after the transaction (as in the traditional business model), but continues in time.

*   *a change in product design,* in order to make profitable the PSS solution; in this sense the vehicle's requisites should be, besides consumption-efficient, even easily up-gradable, maintained, disassembled, reused and recycled.

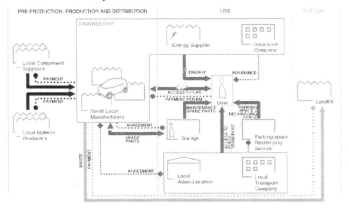

Fig. 2.   Simplified stakeholders system map visualizing all the actors and the related interactions (in terms of material, informational and financial flows), of the alternative business model for a sustainable automotive industry.

4.2   The Eco-Efficiency of the Business Model

As previously described, the alternative business model has been designed in order to make the economic interest of each single stakeholders coincident with the resources optimization on a system level. And this characteristic has been reached through the design of innovative interactions and relationships between the various stakeholders. Looking to the elaborated business model, the partnership has a direct economic interest in reducing the energy consumed in use by vehicles, in order to decrease costs and maximize profits; in fact, being the payment of the service "per km covered", less energy is used by the vehicle per km, minor will be the costs and consequently higher the profits. In this sense the energy supplier and the producer have an economic incentive in developing vehicles and energy systems based on renewable sources (sun, hydrogen, etc.), to save on the cars' energy recharging costs (paid by the partnership and no more by clients). Moreover, since the partnership remains the owner of the vehicle, it is economically interested in extending the product's life span, in order to postpone the disposal cost and the cost for the manufacturing of a new vehicle. For the same reason the partnership has an economic incentive in re-use or re-manufacture components to avoid landfill costs and new component production costs, and in extending material life, though recycling or energy recovery. Furthermore the partnership, through the agreement with the local administration and public transport company, is motivated in facilitating the integration between different transportation modes. In this way the local administration obtains a potential reduction of traffic congestion and emissions and an intensification in the public transport use; on the other hand the partnership gains facilitation like parking and recharging spaces. Finally it has to be underlined that the partnership is also motivated in avoiding accidents, in order to preserve cars and have less insurance costs. In this sense they could be potentially interested in reducing the vehicle acceleration and in adopting intelligent system for example to narrow down the speed within set limits.

5.0   Directions for Future Research: Designing Transition Paths for Sustainable System Innovation Introduction and Diffusion

Before it has been underlined that design could play a key role in orienting and supporting the design process towards the definition of environmental sustainable solutions. Now the research challenge is to understand which could be the potential role of design in defining the proper conditions to foster the introduction and dissemination of sustainable (product service) system solutions.

In this sense DIS research unit is now working on the elaboration of a so called "evolutionary transition path": a strategy for the introduction and diffusion of sustainable system innovations starting form an university research context and through an "open-source" philosophy. A transition path that can be described as a strategic orientation and adaptation of the steps that, through a continuous iterative multi-stakeholder learning process, brings to: the *design of a sustainable solution (I)*, its *experimentation in a pilot project (II)*, its *implementation (III)* and its consequent *diffusion (IV)*.

References

[1] Suh, S., Materials and energy flows in industry and ecosystem netwoks : life cycle assessment, input-output analysis, material flow analysis, ecological network flow analysis, and their combinations for industrial ecology. Leiden, Netherlands: CML Leiden University, PhD Thesis, 2004.

[2] Weidema, B.P., A.M. Nielsen, K. Christiansen, G. Norris, P. Notten, S. Suh, and J. Madsen, Prioritisation within the integrated product policy. 2.-0 LCA Consultants for Danish EPA, Copenhagen, Denmark, 2005.

[3] EU COM551, Green paper. Towards a new culture of urban mobility, Brussels, 2007.

[4] Geerken, T., Sustainable consumption and production in the mobility domain, working paper, SCORE!, 2008.

[5] M. Carley and P. Spapens, Sharing the world – sustainable living and global equity in the 21st century, Earthscan, London, 1998.

[6] Goedkoop MJ, van Halen CJG, te Riele HRM, Rommens PJM, Product service systems – ecological and economic basics, The Hague, Den Bosch & Amersfoort: Pi!MC, Stoorm C.S. & PRé Consultants, 1999.

[7] Brezet, H. et al., The design of eco-efficent services. Methods, tools and review of the case study based "Designing eco-efficent Services" project, report by VROM, The Hauge, 2001.

[8] Manzini E., Vezzoli C., Strategic design for sustainability, in TSPD proceedings, Amsterdam, 2001.

[9] UNEP, Product-Service Systems and Sustainability. Opportunities for sustainable solutions. UNEP, Division of Technology Industry and Economics, Production and Consumption Branch, Paris, 2002.

[10] Vezzoli C., System design for sustainability. Theory, methods and tools for a sustainable "satisfaction-system" design, Maggioli editore, Rimini, 2007.

[11] Van Halen C., Vezzoli C., Wimmer R. (edit by), Methodology for Product Service System. How to develop clean, clever and competitive strategies in companies, Van Gorcum, Assen, 2005.

[12] Manzini E., Collina L., Evans S. (edit by), Solution oriented partnership, Cranfield University ed., Cranfield, 2004.

[13] Welles P., Alternative business model for a sustainable automotive industry, proceedings, Perspectives on Radical Changes to Sustainable Consumption and Production (SCP), SCORE! Network, Copenhagen, 2006.

[14] Williams, A. Product service-systems in the automotive industry: a case for micro-factory retailing, *Journal of cleaner production*, volume 14, issue 2, pp.172-184, 2006.

[15] Nieuwenhuis P. and P. Wells, The automotive industry and the environment, Woodhead Publishing Limited/CRC Press LLC, Cambridge England/Boca Raton, FL, USA, 2003.

[16] Wells P. and P. Nieuwenhuis, The automotive industry – a guide, CAIR, Cardiff, UK, 2001.

[17] Department of Trade and Industry (DTI) (UK), The environmental impacts of motor manufacturing and disposal of end-of-life vehicles – moving towards sustainability, Cleaner Vehicles Task Force Report, HMSO, London, 2000.

[18] SustainAbility & United Nations Environment Programme (UNEP), Driving sustainability – can the auto sector deliver sustainable mobility, Paris, France, 2001.

[19] Official Journal of the European Communities (OJEC), Directive 2000/53/EC of the European Parliament and of the Council on 18 September 2000 on end-of-life vehicles, Brussels, 2000.

[20] Nieuwenhuis P., An ecosystem approach to the transition to new business models, proceedings, Framework for Action for Sustainable Consumption and Production (SCP), (SCORE!) Network, Brussels, 2008.

**PSS IN THE AUTOMOTIVE INDUSTRY: AN ALTERNATIVE BUSINESS MODEL FOR A
SUSTAINABLE SATISFACTION SYSTEM**

The 6th International Conference on Manufacturing Research (ICMR08)
Brunel University, UK, 9-11th September 2008

CHALLENGES OF PRODUCT-SERVICE SYSTEMS: A REAL-LIFE CASE STUDY

Essam Shehab, Steve Evans, Tim Baines, Howard Lightfoot, Ashutosh Tiwari, Mark Johnson, Joe Peppard

Cranfield Innovative Manufacturing Research Centre, Cranfield University, MK43 0AL, UK

Abstract

A Product-Service System (PSS) is an integrated product and service offering that delivers value in use. This paper presents a real-life case study of a large company which has moved towards PSS. A research protocol has been created to conduct an extensive series of interviews with key personnel within the case study company. The results of the study and implications for research are explored.

Keywords: Manufacturing, Service, Case-study, Product-Service System (PSS).

1.0   Introduction

Western manufacturing companies are moving their attention away from old business model of selling products to a new business strategy of selling functions and results that effectively fulfill the final-users' needs. This business model is referred to product-service system (PSS). A Product-Service System (PSS) is an integrated product and service offering that delivers value in use. A PSS can be thought of as a market proposition that extends the traditional functionality of a product by incorporating additional services as shown in Figure (1). The emphasis is on the 'sale of use' rather than the 'sale of product'. The customer pays for using an asset, rather than its purchase, and so benefits from a restructuring of the risks, responsibilities and costs traditionally associated with ownership. Conversely, suppliers/manufacturers gain from this extended relationship by learning more effectively from customers [1], locking customers in to longer relationships [2], and reducing competition due to the inimitable nature of services [3].

The concept of servitization encompasses product service-system. Servitization is now widely recognised as the innovation of an organisation's capabilities and processes, to better create mutual value, through a shift from selling product to selling Product-Service Systems [4, 5]. Such a strategy is now widely advocated as a means by which western manufactures can face-up to the challenges of competitors in lower cost economies. The terms service and product are intrinsically linked to discussions about servitization. The term 'product' is generally well understood by manufacturers. Goedkoop et al. [6] defined a product as a tangible commodity manufactured to be sold, and quite simplistically is capable of 'falling on your toe' and of fulfilling a user's needs. Invariably, in the world of manufacture, it is usually considered to be a material artefact (e.g. car, boat, plane), by comparison services are classed as intangible, heterogeneous, inseparable and perishable.

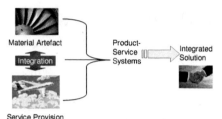

Fig.1. Overall structure of Product-Service System

Few researchers have documented the associated consequences to the organisational design of the host manufacturer as they seek to pursue such a strategy. This research describes a real-life case-based research that gained an in-depth and multi-disciplinary understanding of the implications of a servitization strategy. The focal firm – GreatServ (A fictitious name to protect confidentiality) - is a large manufacturer that, through the successes of integrated products and services, now generates a large portion of revenue from product-centric service contracts (i.e.: services that are tightly coupled to the product offering). The research with GreatServ has helped to appreciate how servitization necessitates companies to make modifications ranging from the language they use to interact with customers, though to their organisation design.

2.0 Related Research

The PSS concept encompasses challenges in different ways and levels within an organisation. From the business management perspective, it requires a substantial change in the way companies see themselves and their businesses. The companies have to adapt their business strategy with this business model. Almost all company functions, including design, purchasing, accounting, management, marketing, etc might encounter extensive changes [7].

Servitization has been studied by a number of authors [8, 3], who have specifically sought to understand the methods and implications of service-led competitive strategies for manufacturers. In addition, during this same period, there has been independent growth in research on the related topics of Product-Service Systems (PSS), Service-Science (SS) and Integrated Vehicle Health Management (IVHM). This increasing body of research indicates a growing interest in this topic by academia, business and government. One reason for this is the belief that a move towards servitized manufacture is a means to create additional value adding capabilities for traditional manufactures [3]. Furthermore, such services are distinctive, long-lived, and easier to defend from competition based in lower cost economies. Indeed, many governments see such moves downstream as key to competitiveness [9]. As a consequence, more Western manufacturers are seeking an ever increasing percentage of their revenues from services [8]. However, there is some concern that servitized manufacturers could be in greater danger of bankruptcy and make lower returns in the longer-term [10]. Nevertheless, it is difficult to argue against a careful adoption of some services in certain situations.

To succeed with servitization a manufacturer is likely to need some new and alternative organisational principles structures and processes [3]. These may be different to those associated with traditionally product manufacture. Authors such as Chase and Garvin [11], argue strongly for reversing the trend of applying operational management based concepts in the services environment. They also suggest that there is a subtle mix of organisational structures that are appropriate to a servitized manufacturer that are distinct and different to those associated with, either a more traditional product manufacturer, or a pure service provider. However, researchers have yet to fully understand the nature of these structures and their associated issues.

3.0   Research Methodology

The study aims to investigate a PSS organisation that designs, builds and delivers integrated product and services, and to identify the challenges they are encountering in the pursuit of such business model. The case research method was employed to study a UK-based manufacturer who gains a large portion of revenue from the provision of services that are closely coupled to their products. The case study was undertaken from June to November 2007.   During this time seasoned researchers from across the disciplines (engineering, manufacturing, management) worked on the study. Firstly a history map with GreatServ was developed to understand how they have arrived at their servitization strategy. Then a research protocol was developed. Working in pairs/triple, researchers conducted interviews with key personnel from across the organisation (e.g. marketing, customer support, engineering, manufacturing operations, and supply chain) and captured their views on how the organisation operates and the issues they are facing. Each interview which lasts for two hours, was recorded and then transcribed. Over 400 pages of transcripts were double or triple marked and then coded and interpreted using mind-mapping techniques to identify the common issues arising across the organisation.

4.0   Key Results

GreatServ provides capital equipment products, and often offers these with a broad range of services that ensure asset availability via a risk and revenue sharing contract. While the origin of this business dates back to the early 1990s it really only took shape in the early 2000s. This market proposition emerged in response to customers who sought to offset their repair and overhaul costs and responsibilities for products. Similarly, GreatServ sought to prevent component suppliers from directly supplying GreatServ customers. Their service business has now grown to such an extent that over 50% of their revenues are now derived from the provision and support of integrated offerings. The changes issues that have arisen as a consequence of this transition from traditional manufacturer are summarised as follows.

4.2   Service Language

One of the most striking differences at GreatServ is the everyday language used by the employees in the delivery of services. Whereas with a conventional manufacturer, personnel use (and fully understand) nomenclature such as product, part and component they may only loosely understand the term service. As a noun, the word 'services' usually refer to the offering (e.g. maintenance, repair, insurance) and a single offering is a service. However, as a verb, service can also be used to refer to a level of performance (e.g. that was good service). This is only one example of many words and phrases whose semantics take on particular and specific meanings. This distinction appears strongest amongst personnel who deal most closely with customers of services. Future challenges are, therefore, to make such language pervasive throughout the organisation.

4.3   Value Dimensions

One reason that language changes, is that a PSS is different. At GreatServ the nature of the relationship with the customer changes from a transaction to that of a long-term relationship. Traditional manufacturers tends to take a linear view of product production (by the manufacturer) which is then sold (a transaction) to the customer for their use (consumption). However, when GreatServ deliver an integrated product and service there tends to be a series of 'touch points' between the host business and customer. For example, initial contract negotiation may be lengthy; monitoring of the asset in-use may be carried out by the business, this may lead to servicing of the product by the business; and finally the host may take-back the product at end-of-life. While the product itself may still be sold to the customer (as is the case with GreatServ) the associated services are more closely associated with long-term relationships. Hence, servitization tends to combine both transactional and relationship elements into the business models. Moreover, revenue, profits and cash flow arise mainly from the relationship aspects of this model with a shift from reducing costs to improving the value for a customer.

The metrics used to define value offered to the customer vary to reflect the changing business model. This is particularly apparent in the measures employed to assess performance. Conventional manufacture will frequently focus on the Cost, Quality and Delivery of products. Here, quality conformance will typically be assessed in terms of rejected components; cost will comprise of labour, materials and overheads; and delivery performance will be assessed by due-date performance. With services at GreatServ, value becomes more associated with asset use, rather than sale or repair, therefore the appropriate measures can be subtly different to those typically employed.

The depth of the manufacturer's understanding of what value has been created for a customer is possibly one of the contingencies that can moderate the association between servitisation strategy and lower returns in the long-term. However, assessing the value created through an integrated offering of products and services can be difficult to gauge. In spite of the nature of the contractual relationship, the product-service provider should be able to assess what value has been created through the asset/service performance as well as through the functional outcome of a product-service provision that is served directly through asset/service consumption. In order to do that the future challenge is to precisely define, distinguish and communicate the key elements of customer value on the basis of the interaction and/or consumption processes of an integrated offering.

4.4   Traditional Products and Design Process

As the value proposition changes, then product designs at GreatServ have also altered to reflect the balance of value gained through asset use rather than simple artefact ownership. As mentioned above, GreatServ sell their product and offer complementary services to assure asset availability. As significant revenue is generated through services, their products incorporate a facility for remotely sensing performance in the field. Here, extra cost is added to product manufacture which can not be recouped at point-of-sale, but rather relies on the customer taking-up the services offered. This is typical of the many product features that are introduced to aid maintenance and servicing to support asset availability in the field. Traditionally, product designs are conceptualised remotely, prototyped and refined, and then put into practice. With services, prototyping does not typically exist and refinement occurs in an organic, experiential manner. Here, one danger is, as GreatServ have found, for engineers to attempt to apply conventional product design processes. Understanding more about how these processes differ is a considerable future challenge.

4.5   Challenges of Integrating Service and Product Delivery Systems

As with product designs, the organisational design required to support the value proposition also changes. The conventional view of materials flowing into a factory, through production, to be consumed by the customer does not occur within GreatServ. While a small portion of this somewhat uni-directional material flow does occur, there is a complex service delivery system that monitors and supports the asset in use superimposed upon the traditional production business. This system transcends the traditional internal / external barriers of the host business; instead calling on partners and suppliers to affect the delivery of the required service.

This delivery system is directly impacted by the relational component of the business model and associated performance measures (as outlined in section 4.3). These requirements are so particular to this context, that GreatServ has decoupled this delivery mechanism from their more conventional production system. However, they recognise that as business pressures increase the sharing of resources and knowledge necessitating that these systems be more tightly coupled. Moreover, a tighter coupling is necessary in the supply network that supports the delivery of a product-service system. As the capital asset is provided by GreatServ and some elements of the service and support by members of the supply network, effective coordination and integration between network members is essential. The complexity of an integrated offering will likely require a different type of supply network for support of new products in comparison to legacy products, including a different network design and shift towards more partnering relationships with key network members. How to achieve this is a topic of some debate within the organisation.

4.6   Transformation Issues

GreatServ illustrates a manufacturer that, in the adoption of a servitization strategy, is encountering changes to language, value, along with designs of product and organisation. Throughout this case, we have been made repeatedly aware that one of the biggest challenges that GreatServ are facing is the need to transition from a service- as opposed to product-oriented organisation. Sections 4.2 – 4.4 above summarise how, across the organisation and its broader supply chain, GreatServ has changed, and continues, to change. Against each of these strands GreatServ is defining new design paradigms, and each of these introduce particular challenges to the mind-sets of customers, employees, and suppliers. For example, educating employees in the language of service, changing process to better suit the nature of service design, and adopting integrated product and service delivery systems. Understanding the specific transformational issues, and how to overcome these, is a principal future challenge.

5.0   Conclusion

CHALLENGES OF PRODUCT-SERVICE SYSTEMS: A CASE STUDY

GreatServ is one example of a UK company that has adopted a product-service system business model. The study has provided a much clearer understanding of the particular issues that are arising as GreatServ attempts to deliver integrated products and services successfully. In brief, these are:

- Language used in service is particular and peculiar.
- Value dimensions are special and biased towards relationships rather transaction.
- Products and design process are different and better enable service support.
- Integrating service and product delivery systems is challenging.
- Transformation issues are both particular and pervasive throughout customers, employees, partners and suppliers.

There is little to suggest that these issues are particular to the GreatServ business or sector. However, for completeness, the future work will now look externally to this organisation to carry out a complementary investigation of the suppliers, partners and customers of GreatServ. In conducting such an investigation we look forward to further developing our understanding of the challenges faced through servitization, and reporting these in future papers.

Acknowledgement

The authors wish to acknowledge the support of the Engineering and Physical Sciences Research Council (EPSRC) for their support in carrying out this work. Also, we are grateful to our colleague Professor Andy Neely for his work in setting-up the case study for this research.

References

[1] Alonso-Rasgado, T., Thompson, G. and Elfstrom, B-O., (2004), 'The design of functional (total care) products', Journal of Engineering Design, Vol. 15, No. 6, pp. 515-540.
[2] Vandermerwe, S. (2000), 'How increasing value to customer improves business results', MIT Sloan Management Review, Vol. 42, No. 1, pp. 27-37.
[3] Oliva R & Kallenberg R. (2003) 'Managing the Transition from Products to Services', International Journal of Service Industry Management Vol. 14, No. 2, pp. 160-172.
[4] Slack, N., Lewis, M. and Bates, H. (2004), 'The two worlds of operations management research and practice: Can they meet, should they meet?' International Journal of Operations & Production Management, Vol. 24, No. 4, pp. 372-387.
[5] Baines, T et al (2007), 'State-of-the-art in Product Service-Systems', Journal of Engineering Manufacture, Vol. 221, Proc. IMechE Part B, pp. 1543-1552.
[6] Goedkoop, M. et al. (1999), 'Product Service-Systems, Ecological and Economic Basics,' Report for Dutch Ministries of Environment (VROM) and Economic Affairs (EZ)
[7] Shehab, E and Roy R. (2006) "Product-Service Systems: Issues and Challenges", The 4th International Conference on Manufacturing Research (ICMR 2006), Liverpool John Moores University, 5th – 7th September 2006 ISBN 0-9553215-0-6, pp 17-22.
[8] Wise R & Baumgartner P. September-October1999, 'Go downstream: The New Profit Imperative in Manufacturing' Harvard Business Review, Vol. 77, No. 5, pp. 133-141.
[9] Hewitt, P. (2002),'Secretary of State for Trade and Industry', No. 4, The Government's Manufacturig Strategy
[10] Neely, A. (2007), 'Servitization of Manufacturing', 14th EurOMA Conf. Ankara, Turkey
[11] Chase, R. Garvin, D. (1989), 'The Service Factory', Harvard Business Review, Vol. 67, No. 4, pp. 61-69.

The 6th International Conference on Manufacturing Research (ICMR08)
Brunel University, UK, 9-11th September 2008

SUPPLY NETWORK INTEGRATION IN COMPLEX PRODUCT SERVICES

Dr Jagjit Singh SRAI, Prof. Mike GREGORY

Centre for International Manufacturing, Institute for Manufacturing, Department of Engineering, University of Cambridge, Mill Lane, Cambridge CB2 1RX. Tel: 01223 765601 e-mail: jss46@cam.ac.uk

Abstract

This paper explores whether a common set of service supply chain process-objectives across the extended supply network could be developed to support more effective product service delivery. Four case studies are compared involving complex product equipment manufacturers and the challenges they face in managing multi-entity service supply chains, where 'services' represent the dominant revenue generator.

The cases included complex product (equipment) service solutions in aerospace, naval, power and telecoms sectors. These cases demonstrated that the provision of a product service solution where complex equipment is involved places a heavy reliance on a network of multiple partners, with the need to constantly upgrade equipment, in many cases in-situ at the customers' premises. The research methodology involved the use of supply chain capability assessment 'process models', to assess supply network integration drivers between key nodes in the supply chain.

Initial findings suggest that the individual entities regard end-to-end integration as a desirable and mutual goal, but view the criticality of particular enabling process-capabilities quite differently, with important differences also on their perspectives of what constitutes strategic and operational processes. This finding suggests that misalignment through the service supply chain is fundamentally a design issue (as well a difficult operational task). The absence of a shared view on critical enabling processes results from contextual complexity of the service supply network rather than competing commercial interests. An approach is presented that enables misalignment in process objectives of the various entities to be addressed, with the development of a common 'multi-entity' set of supply chain process-capabilities, captured within a 'hierarchy' of strategic, operational and routine activities.

Keywords: Complex Product Service, Supply Chain, Capability, Supply Network Integration.

1.0   Introduction

The concept of service supply chains is relatively new and addresses the traditional challenges of Supply Chain Management (SCM), the effective management of materials and information within the network of interdependent organisations in the supply chain, with those operational processes that support the provision of an integrated 'service solution'. These typically include after-sales service processes (often the stage in the value chain where value is captured) but also include other activities and processes in the value chain that support service delivery (often where value is created).

Despite extensive SCM literature over the last two decades and the increasing importance of services too many OEM manufactures (and non-manufacturers), the area of service supply chains (SSCs) is largely unexplored in academia as commented by several authors [1]-[2]. This is particularly surprising since the SSC concept is increasingly prevalent in industry (although sometimes alternative terminology such as service chains, after-sales services etc are used). This gap in the academic arena is now being progressively addressed, directly using the SSC terminology/concepts (e.g. [1]-[5]) and more broadly within the service domain (e.g. [6]-[7]). One of the key challenges in ensuring effective and efficient service operations in complex and dispersed (multi-mode) supply network environments is the integration of demand and supply processes, typically covered by contractual service agreements. Transparency on collective and individual service delivery within an environment where there are multiple interdependencies on effective service provision, often involving bi-directional service supply chains operating in parallel, present particularly complex process integration, accountability and delivery management challenges.

Another key challenge is the migration path to service supply networks. These involve the development of new 'concepts of operation' or the selection of service operating models, and in many cases, the progressive transfer of operational processes between customer and supply organisations. The development of these operational frameworks, need to be supported by organisational routines (process capabilities), some of which may be model-specific. Performance metrics that take into account key inputs, supply chain process development, and output performance become a key component of the operational framework. These metrics need to be considered in a broader context, where the more elusive 'end-to-end' supply network performance and partnering perspectives are assessed, as well as contractual metrics that support service contract delivery.

This paper compares four in-depth case studies involving complex product equipment manufacturers and the challenges they face operating within multi-entity service supply chains, where service and support activities represent their dominant revenue generator. The key focus of the study was to develop a methodology to explore whether a common set of service supply chain process-objectives across the extended supply network could be developed to support more effective product service delivery.

2.0   Key Concepts in Service Supply Chains (SSCs)

Within the limited literature in the field of SSCs several concepts have been identified that provide a useful foundation to support research in the area. Initial research in complex SSCs suggests that the concepts may be usefully grouped into Strategic, Operations Management and Technology aspects. The first two of these dimensions are briefly reviewed below in terms of their relevance to this study.

2.1 Strategic Considerations in SSCs

The literature on service supply chains identifies several concepts that may be classified as strategic level considerations and include;

- SSCs as a new source of value capture ([1], [8]) with service providers moving up the value chain [9]
- Perishability of services, with the inability to store 'inventory' as in conventional SCs, with inventory equivalence being considered as installed 'service capacity' ([1], [2], [4])
- The 'variable capacity' nature of services [2]
- Incentivisation of SSC partners that support value adding behaviours with suitable pain/gain share mechanisms
- The elevation of information and knowledge based 'flows' in SSCs in addition to the effective management of material flow ([4], [6])
- Bidirectional SSCs involving dual customer-supplier roles for principal partners with roles reversed for specific elements (e.g. enabling infrastructure delivery provided by 'customers'), with service delivery and quality highly interdependent (largely involving single tier dependencies), providing complex capability, performance and contract management issues ([3], 10], [11])
- The contractual nature of service delivery in complex equipment maintenance contracts, involving 'enduring' contracts of significant value and scale, rather than the one-off transactional nature of traditional supply chains ([11]).

2.2 SSC Operations Management

From an operations management perspective, the literature presents some unique aspects of service supply chains, namely

- Involving dispersed operations for aftermarket support, with service providers co-located at customer sites ([11],[12])
- Complexity of SSC operational processes and capabilities, with performance management challenges [13]), decision trees, metrics [14], SC performance hierarchies [15], capability models and capability hierarchies ([6], [11])
- Multi-entity contracting, partnering and sub-contracting ([3], [12])
- The specific demand characteristics in complex equipment and service contract environments (large contracts) and the management of ongoing demand on-contract ([1], [4])
- The influence of on-site service (real-time operational and near-future) demand signals leading to capacity and capability development supporting both primary volume demands and new service development opportunities.

SUPPLY NETWORK INTEGRATION IN COMPLEX PRODUCT SERVICES

3.0   Key Research Challenges

The research extends previous work undertaken in the area on supply chain capability model development, capability development paths, capability and performance metric architectures and hierarchies, taking both a strategic supply chain and operational perspectives. Literature on aftermarket support [6], supply chain performance metrics [15], capability hierarchies [11], provide potential approaches to these elements of the research. The extendibility of SCM concepts to SSCs is addressed by understanding the equivalence of concepts such as inventory, demand, capacity etc.

A sub-theme within this research is on 'end-to-end' supply chain integration ([3], [11]) by capturing those supply network capabilities that facilitate customer-supplier alignment, and the combinations of operational-routines that support particular service supply chain models. The hierarchy of service supply chain capabilities is seen as key to providing linkages between discrete strategic and operational processes, including complex support activities, providing a platform for process alignment, metrics development and 'end-to-end' integration. Typology/classification considerations in this research are restricted to the service supply chain domain identifying service supply chain based segmentation and differentiation concepts extending from other authors in the area (e.g. [17]). The focus in this area is on future supply model configuration options [16].

The development of suitable SSC configuration parameters and supply chain mapping techniques are also considered to understand how configuration influences service delivery, and which configurations support particular service models. Due to the integral nature of product development in many service solutions, the configuration of the value chain (or 'footprint') and its impact on service delivery modes and capabilities is considered; the research methods involve application at a top-line level value stream mapping and supply network configuration mapping techniques [18]. The 'service product' dimension within this research is on complex equipment (supply/upgrade/maintenance) centric services where the SSC concepts of relationship management [1], bidirectional SC's ([3], 10]) and complex capability hierarchies manifest [11]. These environments also provide opportunities to understand the complexities of mass-partnering [3] and the emerging role of (service and support) systems integrator within a SSC context. The evolution journey from product manufacturer (or SCM) to systems process integrator and expert partner management (or SSCM) is facilitated by these complex dispersed service networks ([1]-[3], [6], [7], [9]).

A potential output from this research is informing the future development of SSC process models and frameworks, beyond concepts currently reported ([1], [2], [12]), providing a 'process-based' foundation for service operations management. The research aims to enrich traditional operating frameworks by introducing the concepts of 'service and support' operations, integrated with equipment 'design and build' processes.

4.0   Methodology

The principal aim was to establish the relative alignment of service supply chain process objectives across key operational nodes in the supply chain, using process-capability model assessments. Further, to evaluate reasons for any differences in their strategic and operational classification, and possible causes for differing perspectives. The multiple case study method was selected as most appropriate to address the research agenda, as the operations for equipment based product service solutions are complex.

Four case studies were identified as meeting the criteria for the study (complex equipment large-contract-based service provision); the cases included large service contracts, each providing complex 'product service solutions' in aerospace (aircraft maintenance and support), naval (naval-base service operations), power (power supply systems) and telecoms (equipment) sectors. Cross-case comparisons were necessary for deriving generalizable observations.

The research methodology involved the application of a number of capability assessment and configuration mapping techniques previously developed by the authors ([11], [16], [18], [19]), but tailored to the complex dispersed bidirectional SSC context described above. Supply chain capability assessment 'process models' [19] were used to assess from an extended supply network perspective, supply network integration drivers between key nodes in the supply chain; between 'end-customers', 'on-site service' teams, 'original equipment manufacturing hubs' and key 'tier 1 suppliers'. Key elements of the methodology involved the following activities;

- An outline configuration mapping activity, capturing the principal entities involved in service delivery, was undertaken to improve understanding of the dynamics of 'end-to-end' SC integration using established methodologies from the SC literature [16], [18].
- Capturing the key types of material and information flows as part of an 'end-to-end' (bidirectional) supply chain mapping activity using supply network configuration mapping tools [18]
- The application of SC capability models (those with sufficient operational granularity) in a service & support environment; specific methods varied depending on either in-company capability models and generic models available in the literature [19]
- The exploration of capability hierarchy concepts using the framework depicted in Fig.1, adapting previous concepts on SSC Capability Hierarchies [11], and work on performance measurement hierarchies [15].

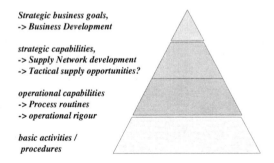

Strategic business goals,
-> Business Development

strategic capabilities,
-> Supply Network development
-> Tactical supply opportunities?

operational capabilities
-> Process routines
-> operational rigour

basic activities /
procedures

Fig. 1.   Developing Capability and Performance Hierarchies to Support Strategic and Operational Alignment [11]

The service supply chain process capabilities, for each of the cases in Table 1, were then evaluated using the capability hierarchy shown in Fig1. In the first two cases, this was extended to multiple 'nodes' in the service supply chain, with results from multiple nodes compared to assess the principal reasons for any capability

SUPPLY NETWORK INTEGRATION IN COMPLEX PRODUCT SERVICES

hierarchy classification differences. In the in-depth pilot case study (Case 1) an approach to the development of a shared perspective was tested; this involved the (multi-nodal) group review of the process-capabilities where there was a 'mismatch' either in the perceived importance of a process, or its strategic and operational classification. Reasons for the mismatch were then discussed.

Table 1 sets out the case service networks studied, the process-capability tools used, and the scope of the capability hierarchy assessment.

Table 1: Case Studies

Case		description	capability model used	informant scope
Case 1	Aerospace	complex multi-partner	in-company, generic ref [19]	extended service chain
Case 2	Naval	complex multi-partner	in-company, generic ref [19]	extended service chain
Case 3	Power	complex downstream	generic ref [19]	service provider
Case 4	Telecoms	complex upstream	generic ref [19]	service provider

In each of these case studies, the SSC data collection and capability hierarchy classification involved interactions with the supply chain leadership teams of the major OEMs. Case 1 and Case 2 also involved in-depth interviews with multiple supplier and customer organisations as part of a review of processes, and supporting tools. In addition to existing service solution projects, a review of exemplar Pioneer Projects was undertaken in the pilot case (Case 1) to capture key transition themes, capturing evolution path history.

The results of the relative 'alignment' between supply-chain process capabilities are shown in Table 2.

5.0 Results

5.1 Multiple Case Review

These cases demonstrated that the provision of a product service solution where complex equipment is involved places a heavy reliance on a network of multiple partners, with the need to constantly upgrade equipment, in many cases in-situ at the customers' premises. Furthermore, maintenance activities were often in partnership with the prime service provider (the holder of the design authority) and involved complex bi-directional supply chain arrangements.

Table 2: Case Studies Summary Results

Case		Network Complexity	Nature of Partnership	Capability Hierarchy Match/Mismatch
Case 1	Aerospace	High multiple-prime(s)	Co-located and Enduring	shared objectives but hierarchy mismatch
Case 2	Naval	High Multiple-primes(s)	Co-located and Enduring	shared objectives but hierarchy mismatch
Case 3	Power	Downstream complexity /single prime	Transactional, Short-term contracts	downstream match (limited KPI based data)
Case 4	Telecoms	Upstream complexity /single prime	Transactional, Fixed-term service contracts	upstream match (limited KPI based data)

Initial findings suggest that the individual entities regard end-to-end integration as a desirable and mutual goal, but (as shown in Table 2) view the criticality of particular enabling process-capabilities quite differently, with important differences also on their perspectives of what constitutes strategic and operational processes. This finding suggests that misalignment through the service supply chain is fundamentally a design issue (as well a difficult operational task). This observation was explored in further detail in Case 1 and Case where multiple

SUPPLY NETWORK INTEGRATION IN COMPLEX PRODUCT SERVICES

node results were compared. The mismatches appeared to be driven by different operational perspectives, and lack of understanding of the extended service supply chain, rather than what might result from competing commercial interests.

5.2   Pilot Case Review

For the pilot study case, Case 1, an in-depth review of the mismatch between hierarchy classifications was conducted to establish the nature of the determinations by the different organizational entities, within the service supply chain. The analysis involved the capturing of the supporting rationale for capability hierarchy classification.

Initial results of this analysis, suggest that the differences result from an absence of a shared view on critical enabling processes and that this largely results from contextual complexity (supply network and product service) rather than competing commercial interests. To further verify this observation, the 'group' sharing of the classification of partner-organisations was then conducted. The different classifications of supply chain process-capabilities appeared to be driven from differing operational perspectives, and suggested that a common perspective can be arrived at, with the supporting rationale discussed collectively, and thus contributing to common set of process objectives. The agreement of a common set of Key Performance Indicators (KPIs) based on a shared view of the critical enabling processes, and their strategic and operational relevance, represented a potential outcome of the data review, providing opportunities for developing shared goals.

6.0   Conclusions

The main conclusions from this study include;

- There is an absence of a shared view on critical enabling processes in complex multi-partnered service supply chain cases studied, particularly evident in the cases where multiple primes are active.
- A significant contribution to the different strategic-operational classification of capability-hierarchy results from contextual complexity (supply network and product service) rather than competing commercial interests
- An approach to make transparent the misalignment in process objectives and priorities of the various supply network entities suggest 'common perspectives' can be arrived at by sharing operational information about criticality of key processes and their strategic and operational relevance
- A common set of service supply chain capability hierarchies may lead to the development of better understood process enablers and their strategic and operational relevance.

The pilot explores possible processes for achieving a common multi-entity set of supply chain process-capabilities, captured within a 'hierarchy' of strategic, operational and routine activities. Follow-up research will consider potential approaches to formulating a shared (multi-entity) supply chain process-capability hierarchy, extending the work of this limited study to understand more fully the contextual factors that may contribute to mismatches in process objectives, and exploring their practical and commercial implications.

References

[1] Baltacioglu T., Ada E., Kaplan M., Yurt O., Kaplan C., "A new framework for service supply chains", *The Service Industries journal*, Vol. 27, No. 2, 105-124 (2007).

[2] Niranjan T.T., "Equivalence of 'goods' and 'services' supply chain concepts", *14th International Annual EurOMA Conference*, (2007).

[3] Sampson S., "Customer-supplier duality and bidirectional supply chains in service organizations", *International Journal of Service Industry Management*, Vol.11, No. 4, 348-364, (2000).

[4] Anderson E.G., Morrice D.J., Lundeen G., "The 'physics' of capacity and backlog management in service and custom manufacturing supply chains", *System Dynamics Review*, Vol. 21, No. 3, 217-247, (2005).

[5] Ellram L., Tate W., Billington C., "Understanding and managing the services supply chain", *Journal of Supply Chain Management*, Vol. 40, Issue 4, (2004).

[6] Cohen M.A., Agrawal N., Agrawal V., "Winning in the aftermarket", *Harvard Business Review*, 129-138, May (2006).

[7] Oliva R., Kallenberg, R., "Managing the transition from product to services", *International Journal of Service Industry Management*, Vol. 14, No.2. (2003).

[8] Chamberlain J., Nunes J., "Service-parts management: A real-life success story", *Supply Chain Management Review*. 38-44 September (2004),

[9] Neely A., "The Servitization of Manufacturing: An analysis of global trends", *14th International Annual EurOMA Conference*, (2007).

[10] Sampson S., "Why do we need an Operations paradigm for services?", POMS College of Service Operations and EurOMA Conference, London Business School, (2007).

[11] Srai J., "Developing a more integrated supply network through process and capability alignment – An initial review of an output-based service supply contract", *SEIC Conference*, Loughborough, (2007)

[12] Farris T.M., Wittmann M.C., Hasty R., "Aftermarket support and the supply chain: Exemplars and implications from the aerospace industry", *International Journal of Physical Distribution and Logistics Management*, Vol. 35 (1) pp 6-19, (2005).

[13] Pavlov A., Bourne M. "Responding to contemporary challenges in performance management: Measuring organisational routines", *14th International Annual EurOMA Conference*, (2007).

[14] Chibba A., "Measuring supply chain performance upstream and downstream the supply chain – two case studies from Swedish heavy vehicle manufacturers", *14th International Annual EurOMA Conference*, (2007)

[15] Hofman D., "The Hierarchy of Supply Chain Metrics", *Supply Chain Management Review*, 28-37 (2004).

[16] Srai J.S., "Global Solutions; Supply Chains - Emerging Models. Manufacturing Engineer", *The Institution of Engineering and Technology*, Vol. 86 (5) 32 – 35, Oct-Nov (2007).

[17] Deshpande V., Cohen M., Donohue K., "An empirical study of service differentiation for weapon system service parts", Operations Research, Vol. 51, No. 4, (2003).

[18] Srai J.S., Gregory M.J., "A Supply Network Configuration Perspective on International Supply Chain Development." *International Journal of Operations Management*, Vol. 5 386-411. May (2008).

[19] Srai J.S. "Process Organisation, Capabilities and Supply Networks - Enterprise organization and operation", Chapter 13 In: *Springer Handbook of Mechanical Engineering*, Editors: Karl-Heinrich Grote, Erik K. Antonsson, Springer, Heidelberg, (2007).

The 6th International Conference on Manufacturing Research (ICMR08)
Brunel University, UK, 9-11th September 2008

DESIGN OF GENERIC MODULAR RECONFIGURABLE PLATFORMS (GMRPS) FOR A PRODUCT-ORIENTED MICRO MANUFACTURING SYSTEM

Xizhi Sun, Kai Cheng

School of Engineering and Design, Brunel University, Uxbridge, UB8 3PH, UK xizhi.sun@brunel.ac.uk, kai.cheng@brunel.ac.uk

Abstract

With the proposition of the concept of product-service systems, many manufacturers are focusing on selling services or functionality rather than products. Industrial production is shifting production models from mass production to mass customization and highly personalized needs. As a result, there is a tendency for manufacturing system suppliers to develop product-oriented systems to responsively cope with the dynamic fast moving competitive market. The key features of such a manufacturing system are the reconfigurability and adaptability, which can enable the system respond to the changeable needs of customers quickly and adaptively. Therefore, one of the challenges for the micro manufacturing system provider has been the design of a reconfigurable machine platform which will provide the functionalities and flexibility required by the product-oriented systems.

In this paper, a new micro manufacturing platform, i.e. a generic modular reconfigurable platform (GMRP) is proposed in order to provide an effective means for fabrication of high quality micro products at low cost in a responsive manner. The GMRP-based system aims to be a product-oriented reconfigurable, highly responsive manufacturing system particularly for high value nano/micro manufacturing purposes. To reuse components and decrease material consumption, GMRP is characterized by hybrid micro manufacturing processes, modularity of key components, and reconfigurability of machine platforms and key components. Furthermore, a practical methodology for the design of reconfigurable machine platforms is discussed against the requirements from product-driven micro manufacturing and its extension for adaptive production.

Keywords: Product-oriented micro manufacturing, reconfigurable manufacturing, micro manufacturing system.

1.0   Introduction

The concept of product-service systems has been proposed for one decade or so as a possible solution to unlink environmental pressure from economic growth. Godekoop et al [1] defined a product-service system as "a marketable set of products and services capable of jointly fulfilling a user's need and has a lower environmental impact than traditional business models". The key idea behind product-service systems is that consumers' specific needs can be met more properly by using service engineering to meet some needs rather than a merely physical object. Product-service systems respond more appropriately to the current demands than the conventional systems of mass production because of the flexibility of customers' demands in current vibrant market place. This is an evolution of the economic transition away from standardized and mass production towards flexibility, mass-customization and markets driven by quality, innovative products and added value rather than cost [2-5]. Therefore, most advanced manufacturing companies are shifting their business strategy from traditional business model towards services-oriented or functionality-driven instead of merely products.

Three types of product-service system have been proposed by Aleksejs Azarenko for machine tool industries. They are product-oriented product-service system, use-oriented product-service system and result-oriented product-service system [6-7]. To meet the variable needs of different customers and providing suitable services, design of a modular reconfigurable machine tool is therefore essential for the success of the proposed industrial product-service systems. It can be argued that the key features of such systems are their modularity and reconfigurability, which will lead to responsive and cost effective solutions to dynamically changing competitive global market. This of course equally applies to micro manufacturing systems because of the system cost, complexity and high value manufacturing in nature. In deed, the current challenges for the micro manufacturing include the hybrid manufacturing capability, reconfigurability, modularity, adaptability and energy/resource efficient. Therefore, a generic modular reconfigurable micro manufacturing platform is in deeded for fulfilling the essential needs above. Such kind of machine platform will play as a basic but key modular unit to provide the functionalities and flexibility required by the product-oriented production systems.

Recently, it is proposed that the emergence of "point-of-care" service systems as a major model for the future of healthcare. Similarly, in the manufacturing domain, there is a swing back from the existing largely centralized manufacturing model to a more distributed manufacturing model that co-exits with the centralized model [8] [9] [10]. That means manufacturing service location will move to the point of consumption from factories in the future. Therefore, the proposed reconfigurable machine platform for product-service system should not only have the ability to provide product-oriented manufacturing but also can enable the micro manufacturing to take place at the "point-of-use" in a timely and economic fashion.

It is against such a background that this paper has proposed a new micro manufacturing platform, i.e. a generic modular reconfigurable platform (GMRP), to provide an effective means for fabrication of high value micro products including customer goods, automotive optics and medical devices, etc. at low cost in a responsive manner. The GMRP has the potential to satisfy the dynamic fast moving demands and the applications of "point-of-use". The GMRP features hybrid micro manufacturing processes, modularity of key components, reuse of machine components, reduced material consumption, and reconfigurability of machine platforms and key components. Furthermore, this paper also proposes and discusses a practical methodology for the design of reconfigurable machine platforms for product-oriented micro manufacturing systems intended as a key element of industrial product-service system.

**DESIGN OF GENERIC MODULAR RECONFIGURABLE PLATFORMS (GMRPS) FOR A
PRODUCT-ORIENTED MICRO MANUFACTURING SYSTEM**

2.0   GMRP Conception

   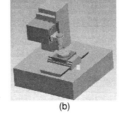

(a)   (b)

Fig.1   Virtual models of two GMRP configurations

As shown through the viral models in Fig.1, two GMRP configurations have been proposed by the authors. Each GMRP is a bench-top hybrid processing machine designed for industrial feasible nano/micro manufacturing. The base of each platform is generic, and manufacturers can add, change, or remove modular components such as spindles, slideways, tool holders, etc., forming a specified nano/micro hybrid machine as new components/ products manufacturing is required. Moreover, a GMRP is modular and reconfigurable in structure, so it can thus be used as a generic machine unit for forming a product-oriented micro manufacturing system at low cost.

2.1   Hybrid Manufacturing Capability

Micro components/products are normally integrated products with different materials and of diverse micro features, which make it necessary for manufacturers to possess hybrid micromachining ability to cope with varied features and materials. The GMRP has hybrid manufacturing capability aiming to broaden the limits of its application and to improve the product manufacturing quality. As illustrated in Fig. 2, the GMRP may integrate many micro processes such as micro-electrical discharge machining (EDM), micro grinding, micro milling, micro drilling, etc. because of their similar kinematic configurations. The seamless integration of micromachining processes on a GMRP will lead to predictability, producibility and productivity of nano/micro manufacturing, with the capability to be adaptive, which is essential for the future industrial product-service system.

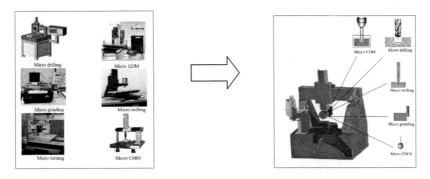

Fig.2   Hybrid manufacturing capability of a GMRP

**DESIGN OF GENERIC MODULAR RECONFIGURABLE PLATFORMS (GMRPS) FOR A
PRODUCT-ORIENTED MICRO MANUFACTURING SYSTEM**

2.2   Machine Platform and Modularity

Modular structure and reconfiguration are required for industrial product-service system which can appropriately responds to personalised individual needs low-costly and quickly. Modularity is one solution for micro manufacturing systems to outlive the products they were originally designed for. The manufacturer can easily configure the platform and later reconfigure it to meet customer's future needs [11]. Modularity is also a cost-efficient solution, and makes later upgrades or modifications to the platform easier.

2.3   Machine Platform and Reconfigurability

According to the definition of product-service system, key factors for the success of product-service system should include: to customize solutions to meet specific customer needs and to create new functions or to make unique combinations of functions. Consequently, GMRP is designed highly reconfigurable in order to be adaptive to the introduction of new technologies, manufacturing changes and mobility requirements.

Mechanical reconfigurability GMRP is able to be easily reconfigured for changes due to its modular components and modules. For example, reconfigurability for changes of products and processes is achieved by changing machine modules, such as spindle units, rotary tables, and linear slideways, with different sizes, accuracy and functionalities.

Electrical reconfigurability Electrical installation at the GMRP can be reconfigured by choosing modules from the library of electrical components and hardware. This library possibly includes rotary motors, linear motors with diverse specifications, encoders and amplifiers. Rotary motors, for example, can be replaced with linear motors to get better motion performance and neat design of the drive and actuation system. Different types of encoder are also possible to be selected to reconfigure the system for different level of performance requirements.

Control system reconfigurability Similar to reconfiguring machine modules and electrical systems, control systems are also capable of being reconfigured by selecting needed software modules (e.g., servo control algorithms, interpolators) and hardware modules (controllers) in the development of open-ended control architecture. Selection of control modules is directly influenced by the electrical components.

2.4   Formation of a Product-oriented Micro Manufacturing System

Fig.3 depicts that a micro manufacturing system formed with GMRPs can be developed to fabricate various micro products, covering the full process chain from different machining operations (e.g. micro milling, drilling, EDM) through inspection (e.g. micro CMM) to the final assembly. Such a system can be used to produce high quality products competitively due to its reconfigurability, modularity and adaptivity, offering excellent responsiveness, short lead time, low cost and mass customization. In this micro manufacturing system, each GMRP can be configured as a specified functional machine by choosing corresponding modular components from the library of modules, which greatly reduces the set up and the cost of the whole manufacturing system. The system is highly flexible and can be easily reconfigured and reused because of the adoption of GMRPs.

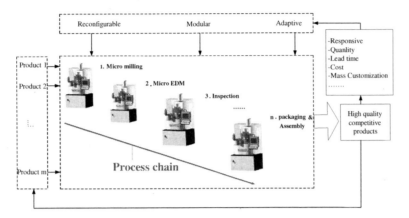

Fig. 3   Principle of a product-oriented micro manufacturing system

3.0   Design Methodology of GMRP

The GMRP-based system aims to be a product-oriented reconfigurable, highly responsive manufacturing system particularly for high value nano/micro manufacturing purposes. The methodology of the design of GMRP is illustrated in Fig. 4.

The methodology consists of four important parts, namely, design interface, knowledge base, design engine and component library, which may be basically regarded as a design expert system.

The design interface provides a user-friendly HCI for accessing different modules and functionalities. Through the interface, the designer will be able to specify the design requirements according to the customer needs such as the type of machining, the number of axis of the machine tool, etc. (Fig. 5). The system will use the knowledge base to display relevant design suggestions and/or solutions (Fig. 6) for designer to choose suitable design options or parameters. The interface presents an integrated platform for the interactive design process.

The rule-based knowledge base is the essential element of the system, which stores and represents the expert knowledge of good designers. It is implemented as a part of a standard expert system. The design engine is largely based the axiomatic design theory, which will be detailed in the next section.

The component library is basically a database to support the design process. The detailed information of the components will be used for analysis and evaluation of different design configurations in the design engine and knowledge base. They will also be directly used in the representation and display of actual designed modules or systems (Fig. 7).

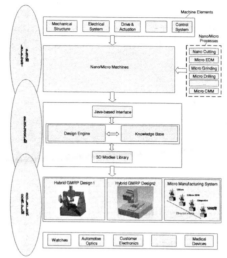

Fig. 4   GMRP and micro manufacturing architecture

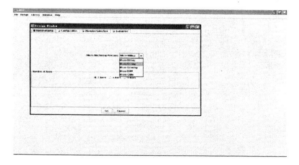

Fig. 5   Design requirements interface

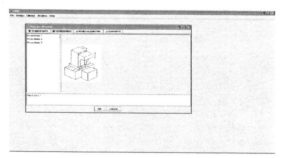

Fig. 6   Recommend design solutions

DESIGN OF GENERIC MODULAR RECONFIGURABLE PLATFORMS (GMRPS) FOR A
PRODUCT-ORIENTED MICRO MANUFACTURING SYSTEM

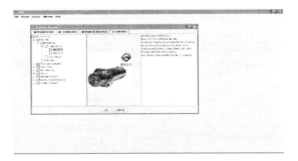

Fig. 7   Detail information of components

3.1   Extended Axiomatic Design

Axiomatic design is a design methodology which systematically processes information between and within four design domains: the consumer domain, the functional domain, the physical domain and the process domain. The domain structure and the specific domains in micro manufacturing of various micro parts are illustrated schematically in Fig. 8. The domain to the left relative to the domain on the right represents "what we want to achieve," whereas the domain on the right represents the design solution, "how we propose to satisfy the requirements specified in the left domain" [12].

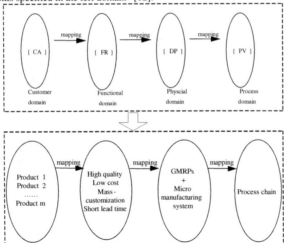

Fig. 8   Four domains of the micro manufacturing of various micro parts

Customer needs is described in the customer domain by the vector {CAs}. In the functional domain, the customer needs are translated to functional requirements {FRs}. To satisfy the specified FRs, design parameters {DPs} in the physical domain are conceived. Finally, to produce the product specified in terms of DPs, we develop a process that is characterized by process variables {PVs} in the process domain [12-14]. In the micro manufacturing field, what customer need are various micro parts, so the micro manufacturing system has to be able to offer high quality, low cost and customized products. In the physical domain, GMRPs and GMRPs based micro manufacturing system are designed to provide the needs required in function domain.

**DESIGN OF GENERIC MODULAR RECONFIGURABLE PLATFORMS (GMRPS) FOR A
PRODUCT-ORIENTED MICRO MANUFACTURING SYSTEM**

Process chains in process domain can provide the fabrication of products required by customers. The mapping process between the domains can be expressed mathematically in terms of the characteristic vectors that define the design goals and design solutions. The relationship between functional requirements {FR} and design parameters {DP} which satisfy the functional requirements can be written as:

$$\{FR\} = [A]\{DP\} \tag{1}$$

where [A] is a design matrix for design process.

Two axioms that govern the design process in axiomatic design are stated as:
Axiom 1: The Independence Axiom. Maintain the independence of the FRs.
Axiom 2: The Information Axiom. Minimize the information content of the design.

Independence axiom states that the independence of functional requirements must always be maintained. It means that when there is two or more FRs, the design solution must be such that each one of the FRs can be satisfied without affecting the other FRs.

Information axiom states that among those designs that satisfy the Independence Axiom, the design that has the smallest information content is the best design because it requires the least amount of information to achieve the design goals. Information content I for a given FR is defined in terms of the probability P of satisfying FR:

$$I = \log_2 \frac{1}{P} = -\log_2 P \tag{2}$$

The information content for an entire system I_{sys} with m FRs is

$$I_{sys} = -\log_2 P_{\{m\}} \tag{3}$$

where $P_{\{m\}}$ is the joint probability that all m FRs are satisfied.

In simple cases where the distributions can be approximated as uniform distributions, equation (2) may be expressed as:

$$I = \log_2 \left(\frac{System\ Range}{Common\ Range} \right) \tag{4}$$

where System Range and Common Range are defined in Fig. 9. The Design Range corresponds to the required tolerances.

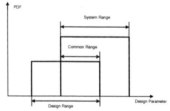

Fig. 9   Probability distribution of a system parameter

DESIGN OF GENERIC MODULAR RECONFIGURABLE PLATFORMS (GMRPS) FOR A PRODUCT-ORIENTED MICRO MANUFACTURING SYSTEM

3.2 Application of Axiomatic Design

A number of corollaries can be derived from the above two axioms and some of them are very relevant to the design discussed in this paper, i.e.

Corollary 2:   Minimization of FRs.
Corollary 3:   Integration of physical parts.
Corollary 4:   Use of standardization
Corollary 6:   Largest tolerance.
Corollary 7:   Uncoupled design with less information.

They can be directly used to guide the design process. A typical design process based upon the axiomatic design theory is as follows [15]:

Step 1:   Establishment of design goals to satisfy a given set of perceived needs.
Step 2:   Conceptualization of design solutions.
Step 3:   Analysis of the proposed solution.
Step 4:   Selection of the best design from among those proposed.
Step 5:   Implementation.

For the design of GMRP, the customer needs can be therefore identified as:
CA1=reconfigurable
CA2=highly responsive
CA3=nano/micro manufacturing

These needs can be further translated into functional requirements:
FR1=machining functions
FR2=flexibility
FR3=accuracy
FR4=machining volume

The functional requirements can be each related to a design parameter:
DP1=machine type
DP2=set up time
DP3=accuracy of machine
DP4=maximal machinable part volume

It is possible to determine the mathematical relationship between the functional requirements and design parameters:

$$\begin{Bmatrix} FR1 \\ FR2 \\ FR3 \\ FR4 \end{Bmatrix} = \begin{bmatrix} X & 0 & 0 & 0 \\ 0 & X & 0 & 0 \\ X & 0 & X & X \\ X & 0 & 0 & X \end{bmatrix} \begin{Bmatrix} DP1 \\ DP2 \\ DP3 \\ DP4 \end{Bmatrix} \tag{5}$$

The first axiom has been used in the generation of the design parameters due to characteristics of design matrix of equation (5). Given these design parameters, there are many feasible solutions. The second axiom may be used to select the best design using the information content measure, calculated based upon equation (4) when system range and common range are known.

DESIGN OF GENERIC MODULAR RECONFIGURABLE PLATFORMS (GMRPS) FOR A PRODUCT-ORIENTED MICRO MANUFACTURING SYSTEM

The functional requirements and design parameters could be further expanded into a hierarchical structure with the design parameter decomposition corresponding to the functional requirements decomposition. One obvious way of decomposition is a top down approach from the whole system through subsystems down to component level.

4.0   Conclusions

This paper has presented a generic modular reconfigurable platform (GMRP) intended for a product-service system in micro manufacturing, as well as its design methodology based upon the axiomatic design theory. The axiomatic design offers many benefits and can subsequently lead to optimum design.

The methodology is currently being implemented. The implementation is based on Java-based interface, axiomatic design and integration knowledge-base and 3D models library. The design and evaluation of the full system will be presented in a future paper.

Acknowledgement

The authors would like to thank the assistance from Dr. D. Huo and Mr. P. Yates at Brunel University and F. Wardle at UPM Ltd.

References

[1] M. Goedkoop, C. van Haler, H. te Riele and P. Rommers. 'Product service systems, ecological and economic basics'. *Report for Dutch Ministries of Environment (VROM) and Economic Affairs (EZ)*, 1999.
[2] O. Mont. 'Clarifying the concept of product-service system'. *Journal of Cleaner Production,* 2002, 10(3): 237-245.
[3] M. Kang, R. Wimmer. Product service systems as systemic cures for obese consumption and production. *Journal of Cleaner Production.* 2008, 16(11): 1146-1152.
[4] A. Williams. Product service systems in the automobile industry: contribution to system innovation? *Journal of Cleaner Production.* 2007, 15: 1093-1103.
[5] N. Morelli. Developing new product service systems (PSS): methodologies and operational tools. *Journal of Cleaner Production.* 2006, 14: 1495-1501.
[6] A. Azarenko. 'Development of technical product-service system scenarios for machine tool industry'. *MSc thesis,* Cranfield University, 2007.
[7] Azarenko, A., Roy, R., Shore, P., Tiwari, A., and Shehab, E. (2007), "Technical Product-Service System: Business Models for High Precision Machine Tool Manufacturers", Proceedings of the 5th International Conference on Manufacturing Research (ICMR 2007), September 11-13, 2007, Leicester, UK
[8] K. F. Ehmann. A synopsis of U.S. micro-manufacturing research and development activities and trends. *Proceeding of 4M2007 Conference on Multi-Material Micro Manufacture,* 2007.
[9] R. Bateman, K. Cheng. Devolved Manufacturing: theoretical perspectives. *Concurrent Engineering: Research and Applications,* 2002, 10(4): 291-297.
[10] R. Bateman, K. Cheng. Extending the product portfolio with 'devolved manufacturing': methodology and case studies, *International Journal of Production Research,* 2006, 44(16): 3325-3343.
[11] J. Heilala, J. Montonen and K. Helin. 'Life cycle and unit cost analysis for modular re-configurable flexible light assembly systems'. *Proceeding of 2nd IPROMS virtual international conference,* 2006, pp: 395-400.
[12] N. P. Suh. 'Axiomatic design: advances and applications'. Oxford University Press, 2000.
[13] K. Chen, X. Feng and B. Zhang. 'Development of computer-aided quotation system for manufacturing enterprises using axiomatic design'. *International Journal of Production Research,* 2003, 41(1): 171-191.
[14] K. Yang and H. Zhang. 'Comparison of TRIZ and axiomatic design'. *Proceeding of ICAD2000 first internal conference on axiomatic design,* Cambridge, 2000.
[15] B. Babic. 'Axiomatic design of flexible manufacturing systems'. *International Journal of Production Research,* 1999, 37(5): 1159-1173.

The 6th International Conference on Manufacturing Research (ICMR08)
Brunel University, UK, 9-11th September 2008

DESIGN OF MODULAR SERVICE ARCHITECTURES FOR PRODUCT SERVICE SYSTEMS

Horst Meier[(2)], Katja Sadek[(2)]

2. **Institute of Product and Service Engineering, Chair of Production Systems, Ruhr-University Bochum, Germany**

Abstract

The product-oriented business strategy of traditional manufacturing companies directly imposes the responsibility of a product's use, its maintenance and disposal to the customer. By shifting the business focus from designing and selling physical products only to offering integrated Product-Service Systems (PSS) those combined solutions represent an innovative strategy to fulfill client demands jointly. Since there are currently neither sufficient methods nor capable computer-aided tools to develop PSS efficiently, especially with focus on its service design, costs increase and customer requirements are only deficiently identified. Therefore, a novel approach to methodically develop a Modular Service Architecture (MSA) for PSS will be presented. The architecture's design is heavily influenced by the characteristics of services as well as the principles of modularization. The development method is conducted in order to generate a variety of service modules, to construct standardized service interfaces and to establish an architecture which consistently combines service modules and interfaces. The MSA is used in the early development phase of a PSS in order to embed different combinations of such developed service modules into a PSS concept model depending on the respective customer requirements.

Keywords: Product-Service-System (PSS), Modular Service Architecture development, Product and Service Modularization

1.0   Introduction

In traditional manufacturing companies physical products are considered to be at the core of the offering. Therefore, value is based on the exchange of physical technological artifacts between a providing company and a receiving customer. This product-oriented business strategy imposes the responsibility of a product's use, its maintenance and disposal to the customer who may not be aware to an appropriate behavior. [1] [2]. Due to the ever increasing global competition as well as the demands for greater company responsibility of products throughout their entire life cycle enterprises are forced to shift their business focus from designing and selling physical products only to offering integrated solutions in the form of Product-Service-Systems (PSS). Those combined solutions continuously provide value to the customer and therefore represent an innovative strategy to not only jointly fulfill client demands but also to successfully compete on the global market [3]. In this regard services are no longer seen as product add-ons, but are to be systematically integrated into a problem solution.

In the following a novel approach to methodically develop a Modular Service Architecture (MSA) for PSS, is presented. The architecture's design is heavily influenced by the characteristics of services as well as the principles of modularization. The MSA is used in the early development phase of PSS in order to embed different combinations of such developed service modules depending on the respective customer requirements into a PSS problem solution in an effective, efficient, standardized and consistent manner.

2.0 Modular Service Architecture (MSA) – Influencing Variables

To systematically develop a Modular Service Architecture (MSA) several so called 'influencing variables' are to be considered. In this regard the characteristics of services as well as the principles of modularization are to be analyzed.

2.1 Service Characteristics

Services are defined as a heterogeneous, mainly immaterial and perishable activity or process. They are offered by a company or an institute and are consumed simultaneously to their production [4]. Another distinguishing characteristic of services is the necessity of integrating an external factor, provided by the service recipient, into service provision. Such external factors can consist of persons, goods, rights and information, etc. Constitutive approaches for the definition of services are further founded on three different dimensions. The structure dimension determines the ability and willingness of a provider to deliver the service in question. The process dimension explains services as processes which are performed on or with external factors integrated. The outcome dimension refers to the tangible and intangible outputs as a result of rendering a service [5].

2.2 Modular Design

Module, modularity, modularization and modular design are well known terms in industry as well as in academia. Nevertheless, it is quite difficult to find one unambiguous explanation to those various terms [6]. In general modularization is used in order to reduce the complexity of an overall system. The term module is defined as a logical and physical unit performing a precisely defined function within an overall context. Such modules are linked with each other through standardized interfaces [7]. These modular systems are subject to the rules of decomposition, abstraction, nested hierarchy, loose coupling and limited access. The term decomposition defines the segmentation of a system into its subsystems. Depending on the chosen level of abstraction and with the aid of nested hierarchy these subsystems can be systematically subdivided into further part systems to the point of elemental functions or to the limits of knowledge. In regard to modularization the principles of loose coupling and limited access play a decisive role concerning the interfaces' design. Loose coupling describes the request for strong dependencies between the embedded elements within one module. Whereas the principle of limited access uses the definition of public attributes in order to design standardized module interfaces. In this regard it is essential that the more the description of the interface differs from the module's internals and the less those internals are revealed by such in- and output information the merrier modules can be independently used and exchanged of a particular context [8].

Modularization is currently used in the context of product development and software engineering. Within the scope of software developing interface descriptions are primarily limited to the exchange of data and control instructions. Due to the fact that services are socio-technical systems their interfaces must be designed in consideration of a series of other interdependencies. By rising to this challenge with the aid of service modularization companies can strike a balance between standardized and individual ranges of services offered [8].

3.0   The Transferability of Modular Product Architectures to the Service Sector

3.1   Modular Product Architecture

Modularity arises from a product's division into independent components and allows for the creation of product variety by decoupling, reusing, exchanging or extending such standardized elements. In this regard modular product architectures are defined as a scheme in which each physical chunk implements a specific set of functional elements. The interactions between these chunks are to be defined precisely and in general of fundamental importance to the primary product's function [6]. The more a product component differentiates in its physical and functional use from the other parts the higher is the level of the product architecture's modularity [9]

The modularization of products not only reduces the development efforts, times and costs by using already existing modules, it also decreases the assembly complexity due to the lower degree of interactions. Product failures can be eliminated quickest possible by simply replacing the defect component using an equivalent product module. On the other hand modeling and realization of product interactions still pose a major challenge. Furthermore, due to the high level of standardization unitized products may not meet individual customer requirements [9]. In this regard a company has to weigh up between the advantages and disadvantages of product modularization according to the group of customers they want to address.

3.2   To What Extend Give Modular Product Architectures Direction to the Service Sector?

The concept of modular product architectures is very suitable for the service sector. Thereby, the service module design can be performed in an analogous manner to the product modularization. Whereas the definition of service module interfaces poses a major challenge due to the fact that services consist of tangible and intangible elements and further because of their process-related character.

In accordance with the advantages that come along with the modularization of products, modular service architectures are used in order to shorten service development times and costs by decoupling, reusing, exchanging or extending standardized service modules. In this regard the ability to respond to changes at the point of sale increases. Moreover, the recombination of service modules allows for customized service configurations requiring minimum development efforts.

4.0   Development of Modular Service Architectures

In the following a novel approach to methodically develop modular service architectures is presented. The method is subdivided into four different phases. A description of the method execution is illustrated in figure 1.

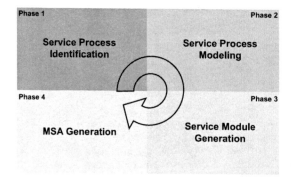

Fig. 1 Development of a Modular Service Architecture

Phase 1: The systematical development of a MSA is initialized by the analysis of a company's portfolio which provides a detailed description of products and services currently offered by that company. Building on this information the service developer starts to identify existing as well as new kinds of services necessary to jointly create value. Such identification of new services is based on so called "*7 types of services*" (function creating, function keeping, optimization, logistics, planning, schooling and consulting [10]) which serve as categories containing an overall number of 86 different kinds of performances.

Phase 2: Based on the information generated during phase one the developer starts to model all identified services using what is termed "event-driven process chains". Those process chains are to be modeled using the purchasable software tool *ARIS* (architecture of integrated information systems). In this regard a service is visualized with the aid of functions, so called events, technical and human resources as well as data and information. Functions describe a specific task within the overall service, while events declare that the function in question has been carried out. The data and information mentioned are dedicated to a particular function in order to render the overall service. Such visualization allows for the design of external factors as well as the integration of immaterial aspects like data and information. Depending on the level of abstraction services can be composed of an indefinite amount of such process elements

After identifying and modeling all service processes the service developer has to methodically generate what is termed "service process units". These units form context-related clusters enabling the identification of equivalent service process sections from the whole of all modeled services.

In the following it is distinguished between three different types of such service units:

- basic service process units (BPU)
- variable service process units (VPU)
- specific service process units (SPU)

"Basic service process" units are defined as a selection of process elements which are usually carried out the same way, but independently of the overall function a service tries to render. An example for such performances is the order acceptance or the order invoicing. Additionally "variable service process units" exist. These contain functions which are used within several of the modeled services, e.g. a functional test repeatedly performed within different maintenance related services. As a third type, "specific service process units" are used in order to fulfill a specific function, e.g. the performing of a preventive maintenance or an installation which are only used in regard to one specific service.

A description of such unit determinations is shown in figure 2.

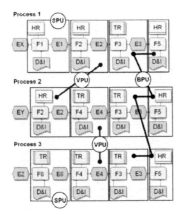

Legend:
Service Event (**E**), Service Function (**F**), Human Resource (**HR**), Technical Resource (**TR**), Data and Information (**D&I**), Basic Service Process Unit (**BPU**), Variable Service Process Unit (**VPU**), Specific Service Process Unit (**SPU**)

Fig.2   Determination of Service Process Units

This fragmentation into three different service units is essential for the generation of service modules. It allows for the decomposition of the overall service system in a methodical way.

Phase 3: Based on the previously established service units so called 'basic, variable and specific service modules' are to be defined. Thereby, the unit's functions are embedded conforming to the principle of loose coupling inside the module, whereas the module interface (in- and output) is designed using technical and human resources as well as data and information in accordance with the role of limited access. An example of such modules is shown in figure 3.

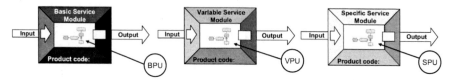

Fig. 3 Service Modules

Each service module is marked by what is termed 'product code'. It defines the relation between a product and its related service module within a PSS. For example the product code 'maintainable product' refers to the related 'service code: maintenance service' which is marked on a specific product. Thereby, the systematical combination of products and their related services within the early development phase of a PSS is much more simplified.

Phase 4: In order to consistently illustrate the developed service modules as well as the relations between them the notation of a class diagram has been chosen. In general a class diagram is used in order to describe the structure of a system by showing the system's classes, their attributes and operations, and further the relationships between all classes. In this regard the service module's in- and output information (human and technical resources, data and information) as well as its product code are listed in the form of attributes, whereby the module's functions are described with the aid of operations. The relations between these modules are to be generated using the service unit's dependencies illustrated in phase 3.

Figure 4 shows the generation of such a class diagram in detail.

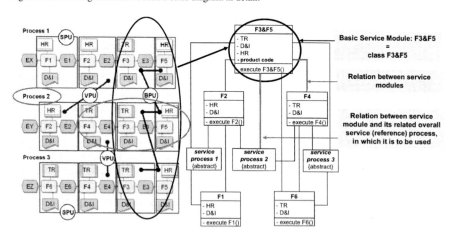

Fig. 4 Generation of the Class Diagram

In order to consistently combine the previously developed service modules a reference process, representing the Modular Service Architecture, is to be generated. Such a process consists of so-called "placeholders" which are linked to each other through standardized interfaces, whereby different service modules can fit into one placeholder. In this regard the previously developed class diagram serves as a blueprint or further catalogue which allows it to choose the necessary service modules under consideration of their relations to other modules/processes and in accordance with the customer's requirements. A detailed illustration of the previous descriptions is shown in figure 5.

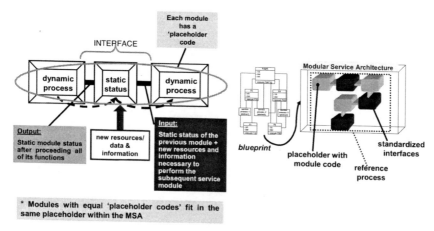

Fig. 5   Modular Service Architecture

A Modular Service Architecture can be developed context-related, e.g. regarding maintenance services (or in accordance with '7types of industrial services'). In this context a maintenance reference process is to be generated in order to consistently combine all modules which had been identified in the context of maintenance through the method execution and further illustrated in a 'maintenance class diagram'.

Hence, a Modular Service Architecture consists of a reference process embedding basic, variable and specific modules which are linked to each other in compliance with the roles of loose coupling and limited access through standardized interfaces. In this regard, the product code of each module simplifies the systematical combination of products and services within the early phase of PSS development.

5.0   Conclusion

Due to the ever increasing global competition as well as the demands for greater company responsibility of products throughout their entire life cycle enterprises are forced to shift their business focus from designing and selling physical products only to offering integrated solutions in the form of Product-Service-Systems. In this regard services are no longer seen as product add-ons, but are to be systematically integrated into a problem solution.

In this context the methodical development of Modular Service Architectures has been presented. Several variables which might influence its development have been analyzed and taken into account, if appropriate. The developed method is to be used in the early development phase of PSS in order to embed different combinations of service modules depending on the respective customer requirements into a PSS problem solution in an effective, efficient, standardized and consistent manner. Thereby, a PSS designer is capable of reducing its service development efforts, times and costs.

References

[1] Tan, A.R.; McAloone, T.C., 2006, What happens to integrated product development models with product/service-system approaches?, 6th Integrated Product Development Workshop, October

[2] Meier, H.; Kortmann, D., 2006, Leadership – From Technology to Use, 14th CIRP Conference on Life Cycle Engineering

[3] Tan, A.R.; McAloone, T.C., 2006, Characteristics of Strategies in Product/Service-System Development, International Design Conference, May 15-18

[4] Matzen, D.; Tan, A.R.; Myrup Andreasen, M., Product/Service-Systems: Proposal for Models and Terminology, 16. Symposium "Design for X", Neukirchen, Oktober 2005

[5] Fähnrich, K.-P., Meiren, T., 2007, Service Engineering State of the Art and Future Trends, in: Spath, D.; Fähnrich, K.-P. [ed.], 2007, Advances in Service Innovations, Springer-Verlag, Berlin et. al.: 3-16

[6] Erixon, Gunnar, 1998, Modular Function Deployment –A Method for Product Modularisation: 50-57, ISSN 1104-2141

[7] Kahlbrandt, B., 2001, Software-Engineering mit der Unified Modeling Language; Springer-Verlag Berlin et. al.: 75, ISBN 3-540-41600-5

[8] Böhmann, T.; Krcmar, H., 2003, Modulare Servicearchitektur, in: Bullinger, H.-J., Scheer, A.-W., Service-Engineering – Gestaltung und Entwicklung innovativer Dienstleistungen, Springer-Verlag Berlin et. al.: 391-415, ISBN 3-540-43831-9

The 6th International Conference on Manufacturing Research (ICMR08)
Brunel University, UK, 9-11th September 2008

APPLYING SEMANTIC WEB SERVICES TO ENTERPRISE WEB

Yang Hu, Qingping Yang, Xizhi Sun, Peng Wei

School of Engineering and Design, Brunel University

Abstract

Enterprise Web provides a convenient, extendable, integrated platform for information sharing and knowledge management. However, it still has many drawbacks due to complexity and increasing information glut, as well as the heterogeneity of the information processed. Research in the field of Semantic Web Services has shown the possibility of adding higher level of semantic functionality onto the top of current Enterprise Web, enhancing usability and usefulness of resource, enabling decision support and automation. This paper aims to explore the use of Semantic Web Services in Enterprise Web and discuss the Semantic Web Services (SWS) approach for designing Enterprise Web applications. A Semantic Web Service oriented model is presented, in which resources and services are described by ontology, and processed through Semantic Web Service, allowing integrated administration, interoperability and automated reasoning.

Keywords: Semantic Web Service, ontology, Enterprise Web, e-business, SOA.

1.0   Introduction

Although Enterprise Web achieved enormous success in many ways, the deficiencies of the current architecture, such as lack of interoperability, massive unstructured data, an increasing number of various systems waiting to be linked, have posed serious problems. Once promising decision-management support is still unsatisfactory, even the enterprise searches are highly limited. To address these problems, new approaches are being proposed and developed, and Semantic Web Service (SWS) appears to be one of the soundest solutions.

Existing Web Services (WS) for enterprises offer very few automation capabilities. For example, the activity of finding proper Web Services, which should deliver expected enterprise functionality, has to be driven by human. The process of assembling pieces of functionality into complex business process also involves human interaction. Finally, translating between different message formats, which are exchanged between enterprise systems and various Web Services, cannot be done automatically [1]. The lack of machine-readable semantics is hampering the usage of Web Services in complex business environment [2]. Semantic Web Services provide a solution, in which a semantic framework is added to extend the current architecture of Web Services, enabling automated discovery, dynamic mediation and invocation.

A general overview of Enterprise Web Service is provided in section 2. And in section 3, three most prominent approaches to define SWS are compared. Finally, a Semantic Web Service oriented model for Enterprise Web is proposed and discussed.

2.0   Enterprise Web Service

Web Service is defined by W3C as "a software system designed to support interoperable Machine to Machine interaction over a network". More specifically, Enterprise Web Services are software applications available on the Enterprise Web, providing specific functions, and can be discovered, described, and accessed using web protocols, transcending platforms, operating systems, programming languages, etc. Enterprise Web Services facilitate integration of enterprise operations, reduce the cost of web application development and deployment. Enterprise Web Services are based on XML and following industry standards: Web Services Description Language (WSDL), SOAP, and Universal Description, Discovery, and Integration (UDDI).

WSDL [3] is the W3C recommended language for describing the service interface. It is one of the three activities of the Web Service Modelling Ontology (WSMO) initiative that aims to provide a complete framework enhancing syntactic description of Web Service with semantic metadata. WSDL can be used to describe a Web Service by specifying the functions the service provides. WSDL-based document provides enough information about how to interact with the target Web Service.

SOAP is a lightweight protocol designed for exchanging XML-based messages between applications over networks. It forms the foundation layer of the Web Services architecture, provides the basic messaging framework upon which abstract layers can be built. SOAP messages can carry an XML payload defined using XML-S, thus ensuring a consistent interpretation of data items between different services [4].

UDDI is a platform-independent, XML-based registry for businesses to publish service listings and discover each other and define how the services or software applications interact over the networks, thus allowing potential users to find services that are offered by providers. UDDI Web Service discovery is typically human oriented but it may also include references to WSDL descriptions, which may facilitate limited automation of discovery and invocation [5].

In the typical scenario of enterprise environment, Web Services applied to Enterprise Web should be self-contained, self-describing, modular applications that can be published, located, and invoked over the Enterprise Web. However, in almost every step of these processes, humans are always involved, to publish, to locate and to invoke the Web Services. Existing architecture lacks an appropriate semantic framework allowing for automation of many of these processes that are currently handled manually [1].

3.0 Comparison of Semantic Web Service Approaches

Semantic Web is an extension to the current Web with the purpose of allowing people and machines to find, share, reuse and integrate information more easily. It is essentially a web with semantics, which are usually added with ontologies. It provides the necessary infrastructure for publishing and resolving ontological descriptions of terms and concepts. In addition, it provides the necessary techniques for reasoning about these concepts, as well as resolving and mapping between ontologies, thus enabling semantic interoperability of Web Services through the identification (and mapping) of semantically similar concepts [2].

Analogously, Semantic Web Services extend the capabilities of original Web Services by describing the services with semantics annotations, enabling automated service discovery, binding and invocation. Also SWS can help facilitate the integration of various resources and services in enterprise scope. Many approaches are proposed to implement Semantic Web Service, three of the most promising ones are WSMO, OWL-S and IRS-III.

The Web Service Modeling Ontology (WSMO) provides ontological specifications to describe the various aspects of Semantic Web Services, aiming at an integrated technology for turning into the next generation Internet from an information repository for human consumption to a worldwide system for distributed web computing [6]. Its top-level elements are Ontologies, Web Services, Goals and Mediators.

1) Ontologies provide the formally specified semantics for the terminology used by all other WSMO components.
2) Web Service offers service description to describe the functionality and behaviors of the service, provided by service providers. It also outlines how Web Services communicate (choreography) and how they are composed (orchestration) [2].
3) Goals are used by service requesters to specify what functionality and behaviors they would like that service to have. Goals are described in ontologies that are used as the semantically defined terminology, modeling the user view in the SWS architecture.
4) Mediators handle the potential mismatches that may occur at both data level and protocol level between the components that shall interoperate.

OWL-S is an ontology for describing Semantic Web Services represented in OWL. It combines the expressivity of description logics and the pragmatism found in the emerging Web Services Standards, to describe services that can be expressed semantically, and yet grounded within a well-defined data typing formalism [7]. It is comprised of three top-level notions: Service Profile, Service Model and Service Grounding.

1) Service Profile describes both the functional and non-functional properties of a Web Service, for the purpose of service discovery.

2) Service Model contains descriptive information on the composition or orchestration of one or more services in terms of their constituent processes. This can be used for reasoning about possible compositions and controlling the service publishing and invocation.

3) Service Grounding gives details of how to access the service, mapping from an abstract to a concrete specification for service usage [6].

IRS-III [6][8], the Internet Reasoning Service, is a framework and implemented infrastructure which supports the developing and execution of Semantic Web Services by utilizing the WSMO ontology. It has the overall aim of supporting the automated or semi-automated construction of semantically enhanced systems over the Internet [9]. IRS III has four features that distinguish it from other work on Semantic Web Services.

1) It can automatically transform programming code (currently Java and Lisp are supported) into a web service, by automatically creating the appropriate wrapper. This feature allows converting existing standalone software into web services very easily.

2) IRS-III supports capability-driven service execution. Users of IRS-III can directly invoke web services via goals.

3) IRS-III is programmable. Users can substitute their own Semantic Web Services for some of the main IRS III components.

4) IRS-III services are web service compatible – standard web services can be trivially published through the IRS III and any IRS III service automatically appears as a standard web service to other web service infrastructures.

Both WSMO and OWL-S share the same WSDL/SOAP foundation. However, while WSMO provides service interface description including definitions of both orchestration and choreography, OWL-S does not have an explicit definition of choreography but instead focuses on a process based description of how complex web services invoke atomic web services [2]. IRS-III is also based on WSMO ontology, considered as a more user-oriented infrastructure that has the concentrated efforts in allowing users easily convert current available service code into Semantic Web Service.

Many researches and studies have been carried out, using or combining these and other approaches, to enhance and semanticize applications in various aspects of enterprise web, such as decision support [10], e-commerce [2][11], supply chain management [12], resource discovery [13], etc. And some attempts have been made to construct new architectures that allow enterprise application integration [14][15].

4.0   Proposed Semantic Web Service-oriented Model for enterprise

Fig. 1 outlines a Semantic Web Service model for Enterprise Web. This architecture is based on ontologies and centered on modules of Mediators running on ISR-III platform. Ontologies serve as the enterprise knowledge base, including: domain ontologies, which represent all the concepts and information of the enterprise and related industry; user ontologies, containing the user-oriented concepts, which can be used to automatically process user-related task or even auto-characterize user interface; WS ontologies, and so on. The typical process of knowledge discovery and production (i.e. in this case, the production of the corporate ontology base) in a Semantic Enterprise Web is also shown, which has distinct difference from the process in current enterprises where information is kept unstructured or in various separate systems. Mediators are very useful components acting as the "connectors" between the Web Services, ontologies and users. By different usage, mediators can be divided into four classes: ontology-to-ontology mediator, goal-to-goal mediator, web services-to-goal mediator and web services-to-web services mediator, each copes with the heterogeneity problems that might occur between respective elements. Further to a standard WSMO framework, IRS-III platform is chosen to be combined with mediators as additional "middleware". IRS-III provides a convenient and flexible way for upgrading old web service or even standalone software to Semantic Web Service thus saving the cost. It also facilitates compatibility with other non-semantic Web Services by automatically appearing as standard web services to other web service infrastructures. The combination of IRS-III platform and WSMO mediators is very natural and technically feasible, as IRS-III and WSMO frameworks are both based on WSMO ontology and have similar mechanisms.

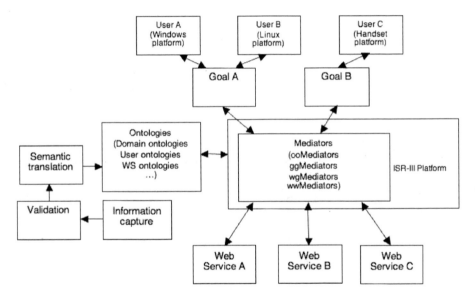

Fig. 1.   Semantic Web Service Model for Enterprise Web.

The publishing and invocation of standard Web Services require the interaction between requester and provider to be tightly coupled together. For example, when a Web Service is published, it must be registered in a UDDI repository. A requester may try looking for the service required by searching the name or human-oriented descriptions through the repository. However, these descriptions are informal and non-semantic, the requester must assume they have the same understanding as the service provider. If the service has been proved to be satisfactory, the requester may have to adjust their data to fit the service description provided by the WSDL document (like what type of data can be accepted and which protocol should be used when interacting with the service, etc.). In proposed model, both Web Services and Goals are described separately using the WSMO ontology, regardless of the different platforms (both user side and service side). This relieves the requester of the responsibility of matching service requests to service descriptions. Goals can be automatically interpreted and matched at run-time to the services that have the required functions and behaviours in the semantic level, enabling automated service discovery, binding and invocation.

When a request occurs, it should be presented as semantically defined Goals, using predefined WS ontologies, from whatever client platform. When Goals are passed to servers, mediators handle the potential heterogeneity between Goals and other parties, then IRS-III service will be called to retrieve the semantic description of Web Service and invoke the services that address the user requests by means of their semantic description. Finally, the expected Web Services are executed.

5.0   Conclusions

Semantic Web Service provides a very promising approach which enterprise can utilize to connect current systems and services regardless of their underlying platform and their location, integrating and structuring all its resources and applications into a new generation Enterprise Web. In this work, an SWS oriented Enterprise Web Model is proposed to extend existing Enterprise Web with Semantic Web technologies. Research in this area shows great potential of Semantic Web Service, but barriers on the road of applying SWS to Enterprise Web are also inclement and real. Firstly, there are still gaps between lab technology and practical usage. The power and value of Semantic Web Service can easily be seen in a lab, however, when it comes to reality, it is still a very difficult task to create and maintain a descent sized Semantic Enterprise Web. Besides other technical problems, the ontology alone will become extremely hard (if not impossible) to create or maintain when modeling a large-scale enterprise. Some other approaches are developed, and can be considered as gap-fillers between existing and Semantic Enterprise Webs, such as Mashups [16], and will provide valuable source of information when semantic technology become mature. Secondly, many enterprises have huge amount of information and systems that may be up to 40 years old, probably some of these information are not even documented, the cost of semanticizing all these information and systems may become unaffordable. Also there are some capabilities that Enterprise Web should have, are still being explored or still a vision, such as collective intelligence platforms and enterprise decision management support applications. And some very important features like security, enterprise search, are still quite limited and far from satisfactory. These aspects will become major concerns in the future research and development.

References

[1]   M. Zaremba, M. Kerrigan, A. Mocan, M. Moran. "Web services modeling ontology". In: J. Cardoso, A.P. Sheth (eds). *Semantic Web Services, processes and applications*. New York: Springer, pp 63-64. 2006.
[2]   J. Ni, X. Zhao, L. Zhu. "A semantic web service-oriented model for e-commerce". In: *International Conference on Service Systems and Service Management*, Chengdu, June 9-11, 2007.
[3]   E. Christensen, F. Curbera, G. Meredith, S. Weerawarana. "Web services description language (WSDL) 1.1". *W3C Note*. Available from World Wide Web: <http://www.w3.org/TR/2001/NOTE-wsdl-20010315>. 15 March 2001.
[4]   N. Mitra. "SOAP version 1.2 part 0: Primer". *W3C Recommendation*. Available from World Wide Web: <http://www.w3.org/TR/soap12-part0/>. 2003.
[5]   L. Clement, A. Hately, C. von Riegen, T. Rogers (eds). "UDDI version 3.0.2". *UDDI Spec Technical Committee Draft*. Available from World Wide Web: <http://uddi.org/pubs/uddi_v3.htm>. 2004.
[6]   J. Domingue, D. Roman, M. Stollberg. "Web service modeling ontology (WSMO) - An ontology for semantic web services". *Position paper at the W3C Workshop on Frameworks for Semantics in Web Services*, Innsbruck, Austria, 9-10 June 2005.

[7] L. Cabral, J. Domingue, E. Motta, T, Payne, and F. Hakimpour. "Approaches to semantic web services: An overview and comparisons". *1st European Semantic Web Symposium*, Heraklion, Greece, 2004.

[8] J. Domingue, L. Cabral, F. Hakimpour, D. Sell, E. Motta. "IRS III: A platform and infrastructure for creating WSMO based semantic web services". *WSMO Implementation Workshop*, Frankfurt, Germany, 2004.

[9] J. Domingue, L. Cabral, S. Galizia, V. Tanasescu, A. Gugliotta, B. Norton, C. Pedrinaci. "IRS-III: A broker-based approach to semantic Web services". *Web Semantics: Science, Services and Agents on the World Wide Web*, Volume 6, Issue 2, Pages 109-132, April 2008.

[10] O. Byung Kwon. "Meta web service: building web-based open decision support system based on web services". *Expert Systems with Applications*, Volume 24, Issue 4, Pages 375-389, May 2003.

[11] D. Trastour, C. Bartolini, C. Preist. "Semantic Web support for the business-to-business e-commerce pre-contractual lifecycle". *Computer Networks*, Volume 42, Issue 5, Pages 661-673, 5 August 2003.

[12] J. Yue, W. Mu, X. Liu, Z. Fu. "Using Protégé to construct vegetable SCM knowledge ontology". *Proceedings of the 6th World Congress on Intelligent Control and Automation*, Dalian, 21-23 June 2006.

[13] S.C. Buraga, T. Rusu. "Using Semantic Web technologies to discover resources within the intranet of an organization". *Intelligent Production Machines and Systems*, Pages 158-163, 2006.

[14] M. Contreras, L. Sheremetov. "Industrial application integration using the unification approach to agent-enabled semantic SOA". *Robotics and Computer-Integrated Manufacturing*, In Press, Corrected Proof, Available online 28 January 2008.

[15] N. Anicic, Z. Marjanovic, N. Ivezic, A. Jones. "Semantic enterprise application integration standards". *International Journal of Manufacturing Technology and Management*, Volume 10, Numbers 2-3, pp. 205-226(22), 28 December 2006.

[16] C. Warner. "The semantic enterprise: Are semantics the future of mashups?". *The Enterprise Web 2.0 Blog* [online]. [Accessed 7 April 2008]. Available from World Wide Web: <http://blogs.jackbe.com/2008/03/semantic-enterprise-are-semantics.html>. 2008.

APPLYING SEMANTIC WEB SERVICES TO ENTERPRISE WEB

The 6th International Conference on Manufacturing Research (ICMR08)
Brunel University, UK, 9-11th September 2008

VR-BASED APPROACH TO ASSEMBLY AND DISASSEMBLY FOR LARGE-SCALE COMPLEX PRODUCTS

P. J. Xia, Y. X. Yao, W. Y. Tang, Y. D. Lang, P. Chen

P. O. Box 422, School of Mechanical and Electrical Engineering, Harbin Institute of Technology, Harbin 150001, P. R. China

Abstract

VR-based assembly and disassembly is one of the most challenging applications of virtual reality in engineering, and has been studied by many researchers for more than two decades. This paper studies on the virtual assembly/disassembly technology for large-scale complex products. The progress of virtual reality technology and related works are surveyed and classified, the characteristics and problems during assembly/disassembly process for complex products are analyzed, and then a new type virtual environment system is designed and implemented for large-scale complex products. This system can overcome the deficiencies of the existing virtual reality systems such as Desktop system, HMD system and CAVE system. A special machine is designed and can achieve the operator's free walking in the spherical virtual space, and then the assembly/disassembly process simulation can be realized considering human activities and ergonomic factors. An information decomposition and transformation method is put forward to transform data from CAD to virtual reality, a geometry constraint-based virtual environment is set up to support interactive assembly/disassembly tasks, and a hybrid approach based on virtual reality and intelligent algorithm is applied to generate optimal or near-optimal assembly/disassembly sequence. The applications and examples given at last demonstrate the usefulness of the new virtual environment system for large-scale complex products.

Keywords: Virtual reality, assembly and disassembly, complex products.

1.0   Introduction

Assembly and disassembly is a difficult task for complex products. The traditional assembly design is finished by experienced workers by means of fabricating a physical model, which leads to increase development cycle, difficulty and cost. Recently even if computer aided assembly planning (CAAP) with CAD systems has been the subject of considerable research, it doesn't achieve significant up-take in manufacturing industry. The main reason is that the 3D visualization is limited in CAD system, the human experience and knowledge is difficult to exert, and some factors such as quality testing, shop floor layout and human ergonomics can't be taken into account.

Virtual reality, as an innovative and promising technology emerged in recent years, provides a new and low-cost approach to solve assembly and disassembly problems for complex products. In immersive virtual environment, the designer can not only visualize the product to appreciate its inner structure and spatial relationships of components, but also can plan assembly sequence and path, consider assembly and disassembly operation, evaluate human ergonomics and safety etc, and then obtain an optimal assembly or disassembly scheme. Especially for large-scale complex products such as satellite, airplane and rocket, since their characteristics are multifarious components, small batches, high precisions and various resources, the application of virtual reality technology has an important theoretical significance and practical value. It can not only optimize product design, avoid mock-up fabricating, shorten development cycle, reduce cost and risk, but also can guide and train assembly workers, improve assembly quality and efficiency.

2.0   Related Work

As a typical application of virtual reality in engineering, virtual assembly and disassembly has evoked great interest by many researchers. The first virtual assembly and disassembly system was VADE[1] developed by Washington State University in 1995, which announced the successful application of virtual reality technology in assembly and disassembly. Then Fraunhofer-Institute for Industrial Engineering (IAO)[2] in Germany proposed another virtual assembly planning prototyping system, which applied a virtual model of a person VirtualANTHROPOS to carry out assembly operation, and based on the user interactions with the virtual objects, a precedence graph was generated and the time of assembly and cost was determined. In 1997 Heriot-Watt University in England developed UVAVU[3] system which provided a method of extracting human knowledge in virtual environment, and Bielefeld University in Germany realized CODY[4] system combining VR technology and artificial intelligence in 1998. Then in 1999 Wichita University developed JIGPRO[5] system to evaluate the alternate assembly sequence and the jig design, Nanyang Technological University developed a desktop virtual reality system (V-REALISM)[6] for assembly, disassembly and maintenance tasks in 2003, and in 2004 New York University built up a virtual assembly prototype system VPAVE[7] to analyze how the actual factors in machining process influencing product assemblability. At the same time the virtual reality application center of Iwoa State University developed VEGAS[8] system, which could support assembly, disassembly and maintenance tasks in CAVE environment. Considering with these typical systems, the following section discusses the related technology from two aspects.

2.1   Virtual Reality System

Virtual reality is a technology that is often regarded as a natural extension to 3D computer graphics with advanced input and output devices, and it provides multi-modal feedback and interactive immersion to the users for a visual estimation of real process. At present, the existing virtual reality systems can be divided into four categories: Desktop, HMD, CAVE and Cybersphere. These virtual reality systems have been used in different occasions and have their own merits and demerits.

(1) Desktop system[9]. Desktop system employs the display screen of ordinary computer or low-level workstation as the window to observe the virtual scenes. The operator wears stereoscopic glass to observe the 3-D virtual scenes. With the help of data gloves and 3-D trackers, the operator can interact with the virtual scenes. Although the cost of forming this type of system is low, the immersive sense is worse because the display device is only a relatively smaller computer screen.

(2) HMD system[10]. HMD system employs head mounted display, data glove and various interactive devices to seal the operator's vision, hearing and other feelings. In the system, the operator really becomes a participant within the system and can interact with the virtual scenes by interactive devices. The immersive sense of this system is better than that of the desktop system. For the restriction of the head mounted display, the system has the deficiencies of intensive restraint sense, low-resolution ratio, easy visual fatigue etc.

(3) CAVE system[11]. CAVE system was evolved at the beginning of the 1990s. Its main body is a room of which the wall, floor, and ceiling are composed of large screens. The high-resolution images are projected on these screens by high power projectors. Wearing stereoscopic glass, the operator can observe 3-D virtual scenes in any position of the space. CAVE has realized a VE of large view angle, panorama and sharing by several people. But there are also some deficiencies for this system. Its cost is very high because lager space and more hardware equipments are required. Furthermore the operator is still restricted in a limited narrow space and is not able to walk for a long distance in the virtual environment.

(4) Cybersphere system[12]. With all the systems described above, there exists one important limitation. The operator is constrained in either a fixed position or a limited space. But in real world, people should be able to move about in wide space. In order to remove this limitation, Warwick university of Britain cooperating with some companies, has developed a new type of environment system — Cybersphere. A large, hollow, translucent sphere supported by means of a low-pressure cushion of air is adopted as the display device in the Cybersphere system. This air cushion enables the sphere to rotate in any direction. An operator is able to enter the large hollow sphere by means of a close entry hatch. Walking movements of the operator cause the large sphere to rotate. Images are projected upon the surface of the large sphere by means of high power projectors. Signals provided by the sensors, fed to the computer via cables, are used by the computer to update the projected images in order to provide the operator the illusion of walking freely through the computer generated virtual environment.

2.2   Virtual Assembly and Disassembly

In fact, virtual assembly or disassembly mainly realizes two hierarchical mappings. The bottom mapping maps product physical model into 3D digital model, which enables engineering analysis and evaluation to become possible. The top mapping maps actual assembly or disassembly process into virtual assembly or disassembly process, which enables operation planning, simulation and evaluation to become possible. At present, according to the realizable function and aim, the research on virtual assembly and disassembly can be classified into the following three types.

Virtual assembly and disassembly for product design[13,14]. Virtual reality provides a method to analyze the assembly relations between computer data models in VE during product design phase in order to assist design decision-making. It combines with the theory and method of Design for Assembly (DFA), and its basic task is to seek the optimal solution of assembly structure from design principle and operation factors. It aims at the comprehensive improvement of product assemblability. Through assembly simulation and ergonomic analysis, the designer can find out the unsuitable or unfeasible structure features for assembly and disassembly, and then redesign and modify them. It ultimately ensures the product assembly structure is reasonable and feasible, and the total assembly cost and cycle can be decreased.

Virtual assembly and disassembly for process planning[15-17]. Aiming at the operation problem of product assembly and disassembly process, based on product information model and resource model, computer simulation and VR technology are used to carry out assembly and disassembly operations, which include planning assembly or disassembly sequence and path, using tools and fixtures, verifying operation space and analyzing human-related factors, then an optimal assembly or disassembly scheme can be obtained and the assembly documents and process cards can be generated to guide practical assembly production in workshop.

Virtual assembly and disassembly for virtual prototype[18-20]. Virtual prototype is using computer simulation system to simulate the shape, function, and performance of the product, so that to check, analyze and evaluate product characteristics. The traditional virtual assembly and disassembly systems are almost based on the ideal rigid models. The combination of virtual reality and virtual prototype technology can analyze and verify the effect of force and deformation on product assemblability during part machining and assembly process, and then provides a visualize approach for shape precision analysis and tolerance optimization design.

3.0   Characteristics and Problems of Assembly and Disassembly for Large-scale Complex Products

Large-scale complex products denote the products that have complicated composition structure, complicated manufacturing and assembly method, and complicated process management etc, such as aircraft, rocket, satellite and ship. During assembly or disassembly process, this type of products require multifarious parts and components, high quality and precision, various fixtures and jigs etc, thus, compared with ordinary mechanical products, there exist several important characteristics and problems in assembly or disassembly process.

(1) **Organization form of assembly production.** There are two organization forms for assembly production, one is production line mode, and the other is fixed place mode. The production line mode means to set up assembly line according to assembly procedure of mechanical product, and different parts are assembled in different assembly steps according to the stream line. This mode mainly adapts to mass production and automatic assembly. The fixed place mode means to fix the main product frame in an assembly region, the workers are demanded to move around the working positions to assemble each part onto the product frame step by step, and then form the whole product. For large-scale complex products, the production mode is numerous varieties, small batches and manual assembly, so their assembly production mainly adopt fixed place mode. For example, during the assembly process of airplane, the airframe is static and fixed, the workers move around in the workshop to assemble the other parts onto the airplane, and this mode is especially suitable for hand assembly.

(2) **Human activity during assembly process.** For large-scale complex products, the main product frame are fixed, the workers need to move around the product to execute assembly or disassembly operation. Compared with the production line mode, the workers need to move long distance in workshop, and to carry out assembly and disassembly operations at different workplace, so more human activities are involved. Especially for the products such as airplane, satellite etc, the workers sometimes need to move into the product

to perform assembly task, because the assembly space is very limited into the product, the human assembly operation is very difficult to accomplish, and the human ergonomics factors such as fatigue, safety etc should be considered. Therefore, human participation is a very important and valuable factor during the assembly and disassembly process for large-scale complex products.

(3) **Evaluation and optimization for assembly planning.** Nowadays the planning and evaluation of assembly process are mainly accomplished by manual work, which inevitably depends on the designer's experience and knowledge, leads to long cycle, low efficiency and poor quality. For large-scale complex products, the optimization of assembly process has important significance. A good assembly sequence can not only be a feasible one, but also an optimized one. That's to say, the assembly sequence should not only satisfy the technical requirements, but also take economical, quality and ergonomic factors into account, so as to shorten assembly cycle, reduce assembly cost and facilitate to assembly operation.

(4) **Guiding and training for assembly workers.** For large-scale complex products, the assembly and disassembly operations need special skills and experiences, and it takes the new workers a long time to master these operation skills and experiences. At present, they mainly depend on 2D drawings and process cards to resort help, and it is difficult to imagine the 3D shape and structure of products, which usually leads to mistakes during assembly operations, such as some parts being assembled incorrectly, or the parts being omitted. An efficient tool is urgently needed to guide assembly operation and industrial training.

All of these problems need new method and technology, virtual reality provides a new low-cost approach to solve these problems. Nowadays VR is regarded as the most valuable training tool in industry and education, in immersive virtual environment, the designer can walk long distance to execute assembly and disassembly operation, can visualize the product to appreciate its inner structure and spatial relationships of components, and can interactively plan assembly sequence and path, and then obtain an economical, rational and practical assembly scheme.

4.0   A New Type VR System for Assembly and Disassembly of Complex Products

Currently the existing VR system (such as *Desktop*, *HMD*, *and CAVE*) has one important limitation that restricts the operator's activity during assembly or disassembly process. Especially for large-scale complex products, this restriction is particularly obvious. A new type VR system considering human activity is designed as shown in Fig.1. A special machine is designed to implement the operator's free walking, and a spherical cap screen is established as the display device. A pair of stereoscopic glass is worn by the operator to observe the 3-D virtual scenes, and the trackers are connected with the head, hands and feet of the operator to reflect the variations of his positions and attitudes. Also the operator wears data loves to implement the interaction with the virtual scenes. The operator as stated is able to walk straight and change his direction side to side on the platform of the free walking machine. The virtual scenes generation system produces the corresponding scenes according to the eyes' position and sight direction of the operator. The varying scenes are projected upon the spherical cap screen by the high power projectors. The operator inside the spherical cap screen can observe the virtual scenes and a strong sense of immersion can be obtained. This new type virtual reality system can break the restriction of the space and realize the free walking of the operator. It is very suitable for assembly and disassembly operation of large-scale complex products, and it can be described as two main parts which are hardware subsystem and software subsystem.

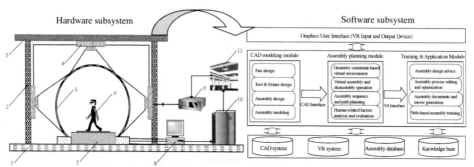

Fig.1   A new type virtual environment system for assembly and disassembly

4.1   Hardware Subsystem

The hardware subsystem consists of the following four components: virtual scenes generation module, the machine for free walking, projection and display module and human-computer interactive devices.

(1) Virtual scenes generation module. It is the core of the whole virtual reality system. It is composed of computer and application software, which implements the real-time generation of virtual scenes and interaction between the operator and the virtual scenes. To ensure the whole performance of the system, the computer should have enough strong abilities to complete the real-time calculation and display of the images and coordinate all the interaction devices. For VE system at present, the computer may be the common PC, computer workstation or supercomputer etc. As to this system, the computer workstation specially used in virtual reality is adopted. This kind of computer workstation has several processors and strong graph processing functions to fulfill the real-time display of the images and coordinate the work of the various interactive devices.

(2) The machine for free walking. It is the key elements of the system. On the platform of the machine, the operator is able to walk straight and turn from side to side while his physical position is not changed. In this machine, two sets of footplates driven by servomotors are adopted to follow the operator's feet. The footplates can move back and forth and rotate along a fixed axis. Each foot of the operator is connected with a tracker to get its position information. The walking activities of the operator are implemented through the cooperation between the footplates and his steps.

(3) Projection and display module. The projection device consists of several high power projectors, by which the virtual scenes are exhibited to the operator. The projectors are capable of presenting images with suitable intensity and resolution. Some of them are mounted on the surrounding walls and a further one is on the ceiling. The height of the projectors on the wall is designed to coincide with the eye-line of the operator on the platform of the walking machine. The display device is a large, hollow and translucent spherical cap screen and its diameter is five meter. By means of a close entry hatch, the operator is able to enter the screen. It is much convenient to communicate with the external devices because the screen is not entirely close. In the system, the virtual scenes are projected upon a curved surface by projectors, so the conjunction of projection channels and the image distortion correction are the main problems to be solved.

(4) Human-computer interactive devices. Interactivity is one of the main features of virtual reality system. Through special human-machine interfaces and peripheral hardware, not only information from the operator can be put into the computer, but also that from the computer can be feedback to the operator. The human-computer interactive devices used in this system include trackers, data glove, and stereo glasses etc, all of them can be obtained from the market.

4.2   Software Subsystem

The software subsystem, which is modularized based on the functional requirements, can be also summarized into five aspects which are three modules and two interfaces.

(1) CAD modeling module. The parts, tools and fixtures are designed in CAD system and stored in assembly database. By means of defining a series of mate constraint relationships, which realize the relative positioning of parts to one another, these individual parts are assembled together. Then an assembly model of the product is obtained. Only the final part position and mate relationships between parts are considered, the assembly sequence and process details of assembly operation are not taken into account in this phase.

(2) Assembly planning module. The geometry constraint based virtual environment is set up at first, and efficient geometry constraint recognition and management method is supplied to support interactive assembly or disassembly operation. By simulating the process of how the constraints are applied and realized, the system can provide a valuable way to analyze the assembly design, optimize the assembly or disassembly operations, plan assembly sequence and path, use tools and fixtures, determine convenient point for quality testing and surface preparing, consider human activities and evaluate human-related factors etc, then generates an optimal assembly planning scheme.

(3) Training & application module. For complex products, the assembly operations require dexterous operation skills and experience. The VR system can be used as an efficient training medium for engineers to familiarize with the assembly process as many times as they want. The practical assembly documents and cards can be generated and applied in the assembly floor, a web-based assembly training system including graphical simulation based on the best assembly sequence can be developed to guide the operators. The workers can jump back and forth between assembly operations and can also slow down the simulation to study a particular operation process.

(4) CAD interface. Because VR software uses polygon representation to visualize objects, after the CAD models are loaded into virtual environment, the useful information must be extracted from CAD system and transfer into virtual environment, including part's geometrical information, topological information and assembly information etc. A data transformation interface is needed to transfer the information from CAD to VR system.

(5) VA interface. In virtual assembly environment, the product assembly process is optimized by interactive assembly planning and evaluation. All the relative assembly information and process data including optimized assembly sequence and path, engaged assembly tools and fixtures etc, should be exported from virtual environment with VA interface, and imported into the training and application module to generate assembly documents and web-based training system for assembly workers.

5.0   Implementations and Applications

VR-BASED APPROACH TO ASSEMBLY AND DISASSEMBLY FOR LARGE-SCALE COMPLEX PRODUCTS

5.1   Design of the Free Walking Machine

The principles of free walking machine as shown in Fig.2, can be described as the following contents: two sets of footplates are adopted to follow the operator's feet, each footplate can slide in its slide way perpendicular to the paper, and each footplate can rotate along the same fixed axis which can be driven by the corresponding servomotor. After investigate people's walking activities in real world, which include walking straightly, turning left and turning right, the related walking data can be obtained as Fig.3 and Table1. According to these data, the free walking machine is designed as shown in Fig.4, which is composed of two main parts: main transmission part and supporting frame. Through the main transmission part, the servomotors are able to drive the footplates to rotate along a fixed axis, and the servomotors are driven by computer according to the signals from the trackers attached to the operator's feet. The supporting frame burdens the main transmission part and also supports the operator weight. Key features of the free walking machine can be described as followings. (1)Each footplate is able to slide back and forth along the guide pole and is connected with the slide way board by return springs. The return springs implement the return stroke of the footplate and create the obstruction sense of walking. There is an angle α between the guide pole and the horizontal direction, which can help the operator move with the help of his gravity. The guide pole is asymmetrically assigned to the rotation center and the extension length of the front are far greater than that of the back end, which are to satisfy the movement of the footplates and the rotating plate. (2)Each of the two footplates is able to rotate along the same fixed axis and the rotation is driven by the corresponding servomotor through the transmission system. The left footplate is directly driven by the servomotor through the joint and the right footplate is driven by the other servomotor through gear drive transmission system. (3)There are grooves in the rotating plate and the footplate stanchion can slide in the groove. By the stanchion, the footplate can drive the rotating plate to rotate freely.

During the working course of the machine, the operator whose feet are connected with trackers stands on the footplates. When the operator walks straight, the servomotors do not act and the footplates only slide back and forth to follow the operator's feet. When the operator changes direction, the control computer obtains the signals from the corresponding tracker attached to the foot of the operator and drives the corresponding servomotor to rotate. Through the transmission system, the servomotor drives the corresponding footplate to rotate exact angles to follow the operator's foot. For this machine, independent servomotor is adopted for each footplate, which can avoid the influence between the two footplates.

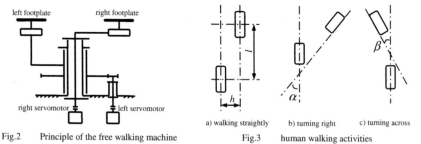

Fig.2   Principle of the free walking machine   Fig.3   human walking activities

a) walking straightly   b) turning right   c) turning across

VR-BASED APPROACH TO ASSEMBLY AND DISASSEMBLY FOR LARGE-SCALE COMPLEX PRODUCTS

Table 1 Measuring data of human walking activities

序号	身高 (cm)	脚间距离 h (cm)	步距 l (cm)	正常转向角度 α (° ?	交叉转向角度 β (° ?
1	160	10	58	40	35
2	165	12	60	50	45
3	168	13	68	45	40
4	172	15	65	48	30
5	175	15	70	50	35
6	178	16	70	48	38
7	180	15	75	55	40
8	182	18	75	45	35
9	185	20	80	50	35

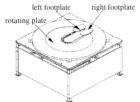

Fig.4.   Appearance of the free walking

5.2   Data Translation from CAD to VR

There is a great difference between CAD system and virtual reality system in the expression of data model. In CAD system, a product can be expressed by precise mathematic model. However, in VR system the models are usually expressed by polygons, and the topological information and assembly relation information are lost, so cannot be used for assembly planning and evaluation. An integrated data interface should be developed to transform data from CAD to VR. Generally, the geometry information, topology information and assembly information are necessary for virtual assembly and disassembly. These three kinds of information can be extracted from CAD system respectively and transformed into virtual environment. Fig.5 shows the process of data transformation from CAD to VR. Through the VRML or STL files exported from CAD system, the surface of part can be divided into many polygons. The information of each polygon in color, texture and material, vertices coordinates and normal vector can be extracted from CAD. Then it can be recognized and written into corresponding NFF file, which can be loaded into virtual environment directly. Topological relationships need to be rebuilt in virtual environment. A part is composed of assembly features, a feature is the aggregation of geometry surfaces, and a surface is the aggregation of polygons. The polygons are the mesh unit to visualize in virtual environment and the surfaces are the foundation to define geometry constraints such as against, collinear, concentric etc. The assembly object, part object, surface object and polygon object are recognized by an identity number as the same written into .nff file, for example, a polygon recognized by the identity number in virtual environment corresponds to a unique surface object, and a surface corresponds to a unique part, and a part object corresponds to a unique assembly object, these relationships can be represented by a hierarchical mapping structure. The assembly information mainly includes product structure tree information and assembly constraint information, which can be extracted from CAD inner database, and the detailed description can be found in reference [21].

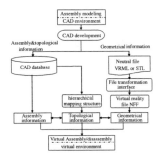

Fig. 5.   Flow chart of data

VR-BASED APPROACH TO ASSEMBLY AND DISASSEMBLY FOR LARGE-SCALE COMPLEX PRODUCTS

5.3 Geometry Constraint-based Virtual Environment for Assembly and Disassembly

Geometry constraints are the main implementation approach of virtual assembly and disassembly operations, the key techniques employed in this process are direct interaction, automatic constraint recognition, constraint satisfaction and constrained motion navigation. After data transformation from CAD to VR, a hierarchical constraint-based virtual assembly model can be represented as shown in Fig.6, which is composed of product layer, subassembly layer, part layer, feature layer, surface layer and polygon layer. The product layer includes subassembly layer and part layer, and a part can belong to a subassembly, or belongs to product general assembly directly. The constraint relationships between parts (C_{11}, C_{12}, C_{13}, etc.) mainly point to assembly constraint relationships. And the part is composed of features, so the constraint relationships between parts can be decomposed as the constraint relationships between features. The constraint relationships between features may be divided into two types, one is the inner constraints (C_{21}, C_{22}, C_{23}, etc.), which are used to define the feature shape and position, and the other is the outer constraints (C_{31}, C_{32}, C_{33}, C_{34}, etc.), which are mainly pointed to assembly constraint relationships. The feature object is composed of geometry surfaces, so the constraint relationships between features can be decomposed as the constraint relationships between surfaces. The constraint relationships between geometry surfaces can be divided into two types too, and the outer constraints (C_{51}, C_{52}, C_{53}, C_{54}, etc.) are mainly pointed to assembly constraint relationships, such as parallel, coincidence, against and coaxial etc. The surface object is composed of polygons, which are used for geometry display and collision detection in virtual environment.

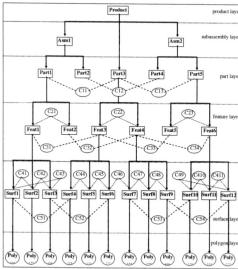

Fig.6.   The hierarchical constraint-based virtual assembly model

According to virtual assembly model, the scene graph structure can be organized as shown in Fig.7. The root node of scene graph includes light node, virtual factory node, product node and virtual human node, and the product node is organized according to subassembly node, part node and surface node hierarchically. Each separate node has its transform node and geometry node, the transform node is used to dominate the position and direction of the node, and the geometry node is used to display the object in virtual environment. According to the scene graph, the user can select and recognize each geometry surface for constraint recognition and satisfaction, and can operate the part or subassembly object in virtual environment.

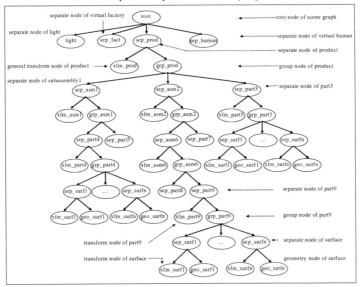

Fig.7   The structure of scene graph

Based on the hierarchical constraint-based virtual assembly model and scene graph, the user can carry out virtual assembly and disassembly operations as realistic as in real word. The automatic recognition of geometry constraint can simulate realistic assembly and disassembly behavior interactively. While an object is being manipulated, the position of the moving object is sampled to identify new constraints between the manipulated object and the surrounding objects. A constraint is recognized between two planes when the angle between their normal is less than the angular tolerance, and that the distance between the planes is less than the linear tolerance. Two cylinders have a potential constraint when their axes make an angle within the angular tolerance and are less than the tolerance apart. The constraint between a plane and a cylinder is recognized when a plane's normal is perpendicular within the tolerance to the cylinder's axis and the distance between the cylindrical and the planar surface is less than the linear tolerance. During virtual assembly and disassembly process, the parts can be in various stages in virtual environment: only one constraint is applied, or two constraints are applied, or maybe just lie on the table, so geometry constraint based motion navigation make the object move only in its allowable space.

5.4   Intelligent Assembly/Disassembly Sequence Planning and Optimization

Assembly or disassembly sequence planning can be generated by two approaches: automatic approach and interactive approach. The automatic assembly and disassembly sequence planning mainly depends on reasoning mechanism based on product geometric and topological structure, and this approach inevitably has shortcomings. On one hand, as the number of components increases, the computation complexity increases exponentially and leads to combined explosion problem. On the other hand, some process and operation factors such as quality testing, shop floor layout, assembly accessibility, and human ergonomics cannot be taken into account for automatic reasoning. Virtual reality provides a new interactive approach for assembly and disassembly sequence planning. In an immersive virtual environment, utilizing multimodal interaction devices (visual, auditory, haptic), the user can plan product assembly and disassembly sequence. However, because virtual assembly and disassembly operation mainly depends on human experience and knowledge, for different operation human their assembly experience and knowledge are different, and may be affected by many factors, so this approach has indeterminacy and blindness, lack of necessary intelligent guiding and optimization. Especially for large-scale complex products, because of the complexity of assembly and disassembly process, the interactive approach can only generate the feasible assembly or disassembly sequence, but not the best sequence.

A hybrid approach is provided to generate optimized or near optimized assembly and disassembly sequence by combining intelligent planning and interactive evaluation. On one hand, it can utilize the advantage of computer reasoning to generate initial optimized assembly or disassembly sequence, so as to guide and optimize the planning process. On the other hand, this initial optimized sequence can be interactive simulate, analysis and evaluate in immersive virtual environment, considering operation related factors and human ergonomics, a more practical and optimal sequence can be obtained. As given in Fig.8, at first precedence constraints and evaluation rules can be generated, an intelligent optimization algorithm is applied to generate initial optimal assembly or disassembly sequence. Then, interactive assembly and disassembly operations can be carried out in virtual environment. During the simulation and evaluation process, new precedence constraints and evaluation rules will be recognized, a more practical and optimal sequence is then replaned and evaluated once again by virtual reality technology until the best assembly or disassembly sequence is obtained. The detail of planning process can be found in reference [22].

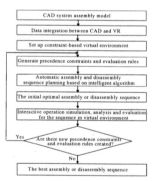

Fig.8 The intelligent assembly and disassembly sequence planning

5.5   Application Examples

An integrated virtual assembly planning and training system (I-VAPTS) for a large-scale complex product is developed and applied in the assembly production. Fig.9 shows the spherical cap screen for stereo display, Fig.10 is the designed machine for operator's free walking. After data transformation from CAD to VR, a geometry constraint based virtual environment is set up, and in the virtual environment, interactive assembly and disassembly operations are implemented as shown in Fig.11. and Fig.12. The assembly process documents and cards are generated as shown in Fig.13, and web-based training in assembly workshop is shown in Fig.14.

Fig.9 Spherical cap screen for stereo display   Fig.10 The designed machine for free walking

Fig.11 Collision detection during interactive assembly and disassembly operation

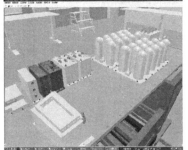

Fig.12 Constraint recognization during interactive assembly and disassembly operation

Fig.13 Assembly process card generated by the system   Fig.14 Web-based assembly training

6.0   Conclusion

**VR-BASED APPROACH TO ASSEMBLY AND DISASSEMBLY FOR LARGE-SCALE COMPLEX
PRODUCTS**

A new type virtual environment system is designed and realized in this paper to assembly and disassembly for large-scale complex products. This system can strengthen the immersive sense and enhance the realistic of simulation by breaking the space restriction and realizing the operator's free walking. Comparing with Cybersphere system, the new system has the following advantages. As the spherical cap screen only acts as display device, the requirements of material and structure are low and the difficulty of manufacturing can be reduced. For the spherical cap screen is not entirely closed, the interaction devices such as trackers and data gloves and so on can be obtained from market without developing new wireless products. At the same time, the operator does not have to bear some devices such as power supply and so on, which will increase the operator's burden.

The future works mainly concentrate on the following aspects: (1) Optimization of data model. The large-scale complex products have many parts. To satisfy the real-time requirement of VA system, the optimization and simplification for data model is necessary to improve efficiency and real time. (2) Analysis and evaluation of human ergonomics. Now the system only supplies a simulation and verification approach for human assembly/disassembly operations, the quantitive analysis and evaluation of human-related factors should be strengthened, which includes efficiency, safety, reliability and tiredness during assembly process.

References

[1] H I Connacher, S Jayaram. Virtual Assembly Design Environment. Proceedings of the Computers in Engineering Conference and the Engineering Database Symposium. 1995: 875~885.
[2] H. J. Bullinger, M. Richter, K. A. Seidel. Virtual Assembly Planning. Human Factors and Ergonomics In Manufacturing. John Wiley & Sons Inc, 2000: 331~341.
[3] Richard G. Dewar, Ian D. Carpenter, James M. Ritcher, et al. Assembly Planning in a Virtual Environment. Proceeding of Portland International Conference on Management and Technology. Portland: 1997, 664~667.
[4] B Jung, M Hoffhenke, I Wachsmuth. Virtual Assembly With Construction Kits. Proceedings of 1997 ASME Design Engineering Technical Conference, Sacramento, September 14-17, 1997
[5] Venkat N. Rajan, Kadiresan Sivasubramanian, Jeffrey E. Fernandez. Accessibility and Ergonomic Analysis of Assembly Product and Jig Designs. International Journal of Industrial Ergonomics. 1999, 23: 473~487
[6] J R Li, L P Khoo, S B Tor. Desktop Virtual Reality for Maintenance Training: An Object Oriented Prototype System (V-REALISM). Computers in Industry. 2003, 52: 109~125
[7] T Deviprasad, T Kesavadas. Virtual Prototyping of Assembly Components Using Process Modeling. Journal of Manufacturing Systems, 2003, 22(1): 16-27
[8] VRAC.VEGAS: a Virtual Environment for General Assembly Simulation. http://www.vrac.iastate.edu/ ~ jmvance /ASSEMBLY/ Assembly.html, 2004-10-25
[9] Liu Jianhua, Ning Ruxin,Tang Chengtong. Journal of Institute of technology, 2005: 400-405
[10] Sankar J, Judy V, Rajit G, Uma J, Hari S. Transactions of the ASME, 2001: 72-83
[11] Jukka R, Jussi M, Raimo L, Marinella F. Human-Computer Studies. 2006,64: 182-191
[12] Hiran Jude Fernandes, Vinesh H. Raja, Julian Eyre. Immersive learning system for manufacturing industries. Computers in Industry, 2003, 51(1): 31-40.
[13] Huang Xiang, Liao Wenhe. Chinese Journal of Mechanical Engineering. Vol.16, 2003: 64-67
[14] S.F.Qin , R.Harrison, A.A.West, D.K.Wright. Computers in Industry, 2004, 54: 69-81
[15] Yao Jun, Jianhua Liu. International Journal of Comup Integrated Manuf. 2005,Vol 18: 442-451
[16] Tianyang Dong, Ruofeng Tong. Advanced Engineering Informatics, 2005, 19: 155-168
[17] Zhang Y, Ning R.X. Computer Integrated Manuf Systems. 2006, Vol 12: 90-94 (in Chinese)
[18] Qing S, Jochen B. Advanced Engineering Informatics, 2005, 19: 169-177
[19] Jiang Z H, Yan J Q. Chinese Journal of Mechanical Engineering. Vol. 15, 2002: 94-96
[20] Siddique Z, Rosen D W. Computer-Aided Design, 1997, 29(12): 847-860
[21] Yao Yingxue, Xia Pingjun, Liu Jiangsheng, Li Jianguang. A Pragmatic System to Support Interactive Assembly Planning and Training in Immersive Virtual Environment (I-VAPTS). International Journal of Advanced Manufacturing Technology, 2006, 30(9)
[22] Xia Pingjun, Yao Yingxue, Liu Jiangsheng, Li Jianguang. Optimizing assembly planning based on virtual reality and bionic algorithm. International journal of manufacturing technology and management. 2006, 5/6.

VR-BASED APPROACH TO ASSEMBLY AND DISASSEMBLY FOR LARGE-SCALE COMPLEX PRODUCTS

The 6th International Conference on Manufacturing Research (ICMR08)
Brunel University, UK, 9-11th September 2008

SERVICE ATTRIBUTE IMPORTANCE AND STRATEGIC PLANNING: AN EMPIRICAL STUDY

Vahid Pezeshki, Ali Mousavi

School of Engineering and Design, Brunel University, Middlesex, UK

Abstract

There is growing evidence that attribute importance is a function of attribute performance. Several studies reported that service quality attributes fall into three categories: basic, performance, and excitement. Thus, the identification of attribute importance is significantly important as a key to customer satisfaction evaluation and other behavioural intentions. According to customer behaviour literature, attribute importance can be measured in two ways: (1) self-stated importance, and (2) statistically inferred importance. The article evaluates two methods according to their impact on overall customer satisfaction measurement and, managerial implementation. A case study is conducted on the telecommunication industry for analysis.

Keywords: Customer satisfaction; Importance-performance analysis (IPA); Strategy.

1.0   Introduction

The importance of service attributes to customers is a central element to the management within the context of customer behaviour analysis, resource allocation process, and organisational behaviour. According to service marketing literature, there are two key characteristics of service quality attributes namely *importance* and *performance*. Using these two dimensions together facilitates the prescription of prioritising customer attributes when enhancing service quality and customer satisfaction [1]. In other words, measuring attribute importance and performance certainly draw a clear image for top managers to best deploy scarce resources, using importance-performance analysis (IPA).

There are several methods for measuring attribute importance in behavioural sciences such as free-elicitation method, direct rating method, direct ranking method, analytical hierarchy process, and information-display board, multi-attribute attitude methods. However, there is a lack of convergent among and nomolological validity of different methods [2]. These issues can cause inconsistent outcomes among methods. Previous research argues that the main reason of the lack of validity among methods is multi-dimensionality of attribute importance [3]. As a result, all inconsistency among methods can be interpreted by the fact that different methods measure different dimensions of importance. According to literature, key dimensions of attribute importance can be classified into three groups: (1) salience, (2) relevance, and (3) determinance [4], [5], see Fig 1.

In this article, we investigate the validity of two existing methods that are proposed to measure the determinance of service attributes in overall customer satisfaction in the mobile telecommunication industry, using statistical inferred importance and customers' stated importance. The findings show that the type of importance measure and the dynamic nature of importance to response influence management decision making. As a result, there are significant differences in nomological validity- the relationship between the importance of service attributes and overall customer satisfaction.

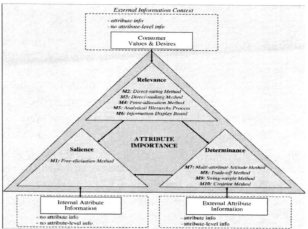

Fig. 1.   The three dimensions of attribute importance (Adopted from [3])

We begin by describing the impact of attribute importance on customer behaviour and the methods we compare. We examine two different statistical methods for driving importance measures including multiple regression and regression with dummy variables. An empirical analysis of three data sets highlights interesting results.

2.0   Service Attribute Importance

Indentifying the importance that consumers place on the service attributes that affect customer satisfaction, customer retention (e.g., repurchase intention), and loyalty (e.g., feedback, and word-of0mouth) is an important element for resource allocation process. Thus, the study of importance of service attributes has been a central topic in consumer behaviour and market research for decades. Most importantly, the focus of attribute importance has shifted from traditional evaluations of service concepts within controlled settings, such as conjoint analysis [6] and choice modelling [7], to understanding the determinants of behaviours intentions [8], [9].

In this study we focus specifically on the impact of service attribute on cumulative customer satisfaction, defined as an overall evaluation of a customer perception of service performance to date [10], [11]. As previous research reported, customer satisfaction has significant impact on other customer behavioural intentions in the form of retention and loyalty. In other words, it plays as mediating attitude between service quality or attribute performance and other behavioural variables. Thus, indentifying the determinants of customer satisfaction can help managers within their long term business planning.

3.0   Methodology

Most research studies which have investigated the importance of service attributes in customer behaviour employed two methods: *customers' self-stated* or *explicitly derived importance* (direct method), and (2) *implicitly derived importance* or *statistically derived importance* (indirect method). By using explicitly derived importance, customers are asked to rate a list of service or product attributes according their importance (e.g. rating scales, constant sum scales, etc.). As a result, basic attributes usually receive the highest rating levels as they are naturally expected by customers (minimum requirements). However, they have literally no impact on overall customer satisfaction and future intentions even if they performed at a satisfactory level. For instance, consider an airline safety. Most customers would rank safety as highly important attribute. But in reality it does not contribute significantly to the prediction of airline choice, since it is more of a minimum requirement (basic attribute). So, do we need to take resources away from this kind of attributes?

It is argued that direct methods do not effectively measure attribute importance [12], [13]. The main issue with this method is that respondents may not take into account the current level of attribute performance. Moreover, there is an asymmetric and nonlinear relationship between attribute importance and performance [12], [11], [14], [15]. Therefore, the customer's self-stated importance is not the actual value for attribute importance.

Importance performance analysis (IPA) is widely used technique indentifying the relative importance of service attributes with associated performance of service attributes [16]. The technique determines where a company should focus its resources to produce the greatest impact on customer satisfaction and subsequent behavioural intentions like retention and loyalty.

3.1   Self-Stated Importance

For the purpose of the evaluation of service attribute importance (explicitly derived), we employed methodology from previous study [17]. Respondents were asked to rate just the three most important attributes; from "1=most important2 to "3=least important". In order to assign each attribute (i) an importance value (P_i) lying between 0 and 1, we integrate the ranked assigned by respondents, using Equation 1, to a ranking score (h_{ij}) using Equation 2. Table I lists the frequency of ranks 1, 2 and 3 for each attributes and also the aggregate importance value (using Eq. 2).

$$h_{ij} = \begin{cases} (k - g_{ij} + 1)/k \\ 0 \end{cases} \qquad (1)$$

$$P_i = (n^{-1} \sum_j h_{ij})^{k/s} \qquad (2)$$

3.2.   Multiple Regression Analysis (MR)

There are various statistical methods for measuring attribute importance such as multiple regression (MR), structural equation modelling or partial correlation [18], [19], [20]. Several researchers have suggested multiple regression analysis as a suitable tool for measuring attribute importance. The method simply regresses the relative performance ratings of service attributes against dependent variable (overall customer satisfaction) to generate significant-level for individual attribute. This approach is the easiest to implement statistically. One of the advantages of regression analysis is that the method provides a model of all attributes

SERVICE ATTRIBUTE IMPORTANCE AND STRATEGIC PLANNING: AN EMPIRICAL STUDY

to form the overall rating. As a result, multiple regression analysis estimates the degree of influence that attributes have in determining customer satisfaction (shown in Table I). The primary problem with this approach is multicollinearity among the independent variables.

$$Sat_{total} = \alpha_0 + \alpha_1 X_1 + ... + \alpha_n X_n + \varepsilon \tag{3}$$

3.3. Regression Analysis with Dummy Variables

In order to identify the asymmetric impact of attributes' performance on attribute importance, a regression analysis with dummy variables was used [21], [22], and [13]. Accordingly, two sets of dummy variables; the first dummy variables quantify basic attributes, and the second ones quantify exciting attributes are set. The attribute-level performance ratings are recoded as (0,1) for low ratings, (0,0) for average ratings, and (1,0) for high ratings. As a result, two regression coefficients are obtained (shown in Table I and Fig II).

$$Sat_{total} = \alpha_0 + \alpha_{1\,Att\,.1} \times dummy_{\,1\,Att\,.1} + \alpha_{2\,Att\,.1} \times dummy_{\,2\,Att\,.1} + ... + \alpha_{1n} \times dummy_{\,1\,Att\,.n} + \alpha_{2n} \times dummy_{\,2\,Att\,.n} \tag{4}$$

Sat_{total} is the overall customer satisfaction, and n is the number of quality attributes ($n = 7$), $dummy_1$ indicates lowest customer satisfaction level, $dummy_2$ indicates highest customer satisfaction levels, α_1 the incremental decline in overall satisfaction associated with low satisfaction levels, and α_2 the incremental increase in overall satisfaction associated with high satisfaction level.

4.0 Survey Methods

The survey was conducted with a random sample of 270 students of a University. Questionnaires were completed and returned either via email or were collected in face-to-face interviews. From this sample, 74.4% percent of the respondents were under 27 years old. In this study, market segmentation is highly considered in order to avoid the risk of displacement and strategy application bias.

Respondents were asked to indicate the most three important service attributes in the mobile service with the anchors of "1=Most important" to "3=Least important". In second part, the performance for each service attribute was rated using a seven-point Likert scale from "1=Poor" to "7=Excellent". Finally respondents were asked to rate overall satisfaction using a seven-point Likert scale from "1=Strongly dissatisfied" to "7=Strongly satisfied".

4.1 Findings

Table I presents the results of three methods for perceived importance. Applying the results of two methods (indirect and direct) into IPA grid shows a change in strategic outcomes for service attributes. The difference between two IPA models emphasises the influence of measurement on managerial implementation [23].

(a) $R^2 = .480$, F-value $= 34.936$,

(b) $R^2 = .469$; F-Value $= 15.338$,

$***P < .01$, $** P<.05$, $*P<.1$, ns = not significant

More importantly, the results from regression with dummy variables accommodates the concept of change in the relative importance of attributes with change in attribute performance as a function of overall customer satisfaction, see Fig. II. Since changes to attribute performance affects the relative attribute importance, therefore, the self-stated importance is not appropriate method. However, multiple regression analysis can be

SERVICE ATTRIBUTE IMPORTANCE AND STRATEGIC PLANNING: AN EMPIRICAL STUDY

an inappropriate if multicollinearly exists within independent variables [14]. In the case of multicollinearly, partial correlation analysis with dummy variables and multiple regression with natural logarithmic dummy variables are more suitable [24], [14], [22], [21], [25]. By using regression with dummy variables, we also found two types of service attribute within the mobile industry: Basic and Exciting [12].

Table I:.Attribute importance analysis

Attribute	Ranking order			Explicit derived	Regression coefficient (a)	Dummy-variable regression coefficient (b)		Attribute performance
	1	2	3			Low performance	High performance	
Network performance	82	51	52	0.81	0.302***	0.048 (ns)	.366***	5.44
Customer service quality	9	27	38	0.54	0.199***	-.001 (ns)	.221***	4.88
Service plans	87	47	31	0.79	0.141*	-.009 (ns)	.068 (ns)	5.05
Range of phones	9	22	30	0.51	-0.089*	-.130 **	-.114*	4.36
Accuracy of billing and payment	6	19	18	0.46	0.145**	-.115**	.064 (ns)	5.11
Value for money	56	62	43	0.76	0.222**	-.012 (ns)	.202***	4.92
Total	253	252	249					

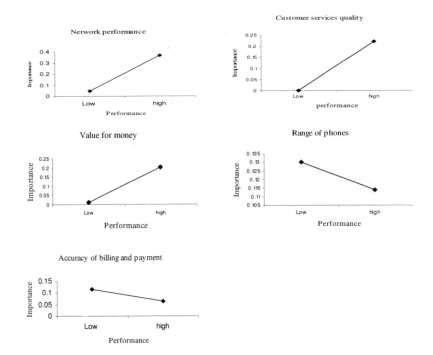

Fig. 2.   Relationship between importance and performance

Fig III demonstrates two IPA models. There are some differences between two methods as some attributes located in different quadrants. However, managers must consider the relationship between importance and performance since changes in performance will affect attrite importance-level.

Statistically importance derived   Customer self-stated importance

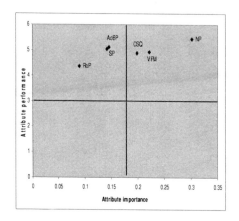
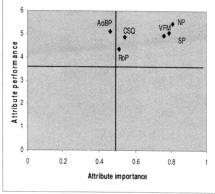

Fig. 3.   IPA models

5.   Conclusion and Management Implications

This article evaluates the effect of importance measurement variation on outcome strategy variance, using IPA technique. The comparative analysis of outcomes from different IPA analysis demonstrates the influence of respective importance measures. In addition, the results of regression analysis with dummy variables highlight the dynamic nature of importance relating to response variance. As a result, managers should consider the fact that changes to attribute performance are associated with changes to attribute importance since quality attributes have impact on customer satisfaction [12]. Differences between two methods of direct and indirect are particularly marked. From managerial perspective, there is absolutely no assurance that increasing scores on attributes with the highest self-stated importance will provide maximised increase in the overall measure [26].

References

[1] Matzler, K., Bailom, F., Hinterhuber, H. H., Renzl, B. and Pichler, J. (2004), "The asymmetric relationship between attribute-level performance and overall customer satisfaction: a reconsideration of the importance-performance analysis", Industrial Marketing Management, Vo. 33, No. 4, pp. 271-277.
[2] Jaccard, J., Brinberg, D. and Ackerman, L.J. (1986), "Assessing attribute importance: a comparison of six methods".Journal of Consumer Research, Vol. 12 (March), pp. 463-8.
[3] Ittersum, K.V., Pennings, J.M.E., Wansik, B. and Trijp, H.C.M. (2007), "The validity of attribute-importance measurement: A review", Journal of Business Research, Vol. 60, pp. 1177-1190.
[4] Myers, J.H. and Alpert, M.I. (1968), "Determinant buying attitudes: meaning and measurement", Journal of Marketing, Vol. 32 (July), pp. 13-20.
[5] Myers, J.H. and Alpert, M.I. (1977), "Semantic confusion in attitude research: salience vs. importance vs. determinance", Advertising Consumer Research, Vol. 4, pp. 106-10.
[6] Green, P.E. and Srinivasan, V. (1990), "Conjoint analysis in marketing: new developments and directions", Journal of Marketing, Vol. 54 (October), pp. 3-19.

[7] Gaudagni, P.M. and Little, J.D.C. (1983), "A logit model of brand choice calibrated on scanner data", Marketing Science, Vol. 2, No. 3 (summer), pp. 203-238.

[8] Gustafsson, and Johnson, (1997), "Determining attribute importance in a service satisfaction model", Journal of Service Research, Vol. 7, No. 2, pp. 124-141.

[9] Ryan, M.J., Rayner, R. and Morrison, A. (1999), Diagnosing customer loyalty drivers: Partial Least Squares vs. Regression", Marketing Research, Vol. 11 (summer), pp. 19-26.

[10] Fornell, C. (1992), "A national customer barometer: The Swedish Experience", Journal of Marketing, Vol. 56, (January), pp. 6-21.

[11] Fornell, C., Johnson, M.D., Anderson, E.W., Cha, J. and Bryant, B.E. (1996), "The American Customer Satisfaction Index: Nature, Purpose and Findings", Journal of Marketing, Vol. 60 (October), pp. 7-18.

[12] Kano, N., Seraku, N., Takahashi, F. and Tsuji, S. (1984), "Alternative quality and must-be quality", Hinshitsu (Quality, The Journal of Japanese Society Control), Vol. 14, pp. 39-48.

[13] Matzler, K. and Sauerwein, E. (2002), "The factor structure of customer satisfaction: an empirical test of the performance grid and the penalty-reward-contrast analysis", International Journal of Industrial Management, Vol. 13, No. 4, pp. 371-32.

[14] Matzler, K., Fuchs, M. and Schubert, A.K. (2004), "Employee satisfaction: Does Kano's model apply?", Total Quality Management and Business Excellence, Vol. 15, No. 9/10, pp. 1179-1198.

[15] Oh, H. (2001), "Revisiting importance-performance analysis", Tourism Management, Vol. 22, No. 6, pp. 617-627.

[16] Matrilla, J.A. and James, J.C. (1977), "Importance-performance analysis", Journal of Marketing, Vol. 41. pp. 77-79.

[17] Abalo, J., Varela, J., Manzano, V. (2007), "Importance values for Importance-Performance Analysis: A formula for spreading out values derived from preference rankings", Journal of Business Research, Vol. 60, pp. 115-121.

[18] Danaher, P.J. and Mattsson, J. (1994), "Customer satisfaction during the service deliver process", European Journal of Marketing, Vol. 28, No. 5, pp. 5-16.

[19] Wittink, D.R. and Bayer, L.R. (1994), "The measurement imperative", Marketing Research, Vol. 6 No.4, pp.14-23.

[20] Varva, T.G. (1997), "Improving your measurement of Customer Satisfaction", ASQ Quality Press, Milwaukee, WI.

[21] Anderson, E.W. and Mittal, V. (2000), "Strengthening the satisfaction-profit chain", Journal of Service Research, vol. 3, No. 2, pp. 107-120.

[22] Brandt, D.R. (1988), "How service marketers can identify value-enhancing service elements", The journal of Service Marketing, Vol. 2, No. 3, pp. 35-41.

[23] Matzler, K., Sauerwein, E. and Heischmidt, K.A. (2002), "The factor structure of customer satisfaction: an empirical test of the performance grid and the penalty-reward-contrast analysis", International Journal of service industry Management, Vol. 23, No. 2. pp. 112-29.

[24] Hair, J.F., Anderson, R.E., Tatham, R.L. and Black, W.C. (1995), "Multivariate Data Analysis", Upper Saddle River, New Jersey: Prentice-Hall (Fourth edition).

[25] Ting, S.C. and Chen, C.N. (2002), "The asymmetrical and non-linear effects of store quality attributes on customer satisfaction", Total Quality of Management, Vol. 13, No. 4, pp. 547-569.

[26] Pennings, J.M.E and Smidts, A. (2003), "The shape of utility functions and organisational behaviour", Journal of Management Science, Vol. 49 (September), pp. 1251-63.

SERVICE ATTRIBUTE IMPORTANCE AND STRATEGIC PLANNING: AN EMPIRICAL STUDY

Design and Manufacturing Simulation

The 6th International Conference on Manufacturing Research (ICMR08)
Brunel University, UK, 9-11th September 2008

NUMERICAL SIMULATION OF REACTION INJECTION MOLDING FOR REFRIGERATOR INSULATION

Stournaras, A., K. Salonitis, and G. Chryssolouris [*]

Laboratory for Manufacturing Systems and Automation, Director, Prof. George Chryssolouris,

Department of Mechanical Engineering and Aeronautics, University of Patras, Greece

[*]exrisol@mech.upatras.gr

Abstract

This paper deals with the computer simulation of the Reaction Injection Molding (RIM) process for refrigerator insulation purposes. The purpose of this simulation work is to investigate the effects of process parameters, such as isocyanate\polyol\blowing agent mixing ratio, flow rate/injection time combination and injection point location on successfully filling the mold and the time required for the complete curing of the mixture, for a real refrigerator application. Reaction Injection Molding simulations were performed using the general purpose CFD software package ANSYS-CFX, designed for the numerical simulation of the fluid flow and the heat and mass transfer.

Keywords: Reaction Injection Molding, Filling, Expansion, Thermal insulation

1.0   Introduction

Reaction Injection Moulding (RIM) is a process for the rapid production of complex parts through the mixing and chemical reaction of two or more components. The liquid components, usually isocyanate and polyol, held in separate temperature controlled tanks, are fed to metering units. When the injection begins, the valves open and the components flow into a mixing chamber, ranging from moderate to high pressures, typically between 10 and 20 MPa. The streams are intensively mixed and the mixture begins to polymerize, or cure, as it flows into the mould cavity. According to and [1], these first developments were applied to the filling stage, in simple geometries ([2]–[10]). In order to expand the previous approaches to more realistic geometries, conformal mapping ([11]–[13]) or decomposition of complex shape cavities, in a number of simple elements ([14], [15]) were used for extending the 1½D approach to more complex flow situations. However, these methods lack sufficient generality to be satisfactory and the solution accuracy strongly depends on how the geometry is partitioned, requiring astute judgment from the user. The real breakthrough came with the development of a general 2½D approach, originally proposed in [16], combining finite elements along the midsurface of the cavity with finite differences along the thickness direction. The pressure field was solved in two dimensions, by the finite element method while the temperature and velocity fields were solved in three dimensions, by means of a mixed finite element / finite difference method. However, based on the Hele-Shaw approximation, the 2½D approach was unable to represent the complex flow kinematics of the flow front region, the so-called fountain flowb, first reported in [17]. The description of this phenomenon has been addressed by many authors by means of experimental ([18]-[21]), analytical ([22]-[24]) and numerical ([19], [25]-[30]) methods, leading to approximate models able to capture its basic flow kinematics without resolving the complex 3D flow details. Different techniques have been used for handling the time-dependency of the flow domain during filling. One solution consisted in the use of the control volume method ([31]-[33]), while alternative solutions included the use of boundary fitted coordinates ([34], [35]) or the use of a front tracking and of remeshing techniques ([36], [37]). To date, several commercial and research three-dimensional simulation programs for injection molding have been developed. In particular, [38] developed a three dimensional finite-element code for predicting the velocity and pressure fields, governed by the generalized Navier-Stokes equations, [39] analyzed the three-dimensional mould filling of an incompressible fluid and the shape of the fountain flow front, ([40], [41]) incorporated the polymer compressibility, by treating its density as a function of temperature and pressure, in a three-dimensional mould filling process. The main purpose of this study is the numerical simulation of RIM for a real refrigerator, in order for the optimization of the process to be investigated, in terms of the mold's volume filled and the time required for completely curing the mixture.

2.0   Numerical Analysis of the RIM Process

The Polyurethane foam molding process can be divided into two main stages: those of polymerization and expansion. During the polymerization process, both viscosity and temperature of the mixture increase due to the exothermic reaction between the two components, isocyanate and polyol. In the second stage, the mixture is expanded by supplying gas to the nucleated bubbles and ends up with the final cellular structure. The assumptions that the polyurethane foam is a homogeneous phase and that the evaporation of the blowing agent is controlled by the heat generation during the process, are necessary in order for the RIM process to be modelled.

The energy balance equation states that the sum of the energy required for the increase in temperature of the entire system and the heat consumption by the evaporation of the physical blowing agent, is equal to the sum of the heat generated by the exothermic polyurethane reaction and the blowing reaction of the chemical blowing agent. If there is no flow of fluid and the material parameters are constant in the temperature range of interest, the energy balance, in a control volume under adiabatic condition, is expressed by [41]:

$$
\left[C_p + r_{CO_2} C_{CO_2} + r_w C_w + r_{BG} C_{BG} + r_{BL} C_{BL} \right] \frac{dT}{dt} = \left[\frac{(-\Delta H)_{OH} [OH]_0}{\rho_p} \right] \frac{dX_{OH}}{dt} +
$$
$$
+ \left[\frac{(-\Delta H)_w [w]_0}{\rho_p} \right] \frac{dX_w}{dt} - \lambda \left(-\frac{dr_{BL}}{dt} \right)
\tag{1}
$$

where C is the heat capacity and r is the mass of each component per unit mass of polymerizing mixture (mixture of un-reacted polyol and isocyanate). The subscript p means the polymerizing mixture, CO2 carbon dioxide, W water, BG physical blowing agent in the gas phase, and BL physical blowing agent in the liquid phase. X is the fractional conversion and (-ΔH) denotes the heat of reaction, whose subscripts OH and W

NUMERICAL SIMULATION OF REACTION INJECTION MOLDING FOR REFRIGERATOR
INSULATION

mean polymerization reaction of the diol and blowing reaction of water molecules. [OH] is the number of moles of the hydroxyl end groups per unit volume of the polymerizing mixture and [W] is the number of moles of water molecules. The mass of each component per unit mass of the polymerizing mixture, ri, can be calculated from the concentration and the fractional conversion:

$$r_w = \frac{[w]M_w}{1000\rho_p} \tag{2}$$

$$r_{CO_2} = \frac{[w]_0 X_w M_{CO_2}}{1000\rho_p - r_{CO_2,D}} \tag{3}$$

$$r_{BG} = r_{BL,0} - r_{BL} \tag{4}$$

M_w and M_{CO_2} are the molecular weight of water and carbon dioxide, respectively. rCO_2, D is the initial mass of carbon dioxide that is dissolved in the polymerizing mixture.

3.1   Polymerization

Reaction of diisocyanate and polyol ends up with the gelling reaction of polyurethane:

$$nNCO - R - NCO + nHO - R' - OH \rightarrow -\big[O - R' - O - CONH - R - NCHCO\big]_n - \tag{5}$$

If molecular diffusion is neglected and second order kinetics are assumed [41], the kinetic equation of the gelling reaction can be represented as:

$$\frac{dX_{OH}}{dt} = A_{OH}e^{\left(\frac{-E_{OH}}{R_gT}\right)}[OH]_0(1-X_{OH})(S_{NCO} - 2s_wX_w - X_{OH}) * \left[1 + r_{BL}\frac{\rho_p}{\rho_{BL}} + r_w\frac{\rho_p}{\rho_w}\right]^{-1} \tag{6}$$

where $s_{NCO} = {[NCO]_0}/{[OH]_0}$, $s_w = {[w]_0}/{[OH]_0}$, A_{OH} is the pre-exponential factor, E_{OH} the activation energy of the gelling reaction and R_g the gas constant.

3.2   Expansion

Since water is used as the chemical blowing agent for the polyurethane foam system, it reacts with isocyanate to form carbon dioxide and urea. Based on the assumption that the water-isocyanate reaction in described from the second order kinetics, the reaction rate is described as:

$$\frac{dX_w}{dt} = A_we^{\left(\frac{-E_w}{R_gT}\right)}[OH]_0(1-X_w)(S_{NCO} - 2s_wX_w - X_{OH}) * \left[1 + r_{BL}\frac{\rho_p}{\rho_{BL}} + r_w\frac{\rho_p}{\rho_w}\right]^{-1} \tag{7}$$

Assuming that the evaporation rate of the physical blowing agent is controlled by the heat generated, due to a chemical reaction, it is based on the fact that the rate of the mass transfer is so fast that the blowing agent in the gas phase can be in equilibrium with the blowing agent in the liquid phase. The boiling point (TB) of the physical blowing agent in the reacting mixture depends on its mole fraction (xBL). The mole fraction is a linear function of the boiling temperature [41]:

NUMERICAL SIMULATION OF REACTION INJECTION MOLDING FOR REFRIGERATOR INSULATION

$$\chi_{BL} = \alpha T_B + \beta \qquad (8)$$

and the relationship between the mass ratio and the mole fraction of the blowing agent in a liquid phase can be given as:

$$r_{BL} = \frac{\chi_{BL}}{(1-\chi_{BL})} \frac{M_B}{M_{no}} \qquad (9)$$

where MB is the molecular weight of the blowing agent and Mno is the initial number average molecular weight of the polymerizing mixture. The expansion rate can be described as:

$$\frac{dr_{BL}}{dt} = \begin{cases} \dfrac{M_B}{M_{no}} \dfrac{1}{(1-\chi_{BL})^2} \dfrac{d\chi_{BL}}{dt} \dfrac{dT}{dt}, \text{for } T \geq T_{BL,0} \\ 0, \text{for } T < T_{BL,0} \end{cases} \qquad (10)$$

With the assumption of the ideal gas, the density of the free rising foam is given by:

$$\rho_F = \frac{1 + r_{BL,0} + r_{w,0}}{\dfrac{r_{CO_2} 1000 R_g T}{p M_{CO_2}} + \dfrac{r_{BG} 1000 R_g T}{p M_B} + \dfrac{r_{BL}}{\rho_{BL}} + \dfrac{1}{\rho_p}} \qquad (11)$$

where p is the ambient pressure.

Concerning the viscosity of the foam, the model of Castro-Macosko [24] is used:

$$\mu_F = \eta_\infty e^{\left(\frac{E_\eta}{R_g T}\right)} \left(\frac{X_{NCO,g}}{X_{NCO,g} - X_{NCO}}\right)^{a + b X_{NCO} + c X_{NCO}} \qquad (12)$$

where X_{NCO} is isocyanate conversion and $X_{NCO,g}$ is its gel conversion.

With the assumption of the ideal gas that the bubbles formed are spherical and that the internal pressure is steady, the bubble radius is given by the following equation [43]:

$$r_{bubble} = \left(\frac{3}{4\pi} \frac{KT}{P_{bubble}}\right)^{1/3} \qquad (13)$$

3.3 Numerical Formulation

Prediction of the mold filling by the self-expanding polyurethane foam has been carried out based on the above theoretical modeling with the use of the commercial Computational Fluid Dynamic software ANSYS-CFX®. The case that was studied had to do with a real refrigerator and particularly with the bottom part of it (Fig. 1).

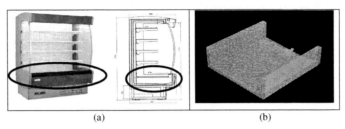

(a)   (b)

Fig. 1.   Test case (a) drawing and (b) CFX model.

The material's properties used for the numerical modeling as also and the parameters of the chemical system and viscosity model are listed in the following tables:

Table I: Material's properties used in numerical simulation

Isocyanate		
Density	Molecular weight	Viscosity
1.214 (Kg/m3)	174.2 (g/mol)	16.1 (mPaS)
Polyol		
Density	Molecular weight	Viscosity
1.1132 (Kg/m3)	62.068 (g/mol)	16.1 (mPaS)
Polyurethane		
Density	Molecular weight	Viscosity
1100 (Kg/m3)	615 (g/mol)	Equation (12)
Blowing agent CFC-11		
Density	Molecular weight	Viscosity
5.86 (Kg/m3)	137.4 (g/mol)	16.1 (µPas)

Table II: Polyurethane chemical system's and viscosity model parameters ([24], [42]):

Polyurethane chemical system		
Pre-exponential factor A_R	Activation energy E_R	Heat of reaction $(-\Delta H_R)$
10560 (m3/mol sec)	53.2 (KJ/mol)	96.3 (KJ/mol)
Viscosity model parameters		
Pre-exponential factor A_n	Activation energy E_n	Heat of reaction $(-\Delta H_R)$
10.3×10^{-8} (Pa s)	41.3 (J/mol)	96.3 (KJ/mol)
factor a	factor b	Gelling point C_{iso}
1.5 (-)	1 (-)	0.65 (-)

In order for the total number of runs to be reduced, the Taguchi method was used for the design of the simulations [44]. Four parameters were selected with three levels each, leading to the use of the L9 orthogonal array (**Table IV**). Since the test case was a refrigerator, in which the density should be 40 ± 5 Kgr/m^3, the mixing ratio was varied only $\pm5\%$ in order not to deviate too much from this value.

Table III: Parameters used and corresponding levels

Parameter	Level L1	Level L2	Level L3
Flow rate	1 Kgr/sec	1,5 Kgr/sec	2 Kgr/sec
Injection time	0.8 sec	1 sec	1.5 sec
Mixing ratio (Iso/Pol/B.Agen.)	0.45/0.35/0.2	0.47/0.34/0.19	0.43/0.36/0.21
Injection point	1	2	3

NUMERICAL SIMULATION OF REACTION INJECTION MOLDING FOR REFRIGERATOR INSULATION

The three injection points used in the simulations are shown in
Fig. 2:

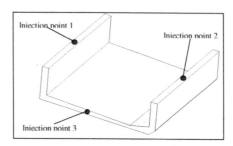

Fig. 2.   Different injection locations used in the simulations.

Table IV: L9 orthogonal array

Experiment	Flow rate	Injection time	Component ratio	Injection point
1	L1	L1	L1	L1
2	L1	L2	L2	L2
3	L1	L3	L3	L3
4	L2	L1	L2	L3
5	L2	L2	L3	L1
6	L2	L3	L1	L2
7	L3	L1	L3	L2
8	L3	L2	L1	L3
9	L3	L3	L2	L1

4.0   Results and Analysis

In the following figures are shown the results obtained from the numerical simulation of the filling stage (**Fig. 3**) and the curing stage (**Fig. 4**), for the nine runs as mentioned in the previous section.

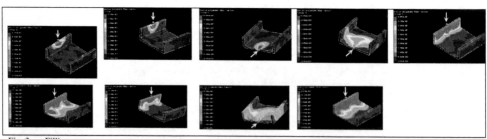

Fig. 3.   Filling stage

NUMERICAL SIMULATION OF REACTION INJECTION MOLDING FOR REFRIGERATOR INSULATION

Fig. 4.   Curing stage

The main purpose of the simulation was to examine the effect of the process parameters, namely flow rate, injection time, component's mixing ratio and injection location, on the volume filled and the time required for the complete curing of the mixture. In the following figures, is shown the effect of process parameters on the volume of the mold filled and the curing time, as resulted from the Analysis of Means (ANOM) and the Analysis of Variance (ANOVA). For the volume filled, it was the "Larger-the-Better" analysis used, whereas for the curing time the "Smaller-the-Better" analysis [45].

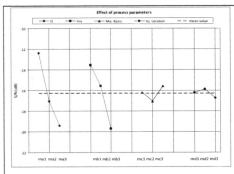 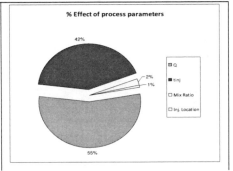

(a) ANOM and ANOVA analysis curing time

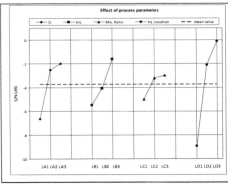 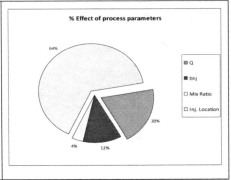

(b) ANOM and ANOVA analysis for volume filled

Fig. 5.   Effect of process parameters on (a) polymerization time and (b) volume filled

As it is shown in Fig. 5, the flow rate and the injection time have the most important effect on the curing time, whereas for the volume filled, on the location of the injection and the flow rate. The ANOM analysis shows that the optimum values of the parameters for the curing time should be L1 for the flow rate and injection time, L3 for the mixing ratio and L2 for the injection location. Correspondingly, for the volume filled, the optimum values should be L3 for all parameters.

NUMERICAL SIMULATION OF REACTION INJECTION MOLDING FOR REFRIGERATOR INSULATION

627

5.0 Conclusion

In the present work, a numerical model of the reaction injection molding of polyurethane foam was presented. The simulation procedure apart from the two stages, the filling stage in which the mixture of isocyanate, polyol and blowing agent is injected in the mold and the curing stage in which the curing and expansion of the mixture is accomplished. Using a statistical analysis of the results, namely the Analysis of Means and the Analysis of Variance, the optimum parameter values and the effect of each process parameter on the time required for the curing of the foam and the volume filled, have been accomplished.

Acknowledgement

This paper is part of the PAVET NE DE9 (COOLRIM) research project, co-financed by National and Community Funds.

References

[1] S.-W. Kim, L.-S. Turng, "Developments of three-dimensional computer-aided engineering simulations for injection moulding", *Modelling and Simulations in Materials Science and Engineering*, Vol. 12, No. 3, pp. S151-S173, 2004.

[2] D. H. Harry, R. G. Parrot, "Numerical simulation of injection mold filling", *Polymer Engineering and Science*, Vol. 10, No. 4, pp. 209-214, 1970.

[3] M. R. Kamal, R. Kening, "The injection molding of thermoplastics. Part I: Theoretical model", *Polymer Engineering and Science*, Vol. 12, No. 4, pp. 294-301, 1972.

[4] M. R. Kamal, R. Kening, "The injection molding of thermoplastics. Part II: Experimental test of the model", *Polymer Engineering and Science*, Vol. 12, No. 4, pp. 302-308, 1972.

[5] J. L Berger, C. G. Gogos, "A numerical simulation of the cavity filling process with PVC in injection molding", *Polymer Engineering and Science*, Vol. 13, No. 2, p. 102-112, 1973.

[6] P.-C. Wu, C. F. Huang, C. G. Gogos, "Simulation of the mold filling process", *Polymer Engineering and Science*, Vol. 14, No. 3, p. 223-230, 1974.

[7] C. Gutfinger, E. Broyer, Z. Tadmor, "Melt solidification in polymer processing", *Polymer Engineering and Science*, Vol. 15, No. 7, p. 515-524, 1975.

[8] G. Williams, H. A. Lord, "Mold-filling studies for the injection molding of thermoplastic materials. Part I: The flow of plastic materials in hot and cold walled circular channels", *Polymer Engineering and Science*, Vol. 15, No. 8, pp. 553-568, 1975.

[9] H. A. Lord, G. Williams, "Mold-filling studies for the injection molding of thermoplastic materials. Part II: The transient flow of plastic materials in the cavities of injection-molding dies", *Polymer Engineering and Science*, Vol. 15, No. 8, p. 569-582, 1975.

[10] J. R. A. Pearson, "Mechanics of Polymer Processing", Elsevier, Amsterdam, 1985.

[11] S. Richardson, "Hele-Shaw flow with a free boundary produced by the injection of fluid into a narrow channel", *Journal of Fluid Mechanics*, Vol. 56, No. 4,pp. 609-618,1972.

[12] Y. Kuo, M. R. Kamal, "The fluid mechanics and heat transfer of injection mold filling of thermoplastic materials", *AIChE Journal*, Vol. 22, No. 4, pp. 661-669, 1976.

[13] M. E. Ryan, T.-S. Chung, "Conformal mapping analysis of injection mold filling", *Polymer Engineering and Science*, Vol. 20, No. 9, p. 642-651, 1980.

[14] S. M. Richardson, H. J. Pearson, J. R. A. Pearson, "Simulation of injection moulding", *Journal of Fluid Mechanics*, Vol. 56, No. 4, p. 609-618, 1980.

[15] S. M. Richardson, "Simplified geometry models", *in Fundamentals of Computer Modeling for Polymer Processing*, Hanser Publishers, Munich, Chapter 4, 1989.

[16] C. A. Hieber, S. F. Shen, "A finite element / finite difference simulation of the injection molding filling process", *Journal of Non-Newtonian Fluid Mechanics*,Vol. 7, No. 1, pp. 1-32, 1980.

[17] W. Rose, "Fluid-fluid interfaces in steady motion", *Nature*, Vol. 191, No. 4785, pp. 242-243, 1961.

[18] L. R. Schmidt, "A special mold and tracer technique for studying shear and extension flows in a mold cavity during injection molding", *Polymer Engineering and Science*, Vol. 14, No. 11, pp. 797-800, 1974.

NUMERICAL SIMULATION OF REACTION INJECTION MOLDING FOR REFRIGERATOR INSULATION

[19] C. G. Gogos, C.-F. Huang, L. R. Schmidt, "The process of cavity filling including the fountain flow in injection molding", *Polymer Engineering and Science*, Vol. 26, No. 20, pp. 1457-1466, 1986.

[20] D. J. Coyle, J. W. Blake, C. W. Macosko, "The kinematics of fountain flow in mold-filling", *AIChE Journal*, Vol. 33, No. 7, p. 1168-1177, 1987.

[21] E. Vos, H. E. H. Meijer, G. W. Peters, "Multilayer injection molding", *International Polymer Processing*, Vol. 6, No. 1, p. 42-50, 1991.

[22] S. Bhattacharji, P. Savic, "Real and apparent non-Newtonian behaviour in viscous pipe flow of suspensions driven by a fluid piston", *Proceedings of the 1965 Heat Transfer and Fluid Mechanics Institute*, Stanford University Press, pp. 248-262, 1965.

[23] Z. Tadmor, "Molecular orientation in injection molding", *Journal of Applied Polymer Science*, Vol. 18, No. 6, p. 1753-1772, 1974.

[24] J. M. Castro, C. W. Macosko, "Studies of mold filling and curing in the reaction injection molding process", *AIChE Journal*, Vol. 28, No. 2, p. 250-260, 1982.

[25] M. R. Kamal, E. Chu, P. G. Lafleur, M. E. Ryan, "Computer simulation of injection mold filling for viscoelastic melts with fountain flow", *Polymer Engineering and Science*, Vol. 26, No. 3, pp. 190-196, 1986.

[26] H. Mavridis, A. N. Hrymak, J. Vlachopoulos, "Finite element simulation of fountain flow in injection molding", *Polymer Engineering and Science*, Vol. 26, No. 7, p. 449-454, 1986.

[27] R. A. Behrens, M. J. Crochet, C. D. Denson, A. B. Metzner, "Transient free surface flows: Motion of a fluid advancing in a tube", *AIChE Journal*, Vol. 33, No. 7, p. 1178-1186, 1987.

[28] M. R. Kamal, S. K. Goyal, E. Chu, "Simulation of injection mold filling of viscoelastic polymer with fountain flow", *AIChE Journal*, Vol. 34, No. 1, pp. 94-106, 1988.

[29] H. Mavridis, A. N. Hrymak, J. Vlachopoulos, "The effect of fountain flow on molecular orientation in injection molding", *Journal of Rheology*, Vol. 32, No. 6, p. 639-663, 1988.

[30] H. Mavridis, A. N. Hrymak, J. Vlachopoulos, "Transient free surface flow in injection mold filling", *AIChE Journal*, Vol. 34, No. 3, pp. 403-410, 1988.

[31] K. K. Wang, V. W. Wang, "Computer aided mold design and manufacturing, in Injection and Compression Molding Fundamentals", Marcel Dekker, Inc., New York, Chapter 9, p. 607-669, 1987.

[32] H. P. Wang, H. S. Lee, "Numerical techniques for free and moving boundary problems", *in Fundamentals of Computer Modeling for Polymer Processing*, Hanser Publishers, Munich, Chapter 8, p. 340-401, 1989.

[33] P. Kennedy, "Flow Analysis of Injection Molds", Hanser Publishers, Munich, 1995.

[34] S. I. Güçeri, "Finite difference solution of field problem", *in Fundamentals of Computer Modeling for Polymer Processing*, Hanser Publishers, Munich, Chapter 5, p. 141-236, 1989.

[35] S. Subbiah, D. L. Trafford, S. I. Güçeri, "Non-isothermal flow of polymers into two-dimensional, thin cavity molds: A numerical grid generation approach", *International Journal of Heat and Mass Transfer*, Vol. 32, No. 3, p. 415-434, 1989.

[36] A. Couniot, M. J. Crochet, "Finite elements for the numerical simulation of injection molding", *Proceedings of The 2nd International Conference on Numerical Methods in Industrial Forming Processes* (Numiform'86), Balkema Publishers, Rotterdam, pp. 165-170, 1986.

[37] F. Dupret, A.Couniot, O. Mal, L. Vanderschuren and O. Verhoyen, Modeling andsimulation of injection molding, in Advances in the Flow and Rheology of Non-Newtonian Fluids, Elsevier, Amsterdam, Chapter 7, 1999, p. 939-1010.

[38] J. F. Hétu, D. M. Gao, A. Garcia-Rejon, G. Salloum, "3D finite element method for the simulation of the filling stage in injection molding", *Polymer Engineering and Science*, Vol. 38, No. 2, pp.223-236, 1998.

[39] E. Pichelin, T. Coupez, "Finite element solution of the 3D mold filling problem for viscous incompressible fluid", *Computer Methods in Applied Mechanics and Engineering*, Vol. 163, No. 1, p. 359-371, 1998.

[40] G. A. A. V. Haagh, F. N. van de Vosse, "Simulation of three-dimensional polymer mould filling process using a pseudo-concentration method", *International Journal for Numerical Methods in Fluids*, Vol. 28, No. 9, pp. 1355-1369, 1998

[41] G. A. A. V. Haagh, G. W. M. Peters, F. N. van de Vosse, H. E. H. Meijer, "A 3-D finite element model for gas-assisted injection molding: Simulations and experiments", *Polymer Engineering and Science*, Vol. 41, No. 3, pp. 449-465, 2001.

[42] Seo D. J.R. Youn, "Numerical analysis on reaction injection molding of polyurethane foam by using a finite volume method", *Polymer*, Vol. 46, pp. 6482-6493, 2005.

[43] C. Kim, J.R.Youn, "Enviromentaly friendly processing of polyurethane foam for thermal insulation", *Polymers and Plastics Technology Engineering*, Vol. 39(1), pp. 163-185, 2000.

[44] Phadke, S. M., "Quality Engineering Using Robust Design", Prentice Hall, 1989.

[45] G. S. Peace, "Taguchi methods-A hands on approach", Addison Wesley, 1993.

NUMERICAL SIMULATION OF REACTION INJECTION MOLDING FOR REFRIGERATOR INSULATION

MODELLING AND SIMULATION OF GRINDING FLUID NOZZLES

V.A. Baines-Jones [1], M.N. Morgan [2], A.D. Batako [2], E. Brown [1]

1. Cinetic Landis Ltd

2. AMTReL, GERI, Liverpool John Moores University

Abstract

The recent advances in grinding technology could not have succeeded without being accompanied by parallel developments in the area of fluid application. In spite of the known successes there remains a potential to accelerate the progress by under-pinning practical experiences in process development with a better understanding of nozzle flows, nozzle positioning and delivery system design. Improvements can be suggested using performance analysis to optimise pre-nozzle fluid supply removing turbulent effects and smoothing out internal flows. The function of a nozzle in grinding is to provide the grind zone with fluid to aid lubrication, grinding chip flushing and cooling. Against this, the presence of reverse flows inside the nozzle and stagnated flows in the region from the inlet to the outlet, reduce nozzle efficiency. These factors influence the exit flow and reduce the coherence length of the jet. The flow simulation process has been used to investigate the flow path in coolant nozzles and pre-nozzle arrangements. The behaviour of turbulent coolant flow motion with massless particle paths in a computational domain are obtained through Computational Fluid Dynamics (CFD)/CAD (Computer Aided Design) software packages. The new information is presented here on recirculation flows in the inlet duct and non-uniform flow within the coolant nozzle provides valuable insights to designers for optimisation of nozzles and more efficient delivery of grinding coolant.

Keywords: Grinding, Nozzles, CFD.

1.0   Introduction

With modern manufacturers requiring high process speeds and reduced production costs and times, the correct method of coolant application can be as vital as selecting the correct wheel to meet the demands of the grinding process. Guo & Malkin [1] discussed the possibility of using the grinding wheel and its momentum as a pumping mechanism to force as much as possible of the grinding coolant into the grinding contact. Webster

[2] points out that if the wheel is not used in this way then high contact arc temperatures will exist and will carry on through the grinding zone until bulk cooling takes place after the wheel has passed. If fluid is not forced into the grinding contact then the ability of the coolant to lubricate and cool the grinding contact is reduced and will lead to higher grinding forces and an increased risk of thermal damage. This post zone bulk cooling may also cause another problem; this bulk cooling can create unwanted stresses in the workpiece surface as well as causing the wheel bond and abrasives to overheat. As higher removal rates, longer wheel life and higher quality parts become a necessity, optimum fluid application in the grinding process becomes more and more important. Webster [2] highlights the importance of the correct application of grinding coolant when he makes the comparison between the coolant selection part of the process and that of wheel selection. This paper describes the geometrical modelling of nozzles from part drawings using the state-of-the-art combined CAD CFD software ANSYS package. The paper also highlights the procedure for generation of multi-type meshes and their analysis in the problem set up of the solver. The resultant mesh along with boundary conditions is solved for turbulent incompressible fluid flow internally for nozzle flows. Several physical parameters through contour/vector plots obtained at different planes of the computational domain are discussed.

2.0   CFD Analysis of Internal Flows

Fluid mechanics is a very large area of science and for many years has been a hot topic for research. Numerous theoretical models and numerical solutions for flow problems exist. With the advent of the high speed computer and new computational techniques, comparison of CFD predictions and previously taken numerical solutions now come to the forefront. Ludicello of ESDU [3] recently carried out a comparison between CFX results and those gained numerically for pressure loss in pipes with sudden contractions. Pipes with sudden contractions exist in many engineering applications, most pipe fittings, and most application systems on the lead-up to the coolant nozzles in grinding. To analyse accurately and design these supply systems, the amount of pressure loss and flow separation must be determined to avoid unnecessary pre-nozzle pressure losses [4]. There is little reliable experimental data on pressure loss in sudden contractions. Ludicello [3] used ANSYS CFX to validate existing experimental data. The solver proved very robust, with the solution converging to a high accuracy with only a small number of iterations on meshes that were not completely orthogonal or high quality. This work is taken further and presented within this paper for grinding fluid nozzles.

3.0   Description of Grinding Fluid Nozzles

Nozzles made up of short interlocking plastic tubes (Fig.1) may be adequate for general toolroom application. For high volume production, however, these interlocking tubes are inadequate as they create turbulence, are difficult to direct with accuracy at the grind zone, and cannot be held in the correct position for very long. For these reasons, therefore, these nozzles prevent equal velocity fluid delivery. More suitably designed nozzles have a long straight section of at least 50 mm length, as illustrated in (Fig.2). The nozzle must have very sharp edges at the point of exit and must be free of "nicks" and other damage to reduce nozzle losses. As illustrated, it is recommended that the nozzle should be inclined at an angle of between 0-20° (for standard cylindrical grinding of steels [5]). Jet nozzles supply coolant at high jet speeds to break through the layer of air that builds up around the grinding wheel. This is why the fluid entrains and "sticks" to the wheels surface, as opposed to click nozzles that only operate at relatively low pressures. Alternatively, the shoe nozzle design (Fig.3), ensures equal fluid velocity delivery at lower pressures than the jet nozzle in Fig.2. A chamber fitting tight to the grinding wheel, leaving a gap of only 0.5mm, is flooded with copious amounts of fluid at low pressure. The grinding wheel picks up the grinding fluid and accelerates it to the grinding wheel peripheral speed, attaining equal fluid velocity delivery. A further key factor of the shoe nozzle design is that it acts as an air scraper that directs the layer of turbulent air, following the wheels periphery, away from the grinding wheel [7]. Engineer et al [8] suggested that the method of fluid application using show nozzles is ineffective. This is especially true under high speed grinding conditions, where the energy of the fluid is not sufficient to penetrate the air boundary layer.

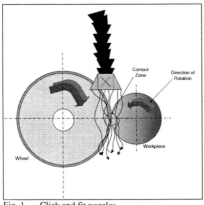

Fig. 1   Click and fit nozzles

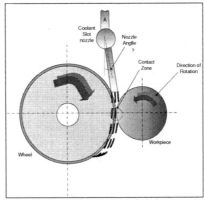

Fig. 2   High-speed nozzle design.

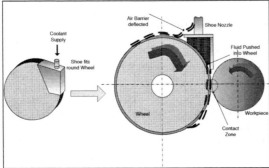

Fig. 3.   Application of fluid into the grinding contact for a shoe nozzle

4.0   CFD Modelling

ANSYS CFX allows modelling of the internal flow profiles for a range of nozzles and fluid situations with different entry conditions. This paper includes internal analyses on the nozzle proposed by Webster et al [9] and work by Cui [10] examined with CFX. Further to this, the nozzles proposed by Gviniashvili [7] were investigated to analyse their internal performance. Each nozzle includes a length of pipe before the inlet to develop the flow before this region. To analyse accurately and design these supply systems, the amount of pressure loss and flow separation must be determined to avoid unnecessary pre-nozzle pressure losses [4].

MODELLING AND SIMULATION OF GRINDING FLUID NOZZLES

There is little reliable experimental data on pressure loss in sudden contractions. To validate existing experimental data, ANSYS CFX was used in [3]. The solver proved very robust, with the solution converging to a high accuracy with only a small number of iterations on meshes that were not completely orthogonal or high quality. This work is taken further and presented within this paper for grinding fluid nozzles. To study the internal flow in grinding fluid nozzles, based on design data, the approach is divided into three aspects, namely geometry creation, mesh generation and flow simulation. To create the geometry for this analysis, a sketch of a section of the pipe was created and then revolved around the axis. After revolving, the section becomes a three-dimensional solid of the flow region. Note that the actual region of flow is created, not the pipe geometry. The interest lies within regions expected for flow recirculation and stagnation. Therefore, checks on dimensional accuracy were performed at these areas of high interest.

For the meshing, ICEM CFD TETRA was used. This meshing tool generates a tetrahedral mesh directly from the CAD geometry. A mesh convergence study of exit velocity permitted some verification of the results. The higher mesh size with the required fineness towards the areas of interest to capture flow phenomenon, is limited in terms of computational power and hardware resources. After meshing, mesh-smoothing was carried out. In smoothing the mesh, the tetrahedral smoother calculates individual cell quality based on the relative aspect ratio of each cell and the ratio between the volume of the cell and that of the largest tetrahedron that could fit inside the sphere that circumscribes the actual cell. Referring then to the user specified cell quality lower bound, the smoother modifies all cells below this quality criterion, nodes are moved and merged, edges are swapped and in some cases, cells are deleted. The quality of the mesh, in terms of skew and aspect ratio were checked. This creates a hybrid mesh with prism elements added at the walls for superior accuracy. The mesh contains both tetrahedral and prismatic elements.

The CFX-Pre module is a modern, consistent and intuitive interface for the definition of the complex physics required for a CFD analysis. The computing method used in this paper is commercial solver CFX, which is based on the finite volume method. It is a fully three-dimensional flow simulation method fulfilling the Reynolds Averaged Navier–Stokes equations of motion, for an incompressible fluid flow. The properties of the cooling fluid with only 10% Hysol X are close enough to that of water in terms of flow and therefore water is assumed as the fluid in the simulation. The simulation is a steady state simulation and therefore, runs continuously. Simulated pressures are related to an atmospheric reference. No heat-transfer analysis is set as this is outside the scope of this work for analysing internal flows of a single fluid at ambient temperature. The SST (shear stress transport) model allows for the best calculation of near wall turbulence in CFD simulations and is therefore chosen. The model works by solving a turbulence/frequency-based model, k–ω at the wall and, k-ε in the bulk flow (the turbulent kinetic energy k, its dissipation rate ε, or specific dissipation rate ω are established numerically [4]). A blending function ensures a smooth transition between the two models. To establish the model, turbulent incompressible fluid flow is considered with varying flow rates and inlet pressures assumed to be entering the inlet and leaving through the outlet where an atmospheric pressure boundary is imposed. The wall boundaries are treated as stationary no slip walls and turbulent intensity of 5% is included. The governing equations are non-linear coupled partial differential equations. Their integration over volumes leads to the system of discrete algebraic equations, which are solved through block iteration methods. The number of iterations for each simulation was set with no maximum so that the solver, within CFX, ran until a converged solution of 0.00001RMS was achieved. This is considered accurate enough for most research activities.

MODELLING AND SIMULATION OF GRINDING FLUID NOZZLES

5.0   Results

The main flow in the nozzle chambers from the inlet is fully developed in the x-y plane expressed by a standard turbulent flow velocity profile except for the region of contraction into the nozzle exit duct (Fig. 4). As the main flow approaches the change in section region, the cross section is continuously decreasing and the main flow is accelerated. The discontinuity of the geometry at the transition of the downwards oriented flow into the constant nozzle exit flow leads to a flow separation. This flow separation is expressed by the formation of a recirculation zone at the beginning of the nozzle exit chamber (Fig. 5). Adjacent to the recirculation zone close to the centre line of the nozzle, a jet is formed with velocities about two times higher than the mean velocity. In the lower and upper parts of the main nozzle chambers, a second recirculation domain establishes itself with extremely low velocities. Those small velocities are due to the fluid backing up against the walls and recirculating (Fig. 6). As the jet exits the nozzle, the jet will start to break up. The distance at which this occurs is the subject for the further work of this paper.

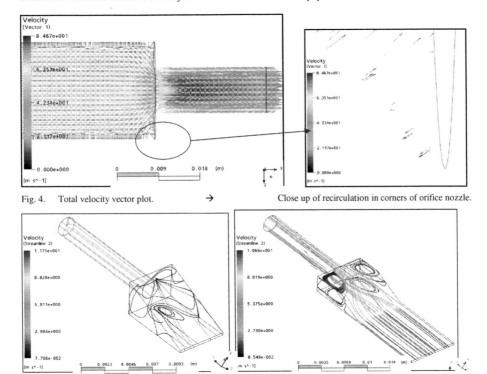

Fig. 4.   Total velocity vector plot.   →   Close up of recirculation in corners of orifice nozzle.

Fig. 5.   Flow patterns in the wedge nozzle.   Fig. 6.   Flow in the conventional slot nozzle.

Velocity profile charts have been produced which show how the flow acts both in the centre of the flow and at the wall of the pipe or nozzle. A number of inputs were tested including the flowrates, fluid velocities, fluid type and sharpness of the contraction. For the first example, the results for water and the contraction angle shown provide an insight into internal nozzle fluid behaviour. The greatest influence on the size of the eddy formation lay with the contraction angle. The steeper this angle, the greater the recirculating flows. The

MODELLING AND SIMULATION OF GRINDING FLUID NOZZLES

smoothness of transition from one point to another also had a smaller effect on the size of the recirculating flow. In terms of improving the nozzle design to reduce the amount of recirculation and losses within the nozzle, aspects of design were changed to monitor the smoothness of the internal flow. The important factors are: recirculation within the flow region, pressure losses due to the influence of the change in section, and the nozzle velocity profile at the exit. These factors all cause the nozzle to perform imperfectly. To remove some of these factors it is critical that a smooth change in section is implemented, such as that proposed in work by Rouse et al [11] and Webster et al [9].

6.0   Jet Breakup Experimentation

Grant and Middleman [12], Hoyt and Taylor [13], Leib and Goldstein [14], investigated the flow of a jet issuing from differing nozzles or hoses in a variety of industrial applications. The major research effort concerns the analysis of jet stability, known in this work as the jet breakup length and more formally the coherence length of that jet. The work described here expands on length definitions based on principles from Grant and Middleman [12]. From this, the coherence length (C_L) of a jet is defined as 'the length of the fluid jet from the point of exit from the nozzle, to a point at which the disturbances (ξ) within the fluid jet reach the same radius (r_j) as the initial nozzle opening, shown schematically in Fig. 7. McCarthy and Molloy [15] describe this area of jet break up mathematically forming relations between the jet break up length in this area and again the numerical constants using the Weber and Reynolds numbers. This is the region under investigation in the experimentation. Cui [10] predicted that nozzle coherence length and its usefulness in the grinding environment is based on the width of the actual jet. Much of this work focused on the splitting of the jet and examined the actual jet width. Originally, this determined the idea of coherence length within this work. On inspection of the experimental results however, the phenomenon of peak velocity was observed. With the accepted relationship of $Vj = Vs$, to match the wheel speed at the point of entry to the grinding contact [3], the fluid must be at this peak velocity. Therefore, the areas of the jet not at this peak velocity are of little use in the grinding contact region.

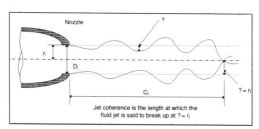

Fig. 7   Schematic for the definition of coherence length

The best performing nozzle, and the one dealt with in detail here, is the round coherent jet nozzle. Fig. 8 shows the velocity profiles at each of the eight measurement points downstream of the nozzle orifice. The fluid stream with minimum distance connection is shown in Fig. 9. Figures 8 and 9 show plots for the fluid stream with nozzle 2 (9mm Rouse based nozzle). This nozzle is predicted as being the most coherent according to Cui [10] and Webster et al [6]. Fig. 9 shows this general trend and pattern for a coherent jet. The fluid profiles for nozzle 2 have a greater amount of peak velocity than those for the straight pipe (nozzle 1). The profile follows the inlet turbulent profile for a distance up to 500mm. At this point, the jet begins to loose central core velocity, but does not break up over the entire measured area. The surface graph confirms this as uniform velocity is observed up until this point.

MODELLING AND SIMULATION OF GRINDING FLUID NOZZLES

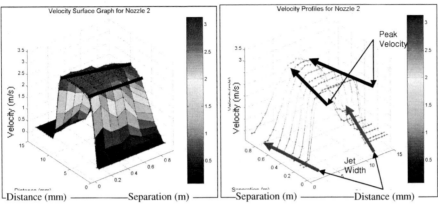

Fig. 8.   Velocity profiles nozzle 2.   Fig. 9   Velocity surface graph nozzle 2.

Fig. 10 is a graphical representation of the fluid jet break up and the inner-core peak velocity profile. The jet appears to hold its shape until the said 500mm mark. At this point, the jet thickness begins to increase. Observing the inner core, this maintains its initial width with only slight loss up to this point. After this, it begins to narrow but extends beyond the measurement zone. Extending the lines forward gives a coherence length of approximately 1300mm. This is a 50% improvement over the straight length of pipe and shows the value of the Rouse type coherent jet nozzle.

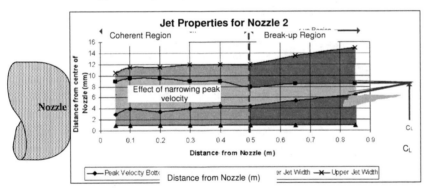

Fig. 10.   Coherence length and Jet width for nozzle 2

Two other nozzles were tested for shape comparison for inclusion into the theory for jet break up length; the slope and the step, 9mm round nozzles. The sloped nozzle (nozzle 4) exhibits a similar profile break up to the Rouse based nozzle (nozzle 2). The break up length is longer than the measurement area but projecting the lines gives a jet break up of around 1100mm. This is an improvement on the straight 9mm pipe of approximately 33%. In comparison, the stepped nozzle begins to break up as soon as the fluid emerges from the orifice. This point shows a jet break up length of approximately 650mm. This is a percentage reduction on the standard coherence length in the region of 24%. These tests, based on the 9mm nozzle exit and compared with the original 9mm straight pipe, gave an insight into the coherence length of a range of nozzle body shapes. Without knowing the internal structure and simply measuring the jet thickness, this phenomenon would have been missed.

MODELLING AND SIMULATION OF GRINDING FLUID NOZZLES

7.0 Conclusion

- Simulation of nozzles for flow prediction is modelled and draws several physical observations from flow results at different planes corroborating theory on flow separation and recirculation.
- Behaviour of flow exiting the nozzle was attempted under idealistic conditions. This lead to experimental validation of the importance of peak velocity.
- Simulation of interior nozzle flows impacts on design, understanding of interior flow phenomenon as well as nozzle efficiency
- The results present a comparative (performance) evaluation of various nozzles not previously analysed within relation to coherence length.
- The work provides an established experimental arrangement for fluids tests.

Acknowledgement

This research was supported by the Engineering and Physical Sciences Research Council under Grant No.: GR/S82350/01. This support is gratefully acknowledged. Invaluable insight into grinding fluid application by two of the leading experts namely Professor B. Rowe and Dr J. Webster is gratefully appreciated. Thanks also to the AMTReL technical staff for support and encouragement with the experimental program. Thanks to Cinetic Landis for financial support and sponsoring of this conference paper and the ongoing work into fluid application optimisation.

References

[1] Guo, C., Malkin, S., 1992 "Analysis of fluid flow through the grinding zone". *J. Eng. Ind.* Vol. 114, pp. 427–434.
[2] Webster. J.A., (1995), "Selection of Coolant Type and Application Technique in Grinding", Supergrind 1995 – *Grinding and Polishing with Superabrasives.*, USA, Nov 2-3, pp.205 – 220.
[3] ESDU TN 06023, "CFD Validation Studies for Pressure Loss and Flow Characteristics in Sudden Contractions," ISBN: 1 86246 600 9. DOI: 10.1912/ESDUtn06023, 2007
[4] ANSYS Solutions Magazine, 2006. [Online] Cited: May 2007. From: http://www.ansyssolutions.com/
[5] Furutani, K., Ohguro, N., Trong Hieu, N., 2002. "In-process measurement of topography change of grinding wheel by using hydrodynamic pressure". *Int. J. of Machine Tools and Man.* 42, pp. 1447–1453.
[6] Webster J.A., (1999) "Optimizing coolant application systems for high productivity grinding", *Abrasives* October/November 34–41.
[7] Gviniashvili, V, K. Woolley, N.H. Rowe, W.B. (2004) "Useful coolant flowrate in grinding", *International Journal of Machine Tools and Manufacture* 44 (6) 629–636.
[8] Engineer F., Guo C., and Malkin S., "Experimental measurement of fluid flow through the grinding zone". *Trans. ASME.* 114 (1992), pp. 61–66.
[9] Webster J.A., Cui C., Mindek R.B. Jr., (1995) "Grinding fluid application system design", *CIRP Annals* 44 (1) 333–338.
[10] Cui C, (1995) "Experimental investigation of thermofluids in the grinding zone", PhD dissertation, University of Connecticut.
[11] Rouse H., Asle M., Howe J.W., Metzler D.E., (1952) "Experimental investigation of fire monitors and nozzles", 117th *ASCE Transactions.*
[12] Grant, R.P., Middleman (1966) Newtonian jet stability. *AIChE J* 15: 669 ± 681
[13] Hoyt, J.W., Taylor, J.J., (1974) "Turbulent Structure in a Water Jet Discharging in Air", *J. Fluid Mech.*, Vol. 63, pp 635-6.
[14] Leib, S.J., Goldstein, M.E., (1986). "Convective and absolute instability of a viscous liquid jet". *Phys. Fluids* Vol. 29: pp. 952-954.
[15] McCarthy. M.J., Molloy N.A., (1974) "Review of stability of liquid jets and the influence of nozzle design", *Chem.Eng. J.* 7-1.

The 6th International Conference on Manufacturing Research (ICMR08)
Brunel University, UK, 9-11th September 2008

TOOL PATH OPTIMISATION USING GRAPH ALGORITHMS

Crispin A. J.

Department of Computing and Mathematics, Manchester Metropolitan University, M1 5GD, UK
a.crispin@mmu.ac.uk

Abstract

The CNC route path optimisation problem involves finding a minimum tour distance or time for a movable tool in applications such as the sequencing of punch operations, the drilling of holes and the robotic dispensing of solder paste onto a surface mount printed circuit board. The tool path problem shares many similarities with the travelling salesman problem but becomes more complicated when tool change and other factors specific to the functionality of a machine tool are taken into consideration. This paper describes graph based algorithms to solve the CNC route path optimisation problem. The solution approach developed is a two-pass (stage) procedure consisting of a node insertion tour improvement followed by a 2-opt tour improvement. The node insertion tour improvement stage takes an initial randomly created tour and attempts to improve it by selecting a node and placing it in a different part of the tour. The 2-opt stage takes the tour created from the node insertion stage and improves it by exchanging two edges as it cycles through the tour path. A strategy for minimising the number of tool changes is discussed. Computational experiments have been undertaken using regular grid patterns and randomly generated data sets to establish the efficiency of the developed methods for different problem sizes. The grid patterns are considered to be illustrations of the type of patterns seen when holes are drilled in printed circuit boards. A generic hole-making CNC part program (G-codes) can be automatically generated from the optimised route path.

Keywords: Optimisation, tool path, graph algorithms, hole-making.

1.0   Introduction

There are many manufacturing applications that involve point-to-point operations and the generation of a tool path which is optimised in terms of tool travel distance. One example is the drilling of holes in a printed circuit board (PCB) where holes are used for making contacts between different layers in a board (i.e. vias) and for placing integrated circuit components. Another example is the application of solder paste to surface mount pads using a robotic dispensing tool which requires that the non-productive travel time or airtime is minimised.

These types of problem involve finding a sequence in which points are visited such that travel distance (or time) is minimised. Various solution techniques based on heuristic approaches have been reported in the literature [1, 2].

This work has developed a graph based solution approach for minimising tool path tour distance. The solution approach has been applied to regular grid patterns, randomly generated data sets and data sets where a tool change is required. The grid patterns are considered to be illustrations of the type of patterns seen when holes are drilled in printed circuit boards. A tool change is needed in applications where it is necessary to drill holes with different diameters. A CNC part program can be generated which accommodates a tool change.

2.0   Graph Algorithms

Many combinatorial optimisation problems such as the tool path problem can be solved using graph theory. A graph G=(V,E) is a structure that is built by interconnecting vertices or nodes V and a finite set of edges E as shown in Fig 1. The nodes in Fig. 1 could represent holes to be drilled and each line or edge represents a connection between two nodes. When the edges are labelled with numbers representing the distance between nodes, for example, the numbers can be viewed as weights and the graph is called a weighted graph.

In the tool path problem the objective is to visit every node (hole to be drilled) in a graph exactly once and return to the starting point using a path that costs as little as possible. This problem is a variant of the classic travelling salesman problem [3]. It is assumed that the graph has a Hamiltonian cycle i.e. a path passing through every node in the connected graph and the objective is to find the minimum length (least cost) Hamiltonian cycle in the graph.

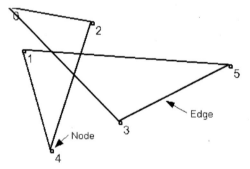

Fig. 1.   A simple graph

If G=(V,E) is a weighted graph where weights correspond to distances between nodes then the length or distance of a path P from node v_1 to v_k in G is the sum of the weights w of the edges in the path.

$$w(P) = \sum_{i=1}^{k-1} w(v_i, v_{i+1})$$

(1)

TOOL PATH OPTIMISATION USING GRAPH ALGORITHMS

In the tool path problem it is reasonable to assume that the maximum distance between points is the Euclidean distance such that

$$w(v_i, v_{i+1}) = \sqrt{(x_{i+1} - x_i)^2 + (y_{i+1} - y_i)^2} \qquad (2)$$

This equation assumes that the tool head is moved by two motors running simultaneously in the horizontal and vertical directions.

A weighted graph can be realised in software using an adjacency matrix data structure. For n nodes or vertices v_1, v_2 to v_n an n-by-n matrix M is constructed with the n rows representing the nodes in order and the n columns representing the same nodes in order. The matrix elements M[i,j] are labelled with the weight (distance cost) for each pair of connected nodes. An infinite (null) value is given for node pairs that are not directly connected. Consequently, this representation allows the determination of adjacencies between pairs of nodes and is implemented in software as a two dimensional n-by-n array such that M[i,j] holds the distance weight for v_i to v_j if they are connected.

With small graphs it is possible to exhaustively search all path combinations to find the path with the minimum tour distance. The problem can be solved by generating all (n-1)! Hamiltonian cycles and comparing their weights. This is because with a directed graph one of the n nodes is fixed thereby leaving (n-1)! different ways of arranging the remaining (n-1) nodes in the cycle. However, as the number of nodes increases, an exhaustive search becomes impractical. For example, a problem with 50 nodes has 49! or approximately 6×10^{62} cycles to search which is too time consuming. Consequently, with this type of problem it is necessary to employ an approximate or heuristic method capable of producing a suboptimal solution that is acceptably close to the optimal solution for practical purposes.

3.0   Solution Approach

The solution developed for this work is based on using the node insertion and 2-opt algorithms which are tour improvement heuristics. Tour improvement heuristics begin with an initial tour and perform operations which attempt to improve it. In this work the initial solution is a random cycle.

The role of the node insertion algorithm is to take a node and attempt to improve the tour by placing it between other nodes. An example of the operation of the algorithm is shown in Fig. 2. With reference to Fig. 2, the algorithm selects and disconnects node 3 and then places it between nodes 2 and 4 to create the new path shown. The distances of the two tours are then compared and the new tour is selected if it has a lower cost. This process is repeated for all nodes in the tour.

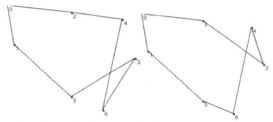

Fig. 2.   Tour improvement by node insertion. The path on the left shows an initial tour. The path on the right shows a new tour with node 3 disconnected and then placed between nodes 2 and 4.

The 2-opt method selects and exchanges an edge pair such that a new tour is created [4, 5]. The algorithm systematically checks all pairs of non-adjacent edges of the tour and tests whether path length would be reduced by exchanging the current edge pair. If the tour length is decreased the exchange is performed and the procedure cycles through the path in search of other edge pairs which, when exchanged, improve the tour length. An example of the operation of the 2-opt algorithm is shown in Fig. 3. Here the edges (3,5) and (4,6) are exchanged with edges (3,4) and (5,6). If a lower cost results then the new graph is retained. Pseudo code and Pascal methods for graph based heuristics are discussed in [6] and Java code [7]. This application has been developed using the C# programming language.

A composite solution approach has been devised for this work. This is referred to as the two-pass method. In the first pass (stage) a random tour is created and improved using the node insertion method. In the second pass the path generated from the first phase is improved using the 2-opt method.

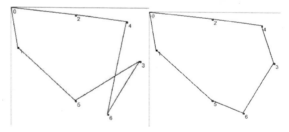

Fig. 3.   Tour improvement by the exchange of two edges (2-opt). The path on the left is an initial tour. The path on the right is the new tour with the edges (3,5) and (4,6) exchanged with edges (3,4) and (5,6)

4.0   Application Software

The work has developed a utility tool (see Fig. 4) which allows tool point data files to be displayed so that an optimised tool travel path can be calculated and a CNC part program automatically generated. The data file format for hole description is (hole-type, x, y) where the hole-type identifier allows different hole diameter types to be defined and (x, y) are absolute coordinate values. The declaration of a hole-type allows problems which involve a tool change to be studied.

The software has been developed as a Microsoft Windows .NET application using C#. The main classes developed for the application include: (i) a point class defining hole positions and a diameter; (ii) a graph class for creating the adjacency matrix; (iii) a path class with random path, node insertion and 2-opt methods; (iv) a user interface (form) class; (v) a file input class and (vi) a CNC postprocessor class for exporting a machine tool part program. The CNC postprocessor class automatically generates a part program using the best order sequence of points obtained by the graph optimiser. Currently, command lines are generated for hole-making cycles which assume a start location (origin) and standard drilling using G81 where X Y values are the coordinates of holes. The postprocessor inserts a tool change command (M06 T0N where N is the tool number) where this is necessary along the path. The output from the CNC postprocessor has been tested using the AutoEditNC simulator [8].

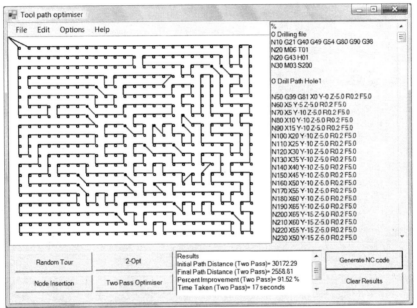

Fig. 4.   Tool path optimisation software

5.0   Algorithm Performance

The performance of the node insertion, 2-opt and two-pass algorithms have been tested on different size problems. All tests were carried out on a PC with an Intel Core Duo E4400 processor with 2MB of RAM.

Performance tests have been completed using grid test patterns ranging from 100 to 600 points in steps of 50. Tests for each pattern were repeated five times to enable average values to be calculated. In all cases the start tour is a random cycle. The percentage path distance improvement for the node insertion, 2-opt and two-pass methods using grid patterns are shown in Fig. 5. In this figure it is seen that the percentage tour distance improvement, as compared to the original random tour length, ranges from 85% to 92%. The two-pass method always produces the best path distance improvement and the trend shows that the percentage distance improvement increases slightly with grid pattern point number.

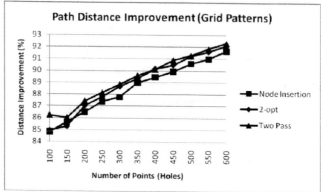

Fig. 5.   Comparison of path distance improvement

Fig. 6 shows the time taken for each of the methods for grid patterns. This shows that in all cases there is a non-linear relationship between problem size and the time taken to find a solution with the time to find a solution in larger problems rapidly increasing. Interestingly the two-pass method shows a similar time performance as the node insertion method and produces superior percentage improvement results as shown in Fig. 5. The reason is likely due to the fact that in the two-pass method the 2-opt method is applied to a partially optimised solution rather than a random cycle.

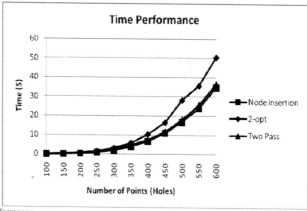

Fig. 6.   Time performance

Performance tests were also performed using random point patterns generated within a fixed area. Fig. 7 shows the percentage path distance improvement for the two-pass method for both grid patterns and random points. The trend is broadly similar. Again tests were repeated five times to enable average values to be calculated.

TOOL PATH OPTIMISATION USING GRAPH ALGORITHMS

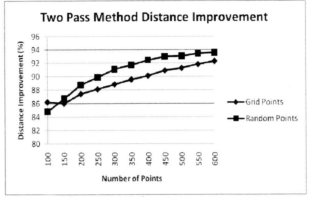

Fig. 7.   Path distance improvement for two-pass method

6.0   Tool Change

In many practical drilling applications a tool change has to be made in order to drill holes with different diameters. It is assumed that the CNC device is capable of changing tools at any hole location. Ideally the number of tool changes along the route tour should be minimised so as to reduce overall process time. One approach that is being investigated for forcing a minimum number of tool changes has been to bias the adjacency weight matrix by hole type. This results in longer paths with fewer tool changes as shown in Fig. 8. An alternative to this approach would be to divide the holes to be drilled into subsets with common diameters and generate independent paths for each subset.

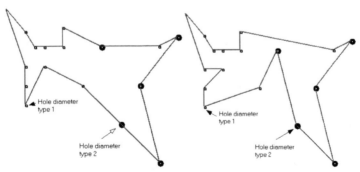

Fig. 8.   Paths relating to minimising tool change. The path on the left shows an initial tour which optimises path length. The path on the right shows a tour generated by biasing the weight matrix to minimise the number of tool changes.

7.0   Conclusion

The paper has described a graph based solution approach for optimising tool path tour distance. This is referred to as the two-pass method. In the first pass (stage) a random tour is created and improved using the node insertion method. In the second pass the path generated from the first phase is improved using the 2-opt method. This algorithm has been shown to be superior, in terms of percentage path distance improvement, to using either the node insertion or 2-opt methods applied to a randomly generated start path. A path improvement of 92% can be obtained using a grid pattern of 600 points. The application has been developed using C#. A strategy for minimising the number of tool changes along a tour path has been developed.

References

[1] Castelino, K., D'Souza, R. and Wright, P. K., Tool-path Optimization for Minimizing Airtime during Machining. Journal of Manufacturing Systems, 2003, Vol 22, No. 3, pp. 173-180

[2] Abu Qudeiri, J., Yamamoto, H. and Ramli, R., Optimization of Operation Sequence in CNC Machine Tools Using Genetic Algorithms, Journal of Advanced Mechanical Design, Systems, and Manufacturing. 2007, Vol. 1. pp. 272-282.

[3] Reinelt, G., The Travelling Salesman: Computational Solutions for TSP, Lecture Notes in Computer Science, Springer, 1994, Vol 840. ISSN 0302-9743

[4] Croes, G. A., A Method for Solving the Travelling Salesman Problems, Operations Research,1958, Vol. 5, pp. 791-812.

[5] Golden, B. L., Bodin, L., Doyle T. and Stewart W., Approximate Travelling Salesman Algorithms, Operations Research, 1980, Vol. 28. Pp. 694-711.

[6] Syslo, M. M., Deo, N. and Kowalik J.S., Discrete Optimization Algorithms with Pascal Programs, Dover Publications , New York, 1983, ISBN 0-486-45353-7.

[7] Grothmann, R., http://mathsrv.ku-eichstaett.de/MGF/homes/grothmann/java/index_en.html [Accessed March 2008]

[8] Mattson, M., CNC Programming Principles and Applications, Delmar-Thompson Learning, 2002, ISBN 0-7668-1888-8.

DEVELOPMENT OF A NEW LEARNING METHODOLOGY FOR DISCRETE EVENT SIMULATION BY REUTILISING PREVIOUS SOFTWARE EXPERIENCE

Alejandro Guerrero [*], Joseph Darlington, Richard Weston, Keith Case, Robert Harrison

Centre of Excellence in Customised Assembly (CECA), Loughborough University, Leicestershire, LE11 3TU, UK : *Tel. +44 (0) 1509 635280; Fax. +44 (0) 1509 635281 A.Guerrero@lboro.ac.uk

Abstract

New discrete event simulation software available to industry has significantly reduced the modelling efforts of complex manufacturing problems. These tools enable analysts to assess the viability of potential solutions that better conform to previously defined requirements. Thus, analysts must be conversant in new technologies applications to deliver top quality solutions to the enterprises analysed.

Traditional approaches of learning a new technology tend to isolate previous knowledge the analyst possesses in similar application fields and concentrate on features and strengths of the particular application under study. A new approach is therefore needed to capitalise on previous experience an analyst might have, enabling reduction of learning a new technological application by minimising the learning curve effort spent learning the technology, and increasing focus on quantitative and qualitative analysis.

The focus of the present research is to reutilise previous experience in a particular research field, i.e., enterprise modelling and discrete event simulation, current researchers possess to adopt a new technological application. Utilising previous case study's information, researchers created models within the new techonology application reutilising previous experience modelling in a particular technology. This enabled researchers to focus on the analysis and the strengths of the new technology rather than to relearn how to model in a discrete event manner thus becoming conversant with the technology application.

By reutilising skills and experience previously acquired by researchers, it has been possible to reduce the effort in learning the new technology and to shift attention to the original problem complexities to produce more detailed analysis of the situation.

The focus of the paper is not to solve particular requirements of the case study, but to develop a new approach to learn new technologies.

Transferring previous experience into similar environments enables minimisation of efforts in the learning curve and allows the student to adapt rapidly to the requirements faced. Change resistance, present in most cases, is minimised as students realise the knowledge they had can be re-used.

Keywords: Discrete event simulation, Models, Learning, Knowledge transfer

1.0   Introduction

Simulation software for discrete event simulation (DES) have enabled practitioners and researchers alike to model, document, experiment and validate requirements posed by manufacturing enterprises (MEs) systems with increasing levels of complexity. There are several technological applications that can analyse dynamic behaviours inherent to the ME's production system. Simulation models are used to analyse current state environment while also being used more proactively for the development of potential candidate solutions that best conform with a proposed strategic intent. Comparisons can be made of variables defined by the analyst, such as throughput, station utilisation, working times, etc. In an increasingly competitive global market, there is a consensus that ME's need to realise their productive activities maximising current resources and being capable of realising any potential change in said environments rapidly. Therefore, researchers and practitioners alike faced to learn state of the art software packages that provide more descriptive models that better capture organisational requirements and proposed candidate solutions.

As discrete event simulation software applications have evolved, new and distinctive sets of tools are offered to the user that facilitate increasingly more complex multiple perspective analysis of a portion of the enterprise understudy. Although basic operations within those applications perform similar functions, distinctive characteristics separates them. The analyst must be conversant in the different features that each package offers so that it may provide the best solution to the problem domain it tackles. The choice of software the analyst does will be directly affected by the tools offered and by the requirements the organisation poses. The analyst will need to be aware of the different software applications that are available, so as to choose the one that which will deliver the maximum benefit to the organisation understudy.

Most software packages include several aids that help the user learn the functionality of the package and guide him through simple tutorials that demonstrate key aspects within a reduced complexity case study. However the experienced practitioner or researcher finds themselves increasingly frustrated at the simplicity of models and disjoint from the help material provided in such software programs which in turn hinders progress to develop a coherent set of models that capture an organisation's requirements or that detail a potential candidate solution. Most materials are aimed at users with no experience whatsoever with similar packages or knowledge within the particular field, i.e., financial background of an experienced user when learning the functionality of a spreadsheet. Learning a state of the art application should benefit from the experience in similar applications and from the knowledge that the average user of such technologies has in the field. By reusing such experiences and knowledge, the typically experienced learning curve in such situations can be minimised, reducing change resistance impact will also be greatly reduced and performance can be enhanced.

DEVELOPMENT OF A NEW LEARNING METHODOLOGY FOR DISCRETE EVENT SIMULATION BY REUTILISING PREVIOUS SOFTWARE EXPERIENCE

2.0   Current Literature Review

Acquisition of skills in a relevant software product is essential in today's working environment. As technology advances rapidly, increasing pressure is centred in learning state of the art applications within a constrained timeframe[3]. Support material has been evolved from textual, i.e., instruction manuals to presentations and reduced functionality software that has enabled students to learn an application [1]. These materials have greatly enhanced the learning experience and have improved the understanding of the application by the student. However, design of such materials has been developed with experimental groups in which individuals possess little or no experience utilising similar applications[1] and [3]. Most of the learning an individual or organisation does come through experience [2]. Increasing amounts of research has been directed towards the processes that occur in learning and knowledge transfer [7]. The role of previous experience in related areas of knowledge has been closely linked to a successful transfer of knowledge in the organisation, and has also been related to a systematic learning from past experiences[7].

Several factors have been identified to produce change resistance within an organisation [4]-[6]. Amongst these causes, technological implementation and the potential employment related risks contribute to an increase from various levels of the organisation to resist such a change. Planning changes in an organisation can potentially mitigate the effects of change resistance, such as low performance from the system. Most technological changes have improved the quality of life, but some have an adverse impact on the workforce, i.e., layoffs [4]. It has been suggested that the change rate in which alterations occur in modern society has outweighed the societal capability to respond leading to the well know adage: "Change is the only constant thing"[4]. However such change resistance can be managed to improve the chances of successful change implementation within an organisation.   Several course of action can be implemented in an organisation to reduce the impact of change resistance and assure a successful implementation of a technology. Training, both conceptual and practical, are amongst the suggested activities needed to achieve success. [6].

3.0   Proposed Approach

Previous sections have highlighted the potential pitfalls utilising the traditional methods of teaching a new software application. With increasing pressure from academia and industry to utilise discrete event simulation software applications to provide optimal solutions to an evolving set of requirements, it follows that there is a need to reduce time spent in learning a new software application. The methodology set forward in this section addresses the issue of reutilising previous knowledge and experience to learn more rapidly a software application and decrease change resistance to embrace a new software application.

MSI Research Institute at Loughborough University has several years of experience utilising simulation modelling and discrete event simulation software in various projects across different industries. The group has used several software applications and has a range of knowledge and experience in applying discrete event simulation software. The authors considered that the collective and individual experience of the MSI Research Institute provided an ideal control group to trial a new learning methodology.

Several discrete simulation software packages have been utilised in the past by members of MSI Research Institute. Software packages such as SIMUL8, Witness and Arena form the principal collection of tools used by the control group, to create complex discrete event models of several case studies. New research interest acquired the UGS Tecnomatix suite, which includes the discrete event simulation tool Plant Simulation. The authors identified this new tool as comparable to SIMUL8 package, which is the main modelling tool utilised by the control group, and therefore presented an opportunity to trial a new learning approach to modelling and simulation on the test set who had little or no knowledge of Plant Simulation software.

Previous experience of the authors when teaching a new technology, highlighted the need of students to find common ground with the known technology application. Throughout a series of courses the authors imparted, the need of relating to previous knowledge or experience was evident in facilitating learning of the new technological application as well as reducing change resistance to adapt a new technology. Therefore it was evident that a new learning methodology that included the reutilisation of previous knowledge was needed to successfully teach new practitioners on a particular technological application.

The methodology consists of thee steps to reutilise knowledge in learning a new software application. The first step is to compare functional, operational and informational capabilities in SIMUL8 and Plant Simulation. A gap analysis is performed to elicit and compare characteristics inherent to both applications is needed to identify which capabilities provide similar functional characteristics. Characteristics that are not common to both software applications can be related to previous experience or knowledge.

After the gap analysis between technologies, the second step explores the commonalities between software packages under review and highlights areas in which knowledge can be reutilised. The objective of this stage is to identify those capabilities that are common and in which potential knowledge held by a user of the first software package can be utilised to learn the second.

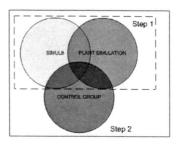

Fig. 1.   parative areas of steps 1 and 2

Third step is to design training materials considering previous knowledge and experience held within the control group. Such information can be elicited in a number of ways, such as, questionnaires, electronic correspondence etc.

4.0   Application of Methodology

The authors previous knowledge of both discrete event simulation software packages and detailed information on the case study previously developed enabled the design of course materials to effectively train researchers at the control group in the software application. The case study developed dealt with the process network of activities of a small manufacturer in the furniture industry. Several models were created to elicit requirements and develop potential candidate solutions. Several areas of interest were modelled to understand the current situation and to gather a more holistic view of the ME. It should be noted that the present paper does not go in to detail of the enterprise or simulation modelling developed for such case. Yet it benefits from the models created as a baseline to introduce a new technological application.

The first step towards creating the course materials was a comparison of each software package, i.e., how does each software application accept parameters to develop models. Similar sets of activities within the software package were compared in order to assess the information needed. Components of the previous software package were mapped into the new software. Table 1 presents a capability mapping done between software applications.

Table 1 Mapping of capabilities between SIMUL8 and Plant Simulation

Capabilities	SIMUL8	Plant Simulation
Work Centre	Single operation	Single/Multiple operations can be modeled
Processing times	Statistical	Statistical
Entry points	Single production unit can be processed	Multiple production units can be processed
Exit Points	Accept multiple production units types	Accept multiple production units types
Resources	No construct	
Human modeling	Number of workers and shifts	Number of workers, services provided, efficiency, shifts
Model statistics	Inside each object within model	Inside each object, can be presented in an external graph
Graphical display	Within objects	External graphical display can be processed
Hierarchy	Only graphical	Reusable objects
Programming	Modifies unit behavior	Modifies units, production flow, object behavior

The second step was to focus on similarities presented between specific tools and methods Plant Simulation offers and mapping previous knowledge held at the control group in similar areas of interest. As there is a veritable wealth of experience in simulation modelling and discrete event simulation, this enabled the focus of the course materials to be on the new capabilities that Plant Simulation offered. Therefore, course materials were oriented to analyse a known case study with a different set of tools.

The third step was to develop the course materials emphasising commonalities. A questionnaire was sent to the control group with three four sections: simulation modelling, discrete event simulation software application proficiency, programming languages and statistical knowledge. The responses facilitated the assessment of capabilities presented within the control group. Development of materials and focus of the training sessions was benefited This led to a reduced level of stress as members were familiar with the model to be represented. The focus of the course was to diminish the change resistance that was perceived by the introduction of the tool by some members of the Institute to adopt new technology.

An existing case study previously addressed by members of the control group was utilised as a baseline to teach the new software packages. The models presented in Fig. 2 and Fig. 3 represent a portion of the ME, a small furniture spray shop, modelled with different software packages. To familiarise the reader to the models presented, a brief description of the process networks is provided The ME produces a wide range in furniture products that are categorised by functionality, colour, finishing, etc. In the spray shop, products are categorised into two main groups: Basic Colours and Sienna/Newhaven as these groups follow two different production routes as the Sienna/Newhaven category undergo additional operations. All product types share the production resources within the ME. The modelling exercise consisted in repeating models created beforehand in Plant Simulation. It should be noted that it is not the intention of the authors to present the results or capabilities of the software packages, rather, to illustrate the reuse of experience and learning obtained

DEVELOPMENT OF A NEW LEARNING METHODOLOGY FOR DISCRETE EVENT SIMULATION BY REUTILISING PREVIOUS SOFTWARE EXPERIENCE

utilising the proposed methodology. This is provided so that the reader might observe similarities between the software applications and abstract into teaching any software application of a given area to users who possess previous knowledge and experience.

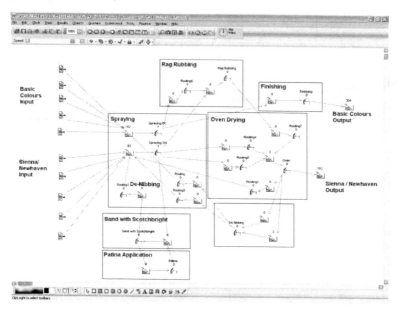

Fig 2.   Model of a spray shop captured with SIMUL8

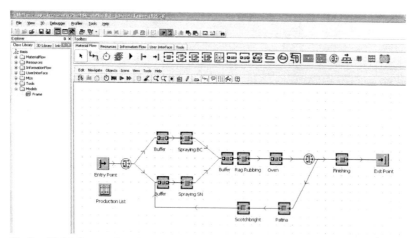

Fig. 3.   Model of a spray shop captured with Plant Simulation

Fig. 2 illustrates model created utilising SIMUL8 by a member of the control group. Fig. 3 illustrates the model created with Plant Simulation during the course of the session. Models served as a baseline of

DEVELOPMENT OF A NEW LEARNING METHODOLOGY FOR DISCRETE EVENT SIMULATION BY REUTILISING PREVIOUS SOFTWARE EXPERIENCE

knowledge that individual members have to further study the functionality and resources the new technology offers to their research interest. It should be noted that the models presented do not present the overall picture of the ME understudy, but enabled the researchers to obtain additional insight into the benefits of the new software application.

5.0   Outcomes of Learning

Members of the control group achieved a significant decrease in time spent in learning the software application. Previously, a two week period time was necessary to get a basic knowledge of the software. This was reduced to a week of training to facilitate creation of simple working models. The time difference enabled members of the control group to explore additional capabilities of the application that better suited their research interest. This methodology facilitated a 'hands on' approach, which enabled a reflection and a comparison between capabilities, strengths and focus of the current and new technological applications. Such an approach proved useful as participants could relate from their research or past areas of expertise to comprehend concepts that are not present in the current software application but can be present in other instances.

Change resistance was reduced as members readily adopted the software application as benefits could be observed in the additional capabilities the package offers. Transition from SIMUL8 to Plant Simulation was perceived to be far smoother. Because the training materials provided to the control group were tailored to their experience users quickly established familiarity with the new software as a result of relational learning to previous knowledge.

6.0   Conclusions

As there is an increase of simulation software available to academia and industry, there is a need for new methodology to improve the effectiveness of learning of such applications. Reutilisation of previous knowledge enables a rapid learning of a new software application by sharing common elements of both packages which minimises the effort spent in learning a new software application. By utilising a previously modelled case study, researchers were able to concentrate on the particulars of the software package and obtain new understandings of the future states proposed as a solution.

Application of the proposed methodology in the design of training materials enabled participants to learn the material quicker as concepts were explained within the collective background. This eliminated the need of lengthy explanations or introductions to simulation modelling and discrete event simulation concepts. There was a significant reduction in the time necessitated to create a new model. Members of the control group created models from a previous case study with little or no assistance and could develop further analysis to that which it was previously realised. Positive feedback was received concerning the difficulty of learning the new software application. However, several potential pitfalls were observed. Detailed knowledge of the candidate technological applications is required to compare and assess similarities in such a manner that course materials might be developed. The authors have experience utilising both technological applications which facilitated the development of the training material, Knowledge of participants is also required, this can be time consuming as well as problematic. In the present case, as the authors knew well the participants, this was not an issue. The number of participants in the present study did not allow for a statistical comparison as to provide improvements in creation time. Consensus was reached that reutilising their previous knowledge was a key factor in reducing time spent in learning the new software application.

The authors consider that such an approach when developing training materials can be beneficial for the wider industry as this can be deployed when training employees to a new software application. It can be concluded that such an approach has potential to be deployed across other areas, such new equipment training. The reader can observe that in deploying a new software tool, knowledge and experience reutilisation will enhance performance as well as reducing change resistance factors that are present. Although such efforts can be perceived as an 'ad hoc' training, it can be argued that benefits of such approach outweigh those of a generic deployment and training.

Acknowledgements

The authors of this paper would like to acknowledge the collaboration of members of the MSI Research Institute of Loughborough University.

References

[1] Spannagel, C.; Girwidz, R.; Lothe, H.; Zendler, A.; Schroeder, U.; "Animated demonstration and training wheels interfaces in a complex learning environment"; Interacting with Computers, Vol. 20; pp. 97 – 111,; 2008
[2] Carayannis, E. G.; "Knowledge transfer through technological hyperlearning in five industries"; Technovation; Vol. 19; pp. 141 – 161; 1999
[3] Kerr, M. P.; Payne. S. J.; "Learning to use a spreadsheet by doing and watching"; Interacting with Computers; Vol. 6; pp 3 – 22; 1994
[4] Azani, H.; Khorramshahgol, R.; "The impact of automation on engineers' creativity and innovation and its implications for reducing resistance to change"; Computers in Industry; Vol 16; pp. 377 – 383; 1991
[5] Canton, E. J. F.; de Groot, H. L. F.; Nahuis, R.; "Vested interest, population ageing and technology adoption"; Vol. 18; pp. 631 – 652; 2002
[6] Krovi, R.; "Identifying the causes of resistance to IS implementation"; Vol. 25; pp. 327 – 335; 1993
[7] Daghfous, A.; "An empirical investigation of the roles of prior knowledge and learning activities in technology transfer"; Technovation; Vol. 24; pp. 939 – 953; 2004
[8] Monfared, R. P.; "A component-based approach to design and construction of change capable manufacturing cell control systems"; PhD Thesis; Loughborough University; 2000
[9] Chatha, K. A.; "Multi-process modelling approach to complex organisation design"; PhD Thesis; Loughborough University, 2004
[10] Ajaefobi, J. O.; Human systems modelling in support of enhanced process realisation"; PhD Thesis; Loughborough University, 2004

The 6th International Conference on Manufacturing Research (ICMR08)
Brunel University, UK, 9-11th September 2008

MOLECULAR DYNAMICS SIMULATIONS FOR NANOMANUFACTURING PROCESSES: A CRITICAL REVIEW

P. Stavropoulos, K. Salonitis and G. Chryssolouris[*]

Laboratory for Manufacturing Systems and Automation, Director, Prof. George Chryssolouris,
Department of Mechanical Engineering and Aeronautics, University of Patras, Greece
[*]xrisol@mech.upatras.gr

Abstract

The future of commercial products with the use of Nanomanufacturing is dependent upon their ability to rationally design and engineer in Nanoscale. The majority of Nanostructures are too small to be reliably characterized through experimentation. On the other hand, the nanostructures are small enough to have a significantly decreased complexity that enables the detailed computation of their structure and properties, compared with that of macro materials. These two facts offer unique chances and grand challenges to simulation and modeling for the understanding and controlling of Nanomanufacturing. However, manufacturing products in the Nanometer scale present many difficulties and differences compared with the manufacturing ones in the traditional length-scales. This is the reason why simulation is of paramount importance in these short length scales. The Molecular Mechanics approach, Monte Carlo simulation and Molecular Dynamics (MD) are some of the tools developed for taking simulation in the Nanoscale. MD simulation is based on solving Newton's second law equation in order for the velocity and displacement of each particle, in the modeled system, to be determined. These results can then be averaged to determine the Macro-scale properties of the simulated materials. Nevertheless, the ability to simulate large systems is obstructed by the limited computational power of modern computers. As this power increases the MD becomes a very powerful simulation tool for Nanomanufacturing processes. This paper reviews and categorizes, studies of simulation Nanomanufacturing processes with focus on the Laser ablation due to the complicated phenomenon that accompanies them. The studies have been categorized depending on the type of interatomic potential, used for describing the interactions of the particles forming the simulation volume and the type of MD method utilized.

Keywords: Molecular Dynamics, Nanomanufacturing Processes, Simulation

1.0   Introduction

The term "computer simulation" is generally used for describing a physical system modeling and its study with computational methods, which demand the use of a computer system to be resolved, because of their high complexity and number of calculations required. Molecular Modeling is used for describing any procedure that takes place with a view to imaging, describing and calculating the attributes or the morphology of one or more molecules. In addition to this, the term Molecular Simulation is used and is identical with the term Molecular Modeling. Molecular Simulation completes an experimental procedure. More specifically, it can indicate or reject a possible physical processing of description models, taking place in a molecular system and explaining the inner mechanism on a molecular base. Molecular Simulation helps define the conditions under which the experiment is executed and understand the mechanisms that take place in the experimental procedure. Compared with correspondent theoretical approaches at macroscopic level, molecular simulations are usually more accurate. The computational power available is a critical parameter for the efficiency and the practical use of the Molecular Simulation. The faster the computational system is the faster the molecular system can simulate. Simultaneously, the approaches, which the computational methods are based on, can be decreased and because of that more accurate results can be derived. The computational power acts restrictively to the results' accuracy. This is the reason why the complex systems' studies (and because of that demanding in computational power) are made with the use of serial connected PCs, where the computational load splits equally. Various studies during the last years tend to simulate processes (physical or chemical) at molecular level, in order to better explain the macromolecular results. For this reason, many simulation methods, on a molecular base, have been recently developed, from which the most frequently applied ones are: Molecular Mechanics (MM), Monte Carlo simulations (MC) and Molecular Dynamics (MD). The main characteristics of the methods above, are shown in the table below.

Table 1: Main simulation characteristics at molecular scale

Method	Main calculation aim	Main result
Molecular Mechanics (MM)	Solitary molecules or small molecular systems (organic molecules)	Optimized geometry, energy minimization, interatomic potential mapping
Monte Carlo (MC)	Large number of atoms or molecules (fluids, alloys, gases)	Thermodynamic attributes, particles movements
Molecular Dynamics (MD)	Large number of atoms or molecules (organic, inorganic molecules, fluids, solids and gasses)	Thermodynamic attributes, dynamic, particles movement

2.0   Molecular Dynamics Simulations

The Molecular Dynamic (MD) method is a deterministic simulation one. On the contrary, the Monte Carlo method is a stochastic simulation method. The Monte Carlo techniques consist of a reliable tool for the calculation of the equilibrium thermodynamic properties, because the molecular movements can be designed in such a way so as to allow for a successful sampling of the probability density required. However, the Monte Carlo methods are not able to provide direct information about the dynamic condition, because the term of time is not included into the system's development. The MD method was initially developed by Alder and Wainwright in 1956 [1] and consisted of the numerical solution of Newton's movement equations, of a number of N atoms, which are supposed to interact with a known potential form [2]. This study has helped to bring forward many and significant new aspects of the simple fluids' behavior. The next big step was made in 1964, when Rahman conducted the first simulation using equations, which state, in a realistic way, the intermolecular forces of Argon (Ar) fluid [3]. The first Molecular Dynamic simulation of a realistic system was performed by Rahman and Stillinger, when, in 1974, they simulated water in a fluid state [4]. In 1977, it was the first protein simulations that took place, with the simulation of the Bovine Pancreatic Trypsin Inhibitor (BPTI) [5]. In the case that information is required about the dynamic condition of a molecule, it is necessary that a different approach be followed, which will be capable of monitoring the evolution of the system over time. The MD simulations, from several points of view, are identical with those of the physical experiments. For example, when conducting a physical experiment the sample is placed in a device connected with e.g. a thermometer and the attribute which is investigated is measured. If noise is included in the measures, their number is increased and the mean average is obtained, in order for the accuracy of the measures to be increased. In an MD simulation, the same process is followed. At first, the sample is prepared and the system as well as the model to be adopted are chosen, considering the minimum number of assumptions applicable. So, if a system consists of N particles, the Newton equations are solved until the system's attributes remain constant during the time intervals. The measurement takes place when the system's equilibrium has been achieved. However, a lot of the common errors that take place during a numerical experiment are similar with those that can occur during a physical experiment. For example, the sample could not be properly prepared, or the time period of the measurement could be too short; during this time, the system could sustain an irreversible change or a wrong measurement could be finally acquired. The basic idea behind the MD method is that after any element/substance is created, from an elementary particle, if the basic dynamic parameters of these particles are appointed, then the macroscopic natural attributes of the element/substance can be determined with the use of statistical methods. The MD analysis is based on the solution of the second Newton's law aiming to monitor every atom's movement in a system [6][7][8]. In the occasion of a reflected atom with transferring movement, the law takes this simple form.

$$\mathbf{F} = m \frac{d^2 \mathbf{r}}{dt^2} \tag{1}$$

Where F, is the vector of the forces resultant that are being exerted on the molecule from the rest of the system's molecules, r is the molecule's space vector, t is the time and m is the molecule's mass. When the equation above is integrated, the values of velocity and distance can be calculated. When these calculations are made for every atom in different time spaces, from a starting position, then the information about the movement of every atom can be accumulated [9]. After the calculation of the mean averages, in time, space or both, the macroscopic physical attributes can be extracted. For molecules with complex geometry, Newton's law is not adequate. Depending on the molecular type of model that is used, the simulation process adopts a general shape of Newton's equation. For example, when a solid body model is used, the molecules' rotations, around their equilibrium position, have to be taken under consideration. Regardless of the movement equation's complexity, the basic simulation process is always identical: initially, the movement equation for every molecule is integrated, the dynamic parameters are calculated and next, the mean averages of the dynamic parameters are calculated in order for the macroscopic natural attributes to be calculated. The calculations of the intramolecular forces, due to their electric/electromagnetic nature, require the existence of proper intramolecular dynamic models, which describe the interactions. These models are usually retrieved from experimental data or from quantomechnical calculations. Frequently, the interaction between two or three molecules is taken into consideration, as the contribution of more particles are inconsistent and therefore, can totally be neglected or can be incorporated as a correction contributor to the dynamic equation [9]. Owing to the great advancement in the computational power, the MD simulation has been developed a lot the last years. It is an important tool for the study of the material formation procedure and their attributes. Additionally, it is used more and more for solving thermal conduction problems. The basic limitations of this method comprise the need for the determination, of an accurate dynamic equation and the maximum system size that can be studied. For the dynamic equation; tested empirical ones that describe adequately the material structure are available in bibliography, namely for silicon, the dynamic Stillinger-Webber is used [10]. The greatest constraint of the MD analysis is the size of the systems that can be simulated. Fluids' simulations can include up to 200,000 molecules, whilst on the other hand, solid simulations can include from 10 up to 100 million atoms, depending on the required simulation time. Unfortunately, even one simulation cube with 1000 A tip, which can include up to 50 million atoms of silicon, requires a long simulation time. In addition to this, the mean free way of the phonons in silicon is approximately 3000 A [11][12]. For the study of the thermal conduction equilibrium or not, the MD simulations have been used in various studies. On the approach of the nonequilibrium, a temperature difference or an energy flow is enforced onto the system, changing the dynamic characteristics of the system's atoms in locally bordered places [13]. The equilibrium approach is based on low temperature variations in order to create a momentary temperature flow. Although chronically, the main average value of thermal flow disappears, the system's thermal conductivity, regarding the disorder, can be calculated from the thermal flow auto covariance function, as is it described in the Green-Kubo equation [14]. The congruity approach is slow, but the equilibrium MD simulation does not suffer from the three disadvantages that were stated before (the periodical boundary conditions abolish the restrains relatively with the mean average way). Although, during the MD equilibrium, simulation caution is required in order that it does not enter unreal size actions, due to the finite size of the simulation model. Through the MD simulation, from the track time evolution and the velocity of every atom separately, characteristics such as time calming, phonon spectrum, velocity and all condition system density can be calculated. This information can be inserted into the Boltzmann equation and confront any mid-level heat transfer problems. Additionally, MD can be considered as the ideal tool for the study of the defective interplay levels and the non-harmonic distribution. A theoretical disadvantage of the classical MD is that this method doesn't include statistical quantum authorities and the mechanisms of the quantum disband. It worth mentioning that the classical MD studies are focusing on the classical systems made of a great number of particles. In classical MD systems, it is assumed that the N atoms are located inside a "box" with dimensions Lx, Ly, Lz . The box volume and the number of atoms determine the system's density. The periodical conditions to the boxes edges simulate the infinite system. These, from a mathematical point of view, are described in the following equation for any size A:

$$A(x) = A(x + nL) \tag{2}$$

Where n=(n1, n2, n3) for all the integers n1, n2, n3 and L=(Lx, Ly, Lz). So, at any time a particle goes out of one side to another with the same velocity it enters from the opposite side (fig.1)

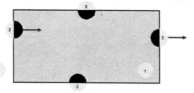

Fig. 1.   Diagram indicating initial application of Periodic Boundary Conditions

In general, the dynamic energy of the N particles for a central and additional dynamic couple is given by:

$$\varphi(r_1, r_2, \ldots r_N) = \sum_{i=1}^{N} \sum_{j>i}^{N} \varphi_{ij}\left(\left|r_i - r_j\right|\right) \tag{3}$$

Where r_i, r_j are the locations of the atoms i and j correspondently and φ is the dynamic developed between the atoms above. The use of the periodical conditions enforces the introduction of a range of dynamic interaction for the calculation of the dynamic and the forces:

$$r_i \leq \frac{1}{2} \min(L_x, L_y, L_z) \tag{4}$$

This range is called cut-off distance ro and it is used for avoiding the interactions between the atoms i and j consimultaneously between the i and the periodical idols of j. the force exerted on the particle i from its neighbors will be:

$$\overline{F}_i = -\sum_{i \neq j} \overline{\forall} \varphi\left(\overline{r}_{ij}\right) \qquad \left|\overline{r}_{ij}\right| \leq r_o \tag{5}$$

Inside the limits of the classical approach, that is for temperatures $T > \Theta_{DEBYE}$ and for time greater than 10^{-16} sec, the movement Newtown's equation is:

$$F_i = m_i \frac{\partial^2 r_i}{\partial t^2} \tag{6}$$

Thus, for a system of N atoms, it is required that the 3N differential equation and the 6N initial conditions need to be integrated. These initial positions can be the atoms' locations and their velocities. For a solid, the atoms' initial conditions can easily be the grading positions and the velocities are chosen with a Maxwell-Boltzmann distribution, in order to correspond with the required temperature in which we want to accomplish the simulation. The speed distribution expression at Maxwell-Boltzmann is given by the following equation:

$$N(v) = 4\pi N \left(\frac{m}{2\pi k_B T}\right)^{3/2} v^2 \exp\left(\frac{-mv^2}{2kT}\right) \tag{7}$$

Where N(v) is the particle number, with speed v, N the total sample's atom amount, m every atoms mass, kB Boltzmann constant and T the sample's temperature. The system described is isolated, so, the particles' number N, the volume V and the energy E are constant. It is possible for the system to interact with the environment, either to obtain the required constant temperature (normal statistical sum, remain constant N, V, T), or to reach the constant pressure (isobaric statistical sum, remain constant N, pressure P, enthalpy H).

3.0 Molecular Dynamics Simulations of Laser Ablation Processes

In the following paragraphs, the MD simulations are presented and analyzed depending on the MD type utilized (hybrid or classic) and the interatomic potential used for describing the forces with the atoms.

3.1 Hybrid Molecular Dynamics Simulations

Aiming not only at the development of the simulation volume but also at a better observation, especially of macro-processes, the hybrid MD simulations have been introduced. The MD simulation volumes are connected with the finite element simulation methods or the twin temperature model. In the study of [15], a numerical method is presented, combining the MD simulation and the finite elements; method, aiming to simulate the mechanical behavior of the materials and the structures in nano-scale.

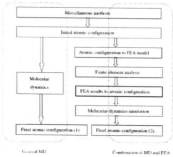

Fig. 2.   Flow chart of combination MD/FEA method [15]

In this combinational method, the initial atomic model is transformed into a continuous model and an approximate solution for the system is produced, with specific initial conditions and charges. Then, the charged continuous model is transformed into a new atomic model, and the MD simulation method is applied, in order for the system to reach the final equilibrium state. The strong point of this method is that it combines the productivity and speed of the continuous simulation models and the simulation accuracy of MD. The result of the part that is being analyzed with finite elements can be assumed as the mean stage of the analysis. The methodology above has been applied in order for the attributes of a nano-beam, in a deformation state, to be checked. A different approach of this combinational analysis method is presented in [16]. The study of the multifunctional dynamical phenomenon claims analysis, in atomic and continues scale length, at the same time. The combined methodology, gives the spotting possibility of the critical mark between an accurate calculation and a calculation load. The method is applied to pressure transmission waves in a material, which is brought about from the applied Laser radiation onto its surface. In order to be successfully combined the MD and FE methods not only does the continuity between the attributes of the atomic and continues mean have to be secured but also the smooth transmission between these two different means. The smooth coupling of the means is succeeded with the use of a transition area, where the FE nodes correspond with the MD particles' places as indicated in figure 3.

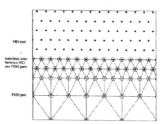

Fig. 3.   Transitional stage where FE nodes correspond to MD particles [16]

The range of this location equals that with the cut-off distance. The particles that are included in this area interact with that of the MD, as determined by the interatomic potential. Simultaneously, these particles correspond to the nodes of the FE area and interact through forces that are being determined from the FE grid. This method has been utilized when high accuracy, at specific points of the situation, is required. In [17], a multiple scale methodology is presented, which is a result of three simulation methods, with aim to explain the phenomena that connect with the Laser ablation of the materials. The methods include: a) MD and specifically,

MOLECULAR DYNAMICS SIMULATIONS FOR NANOMANUFACTURING PROCESSES: A
CRITICAL REVIEW

the model of the breathing sphere for the simulation of the starting stages of the Laser ablation, b) the FE method for the study of the pressure wave propagation c) MC analysis for the simulation enlargement of the cloud that it is created from the Laser ablation. The multiple range methodology takes into consideration all the phenomena that take place during the time of the Laser ablation, with the proper accuracy that requires any one of them and simultaneously describes their interaction satisfactorily.

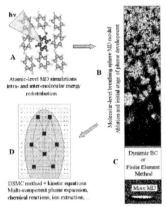

Fig. 4.   Hierarchy of the multi scale molecular simulation method [17]

In study [17], the metal material fusion modeling, associated with the use of MD and the Twin Temperature Model (TTM), is presented. This model combines the classical MD for the simulation of non-equilibrium processes, with a constant excitation description, due to the Laser radiation, making also use of the TTM. This energy, in fractions of femtoseconds, balances within the electrons and then following slower rates, it is transformed into a crystal form vibration. Using this combinational method, MD is being replaced from the TTM method for the calculation of the crystal's temperature. MD method is applied only to the materials' surface, where the processes of fusion and ablation are active. Then, while the depth is increased, the TTM is applied for describing the phenomenon. Similar investigations following combinational MD and TTM models have been used in a number of studies [18]-[21].

3.2   Classical Molecular Dynamics Simulations

The classification of the classical MD simulation has been made with reference to the interatomic potential used for describing the interactions between the atoms and the material to be simulated.
The Embedded-Atom Method (EAM) is a semi-empirical, many-a particle potential for computing the total energy of a metallic system [22]-[24].

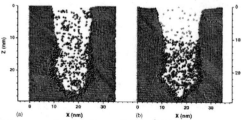

Fig. 5.   Captions of the ablation process for Laser Fluence F=2J/cm^2, 2 ps after Laser irradiation (a) in Vaccum (b) in Ar [22]

Although the majority of the interacting potentials, used in simulation, has been based on the Pair Potential Approximation (PPA), it is so, due to the fact that the PPA provides a good description of the material's properties and also consumes less computing time than do the potentials that utilize three or more body terms. Potential functions that have been phenomenologically derived, often present a more realistic view of the atomic interactions than do the potentials having been exclusively derived. According to [25] the following types of potentials fall into the phenomenological category: Buckingham, Morse, Lennard-Jones (Mie's reduced form) and Barker potentials for Krypton and Xenon. Among the above potential functions, the Morse Potential Function (MPF) is considered being more appropriate for application to metals [25][26]. MPF has been extensively used in the study of lattice dynamics, defect structure in metals, inert gases in metals, equation of state, elastic properties of metals and the interaction between gas particles and crystal surfaces. The comparison between these two methods reveals the optimum areas that the MPF is utilised. In [24], the influence of the MPF and EAM based potential has been studied, on the description of the properties and the ultrashort Laser ablation process of Fe by the Molecular Dynamics Simulation technique. The accuracy of both potentials in evaluating the melting temperature, the linear thermal expansion coefficient and the compression behaviour of Fe is calculated. It has been found by [27] that the phase explosion is responsible for the gas bubble generation and the subsequent material removal at lower Laser fluences. The phase in which the explosion process occurs as the combined results of heating, the thermal expansion, and the propagation of the tensile stress wave are induced by the Laser pulse. At higher fluences, it has been revealed that the critical point phase separation plays an important role in material removal. According to [29], the results from the MD modelling of ultrashort Laser pulse ablation of metals (Al, Ni and Fe) are reported at fluences, ranging from the threshold of ablation up to 0.5 J/cm^2. At Laser fluences, near the ablation threshold, the removal of the material is governed by thermo-elastic stress having been developed due to a fast heating. The fluence increase, results in a strong overheating of the irradiated volume and in a subsequent phase explosion. In study [28], the process of the femtosecond Laser ablation of Ni is demonstrated. The temperature and stress history, as well as the generation and growth of gas bubbles have been traced. For different Laser pulse fluences, the material ablation process is analysed to reveal the effect of temperature as well as the stress. Afanasiev et al (2001) [30] studied, the ablation of iron by ultrafast, whilst the Laser ablation was also investigated experimentally with MD. The experiments were carried out with the use of a Ti:Saphire Laser system (800 nm). The model also accounted for the electron thermal diffusion, by having the effective depth of the Laser energy penetration increased. The results have clearly shown the existence of two different modes of ablation, namely, one at low (<1 J/cm^2) and another at higher Laser fluences. An increase in the pulse duration brings about a significant rise in the heat losses, in order for a lower ablation rate to be observed. Nedialkov in study [31] applied an MD model, in order for the formation and the early stages of ejection of iron, in the ultra-short Laser ablation of metals in vacuum, to be studied.

MOLECULAR DYNAMICS SIMULATIONS FOR NANOMANUFACTURING PROCESSES: A CRITICAL REVIEW

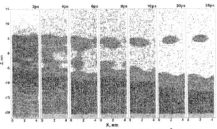

Fig. 6.   Captions of the ablation process of Fe for Laser fluence F=0.5 J/cm^2, λ=800 nm and τ_p=0.1ps [31].

The velocity Verlet algorithm is applied, the equation of motion is integrated and the interaction among the atoms in the system, is described by MPF. In order for the interaction among atoms, at distances longer than the potential cut-off radius to be avoided, the calculations have been organized with the use of the cell structure and the link-list method. The energy of the photons, which is based on the two-temperature diffusion model, is transferred to the system's atoms within a characteristic time, and its kinetic energy is increased. At Laser fluences, above the threshold of ablation (~ 0.1 J/cm^2) the ejection of the material, which mainly consists of single particles, small and medium sized clusters, and big droplets, is mainly governed by the strong overheating of the irradiated volume. Due to the decrease in the amount of deposited energy, in the depth of the material, single particles are mostly located in the front of the plume, medium-sized clusters in the middle part, and big liquid droplets are close to the surface.

4.0   Conclusions

The Molecular Mechanics approach, the Monte Carlo simulation and the Molecular Dynamics are some of the tools developed for allowing the performance of simulations in the Nanoscale. The MD simulation is based on solving Newton's second law equation so as for the velocity and displacement of each particle, in the modeled system, to be determined. These results can then be averaged to determine the Macro-scale properties of the simulated materials. However, the ability to simulate large systems is obstructed by the limited computational power of modern computers. As this power increases, MD becomes a very powerful simulation tool for Nanomanufacturing processes. Precision is a driver in Nanomanufacturing processes and consequently, precision simulation methods are required. The Molecular Dynamics based simulation of machining processes, creates new possibilities for the modelling of complex processes

Acknowledgement

This paper is part of the 03ED375 research project, implemented within the framework of the "Reinforcement Program of Human Research Manpower" (RENED) and co-financed by National and Community Funds (25% from the Greek Ministry of Development-General Secretary of Research and Technology and 75% from E.U. European Social Fund.)

References

[1]   Alder, B. J., and Wainwright, T., E., (1957), "Phase transition of a hard sphere system", Journal of Chemical Physics Vol. 27, pp. 1208-1209.
[2]   Alder, B. J., and Wainwright, T., E., (1959), "Studies in Molecular Dynamics I: General method", Journal of Chemical Physics Vol. 31, pp. 459-466
[3]   Rahman, A., (1964), "Correlations in the motion of atoms in liquid Argon", Physical Reviews Vol. 136, pp. 405-411

MOLECULAR DYNAMICS SIMULATIONS FOR NANOMANUFACTURING PROCESSES: A
CRITICAL REVIEW

[4]   Stillinger, F. H. and Rahman, A., (1974), *"Improved Simulation of liquid water by molecular dynamics"*, Journal of Chemical Physics Vol. 60, pp. 1545-1557.
[5]   McCammon, J. A., Gelin, B. R. and Karplus, M., (1977), *"Dynamics of folded proteins"*, Nature Vol. 267, pp. 585-590
[6]   Frenkel, D. and Smit, B., (1996), *"Understanding Molecular Simulation: from algorithms to applications"*, Academic Press: San Diego.
[7]   Rapaport, D.C., (1995), *"The art of molecular dynamics"*, Cambridge University Press, Cambridge
[8]   Hansen, J.P. and MacDonald, I.A., (1990), *"Theory of simple liquids"*, Academic Press, New York
[9]   Poulikakos, D., Arcidiacono, S. and Maruyama, S., (2003), *"Molecular dynamics simulation in nanoscale heat transfer: a review"*, Microscale Thermophysical Engineering, Vol. 7, pp. 181-206.
[10]   Stillinger, F.H. and Weber, T.A., (1985), "Computer simulation of local order in condensed phases of silicon", Physics Reviews B, Vol. 31 (8), pp. 5262-5271.
[11]   Goodson, K.E. and Ju, Y.S., (1999), "Heat conduction in novel electronic films", Annual Reviews of Materials Science, Vol. 29, pp. 261-293
[12]   Chen, G., (1998), "Thermal conductivity and ballistic-phonon transport in the cross-plane direction of superlattices", Physics Reviews B, Vol. 57 (23), pp. 14958-14973
[13]   Muller-Plathe, F., (1997), "A simple nonequilibrium molecular dynamics method for calculating the thermal conductivity", Journal of Chemical Physics, Vol. 106, pp. 6082-6085
[14]   Kubo, R., Yokota, M. and Nakajima, S., (1957), "Statistical-mechanical theory of irreversible processes. II. Response to thermal disturbance", Journal of the Physical Society of Japan, Vol. 12 (11), pp. 1203-1211
[15]   Wu H.A. Liu G.R., Han X. and Wang X.X., (2005) *"An atomistic simulation method combining molecular dynamics with finite element technique"*, Chaos, Solutions and Fractals, doi:10.1016/j.chaos.2005.08.161
[16]   Smirnova J.A., Zhigilei L.V. and Garrison B.J., (1999), "A combined molecular dynamics and finite element method technique applied to laser induced pressure wave propagation", Computer Physics Communications, Vol. 118, pp. 11-16.
[17]   Zhigilei L.V., (2001), *"Computational model for multiscale simulation of laser ablation"*, Materials Research Society Symposium Proceedings, Vol. 677, pp. AA2.1.1-AA2.1.11
[18]   Zhigilei L.V., Ivanov D.S. and Leveugle E., (2004), "Computer modeling of laser melting and spallation of metal targets", Proceedings of SPIE, Vol. 5448, pp. 505-519
[19]   Ohmura E., Fukumoto I. and Miyamoto I., (2001), "Molecular dynamics simulation of ablation process with ultrashort-pulse laser", RIKEN Review, Vol.32, pp. 19-22
[20]   Zhigilei L.V., (2002), "Metal ablation by picosecond laser pulses: A hybrid simulation", Physical Review B, Vol. 66, pp. 115404-1 - 115404-8
[21]   Yamashita Y., Yokomine T., Ebara S. and Shimizu A., (2006), "Heat transport analysis for femtosecond laser ablation with molecular dynamics-two temperature model method", Fusion Engineering and Design, Vol. 81, pp. 1695-1700
[22]   Nedialkov N.N. and Atanasoy P.A., (2005), "Molecular dynamics simulation study of deep hole drilling in iron by ultrashort laser pulses", Applied Surface Science, Vol. 252 (13), pp. 4411-4415
[23]   Yamashita Y., Yokomine T., Ebara S. and Shimizu A., (2006), "Heat transport analysis for femtosecond laser ablation with molecular dynamics-two temperature model method", Fusion Engineering and Design, Vol. 81, pp. 1695-1700
[24]   Imamova S.E., Atanasov P.A., Nedialkov N.N., Dausinger F. and Berger P., (2005), "Molecular dynamics simulation using pair and many body interatomic potentials: Ultrashort laser ablation of Fe", Nuclear Instruments and Methods in Physics Research B, Vol. 227, pp. 490-498
[25]   Rieth M.,(2000), "Molecular dynamics calculations for nanostructured systems", University of Patras, School of Engineering, Engineering Science Department, PhD Thesis
[26]   Girifalco L.A and Weizer V.G., (1959), "Application of the Morse Potential Function to Cubic Metals", Physical Review, Vol. 114 (3), pp. 687-690
[27]   Chend C. and Xu X., (2005), *"Mechanisms of decomposition of metal during femtosecond laser ablation"*, Physical Review B, Vol. 72, pp. 1-15
[28]   Cheng C. and Xu X., (2004), *"Molecular dynamic study of volumetric phase change induced by a femtosecond laser pulse"*, Applied Physics A, Vol. 79, pp. 761-765
[29]   Nedialkov N.N., Imamova S.E., Atanasov P.A., Berger P. and Dausinger F., (2005), *"Mechanism of ultrashort laser ablation of metals: Molecular dynamics simulation"*, Applied Surface Science, Vol. 247, pp. 243-248
[30]   Afanasiev, Y.V., Chichkov, B.N., Demchenko, N.N., Isakov, V.A. and Zavestovskaya, I.N., (2001), "Ablation of metals by ultrashort laser pulses: Theoretical modeling and computer simulation", ECA, Vol. 25A, pp. 2021-2024
[31]   Nedialkov N.N., Imamova S.E., Atanasov P.A, Heusel G., Breitling D., Ruf A., Hugel H., Dausinger F. and Berger P., (2004), *"Laser ablation of iron by ultrashort laser pulses"*, Thin Solid Films, Vol. 453-454, pp. 496-500

MOLECULAR DYNAMICS SIMULATIONS FOR NANOMANUFACTURING PROCESSES: A CRITICAL REVIEW

The 6th International Conference on Manufacturing Research (ICMR08)
Brunel University, UK, 9-11th September 2008

FINITE ELEMENT SIMULATION OF LASER WELDING PROCESS OF T-JOINT SPECIMENS

N. Siva Shanmugam [2], G. Buvanashekaran [1], K. Sankaranarayanasamy[2]

1. Welding Research Institute, Bharat Heavy Electricals Limited, Tiruchirappalli – 620 015, Tamil Nadu, India.

2. Department of Mechanical Engineering, National Institute of Technology, Tiruchirappalli – 620 015, Tamil Nadu, India.

Abstract

Laser welding is based on high power density welding technologies, which have the capability of focusing the beam power to a very small spot diameter. As it has several characteristics such as high precision and low and concentrated heat input, it minimizes the micro-structural modifications, residual stresses and distortions on the welded specimens. In this paper, finite element method (FEM) is applied for predicting the bead geometry in laser welding of 1.6mm thick AISI 304 stainless steel sheets. A three-dimensional finite element model is used to analyze the temperature distribution in a T-joint weld produced by the laser welding process. Temperature-dependent thermal properties of AISI304 Stainless Steel, effect of latent heat of fusion, and the convective and radiative boundary conditions are included in the model. The heat input to the model is assumed to be a 3D conical Gaussian heat source. The finite element code SYSWELD, along with a few FORTRAN subroutines, is employed to obtain the numerical results. The T-joint welds are made using a Nd:YAG laser having a maximum power of 2 kW in the continuous wave mode. The effect of laser beam power, welding speed and beam incident angle on the weld bead geometry (i.e. depth of penetration and bead width) are investigated. Finally, the shapes of the molten pool predicted by the numerical analysis are compared with the results obtained through the experimentation. The comparison shows that they are in good agreement.

Keywords: Laser T-joint welds, finite element simulation, temperature field, stainless steel.

1.0   Introduction

In olden days, the welding operations were carried out by skilled workers. Later with the advent of scientific tools the workers skill has been replaced by industrial automated machines and robots. The joint made by welding process are extensively used in the fabrication industry, including ships, automobile, electrical and pressure vessels. To obtain the expected productivity through mechanization, high precision of parts to be fabricated and assembled must be kept. Therefore in the industry dimensional accuracy of components produced is important. One such technique used for joining processes with a high joint efficiency, water and air tightness and low fabrication lost is laser welding (keyhole welding). The high power Nd:YAG laser sources with continuous wave mode power distribution are nowadays one of the most used devices especially for welding stainless steel sheets. The laser welding of AISI304 stainless steel is used in numerous areas, including electronics, medical instruments, home appliances, automotive and specialized tube industry. This welding process is characterized by its high energy density with low heat input, high degree of automation, high production rate and low weld distortion. The welded joints employed for various applications can be configured into five basic categories: butt, T, corner, lap and edge [1]. Among these T-joint welds are widely used in ships, pressure vessels, panel blocks etc. The study of Laser welding of T-joints is complex one. It requires analysis involving thermodynamics, fluid flow and heat transfer phenomena which requires several trials before arriving at proper conditions. It is advantageous to analyze the influence of welding parameters on its bead shape so that the number of trials required to arrive at optimum process parameters can be reduced [2]. This can be achieved using a computer simulation based on numerical techniques which is widely employed in research, design and analysis of welded structures. The finite element method is one of the numerical methods which are very useful to predict the thermal field and the bead shape of the welded specimens [3, 4] from the thermal simulation at an early stage of product design and welding process development.

A brief literature review on weld process analysis and weld pool modeling is outlined here. The elementary welding heat source models were based mostly on Rosenthal's solutions [5]. He proposed a mathematical model for a moving heat source under the assumptions of quasi-stationary state and concentrated point heating in 3D analysis. Sabbaghzadeh et al [6] developed two numerical models in finite difference and finite element, to compute thermal phenomena during pulsed laser welding. They found that the temperature contours and depth of penetration were strongly dependent on the pulse parameters of the laser beam. Spina et al [7] investigated the efficiency of numerical simulations to predict the thermo-mechanical fields induced by laser welding of aluminum alloy sheets. The penetration depth, nugget size and bead width of laser spot welds on AISI304 stainless steel were studied by Chang and Na [8] using the finite element method and artificial neural network. They also investigated the shape of the molten pool by keeping the specimen with and without air gap. Teng et al [1] performed thermal elasto-plastic analysis using finite element techniques to analyze the thermo-mechanical behaviour and evaluate the residual stress and angular distortions of the T-joint in fillet welds. They considered the effects of flange thickness, welding penetration depth, restraint condition on residual stresses and distortions. Sarkani et al [9] investigated the possibility of changing a 2D-weld model onto a corresponding 3D-weld model for the purpose of determining the magnitude and distribution of the welding residual stresses. There are many research papers which deal with the shape and size of the molten pool of laser beam butt welds in relation to different laser input parameters. However, the effect of main laser parameters namely beam power, welding speed and beam incident angle on T-joint welds have till date not been extensively reported. Since the orientation of the sheets to be welded is perpendicular to each other, the effect of beam incident angle has to be analyzed in detail.

This paper presents the thermal field and the bead shape of a T- joint made of AISI304 stainless steel sheet by laser welding, using FE transient thermal analysis. The heat source model is assumed to be a 3D conical Gaussian and the required FORTRAN subroutines [10] are developed in order to define a moving distributed heat source for the simulations carried out using finite element code SYSWELD. The depth of penetration and bead width of T-joint laser welds obtained by simulation methods are compared with the T-joints weld specimens produced using the same welding parameters for validation.

2.0 Finite Element Analysis of T-joint Welds

The thermal fields and the bead shape of T-joint laser welds are investigated by means of finite element code, SYSWELD, a software package for numerical analysis of welding processes. It is applied to simulate the various parameters such as temperature distribution, residual stresses, distortion, etc. in laser welding process.

2.1 Specimen and Material for Experimentation

Fig. 1 shows the configuration of T-joint specimen taken for both analysis and for conducting actual experimental trials. The length of the weld, the width of the flange and height of the web are taken to be 60, 40 and 20 mm, respectively. The material used for this purpose is commercial AISI304 stainless steel sheet of thickness 1.6mm. The chemical composition of this material under annealed condition is presented in Table 1. Thermo-physical properties (temperature dependent) of the material are assumed to be isotropic and homogeneous and are taken according to Sabbaghzadeh et al [5].

Table 1: Chemical composition of AISI304 stainless sheet metal vs. the weight percentage

C	Cr	Fe	Mn	Ni	P	S	Si
0.055	18.28	66.34	1.00	8.48	0.029	0.005	0.6

2.2 Laser Welding Parameters

The welding parameters chosen for the analysis are listed in the Table 2. The parameters are selected based on the expertise available at Welding Research Institute, BHEL, Trichy, where laser welding was successfully used for many industrial applications like welding of fins, batteries, dental clips etc.

Table 2: Laser welding parameters

S. No.	Beam Power, Watts	Welding speed, mm/min	Beam Angle, deg.
1	1250		30
2	1500	500	45
3	1750		60

2.3 Finite Element Model

To accurately model the temperature distribution produced by the laser irradiation in steel substrate, FEM is adopted due to its flexibility in modeling and its capability in obtaining full field numerical solutions [3]. The nonlinear finite element code, SYSWELD is employed to solve the transient thermal analysis of the problem. The specimen is taken in the form of two sheets of thickness 1.6 mm connected at the joint as shown in Fig. 1.

The T-profile (Fig. 1a) considered above is analyzed by a three dimensional FEM Model. The model uses 8 noded hexahedron elements and contains 14868 nodes and 12180 elements. This kind of elements has high degree of freedom and gives a good compromise between accuracy and model size. The effect of the weld bead geometry i.e. predefined weld bead has not been taken into the account during the analysis. This is because the reinforcement height is absent in laser welding of T-joint specimens. The mesh is shown in Fig. 1b. As illustrated in Fig. 1b the mesh density increases towards the weld bead which has the highest gradients. The finest mesh density along the weld line is 1 mm per element. The following points are taken into account while developing the finite element model:

- The workpiece initial temperature is 30°C
- Thermal properties of the material such as conductivity, specific heat, density are temperature dependent
- The convection and radiation loads are considered
- There is no predefined weld bead geometry
- It is also assumed that the laser energy is completely transferred to the base metal by direct absorption

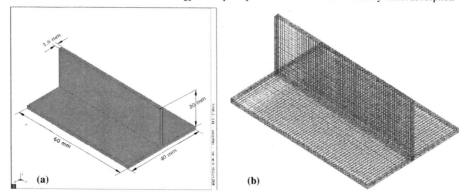

Fig. 1.(a) T-profile (b) The mesh, containing eight nodded solid elements used for the analysis

2.4   Heat Input

In the present work, a three dimensional conical Gaussian heat source (volumetric heat source) is used as a laser source and it is applied to specific elements in the finite element model. The laser heat source is fitted in such a way that the start position can be defined by the user as shown in Fig. 2.

The heat source is rotated at 30°, 45° and 60° around the longitudinal axis, in order to get a position which is normal to the weld line. The heat source, Q_v expressed by Eq. (1), travels from one end to the other. When passing to the final edge, the heat source turns off and T-profile is only influenced by the radiative and convective boundary conditions. The modified expression for 3D conical Gaussian heat source used in the analysis is given by

$$Q_v(r,z) = \frac{2P}{\pi r_0^2 H} e^{1-\left(r/r_0\right)^2}\left(1-\frac{z}{H}\right)$$

(1)

where

r_0 is the initial radius at the top of the keyhole

H is the keyhole depth

r is the current radius, i.e. the distance from the cone axis, z is the vertical axis and P is the absorbed laser power [4].

In the local reference frame of finite element code SYSWELD, it is possible to define the offset of the heat source centre (x_0, y_0, z_0) and the angle of the laser beam relative to z axis and oriented by the y axis (a_y). Based on the orientation of y axis (beam angle), the source intensity Q_v is calculated and applied into the finite element model and moving load is implemented by using a FORTRAN subroutine [3].

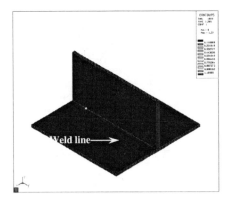

Fig. 2. Laser heat source fitting

3.0   Experimental Work

A GSI Lumonics JK2000 welding system available at WRI, BHEL, Trichy is employed for the T-joint weld specimens. Test coupons with dimensions of 60 X 40 mm are made of AISI304 stainless steel sheets of 1.6 mm thickness. Prior to welding, the test coupons are sanded with #200 sand papers and cleaned with acetone. T-joint laser welds are then carried out down the center of the plate as shown in Fig. 3. The joint setup is autogenous bead-on-plate welding. To study the effects of welding parameters on the weld geometry, the tested coupons are sectioned perpendicular to the welding direction for metallographic examinations. A sample of T-joint laser weld is shown in Fig. 4. It shows the smooth weld bead profile is achieved without any discontinuity. The parameters used for making this T-joint weld are laser power of 1250 Watts, welding speed of 500 mm/min. and beam incident angle of 60°. The length of the weld is around 60 mm. All the welding trials are conducted under the controlled atmosphere with Industrial pure Argon (99.9%) as a shielding medium. The spot diameter of the beam used for these trials is 0.8 mm with 160 mm focal length. After welding, the samples are sectioned, mounted, sanded using sand papers and polished using Alumina (Al_2O_3, 0.05μ) colloidal solution. All the samples are cleaned before being etched with a solution of Ferric chloride + Water. Then they are observed under an Image Analyzer to determine the weld profile.

4.0   Results and Discussion

The temperature distribution profiles are compelled by FEA for different laser power values and beam incident angles listed in Table 2. The bead shapes are determined from the melting (1,728 K or 1455°C) and the vaporization (2,740 K or 2467°C) isotherms [11], in the middle of each seam along the direction of the laser beam. A sample of the temperature distribution computed with the 3D FE model for a T-joint welding is shown in Fig. 5 for a laser beam power of 1250 Watts, with welding speed of 500 mm/min. (8.33 mm/s) and beam incident angle of 60°. In this analysis, a total of 100 load steps are used to complete the heating cycle. Only 37 load increments (42.38 s) are typically required for the weldment to return to its room temperature of 30°C (initial temperature). The time increments are automatically optimized for each time step by the FORTRAN subroutines available in the finite element package. From the Fig. 5, it can be seen that the thermal field around the laser heat source is rising from 30°C to 7208°C for between the time interval from 0 s to 1.697 s, which is called as initial transient stage or initial zone. This can be attributed to the fact that at this stage the T-joint specimen is subjected to all the three modes of heat transfer such as conduction, convection and radiation. The length of the initial zone is approximately 8 times the weld sheet thickness. It is also evident that as the time progresses to 2.62 s the thermal field along the weldment moves steadily with the temperature isotherm of around 7730°C, termed as Quasi-stationary stage or central zone. The elements in this zone get heated up and the heat is conducted to the adjacent elements. At this quasi-stationary stage heat transfer by conduction is more compared to convection and radiation heat transfer. Further, the thermal fields are stationary and only the co-ordinate system moves with the laser source. The central zone is situated at a distance of approximately 9 times the weld sheet thickness away from the inlet. When the laser source moves to the other end of about 56 mm from the starting end of the specimens the second transient stage or final zone starts, wherein the temperature decreases slowly from 7730°C to 6674 °C for the time interval from 5.91s to 7.20s as shown in Fig. 5. At the final edge, the heat source turns off and the profile is only influenced by the radiative and convective boundary conditions (cooling stage).

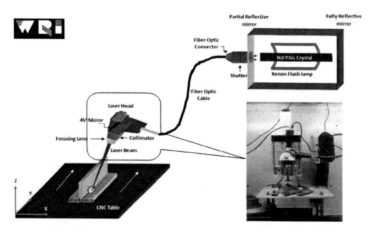

Fig. 3 Schematic representation of laser welding process for T-joint specimen

The 6th International Conference on Manufacturing Research (ICMR08)
Brunel University, UK, 9-11th September 2008

Fig. 4.   T-joint laser weld

In Fig. 6, the isotherm corresponding to the melting of base metal for the laser power of 1250 W with a welding speed of 500 mm/min and the beam angle of 60° at a time of 2.11s is compared with the weld pool shape obtained experimentally with the same laser welding parameters.   Here, the bead width and depth of penetration are estimated along the direction of the beam.   The position of the weld pool boundary (bead shape) in the experimental weld cross section is assessed from the grain structure and is depicted in the white line in Figs. 6 and 7.   In general, the quality of the laser welds presented in this study is considered to be good, since no phenomena such as warpage, porosity, etc. are present. Fig. 8 shows the temperature isotherms for the beam power of 1250 W at three different beam angles.

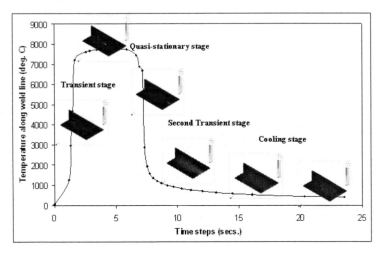

Fig. 5.   Temperature plots at different time periods

The 6th International Conference on Manufacturing Research (ICMR08)
Brunel University, UK, 9-11th September 2008

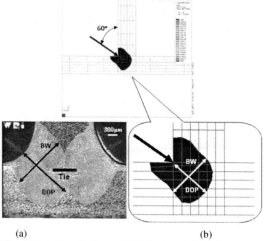

(a)   (b)

Fig. 6. Weld pool shape (a) Experimental investigation and (b) finite element simulation

It shows clearly the three shapes of bead profiles for the T-joint specimens welded with three different beam angles. It is also noted that when the beam angle is maintained at 30° more laser energy is concentrated towards the horizontal sheet compared to vertical sheet. This leads to more fusion of materials in the horizontal sheet. Similarly when the 30° beam angle is used on the other side of joint it means that there is no tie between these two weld profiles leading to non-penetration defect (see Fig. 7). For the beam angle of 60°, this defect can be eliminated, as proper fusion is achieved between horizontal and vertical sheets. Further, a very good tie is achieved between the resulting weld profiles leading to an acceptable weld (refer Fig. 8). When the beam angle is maintained at 45° between the two sheets, proper fusion is achieved but a tie between the weld profiles is not achieved. This work would facilitate the researchers, when contemplating welding of dissimilar materials and thickness. The entire calculated bead shapes shown in Fig. 7 and 8 are similar to the experimentally measured bead shapes. Although not reported, for all the combinations of laser powers and beam incident angles, similar agreement are obtained for the other samples also.

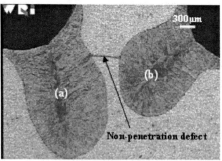

Fig. 7. Macro photograph of T joint specimen welded with (a) 30° and (b) 45° beam angles

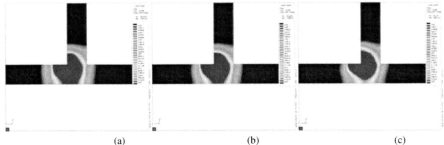

| (a) | (b) | (c) |

Fig. 8.   Isotherms at the middle of the seam for BP = 1250 W at beam angle (a) 30°, (b) 45° and (c) 60°

5.0   Conclusion

- Proper fusion of base material (horizontal and vertical sheets) and tie between the bead profiles is achieved when the laser system is operated with 60° beam incident angle, irrespective of beam power and welding speed.
- A non-penetration defect is established in the macro graph, when the beam angle is maintained at 30°.
- For the beam angle of 45°, proper fusion of base material is achieved between the horizontal and vertical sheets, but there is no tie between the resulting bead profiles.
- A series of experiments have been conducted to verify the finite element simulation results.
- The quality of the T-joint laser welds is good, since no phenomena such as warpage, porosity, etc. are present.
- The computed weld dimensions are found to be in correlation with the experimental measurements. In particular, an error of 6.3% is found between computed temperature profile and experimental measurement.

Acknowledgement

The authors thank Head, Welding Research Institute and Management, Bharat Heavy Electricals Limited, Tiruchirappalli for extending the facilities to carryout this research work and allowing to present the results in this paper. Authors thank NITT for providing computation facilities (SYSWELD).

References

[1].   T.L. Teng, C.P. Fung, P.H. Chang and W.C. Yang, Analysis of residual stresses and distortions in T-joint fillet welds", International Journal of Pressure Vessels and Piping, Vol. 78, 2001, pp. 523-538.

[2].   K.R. Balasubramanian, K. Sankaranarayanasamy and G Buvanashekaran "Analysis of Laser welding parameters using artificial neural network" International Journal for the Joining of Materials, Volume 18 No. 3/4, December 2006, pp. 99-104.

[3].   K.R. Balasubramanian, N. Siva Shanmugam, G. Buvanashekaran and K. Sankaranarayanasamy, "Numerical and experimental investigation of laser beam welding of AISI 304 stainless steel sheet", Advances in Production Engineering & Management Journal, Vol. 3, No. 2, 2008, pp 93 - 105.

[4].   S.A.Tsirkas, P.Papanikos and Th.Kermanidis, "Numerical simulation of the laser welding process in butt-joint specimens," Journal of Materials Processing Technology, Vol. 134, 2003, pp 59-69.

[5]. D. Rosenthal, "The Theory of Moving Source of Heat and it's Application to Metal Treatment," Trans. ASME, Vol. 68, 1946, pp. 849–866.

[6]. J. Sabbaghzadeh, M. Azizi and M.J. Torkamany, "Numerical and experimental investigation of seam welding with a pulsed laser," Journal of Optics & Laser Technology, Vol. 40, 2008, pp. 289-296.

[7]. R. Spina, L. Tricarico, G. Basile and T. Sibillano, "Thermo-mechanical modeling of laser welding of AA5083 sheets," Journal of Materials Processing Technology, Vol.191, 2007, pp. 215-219.

[8]. W.S.Chang and S.J.Na, "Prediction of laser spot weld shape by numerical analysis and neural network," Metallurgical and Material Transactions B, Vol. 32B, August 2001, pp 723-731.

[9]. S. Sarkani, V. Tritchkov and G. Michaelov, "An efficient approach for computing residual stresses in welded joints", Journal of Finite Elements in Analysis and Design, Vol. 35, 2000, pp. 247-268.

[10]. ESI-Group, "SYSWELD Reference Manual", 2007.

[11]. G. Tsoukantas and G. Chryssolouris, "Theoretical and experimental analysis of the remote welding process on thin, lap-joined AISI 304 sheets", International Journal of Advanced Manufacturing Technology, DOI 10.1007/s00170-006-0767-0.

The 6th International Conference on Manufacturing Research (ICMR08)
Brunel University, UK, 9-11th September 2008

A SENSITIVITY STUDY OF THE EFFECTS OF INTERFACE HEAT TRANSFER COEFFICIENT ON FE MODELLING OF MACHINING FOR A WIDE RANGE OF CUTTING SPEEDS

S A Iqbal [*1], P T Mativenga [2], M A Sheikh [3]

Manufacturing and Laser Processing Group, School of MACE, The University of Manchester, UK

[1*] amir.syed@postgrad.manchester.ac.uk
[2] p.mativenga@manchester.ac.uk
[3] mohammad.a.sheikh@manchester.ac.uk

Abstract

Heat transfer plays a significant role in the machining processes, where both the workpiece and tool behaviour are affected by the generated temperature fields. The heat transfer between the chip, the tool and the environment has an impact on tool wear mechanisms and hence on tool life and accuracy of the machined surface. For the finite element modelling of the metal machining processes, the interface heat transfer coefficient is an important input parameter to quantify the transfer of heat between the chip and the tool and to accurately predict the temperature distribution within the cutting tool. This paper discusses the effects of the interface heat transfer coefficient on the output of the finite element model of metal cutting process for a wide range of cutting speeds. An updated Lagrangian finite element code DEFORM 2D simulating continuous chip formation is used for the modelling of two dimensional orthogonal machining process. A sensitivity study has been performed by varying interface heat transfer coefficient in the simulation of orthogonal cutting process. The effects of varying interface heat transfer coefficient on the simulation output: cutting forces, temperature, shear angle, and chip morphology has been analysed. The simulated results are also compared with the temperature measurement results of high cutting speed tests. The comparison of simulation results show that in Finite Element modelling of the machining process, temperature in tool and chip morphology are significantly influenced by selection of the interface heat transfer coefficient.

Keywords: Interface heat transfer coefficient, high speed machining (HSM), Finite Element Modelling (FEM).

1.0   Introduction

A SENSITIVITY STUDY OF THE EFFECTS OF INTERFACE HEAT TRANSFER COEFFICIENT
ON FE MODELLING OF MACHINING FOR A WIDE RANGE OF CUTTING SPEEDS

The heat transfer between the chip, the tool and the environment has a significant impact on wear mechanisms and hence on tool life and accuracy of the machined surface. The heat transfer at the tool-workpiece interface is commonly assumed to be governed by the interface heat-transfer coefficient. The interface heat transfer coefficient can be defined by equation 1:

$$h = \frac{q}{\Delta T} \qquad (1)$$

where q is the average heat flow and ΔT is the temperature drop across the interface. It has been established that interface heat transfer coefficient is a function of several parameters, the dominant ones being contact pressure, interstitial materials, macro and micro geometries of the contacting surfaces, temperature and the type of lubricant or containment and its thickness [1]. For the FE modelling of metal machining processes, the thermal boundary conditions at the tool-chip interface are usually formulated in terms of the interface heat-transfer coefficient. The interface heat transfer coefficient is an important input parameter to quantify the transfer of heat between the chip and the tool, and to accurately predict the temperature distribution within the cutting tool. In the application of interface heat transfer coefficient to the chip formation simulations, very high values of 'h' were used based on the assumption of perfect contact. The survey of literature reveals that for all the previous works on FE modelling of metal machining, the numerical values used for defining thermal interface boundary condition are assumed with background from metal forming processes (mostly metal forging). Table-1 summarises the values of interface heat transfer coefficient used in the FE simulations of metal cutting process.

Table 1: Summary of interface heat transfer coefficient values used for machining simulation

Researcher	Workpiece	Tool	$h(kW/m^{2\,o}C)$
Yen et al [2]	AISI 1020	Uncoated WC	**
Yen et al [3]	AISI 1045	TiC/Al$_2$O$_3$/TiN coated WC	100
Yen et al [4]	AISI 1045	Uncoated WC	100
Yen et al [5]	AISI 1045	Uncoated WC	**
Klocke et al [6]	AISI 1045	SiC-Ceramic	**
Ozel [7]	LCFCS	Uncoated WC	100
Xie et al [8]	AISI 1045	Uncoated WC	10
Miguelez et al [9]	42CrMo4	Uncoated WC	**
Coelho et al [10]	AISI 4340	PCBN	500

** *Value not reported and perfect contact was assumed between tool and workpiece.*

In this work a sensitivity study has been performed utilizing different values of interface heat transfer coefficient 'h' in the FE simulation of orthogonal machining process for a wide range of cutting speeds. The purpose of this sensitivity study is to analyse the effect of interface heat transfer coefficient on the output of FE simulations. The cutting parameters such as, cutting forces, shear angle, chip morphology and tool-chip temperatures are compared for different values of interface hear transfer coefficient 'h'.

2.0   Finite Element Model

A SENSITIVITY STUDY OF THE EFFECTS OF INTERFACE HEAT TRANSFER COEFFICIENT ON FE MODELLING OF MACHINING FOR A WIDE RANGE OF CUTTING SPEEDS

For FEM simulations, an updated Lagrangian FE code DEFORM 2D was used, that employs implicit integration method, designed for large deformation simulations. This implicit Lagrangian code offers very stable remeshing routines, which can handle large gradients of strain, strain rate and temperature. A dense mesh can be easily defined around the tool-workpiece interface. This mesh is adapted as the tool advances and simulation of continuous chip formation is achieved. The simulation inputs such as mesh definition, sizes of the tool and the workpiece were selected so that the simulated results would not be sensitive to these inputs. The workpiece material AISI 1045 steel and uncoated cemented carbide (ISO P20 grade) tool were used. Simulations for orthogonal cutting process were performed at cutting speeds of 198, 399, 628, and 879 m/min. The feed rate was set at 0.1 mm/rev and the depth of cut fixed to the tube thickness of 2.5 mm. For defining material flow stress behaviour, Johnson-Cook material flow stress model was used based on its suitability for a wide range of cutting speeds [11]. The interface friction characteristics were defined by using velocity dependent friction distribution schemes. The details of cutting speed dependent friction distribution scheme can be found elsewhere [12]. For the FE simulations, after the cutting forces achieved a steady-state level, an additional step based on Eulerian analysis was performed to obtain steady-state tool and workpiece temperatures. Due to anticipated high temperature during cutting process, temperature dependent properties of workpiece and tool material cited in literature [13]-[15], were used as inputs to the simulation software. The interface heat transfer coefficient values used for defining the interface thermal boundary conditions ranged from 1 kW/m²ºC to 1x10⁵ kW/m²ºC.

3.0   Simulation Results

3.1   Comparison of the Cutting Forces and Shear Angle

Figures 1 (a, b, c) show the simulation results for cutting (tangential) force, feed force and shear angle respectively, for different cutting speeds using different values of interface heat transfer coefficient. The simulation results suggest that the cutting forces and shear angle are insensitive to any changes in the interface heat transfer coefficient values except for the lowest cutting speed of 198 m/min. At this cutting speed, the three parameters (cutting forces and shear angle) show a noticeable difference for the lowest value of interface heat transfer coefficient i.e. 1 kW/m² ºC. Besides this, the output for the three parameters considered here, is consistent and does not show any noticeable variation, with the interface heat transfer coefficients for all the cutting speeds used. The main reason for the insensitivity of these parameters is that the cutting force and shear angle are mainly dependent on the elastic-plastic properties of the workpiece material and the feed force is dependent on interface friction conditions. Here the workpiece material plastic properties are defined by Johnson-Cook flow stress model and the interface friction characteristics are defined by velocity dependent friction schemes. These two parameters remain the same in all the simulations and the only variable in the sensitivity study is the interface heat transfer coefficient.

3.2   Chip Morphology

The chip shapes obtained from simulations for different values of interface heat transfer coefficient, and for different cutting speeds are shown in Figure 2. This figure shows that chip shapes are influenced by varying the interface heat transfer coefficient values. It is noticed that at low cutting speed and with low interface heat

**A SENSITIVITY STUDY OF THE EFFECTS OF INTERFACE HEAT TRANSFER COEFFICIENT
ON FE MODELLING OF MACHINING FOR A WIDE RANGE OF CUTTING SPEEDS**

transfer coefficient value, the chip morphology is different as compared to high cutting speeds and high 'h' values. The low value of interface heat transfer coefficient means high resistance at the tool-chip interface for the transfer of heat. Due to this reason, a major portion of heat generated in the secondary deformation zone goes into the chip and raises its temperature. However, this is a complex thermo-mechanical phenomenon and high temperature in the chip alongwith other parameters such as workpiece material properties (plastic, physical and thermal) and interface friction conditions, may also influence the chip curl. Iqbal et al [16] reported that the chip curl is influenced by interface friction conditions. Mabrouki and Rigal [17] have also reported sensitivity of chip morphology (chip curvature and chip serrations) to the interface heat transfer coefficient and heat partition in a machining simulation of AISI 4340 steel at a cutting speed of 100 m/min.

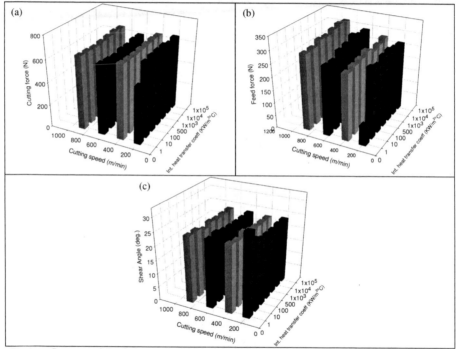

Fig. 1.   Summary of simulation results for (a) cutting force (b) feed force and (c) shear angle at different interface heat transfer values and different cutting speeds

The variation of chip curl at a low value of interface heat transfer coefficient 'h' and at low cutting speed might be the reason for a noticeable variation in cutting force and shear angle results shown in Figure 1. For higher cutting speeds and high values of interface heat transfer coefficient 'h', a noticeable reduction in chip curl (curvature) is observed. It is also observed that at higher values of interface heat transfer coefficient, the chip curl (chip curvature) remains constant for all cutting speeds. These results also suggest that for having longer tool life, during the actual machining operation, a higher thermal resistance at the tool chip interface can be introduced e.g. by using thermally insulated tool coatings.

A SENSITIVITY STUDY OF THE EFFECTS OF INTERFACE HEAT TRANSFER COEFFICIENT ON FE MODELLING OF MACHINING FOR A WIDE RANGE OF CUTTING SPEEDS

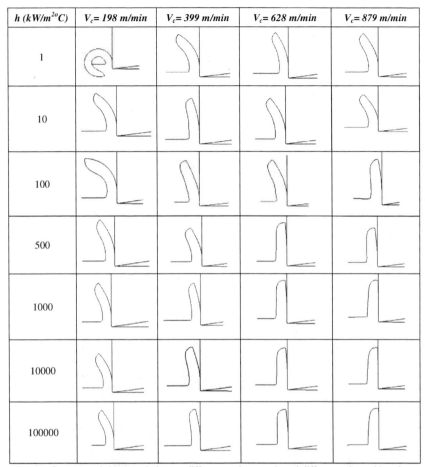

Fig. 2.   Summary of chip morphology at different cutting speeds and different values of interface
heat transfer coefficients

3.3   Temperature in the Tool and the Chip

The steady-state temperatures are obtained from the simulations on both the chip and the tool. A summary of the maximum steady-state tool temperature, for different interface heat transfer coefficient values at different cutting speeds is shown in Figure 3 (a, b). This figure shows that for low values of interface heat transfer coefficient, a high thermal barrier is present at the tool-chip interface and less amount of heat enters into the tool. Typically for the interface heat transfer coefficient value of 1 kW/m^{2o}C, the steady-state temperature is nearly equal to the room temperature. For the cutting speeds of 198 m/min and 399 m/min, and at higher values of 'h' (greater than 500 kW/m^{2o}C), the steady-state tool temperature becomes constant. However, for the two remaining cutting speeds (628 m/min and 879 m/min), the steady-state tool temperature shows an increasing trend with increasing 'h' value.

**A SENSITIVITY STUDY OF THE EFFECTS OF INTERFACE HEAT TRANSFER COEFFICIENT
ON FE MODELLING OF MACHINING FOR A WIDE RANGE OF CUTTING SPEEDS**

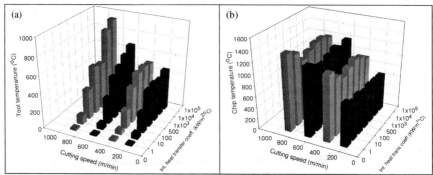

Fig. 3.   Steady-state temperatures for (a) tool and (b) chip at different cutting speed and different
interface heat transfer coefficient values

A summary of the maximum steady-state chip temperatures is shown in Figure 3 (b). For an 'h' value of 1 kW/m^{2o}C, and for cutting speed of 198 m/min, the steady-state chip temperature is highest. In addition, it is also noted that for higher 'h' values the maximum steady-state chip temperatures are nearly constant.

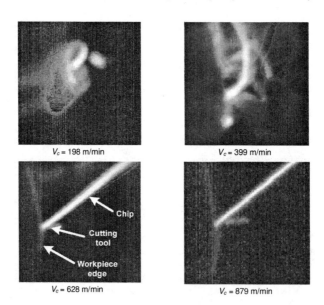

Fig. 4.   Images showing temperature measurement at different cutting speeds (chip shapes are also
observed)

The experimental measurement of cutting temperatures in the cutting process was carried out by using an infrared thermal imaging camera ThermaCAM^{TM}. The cutting conditions, tool and workpiece material used were the same. Due to the anticipated high temperatures during the cutting process, a temperature measuring range between 300°C-2000°C was employed. The camera could record the whole sequence of the cutting process and had excellent data acquisition software (ThermaCAM^{TM} Researcher), with data post processing

A SENSITIVITY STUDY OF THE EFFECTS OF INTERFACE HEAT TRANSFER COEFFICIENT
ON FE MODELLING OF MACHINING FOR A WIDE RANGE OF CUTTING SPEEDS

680

options. The images of the temperature obtained by the camera for different cutting speeds are shown in Figure 4. The chip curls (morphology) at the start of the cutting tests can be observed in this figure. These chip shapes can be compared with chip curl results obtained from simulations shown in the Figure 2, and show good similarity for chip shapes at interface heat transfer values of 100 kW/m^{2o}C and 500 kW/m^{2o}C for all the cutting speeds considered.

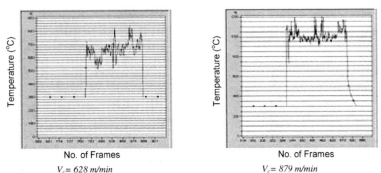

$V_c= 628\ m/min$ $V_c= 879\ m/min$

Fig. 5.   Maximum temperature measured in the region of tool chip interface using thermal imaging camera

Figure 5 shows the maximum temperature measured in the region of the tool chip interface for the cutting speed of 628 and 879 m/min, obtained by using the thermal imaging camera. The average maximum temperatures in the tool chip interface region are measured as 400°C, 550°C, 700°C and 1000°C respectively for the four cutting speeds of $V_c = 198, 399, 628$ and 879 m/min.

This sensitivity study reveals that the interface heat transfer coefficient is an important and influencing parameter in the FE modelling of the machining process. It has high impact on the tool temperature rise and consequently on wear mechanisms. It also has influence on chip morphology (chip shapes) during the machining process.

4.0   Conclusions

Based on the sensitivity study results performed using a wide range of interface transfer coefficient values in the simulation of orthogonal metal cutting process, following conclusions can be drawn:

- The cutting forces involved in the cutting process and the resulting shear angles are insensitive to the variation of interface heat transfer coefficient values. These values are more influenced by material flow stress behaviour and interface friction conditions. However, the cutting tool temperature distribution, maximum cutting tool temperature, chip temperature and chip shape, all show a degree of sensitivity to the variation of interface heat transfer coefficient. This may suggest that introducing a thermal barrier in the tool-chip interface can help promote chip curl and affect tool-chip contact length.

- The comparison of experimental and simulation results, for chip morphology and temperature in the tool-chip interface region, suggests that the interface heat transfer coefficient value in the range of 100-500

A SENSITIVITY STUDY OF THE EFFECTS OF INTERFACE HEAT TRANSFER COEFFICIENT
ON FE MODELLING OF MACHINING FOR A WIDE RANGE OF CUTTING SPEEDS

681

KW/m^{2o}C gives good agreement. However the interface heat transfer coefficient values less than these were used for FE modelling of machining process.

- Interface heat transfer coefficient is an important parameter which quantifies the amount of heat transferred to the cutting tool in the FE modelling of metal machining process. The resulting temperature distribution in the cutting tool is, in turn important for the modelling of tool wear process. The present practice is to use interface heat transfer coefficient values estimated from metal forging process, based on the assumption of perfect contact. However on the basis of operating characteristics such as contact pressure, temperature, nature of contact and strain rates involved, the nature of forging and machining processes are different. In this context, it is necessary to develop an experimental procedure close to machining process for the estimation of this important parameter related to FE modelling machining.

References

[1]   C. V. Madhusudana, Thermal Contact Conductance, Springer, Berlin, 1996
[2]   Y. -C. Yen, A. Jain, T. Altan "A finite element analysis of orthogonal machining using different tool edge geometries" *Journal of Materials Processing Technology* 146 (2004) 72-81
[3]   Y. -C. Yen, A. Jain, P. Chigurupati, W. -T. Wu, T. Altan "Computer simulation of orthogonal metal cutting using a tool with multiple coatings" *Machining Science and Technology* 8(2) (2004) 305-326
[4]   Y. -C. Yen, J. Sohner, B. Lilly, T. Altan "Estimation of tool wear in orthogonal cutting using finite element analysis" *Journal of Materials Processing Technology* 146 (2004) 82-91
[5]   Y. -C Yen, J. Söhner, H. J. Weule, J. Schmidt, T. Altan "Estimation of tool wear of carbide tool in orthogonal cutting using FEM simulation" *Machining Science and Technology* 6(3) (2002) 467-486
[6]   F. Klocke, H.-W. Raedt, S. Hoppe "2D-FEM Simulation of the orthogonal high speed cutting process" *Machining Science and Technology* 5(3) (2001) 323–340
[7]   T. Ozel "The influence of friction models on finite element simulations of machining" *Int. J. Machine Tools and Manufacture* 46(6) (2006) 518-530
[8]   L.-J. Xie, J. Schmidt, C. Schmidt, F. Biesinger "2D FEM estimate of tool wear in turning operation" *Wear* 258 (2005) 1479–1490
[9]   H. Miguelez, R. Zaera, A. Rusinek, A. Moufki, A. Molinari "Numerical modelling of orthogonal cutting: Influence of cutting conditions and separation criterion" *Journal De Physique* 134 (2006) 417-422
[10]   R. T. Coelho, E-G. Ng, M. A. Elbestawi "Tool wear when turning AISI 4340 with coated PCBN tools using finishing cutting conditions" *Int. J. Machine Tools & Manufacture* 47 (2007) 263-272
[11]   S. A. Iqbal, P.T. Mativenga, M.A. Sheikh "Characterization of the Machining of AISI 1045 steel over a wide range of cutting speeds-Part 2: Evaluation of flow stress models and interface friction distribution schemes" *Proc. IMechE Part B: J. Engineering Manufacture* 221(5) (2007) 917-926
[12]   S. A. Iqbal, P. T. Mativenga, M. A. Sheikh "Characterization of the Machining of AISI 1045 steel over a wide range of cutting speeds-Part 1: Investigation of contact phenomena" *Proc. IMechE Part B: J. Engineering Manufacture* 221(5) (2007) 909-916
[13]   V. Kalhori Modeling and Simulation of Mechanical Cutting, PhD thesis, Lulea University of Technology, (2001)
[14]   ASM, Metals Handbook: Properties and Selection: Iron and steels Volume 1 Tenth ed. Vol. 1, American Society for Metals., Metals park, Ohio., 1990, 506-511
[15]   T. H. C. Childs, K. Maekawa, T. Obikawa, Y. Yamane, Metal Machining: Theory and Application, Arnold, London, 2000
[16]   S. A. Iqbal, P. T. Mativenga, M. A. Sheikh "Contact length prediction: mathematical models and effect of friction schemes on FEM simulation for conventional to HSM of AISI 1045 steel" *Int. J. Machinability and Machining of Materials* 3(1/2) (2008) 18-33
[17]   T. Mabrouki, J.-F Rigal "A contribution to a qualitative understanding of thermo-mechanical effects during chip formation in hard turning" *Journal of Materials Processing Technology* 176(1-3) (2006) 214-221

A SENSITIVITY STUDY OF THE EFFECTS OF INTERFACE HEAT TRANSFER COEFFICIENT ON FE MODELLING OF MACHINING FOR A WIDE RANGE OF CUTTING SPEEDS

The 6th International Conference on Manufacturing Research (ICMR08)
Brunel University, UK, 9 – 11th September 2008

EXPERIMENTAL STUDIES AND FINITE ELEMENT SIMULATION OF Al – Fe COMPOSITES DURING COLD UPSETTING

T. Ramesh [1], R. Narayanasamy [2]

1. Department of Mechanical Engineering, National Institute of Technology, Tiruchirappalli – 620 015, Tamilnadu, India tramesh@nitt.edu

2. Department of Production Engineering, National Institute of Technology, Tiruchirappalli – 620 015, Tamilnadu, India narayan@nitt.edu

Abstract

Powder Metallurgy is widely applied to produce mainly automotive parts such as bearings, cams and toothed components. It was emerged as a distinct technology in an era when improved performance for advanced military systems provided a primary motivation for materials development. An experimental investigation on the barreling of aluminium with various percent additives of iron composites, namely, 2, 4, 6, 8 and 10 per cent under triaxial stress state condition has been studied in the present work. Sintered aluminium – iron composites with height to diameter ratio of 0.75 and 1.0 were prepared, sintered, furnace cooled and cold upset forged. A new empirical relationship for the determination of the barrel radius is proposed based on circular radius of curvature and compared with the experimentally measured barrel radius. Various stress ratio parameters, namely, (σ_θ / σ_z) and (σ_m/ σ_z), respectively were determined and their behaviour against the relative density has been systematically analyzed. ABAQUS/CAE, a general purpose finite element code is used for the simulation of the forging process. The powder compaction process has been simulated in order to predict the density distribution of the compacts. An attempt has also been made to simulate the sintering process utilizing the thermo-mechanical modeling. The results obtained through the Finite Element are compared with the experimental results.

Keywords: Barreling, Metal Matrix Composites, Stress Ratio Parameters, Relative Density and Abaqus.

1.0   Introduction

Powder Metallurgy is widely applied to produce mainly automotive parts such as bearings, cams and toothed components. It was emerged as a distinct technology in an era when improved performance for advanced military systems provided a primary motivation for materials development. The Powder Metallurgy includes four major steps: powder preparation and mixing, compacting powders in to appropriate shapes in closed die to produce green compacts, sintering the green compacts at elevated temperature and post sintering secondary operations. The design and control of such processes depend on the characteristics of the work piece material, the conditions at the tool/workpiece interface, the mechanics of plastic deformation, the equipment used and the requirement of the finished products. The cold forging of powder metallurgy composites are subjected to both ductile fracture and the strain hardening. These two predominating mechanisms control the feasibility of the powder forging operations and help to achieve the good quality in the properties of the final products. Powder forging includes the preparation of preforms by conventional pressing and sintering processes, followed by forging of the powder preform in to final shapes. Ductile fracture is the common mode of failure, which is a complicated phenomenon, dependent upon process parameters such as stress, strain, strain – rate, friction etc., and the material parameters such as strain hardening exponent, strength coefficient, density coefficient and the strain rate sensitivity. Ductility of a powder material is the ability to deform plastically without fracture. Because of the complexity of many metal-working operations, models of various types such as analytical and numerical models are often relied upon to design and processes.

(Coube & Riedel, 2000) proposed a numerical simulation process using the finite element method and a phenomenological material model, modifying the Drucker – Prager cap model with the intention of describing the formation of cracks during powder transfer, compaction, unloading and ejection of the parts from die. The density distributions of iron powder compacts were calculated in a successful manner and compared their work with experimental results. Densification behaviour of composite powders under cold compaction was studied by (Kim et al., 2000), proposing a model for densification of mixed – soft and hard – metal powders. They performed an experimental work on mixed powders of copper and tungsten with various volume fractions of tungsten under cold isostatic pressing and die compaction and concluded that very good agreements between the theoretical models proposed by them with the experimental data. (Kim et al., 2000) investigated the densification behaviour of ceramic powder under cold compaction and performed an experimental work on zirconia powder under triaxial compressions loading conditions and further they proposed a novel hyperbolic cap model from the iso-density curves based on the experimental data. Similar type of work has been identified with a large number of referenced authors (Kim & Cho, 2001; Kim et al., 2001; Kraft &Riedel, 2002; Nhou et al., 2002; Kim et al., 2003; Reitere et al., 2004; Biswas, 2005; Tahir & Ariffin, 2006) validating their own proposed model with the experimental work through Abaqus, a general-purpose finite element code.

In this work, an experimental investigation is performed on a metal – matrix composite prepared from aluminium with various percent additions of iron powders. Various stress ratio parameters, which defines the prediction of the ductile fracture and densification mechanism, were determined from the proposed analytical models and a finite element simulation is performed for studying the behaviour of the metal – matrix composites under various loading conditions. The barreling of the compacts under plastic deformation is calculated and verified with the numerical results obtained through Abaqus implementing a standard model, porous metal plasticity.

2.0   Theoretical Foundations

The mathematical expressions used and proposed for the determination of various upsetting parameters under triaxial stress state condition are discussed below.

2.1   New Geometrical Shape Factor

**EXPERIMENTAL STUDIES AND FINITE ELEMENT SIMULATION OF Al – Fe COMPOSITES
DURING COLD UPSETTING**

According to (Narayanasamy & Pandey, 1997), the expressions for circular arc of barreling can be written as follows:

According to mass constancy principle,

$$\frac{\pi}{4} D_o^2 h_o \left(\frac{\rho_o}{\rho_{th}} \right) = \frac{\pi}{12} (2D_b^2 + D_c^2) h_f \left(\frac{\rho_f}{\rho_{th}} \right) \tag{2.1}$$

Where D_0 is the initial diameter, h_o the initial height, ρ_o the initial preform density, ρ_f is the density of the preform after deformation, D_b the bulged diameter, D_c the average contact diameter, h_f the height of the deformed compact and ρ_{th} is the theoretical density of the fully dense material.

The above equation (2.1) can be rearranged as follows;

$$\frac{\rho_f}{\rho_{th}} = \frac{\rho_o}{\rho_{th}} \frac{h_o}{h_f} \left(\frac{3D_o^2}{(2D_b^2 + D_c^2)} \right) \tag{2.2}$$

Taking Natural Logarithm on both sides of the above equation (2.2) yields an equation of the form,

$$\ln \left(\frac{\rho_f}{\rho_{th}} \right) = \ln \left(\frac{\rho_o}{\rho_{th}} \right) + \ln \left(\frac{h_o}{h_f} \right) \left(\frac{(2D_b^2 + D_c^2)}{3D_o^2} \right) \tag{2.3}$$

$$\ln \left(\frac{\rho_f}{\rho_{th}} \right) = \ln \left(\frac{\rho_o}{\rho_{th}} \right) + \varepsilon_z - \varepsilon_\theta \tag{2.4}$$

The above equation (2.4) can be rewritten as follows;

$$\left(\frac{\rho_f}{\rho_{th}} \right) = \left(\frac{\rho_o}{\rho_{th}} \right) e^{\varepsilon_z - \varepsilon_\theta} \tag{2.5}$$

$$\text{Where, } \varepsilon_z = \ln \left(\frac{h_o}{h_f} \right) \text{ and } \varepsilon_\theta = \ln \left(\frac{2D_b^2 + D_c^2}{3D_o^2} \right) \tag{2.6}$$

Since the ratio of (ρ_f / ρ_{th}) is taken to be constant, equation (2.5) would show an exponential relationship between density ratio (ρ_f / ρ_{th}) and the difference between the true strains namely ε_z and ε_θ.

2.2 Various Stress Ratio Parameters under Triaxial Stress State Condition

According to (Narayanasamy & Ponalagusamy, 2001), the state of stress in a triaxial condition is given as follows;

$$\alpha = \left(\frac{(2+R^2)\,\sigma_\theta - R^2\,(\sigma_z + 2\sigma_\theta)}{(2+R^2)\,\sigma_z - R^2(\sigma_z + 2\sigma_\theta)} \right) \tag{2.7}$$

Where α is the Poisson's ratio and R, the relative density

The above equation (2.7) can be rewritten as follows;

$$\sigma_\theta = \left(\frac{2\alpha + R^2}{2 + R^2 + 2\alpha R^2} \right) \sigma_z \tag{2.8}$$

$$\left(\frac{\sigma_\theta}{\sigma_z} \right) = \left(\frac{2\alpha + R^2}{2 + R^2 + 2\alpha R^2} \right) \tag{2.9}$$

Where σ_θ is the hoop stress, σ_z is the axial stress and R is the relative density.

The mean or the hydrostatic stress component can be determined as follows;

$$\sigma_m = (\sigma_z + \sigma_\theta + \sigma_r)/3 \tag{2.10}$$

Under triaxial stress condition, the radial stress component is equal to the hoop stress ($\sigma_r = \sigma_\theta$)

$$\sigma_m = 1/3\,(\sigma_z + 2\sigma_\theta) \tag{2.11}$$

Dividing the above equation (2.11) on both sides by means of σ_z,

$$(\sigma_m / \sigma_z) = 1/3\,[1 + (2\sigma_\theta / \sigma_z)] \tag{2.12}$$

3.0   Experimental Details

Atomized aluminium and iron powders of the characterization stated in the Table 1 were procured and analyzed for its purity. The purity level of the aluminium and iron powders was found to be 99.7 per cent and 99.62 per cent respectively.

Table I: Characterization of Al – Fe Powders

Aluminium Powder	Iron Powder	Aspect Ratio
100 μm	150 μm	0.75

Table II: Compact geometry for various percentage of Iron content

	Al – 2%Fe	Al- 4%Fe	Al – 6%Fe	Al – 8% Fe	Al – 10%Fe
Initial Diameter	26.21	26.22	26.09	26	26.1
Initial Height	18.7	18.66	18.95	19.09	19.29

EXPERIMENTAL STUDIES AND FINITE ELEMENT SIMULATION OF Al – Fe COMPOSITES DURING COLD UPSETTING

The compacts were prepared from aluminium and iron powders with aspect ratio of 0.75 as given in the Table 2 at the compacting pressure range of 200 to 225 MPa in order to obtain the initial preform density ranging from 90 to 93 per cent of the theoretical density. The powder metal compacts were prepared by blending aluminium and iron powders of different iron contents (2 to 10 per cent). The ceramic coating was applied over the surface of the compacts to protect them from oxidation during sintering. The ceramic-coated compacts were sintered in an electric muffle furnace at 550°C for a period of 90 minutes. Immediately after the completion of sintering schedule, the sintered preforms were allowed to cool at room temperature by switching off the furnace power supply. The sintered preforms were cleaned from the sand particles and the dimensional measurements made before and after each deformation. The deformation of the preform was carried out between two flat open dies hardened to 50 – 55 Rc and tempered to 46 – 50 Rc on a 100 tons capacity hydraulic press. Each preform was applied with the compressive loading in the step of 0.01 MN until the appearance of first visible cracks on the free surface. Immediately after the completion of each step of loading, the deformed height, the contact diameters (the top and bottom surfaces), the bulged diameter and the density were measured. The density measurement was carried out using Archimedes principle. Figure 3.1 shows the deformed and un-deformed shapes of the specimen.

Fig. 3.1   Various Composite Preforms before and after deformation.

4.0   Numerical Analysis

The sintered cylindrical powder metallurgy part is considered as a piece of normal metal with relative density involved in it. The metal bock is considered as a cylinder with a radius of 13.105mm and a total height of 18.7mm. Axisymmetric boundary conditions are established for the simplification of the analysis. Porous metal plasticity model, normally found in the situation of modeling compressible materials taking the void closure mechanism in to the consideration, has been utilized for the definition of material properties such as yield stress, elastic modulus, relative density and plastic strain. The friction between the die platen and the powder compacts has been predicted and introduced in to the porous metal plasticity model. The analysis is performed utilizing the following options such as large displacement, constant dilatation and large strain additive provided in the Abaqus/Explicit. An adoptive re-meshing feature can also be used for automatic regeneration of the mesh of the powder compacts. The whole analysis is divided in to 20 steps. The upper punch is allowed to move 8mm of maximum along its axis during deformation. Figure 4.1 shows the finite element model of the cylindrical specimen before and after deformation loads are applied. Symmetric expansion option has been used for plotting the various parameters, such as, von-mises stress contour, plastic strain, axial and radial deformations and are given in the following Figures 4.2 – 4.6. From Figures 4.2 – 4.6, it is clearly understand that the initiation of ductile fracture would be identified at the peripheral surface of the composite where maximum failure stress found. Also a maximum amount of plastic strain is appeared at the inner surface of the compacts, which would permit the initiation of the crack to propagate internally.

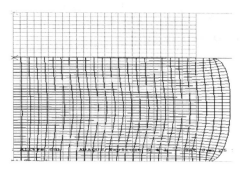

Fig. 4.1   Finite Element Model of the Cylindrical Billet before and after deformation

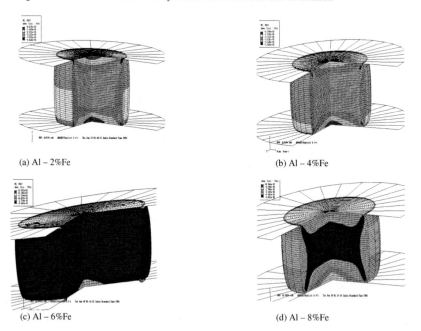

(a) Al – 2%Fe

(b) Al – 4%Fe

(c) Al – 6%Fe

(d) Al – 8%Fe

EXPERIMENTAL STUDIES AND FINITE ELEMENT SIMULATION OF Al – Fe COMPOSITES DURING COLD UPSETTING

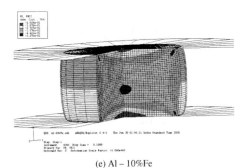

(e) Al – 10%Fe

Fig. 4.2   Plastic Strain Distribution – Al –Fe Composite having Initial Relative Density of 0.90654

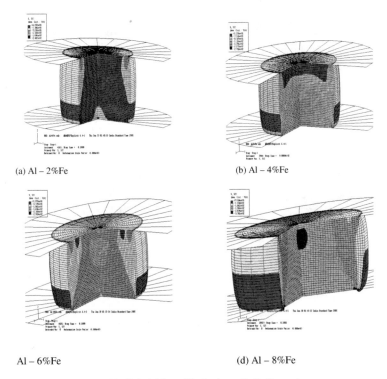

(a) Al – 2%Fe   (b) Al – 4%Fe

Al – 6%Fe   (d) Al – 8%Fe

Fig. 4.3   Contour plot of the Uniaxial Stress Distribution – Al –Fe Composite

**EXPERIMENTAL STUDIES AND FINITE ELEMENT SIMULATION OF Al – Fe COMPOSITES
DURING COLD UPSETTING**

The 6th International Conference on Manufacturing Research (ICMR08)
Brunel University, UK, 9 – 11th September 2008

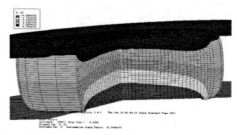

Fig. 4.4 Contour plot of the specimen during uniaxial deformation (Axial Displacement)

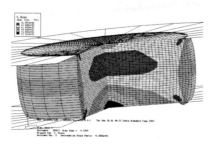

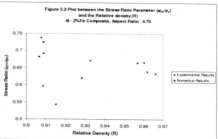

Fig. 4.5   Von-Mise's Stress Distribution

Al -6%Fe Composite

Fig. 4.6   Logarithmic Strain distributions,

Al – 8%Fe Composite

5.0   Results and Discussion

Figures 5.1 – 5.6 have been plotted between two different stress ratio parameters such as (σ_θ/σ_z) and (σ_m/σ_z) and the relative density (R) for different percent of iron contents such as 2, 4 and 6% under experimental and numerical conditions. As shown in the Figures 5.1 – 5.6, as the relative density increases, the stress ratio parameters such as (σ_θ/σ_z) and (σ_m/σ_z) decreases, reaches the lower level and for further increase in the relative density, these parameters maintains almost a constant value. From the above observation it clearly indicates that there is relationship between the stress ratio parameter and densification mechanism developed during cold upset forging operation.

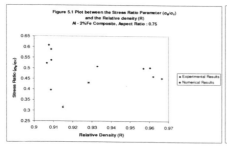

Fig. 5.1   Plot between (σ_θ/σ_z) and R, Al –

Fig. 5.2   Plot between (σ_m/σ_z) and R, Al –

**EXPERIMENTAL STUDIES AND FINITE ELEMENT SIMULATION OF Al – Fe COMPOSITES
DURING COLD UPSETTING**

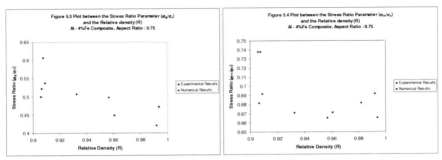

Fig. 5.3   Plot between (σ_θ/σ_z) and R, Al –   Fig. 5.4   Plot between (σ_m/σ_z) and R, Al –

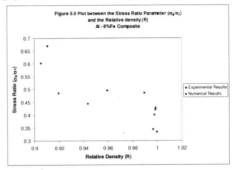

Fig. 5.3   Plot between (σ_θ/σ_z) and R, Al –

Figs. 5.1 – 5.5   Plot between various stress ratio parameters such as (σ_θ/σ_z) and (σ_m/σ_θ) against the Relative density (R)

Figure 5.7 shows the relationship between the axial stress and the axial strain of aluminium – 6% iron composite compacts. Since the metal matrix composite having mixture of Aluminium with 6% Iron exhibits a large amount of stress and strain values, the stress strain curve is particularly discussed here. Fro this Figure 5.7, it has been observed that a greater stress value is obtained for the higher value of the axial strain. A close correlation is found between the experimental and numerical results data.

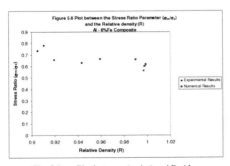

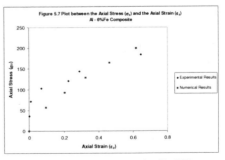

Fig. 5.6   Plot between (σ_m/σ_z) and R, Al –   Fig. 5.7   Plot between σ_z and ε_z Al –6%Fe

EXPERIMENTAL STUDIES AND FINITE ELEMENT SIMULATION OF Al – Fe COMPOSITES DURING COLD UPSETTING

6.0   Conclusion

From the observation of the results through numerical and experimental data, the following conclusions are drawn:

- Stress ratio parameters such as (σ_θ/σ_z) and (σ_m/σ_z) have a strong relationship with the relative density.

- Greater densification is found for the metal matrix composites of Al – 6% Iron.

- Higher stress and strain levels were obtained for the composites of Al – 6%Fe.

Further it has been proposed to conduct experiments adopting various lubricants and is requested to investigate the effect of friction on the powder compaction and deformation and comparisons are to be made by means of simulating the process. Optimized parameters are to be identified in order to predict the suitable and optimum conditions for the conduct of the experiments.

References

[1] Coube, O & Riedel, H. (2000) "Numerical simulation of metal powder die compaction with special consideration of cracking", *Powder Metallurgy*, 43/2 (2000), 123 – 131.
[2] Kim, K.T., Cho, J.H. & Kim, J.S (2000), "Cold compaction of composite powders", *Journal of Engineering Materials Technology*, 122, (January 2000), 119 – 127.
[2] Kim, K.T., Choi, S.W. & Pak, S. (2000), Densification behaviour of ceramic powder cold compaction, *Journal of Engineering Materials and Technology*, 122, (April 2000), 238 – 244.
[3] Kim, K.T. & Cho, J.H. (2001), "A densification model for mixed metal powder under cold compaction", *International Journal of Mechanical Sciences*, 43 (2001), 2929 – 2946.
[4] Kim, K.G., Lee, H.M. & Kim, K.T. (2001), "Near –net-shape forming of ceramic powder under cold combination pressing and pressureless sintering", *Journal of Engineering Materials and Technology*, 123 (April 2001), 221 – 228.
[5] Kraft, T. & Riedel, H. (2002), "Numerical simulation of die compaction and sintering", *Powder Metallurgy*, 45/3 (2002), 227 – 231.
[6] Nhou, Z.Y., Chen, P.Q., Zhao, W.B., Shao, M. & Xia, W. (2002), "Densification model for porous metallic powder materials", *Journal of Materials Processing Technology*, 129 (2002), 385 – 388.
[7] Kim, K.T., Lee, S.C. & Ryu, H.S. (2003), "Densification behaviour of aluminum alloy powder mixed with zirconia powder inclusion under cold compaction", *Materials Science and Engineering A*, 340 (2003) 41 – 48.
[8] Reiterer, M., Kraft, T., Janosovits, U & Riedel, H. (2004), "Finite element simulation of cold isostatic pressing and sintering of SiC composites", *Ceramics International*, 30 (2004) 177 – 183.
[9] Biswas, K. (2005), "Comparison of various plasticity models for metal powder compaction processes", *Journal of Materials Processing Technology*, 166 (2005) 107 – 115.
[10] Tahir, S.M. & Ariffin, A.K. (2006), "Fracture in metal powder compaction", *International Journal of Solids and Structures*, 43 (2006), 1528 – 1542.
[11] Narayanasamy, R.; Pandey, K.S. "Salient features in the cold upset forming of sintered aluminium – 3.5 per cent alumina powder composite preforms", *Journal of Materials Processing Technology*, 72 (1997) 201 – 207.
[12] Narayanasamy, R. & Ponalagusamy, R (2001) "Unpublished report on P/M forging", *National Institute of Technology, Tiruchirappalli – 620 015, India*, (2001).

DESIGN AND DEVELOPMENT OF MIAB WELDING MODULE-INVESTIGATION AND VALIDATION OF ELECTROMAGNETIC FORCE USING FINITE ELEMENT ANALYSIS

S. Arungalai Vendan [1], S. Manoharan [2], G. Buvanashekaran [3], C. Nagamani [4]

1. Research Scholar Department of Electricals and Electronics Engineering, National Institute of Technology, Tiruchirappalli – 620 015 arungalaisv@yahoo.co.in

2. SDGM, Welding Research Institute, BHEL, Tiruchirappalli – 620 014

3. DGM, Welding Research Institute, BHEL, Tiruchirappalli – 620 014

4. Professor and Head, Department of Electricals and Electronics Engineering, National Institute of Technology, Tiruchirappalli – 620 015

Abstract

Magnetically Impelled Arc Butt welding (MIAB) is an efficient two phase process which is used in highly automated factory production lines in high volume industries such as automotive manufactures. In this process heat is generated prior to forging by an arc created between the two clamped and aligned tubes. This arc swiftly rotates along the peripheral edges of the tubes to be welded under the action of the electromagnetic force resulting from the interaction of the arc current and the externally controlled magnetic field created by magnetic systems. This electromagnetic force responsible for the arc rotation is governed by the magnetic flux density in the gap, the arc current and the arc length (gap size). To be precise the radial magnetic flux density is a critical factor in arc rotation and weld quality. An attempt is being made in this study, to develop a laboratory MIAB module and carry out trials to investigate the process parameters and illustrate the result of performance of the system. Further, a non linear electromagnetic analysis is performed to determine the magnetic field distribution and the magnitude of electromagnetic force required for arc rotation using a 3-dimentional finite element model developed using ANSYS. The results of this analysis are compared with the obtained experimental data for steel tubes T11 (outer diameter 47mm and thickness of 2mm). The results obtained in both the experiments and finite element analyses (FEA) establish that magnetic flux density is linear and proportional to the exciting current. It is also evident that faster rotation of arc is achieved with higher electromagnetic force. Added to this, it is observed that

DESIGN AND DEVELOPMENT OF MIAB WELDING MODULE-INVESTIGATION AND
VALIDATION OF ELECTROMAGNETIC FORCE USING FINITE ELEMENT ANALYSIS

693

the results obtained from FEA simulations and the experimental trials are in excellent agreement.

Keywords: MIAB, Electromagnetic force, Magnetic flux density, T11, FEA, Automotive Manufacturers

1.0   Introduction

Magnetically Impelled Arc Butt welding process can be employed to weld steels, stainless steel, aluminum alloys, etc. and pipe to pipe. MIAB leads to higher productivity in manufacturing industry as it reduces welding time by up to 90 percent.

From the available literature the work carried out previously by the researchers on MIAB welding is discussed in brief. Ganowski [1] presented a survey of the state of magnetic arc welding process and its mechanical development. Georgescu et al [2] presented a compact design and development of portable equipment for rotary arc operated pneumatically. The equipment was designed for welding a maximum of 30mm diameter pipes. A two dimensional finite element analysis model for the MIAB welding process was proposed by Kim et al [3] and it was stated that the magnetic flux density is mainly dependent on the gap size between two pipes, the position of the exciting coil that generates the magnetic field, the exciting current in the coil and the relative permeability of the pipes. Georgescu et al [4] presented the principle of ROTARC welding and discussed details of several original equipment developed by them. Also the experimental results with a classical longitudinal magnetizing system and the conclusions of the experiments were presented. Kachinskiy et al [5] discussed the developments in the field of MIAB welding of different compositions of steel and for hollow shapes with wall thicknesses over 10 mm and also for solid parts used in pipeline construction, in automobile and other industries. Johnson et al [6] reported an evaluation of a commercially available MIAB machine used for welding 51 mm (2 in.) diameter, 3 mm (0.12 in.) wall mild steel tubing. The quality of MIAB welds were assessed by bend testing and by the height of the internal upset. The main disadvantage of the MIAB welding as noted by [] was that it is suitable for welding only thin wall components (up to 3-5mm).

Although several studies [1-9] had reported MIAB welding, very little has been mentioned about the design and development of a test module for MIAB welding. An attempt is made here to develop a laboratory module for MIAB welding and to propose a FE based 3 dimensional model for determining the electromagnetic force and magnetic flux density distribution which affect the process of MIAB. Further, experimental data obtained from the designed MIAB module is utilized to verify the proposed FEM model. Their exists excellent correlation between the results of numerical analysis (proposed FEM model) and the experimental results which establishes the validity of the proposed FEM model.

2.0   Principle of MIAB Welding Process

DESIGN AND DEVELOPMENT OF MIAB WELDING MODULE-INVESTIGATION AND VALIDATION OF ELECTROMAGNETIC FORCE USING FINITE ELEMENT ANALYSIS

MIAB welding is a fusion welding process for tubes and pipes in which heat is generated prior to forging by an electric arc moving along the peripheral edges of the weldments with the aid of an external magnetic field. The schematic diagram depicting the principle of MIAB welding process is shown in Fig. 1.

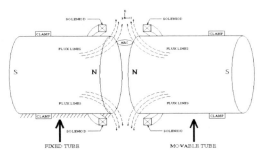

Fig. 1.   Schematic representation of MIAB Welding process

Two tubes to be welded are clamped with proper alignment. The magnetic field is established due to the electromagnetic induction caused by the exciting current flowing through the magnetic coils for the MIAB welding machine. The exciting coils are magnetized in such a manner that the opposite pipe ends have the same magnetic polarity and the path of the magnetic flux becomes radial to the tube axis in the gap between the edges of the two pipes to be joined. Since the arc comes under the influence of the radial magnetic field superimposed upon the gaps, it receives an electromagnetic force due to Fleming's left-hand law (Fig. 2) and begins to rotate along the peripheral pipe ends, the rotating direction being thereby perpendicular both to the magnetic field and to the arc current [9].

The electromagnetic force is the Lorentz force, which is exerted on the arc by the external magnetic field. The electromagnetic force density can be expressed as the following vector equation:

$$F = J \times B \qquad \text{- (1)}$$

Where F - Electromagnetic force density, J - Electric current density and B - Magnetic flux density.

Finally, the magnitude of the total force propelling arc can be represented as the following relationship:

$$F \propto B \times I \times L_a \qquad \text{- (2)}$$

where F - Force propelling arc, B - Radial component of the magnetic flux density, I - Arc current and L_a - Arc length.

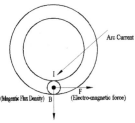

Fig, 2.   Fleming's left hand rule

DESIGN AND DEVELOPMENT OF MIAB WELDING MODULE-INVESTIGATION AND VALIDATION OF ELECTROMAGNETIC FORCE USING FINITE ELEMENT ANALYSIS

From equation (2), it can be observed that magnetic flux density, arc current and arc length are the main variables affecting the force propelling arc. Therefore, in order to have a constant high quality joint, it is necessary that a magnetic flux density, as large as possible, be formed in the pipe gap space.

3.0   Experimental Study

One of the tubes was held stationary by a clamp on one side and the other tube was made movable, fixed by a clamp. For all the experimental trails, T11 grade tubes, having Chromium alloying was used. The movable tube was powered by a pneumatic cylinder. With the help of movable tube the distance between the tubes was adjusted. Magnetic coil arrangement is shown in Fig. 3a. It has a laminated core wounded by magnetic coil. When power supply was given, arc formed between tubes and it was rotating slowly.

Fig. 3,   a) MIAB module illustrating clamped tubes b) MIAB forging system

Trials were conducted with 400 to 500amps current and 90 to 120volts to the tubes using an ESAB power source. DC power of 75 to 200V and 0.3 to 0.5amps was supplied to magnetic coil. Trials showed that arc rotation with this arrangement of the magnetic coils is continuous and uniform. With this help arrangement around 50 to 60% was melted. Upset force required to join the tube was 30 to 100N/mm[2].The provision of forging employed in the experimental set up is shown in Fig 3b.

4.0   Finite Element Analysis

Finite element analysis is carried out for investigating the radial magnetic flux density distribution in the space between the tubes. A three dimensional finite element model is adopted for the analyses as shown in Fig. 4 in which the mesh system in the vicinity of the exciting coils is represented. In the present case, the magnetic flux distribution for MIAB welding process is required, so a non linear electromagnetic analysis must be performed.

This finite element model includes a total of 76,655 nodes and 24,457 elements for the calculation domain. The calculation domain was increased and selected through a series of calculations for this size, which showed a converging distribution of magnetic flux density. An average current density was used for the calculation instead of using the exciting current itself. The boundary condition is that there is no magnetic flux on the outside of the calculation domain. The general assumptions of room temperature and the medium of air are considered for this analysis

**DESIGN AND DEVELOPMENT OF MIAB WELDING MODULE-INVESTIGATION AND
VALIDATION OF ELECTROMAGNETIC FORCE USING FINITE ELEMENT ANALYSIS**

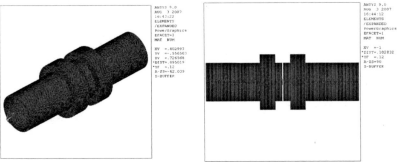

Fig, 4.   Three dimensional finite element model

5.0   Results and Discussion

The results are discussed separately for experimental trails and simulation.

5.1   Experimental Results:

Trials were conducted on the MIAB test setup and the results obtained are tabulated in table I. The main objective of developing the MIAB module is to achieve a good weldment using MIAB welding process. Trials are conducted by varying the electrical parameters namely the welding voltage, welding current, magnetic coil voltage and the magnetic coil current respectively. The arc establishment and rotation is by varying one of the above mentioned electrical parameter or parameters while maintaining at least one other parameter constant. From the experiments the following observations are made.

Table I.Trials on MIAB Welding

Sl. No	Power source	Welding voltage in volts	Welding current in amps	Magnetic coil voltage in volts	Magnetic coil current in amps	Remarks
1		48	450-500	100	0.2	Arc strikes and vanishes instantaneously
2		50	400	100	0.2	Arc strikes and vanishes instantaneously
3	Constant Current Source	50	400	100	0.3	Arc strikes and vanishes instantaneously
4		15	400	200-220	0.3	Arc dint strike Power supply not suitable
5		50	425	110	0.4	Half rotation of arc
6		50	450	100	0.4	Slow rotation of arc-about 60rpm

**DESIGN AND DEVELOPMENT OF MIAB WELDING MODULE-INVESTIGATION AND
VALIDATION OF ELECTROMAGNETIC FORCE USING FINITE ELEMENT ANALYSIS**

The arc establishment is mainly governed by the voltage of welding source. For welding voltages in the range of 15 to 30V the arc does not strike. This may possibly be due to inadequate welding current that flow to cause an arc. A voltage of above 50V is needed to establish the current and thus an arc and also to sustain the arc between the two tubes. The impact of magnetizing coil voltage on the MIAB module performance is not very prominent when the coil voltage is varied between 75 to 200V. Hence an optimum magnetic coil voltage of around 100-110V is considered for the trials

The most significant factor governing the arc initiation, establishment and the rotation is the welding current that flows through the tubes. This welding current contributes the necessary energy to the arc . The specimen (tubes T11) possesses a high melting point. Based on rough calculations it is estimated that the arc current should be in the range of 400 -500A to melt the material. This range of 400 -500A has been obtained taking into account the arc energy that is lost due to convection and radiation. It is next observed that higher the welding current, higher is the speed of arc rotation while maintaining the necessary welding voltage and magnetic coil voltage. Taking into account the characteristics of the magnetic field, the value of coil current is imperative for the rotation of the arc. The electromagnetic force is regulated by the magnetic flux density distribution in the gap between the two tubes, the arc current and the arc length. A considerable arc rotation with about 60 rpm is observed when the exciting current is 0.3A while the welding voltage, welding current and the magnetic coil voltage are 50V, 400A and 100V respectively. A Slow but uniform rotation is noticed when the magnetic coil current is 0.4A while the welding voltage, welding current and the magnetic coil voltage are 50V, 450A and 100V respectively.

5.2   Simulation Result

Simulations are carried out to determine the magnetic flux distribution necessary for the magnetically impelled arc butt welding process. Experimental trials were conducted by varying the current and voltage parameters of the welding circuit and the magnetizing circuit. The simulations mainly focus on the prediction of the magnitude of magnetic flux density and electromagnetic force which is necessary in order to obtain slow rotation. Simulation is carried out by using a finite element code ANSYS.

5.2.1   Simulation of Magnetic Flux Density and Electromagnetic Force Distribution in Case of Slow Rotation of Arc

The input provided for the simulation for this particular case is same as that of the 6th trial conducted in our experiment. The values of welding current, welding voltage, magnetic coil voltage and magnetic coil current are 450A, 50V, 100V and 0.4A respectively.

Figure 7 shows the three dimensional FEM model of the set up to determine the magnetic flux distribution for MIAB welding process. The maximum flux density is found to be 2.032tesla from the simulations. Simulations reveal that the minimum magnetic flux density required to accomplish slow rotation of arc is 2.032tesla.Further, it is noticed that the minimum value of electromagnetic force required to impel the arc at slow speed is 1.059 electromagnetic units. This maximum flux density is concentrated at the centre between

DESIGN AND DEVELOPMENT OF MIAB WELDING MODULE-INVESTIGATION AND
VALIDATION OF ELECTROMAGNETIC FORCE USING FINITE ELEMENT ANALYSIS

698

the two aligned tubes for MIAB welding. It can be noted that the magnitude of flux density decreases from the centre.

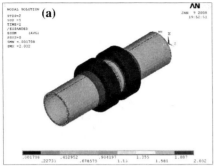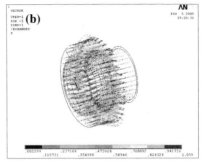

Fig, 5   a) 3-D magnetic flux density distribution b) 3-D electromagnetic force

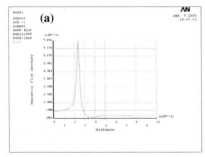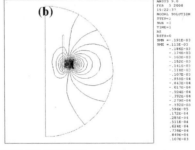

Fig. 6   a) Magnetic flux density along radial distance b) Distribution of flux lines

Fig. 6a shows the variation of the magnetic flux density with radial distance. The magnetic flux density is minimum at bottom of the peripheral edge of the tubes and is observed to be 0.799tesla when the welding current, welding voltage, magnetic oil voltage and magnetic coil current are 450A, 50V, 100V and 0.4A respectively. Then gradually the flux density increases and attains the peak value of 7.976tesla at the centre. Further the value of flux density decreases to almost zero at the top of the exterior edge of the tubes.

The flux lines contributing to the magnetic field is illustrated in the fig. 6b for an exciting current of 0.4 amps when slow rotation of arc is achieved. It is clearly noticed that the flux lines are concentrated more at the gap between the two pipes leading to the achievement of better electromagnetic force which would impelled arc at a requisite high speed.

6.0   Validation of Simulation Result

The results of FEA are validated with the experimental data. In the experiments, the radial magnetic flux density was measured by using a Gauss-meter at the various positions from the pipe surface as shown in figure

DESIGN AND DEVELOPMENT OF MIAB WELDING MODULE-INVESTIGATION AND VALIDATION OF ELECTROMAGNETIC FORCE USING FINITE ELEMENT ANALYSIS

.The gauss meter was initially taken from the outside edge to the inner edge and vice versa for determination of magnetic flux density between the steel tubes. It was observed that the maximum magnetic flux density noted for slow arc rotation with the input considered as in case of the 6th trail in experimentation is 2.018tesla. The values of maximum magnetic flux density that was determined in simulation for slow arc rotation is 2.032 which are almost equivalent to that of the experimental data. The results of numerical analysis have an excellent correlation with that of the experimental ones

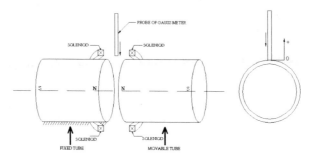

Fig, 7.   Measuring method for magnetic flux density [3]

7.0   Conclusion

The investigation on MIAB welded on steel tubes was carried out and the laboratory module was designed. The electromagnetic force responsible for the arc rotation is governed by the magnetic flux density in the gap, the arc current and the arc length (gap size). To be precise the radial magnetic flux density is a critical factor in arc rotation and weld quality. Thus, the effectual and efficient design of the electromagnetic system is an vital task for construction of the MIAB welding machine. Due to this factor, many trials were conducted on MIAB laboratory module with different magnetic coil system for steel tubes to attain continuous and uniform arc rotation.

The numerical analysis of magnetic flux density distribution using the finite element code ANSYS helps in thoroughly understanding the MIAB welding process and further facilitates in optimizing the design and development of the electromagnetic system. Further the simulation results were validated with the experimental data. The following conclusions are drawn from the results of the analysis,

- The minimum magnetic flux density required to accomplish slow rotation of arc is 2.032tesla for 0.5 amps exciting current in the magnetic coil system.

- By using the numerical model, the magnetic flux density distribution for different exciting currents and welding currents could be analyzed. It is revealed that the magnetic flux density in the gap between the pipes increases with increasing exciting current.

Acknowledgements

DESIGN AND DEVELOPMENT OF MIAB WELDING MODULE-INVESTIGATION AND VALIDATION OF ELECTROMAGNETIC FORCE USING FINITE ELEMENT ANALYSIS

The authors thank Head, Welding Research Institute and Management, Bharat Heavy Electricals Limited, Tiruchirappalli for extending the facilities to carryout this research work and allowing to present the results in this paper. Authors thank NITT for providing computation facilities.

References

[1]. Ganowski, F.J. (1974). The magnetarc welding process, *Welding and Metal Fabrication*, 206-213.

[2]. Georgescu, V.; Iordachescu, D.; Geogescu B. Pneumatically Operated Equipment For Pressure Welding In Magnetic Forces Field, *Dunarea De Jos*, University of Galati, Romania

[3]. Kim, J.W.; Choi, D.H. (2003). A study on the numerical analysis of magnetic flux density distribution by a solenoid for magnetically impelled arc but welding, Proc. Instn Mech. Engrs, Part B:J Engineering Manufacture, Vol. 217, 1401-1407.

[4]. Georgescu, V.; Iordachescu, D.(2000). Original Magnetizing Systems for ROTARC Welding, *The Annals of dunarea De Jos*, University of Galati 1998-2000,10-14.(ISSN 1221-4639)

[5]. Kachinskiy, V.S.; Krivenko, V.G.; Ignatenko, V.Yu. (2002). Magnetically impelled arc butt welding of hollow and solid parts, *Commission III Doc. IIW-1564-02*, 49-56.

[6]. Johnson, K. I.; Carter, A. W.; Dinsdale, W. O.; Threadgill, P. L.; Wright, J. A. (1979) The magnetically impelled arc butt welding of mild steel tubing. *Welding Journal*, Vol. 59, Issue 11, 17-27.

DESIGN AND DEVELOPMENT OF MIAB WELDING MODULE-INVESTIGATION AND VALIDATION OF ELECTROMAGNETIC FORCE USING FINITE ELEMENT ANALYSIS

DESIGN AND FINITE ELEMENT MODE ANALYSIS OF NONCIRCULAR GEAR

Chao Lin [1], Kai Cheng [2], Datong Qin [1], Caichao Zhu [1], Hua Qiu [3], Xiaohu Ran [1]

1. **The State Key Laboratory of Mechanical Transmission, Chongqing University, China**

2. **School of Engineering and Design, Brunel University, UK**

3. **Department of Mechanical Engineering, Kyushu Sangyo University, Japan**

Abstract

The noncircular gear transmission is an important branch of the gear transmission, it is characterized by its compact structure, good dynamic equilibration and other advantages, and can be used in the automobile, engineering machine, ship, machine tool, aviation and spaceflight field etc. Studying on the dynamics feature of noncircular gear transmission can improve the ability to carry loads of, reduce the vibration and noise of, increase the life of the noncircular gear transmission machine, provides guidance for the design of the noncircular gear, and has significant theories and practical meanings. In this paper, the gear transmission technique is used to studied the design method of the noncircular gear, which contains distribution of teeth on the pitch curve, designs of the tooth tip curve and the tooth root curve, design of the tooth profile curve, the gear system dynamics principle is introduced to establish dynamics model for the noncircular gear; basic theory of finite element and mode analysis method are applied, finite element model for the noncircular gear is established, natural vibration characteristic of the noncircular gear is studied. And the oval gear is taken as an example, the mathematics software MathCAD, the 3D modeling software UG and the finite element software ABAQUS are used to realize precise 3D model of the oval gear. The finite element method is used, the natural vibration characteristic of the oval gear is studied, the main vibration types and natural frequencies of the oval gear and that of the equivalent cylindrical gears are analyzed and compared, the conclusions received reflect the dynamics performance of the oval gear, and solid foundation is laid for dynamics research and engineering application of the oval gear transmission.

Keywords: Noncircular gear, Finite element method, Natural frequency, Natural vibration shape.

1.0 Introduction

The noncircular gear is an important branch of gear transmission, can be used to transmit movement and power between two intersectant axes, is characterized by its compact structure, good dynamic equilibration and other advantages, and can be applied in automobile, engineering machine, ship, machine tool, aviation and space flight field etc. The currently, the studying work of noncircular gear concentrates on geometry modeling, kinematics, machining etc, while that on dynamics is much less. Studying on the dynamics feature of the noncircular gear transmission can improve the ability to carry loads of reduce the vibration and noise, increase the life of the noncircular gear transmission machine, provides guidance for the design of the noncircular gear, and there are significant theories and practical meanings.

2.0 Design of the Noncircular Gear

The pitch curve of the noncircular gear is noncircular, which makes the design of the noncircular gear difficult. The keys of the noncircular gear design are to determine the position on the pitch curve of each tooth, the tooth tip curve, the tooth root curve and the tooth profile curve of the noncircular gear.

First, it give a point on the pitch curve as a beginning point. Then determine the positions for left and right tooth profile of each tooth by calculating arc length according to pitch distance and spiral thickness [1].

2.1 The Tooth Tip Curve and Tooth Root Curve

The tooth tip curve and the tooth root curve of the noncircular gear are normal equal-distance curves of the pitch curve, the normal distances between them and the pitch curve are the tooth addendum and the tooth root height respectively[1], the shown in Fig. 1.

From Fig. 1 the tooth tip curve formula can be written as.

$$r_a = \sqrt{r^2 + h_a^2 + 2rh_a \sin \mu} \tag{1}$$

Where: r_a——Tooth tip curve radius, r——Pitch curve radius, h_a——Tooth addendum, μ——Angle between tangential direction and radial direction of a point (P) on pitch curve.

$$\mu = \arctan \frac{r}{\dfrac{dr}{d\varphi}} \tag{2}$$

$$\theta_a = \varphi - \arcsin \frac{h_a \cos \mu}{r_a} \tag{3}$$

Where: θ_a——Polar angle of tooth tip curve, φ——Polar angle of pitch curve.
The tooth root curve formula can be written as.

DESIGN AND FINITE ELEMENT MODE ANALYSIS OF NONCIRCULAR GEAR

$$r_f = \sqrt{r^2 + h_f^2 + 2rh_f \sin \mu} \tag{4}$$

Where: r_f ——Tooth root curve radius, h_f ——Tooth dedendum.

$$\theta_f = \varphi + \arcsin \frac{h_f \cos \mu}{r_f} \tag{5}$$

Where: θ_f ——Polar angle of tooth root curve.

2.2   The Tooth Profile Curve

The tooth profile curve of the cylindrical gear is involute of the basic circle, and can be settled according to the basic circle. The tooth profile curve of the noncircular gear is computed from evolute of tooth profile, and the profile curve of each tooth is different[2]. The tooth profile curve of the noncircular gear can be derived from pitch curve formula by analytic method as shown in Fig. 2.

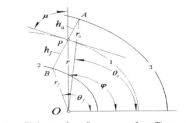

1——Pitch curve, 2——Root curvem, 3——Tip curve.   1——Pitch curve, 2——Left tooth profile, 3——Right tooth profile.

Fig. 1.   Tip curve and root curve   Fig. 2.   Tooth profile curve

From Fig. 2 the right tooth profile curve formula of the noncircular gear can be written as.

$$\begin{cases} x_r = r\cos\varphi \mp an\cos(\varphi + \mu + \alpha_n) \\ y_r = r\sin\varphi \mp an\sin(\varphi + \mu + \alpha_n) \end{cases} \tag{6}$$

Where: x_r ——X coordinates value of right tooth profile, y_r ——Y coordinates of right tooth profile, α_n ——Pressure angle of tool, an ——Distance from intersection point between pitch curve and normal of tooth profile to tooth profile along normal direction of tooth profile.
Left tooth profile curve formula of the noncircular gear can be written as.

$$\begin{cases} x_l = r\cos\varphi \pm an\cos(\varphi + \mu - \alpha_n) \\ y_l = r\sin\varphi \pm an\sin(\varphi + \mu - \alpha_n) \end{cases} \tag{7}$$

Where: x_l ——X coordinates of left tooth profile, y_l ——Y coordinates of left tooth profile.
From the gear meshing theory.

$$an = S \cos \alpha_n \tag{8}$$

Where: S ——Arc length on the pitch from point (a) to intersection point (a₀) between the pitch curve and the tooth profile curve.

The tooth profile curve of the noncircular gear can be realized by two methods: 1) The programming, which is difficult to common designer. 2) The equivalent method, which use the involute of the equivalent cylindrical gear to substitute the tooth profile curve of the noncircular gear, and make the model imprecise. All these

DESIGN AND FINITE ELEMENT MODE ANALYSIS OF NONCIRCULAR GEAR

make the analysis of the noncircular gear difficult. This paper aims at this problem, takes the oval gear as an example, uses the tooth profile curve formula, combines mathematic software MathCAD, software UG and finite element software ABAQUS, and realizes the precise model of the oval gear.

2.3   Oval Gear Modeling

The pitch curve formula of the oval gear can be written as.

$$r = a(1-k^2)/(1-k\cos(n\varphi)) \tag{9}$$

Where: $n = 2$, k ——Eccentricity, a ——Radius of long axis.

The pitch curve of the oval gear is symmetrical with the X-axis and Y-axis of cartesian coordinate. For the design convenience, the tooth number $Z = 4C + 2$ (C is positive integer), and the sections at long and short axes should be tooth and alveolus respectively. The design steps of oval gear modeling are shown in Fig. 3. The parameters of the oval gear in this paper: The tooth number $Z = 22$, modulus $m = 5mm$, eccentricity $e = 0.1$, tooth addendum $h_a = 5mm$, tooth height $h = 11.25mm$, tooth width $B = 25mm$, radius (length half axles) $a = 54.728$ mm, inner radius $r_{in} = 25mm$. The two oval gears are same.

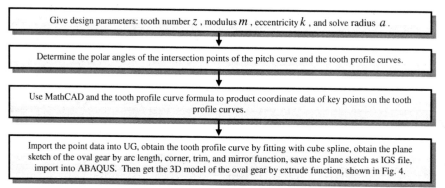

Fig. 3.   Design of the oval gear modeling

3.0   Finite Element Model of the Oval Gear

The ABAQUS is one of the most advanced large-scale general finite element software in the world, and has powerful function in big strain, nonlinear (geometry, material and boundary), viscoelastic, dynamic stress, and contact problem fields etc [3].

DESIGN AND FINITE ELEMENT MODE ANALYSIS OF NONCIRCULAR GEAR

In this paper, the material of the oval gear is 45 steel, Young's modulus $E = 2.0 \times 10^{11} N / mm^2$, Poisson's ratio $\mu = 0.3$, and Density $\rho = 7.85 \times 10^3 kg / m^3$. Create material steel under material module, create the oval gear section, set material steel as property of the oval gear section, and appoint to section of the oval gear.

The boundary condition of finite element model for the oval gear can be set according to the factual working condition. In the meshing process of the oval gears, interference fit is applied between inside surface and axis with spline, the interference fit between axis and the gear can be considered as rigid connection in the finite element model, and the influence of spline is neglected. The tolerance of this simplification is small to dynamic study. In order to reflect the factual condition of gear meshing correctly, the inner surface of the oval gear is restricted, and displacements along X axis, Y axis, Z axis and rotations round with X and Y axis are restricted. In the ABAQUS, the 3D solid unit only has three displacement freedoms. In order to restrict rotation freedom of the oval gear's inner surface, a coupling must be added to couple the inner surface to a point on the center rotating axis of the oval gear, and freedoms of the oval gear's inner surface can be restricted by setting the reference point's freedoms. The boundary condition of the oval gear can be applied to initial step.

The mode is determined by natural property of the gear system, and it is irrespective with outer loads, so it is needless to set the load boundary condition for the oval gear. In course of the meshing, distortion should be reduced farthest, as for the problem that the grids distorts badly, small sized linear reduced integration unit can be used, for the 3D problem, hexahedron unit should be applied utmost, which can get better result with lower cast, the result received form tetrahedron unit is imprecise, so large numbers of units must be applied to get a better result, which makes computing cost increase greatly. According to the principle above, swept meshing technique is applied in the this model, C3D8R unit (8 nodes hexahedron reduced integration unit) is used, and 19600 units and 59433 nodes are received. The finite element model of the oval gear completed is shown in Fig. 5.

Fig. 4. The 3D model of the oval gear   Fig. 5. The finite element model of the oval gear

4.0 Calculating the Natural Mode and Natural Frequency

The methods of calculating the natural mode and natural frequency. According to the mechanical system dynamics theory and the finite element theory, the movement differential equation of the multi-freedom system can be written as[4].

$$[M]\{\ddot{u}\} + [C]\{\dot{u}\} + [K]\{u\} = \{p(t)\} \tag{10}$$

Where $[M]$——Mass matrix, $\{\ddot{u}\}$——Acceleration matrix, $[C]$——Damping matrix, $\{\dot{u}\}$——Velocity matrix, $[K]$——Stiffness matrix, $\{u\}$——Displacement matrix, $\{p(t)\}$——Outer load matrix.

When the damping force is neglected and the system is free of load, the movement differential equation of undamped free vibration system can be written as[4].

$$([K] - \omega^2 [M])\{\phi\} = 0 \tag{11}$$

Where ω——Frequencies of system, $\{\phi\}$——Eigenvector of system.

The LANCZOS method and the subspace iterative method are provided to calculate eigenvalue. When the system has many freedoms and plentiful characteristic modes are requested, it is much quicker by applying the LANCZOS method, while few characteristic modes (< 20) are requested, it is much quicker by using subspace iterative method. In this paper, the LANCZOS method is applied.

5.0   Analytical Result

The structure vibration can be expressed as linear combination of each order natural vibration shape, while lower order vibration shape has big influence on structure vibration, and play a decisive role in structure's dynamic character. First 5 to 10 orders are needed only when mode analysis.

In order to explain the dynamic character of the oval gear contrastively, the finite element models of equivalent cylindrical gears (0 degree, 30 degree, 60 degree, 90 degree) are established, and the natural vibrations and natural frequencies are calculated and analyzed. The 1st, 2nd, 3rd, 5th, 7th, 10th mode vibration shapes are shown in Fig. 6 (a) ~ (f), and the vibration shapes and natural frequencies are shown in Table 1.

The Table 1 and Fig. 7 show that the natural frequencies of the oval gear lie between the corresponding order's natural frequencies of the big section (0 degree) and that of the small section (90 degree), they are bigger than that of the big section and smaller than that of the small section. The natural frequency increases with the order increases. The vibration shapes of the oval gear are same with that of equivalent cylindrical gear, but the orders arisen are different. Compared with the cylindrical gear, the frequencies to each order of the oval gear is different obviously, while the frequencies to each order of the cylindrical gear may be same or similar. The reason is that the cylindrical gear is symmetrical with the rotating center absolutely, while the oval gear is symmetrical with the rotating center incompletely.

The Table 1 and Fig. 6 show that the 3rd, 4th and 6th mode vibration shapes are same, the 5th and 9th mode vibration shapes are same, and the 7th and 8th mode vibration shapes are same. The main differences lie in that the vibration directions of each tooth are different.

The Fig. 8 shows that the natural frequencies to each order of the equivalent cylindrical gear increase while the polar angle of the oval gear increases and the pitch curve radius decrease. The compared with cylindrical gear, the distance among the amplitudes of each tooth to each mode of the oval gear is quite big. For example, for the 2nd SZ mode, the amplitude of the tooth about the big section (0 degree) is quite big, while the tooth about the small section doesn't vibrate basically.

The Fig. 6 and Table 1 show that the main vibration shapes of the oval gear is the DZ mode and YZ mode, while radial vibration is quite small. So the DZ mode and YZ mode is the vibration shape which is most possible to arouse resonance of the oval gear. In design of the oval gear transmission system, the natural vibration shapes and natural frequencies should be considered adequately, the working frequency should keeps away from the natural frequencies to avoid resonance.

Table 1: Natural frequencies and vibration shapes of the oval gear and the equivalent gears

Model	Order	1	2	3	4	5	6	7	8	9	10
Oval gear	Frequency	12170	12235	14896	15179	16739	18203	19274	20348	22882	23925
	Type	DZ1	SZ	DZ2	DZ2	YZ	DZ2	DZ3	DZ3	YZ	DZ4
0^0	Frequency	11000	11000	11377	11719	11720	15275	15277	17004	17007	20343
	Type	DZ1	DZ1	SZ	DZ2	DZ2	DZ3	DZ3	YZ	YZ	DZ4
30^0	Frequency	12834	12835	13202	13516	13523	16969	16979	18457	18474	21982
	Type	DZ1	DZ1	SZ	DZ2	DZ2	DZ3	DZ3	YZ	YZ	DZ4
60^0	Frequency	17084	17085	17411	17699	17701	20802	20806	21646	21652	25485
	Type	DZ1	DZ1	SZ	DZ2	DZ2	DZ3	DZ3	YZ	YZ	DZ4
90^0	Frequency	19622	19692	19693	20997	20999	24472	24485	24542	24543	29489
	Type	SZ	DZ1	DZ1	DZ2	DZ2	YZ	YZ	DZ3	DZ3	DZ3

DZ1—1st folio vibration,DZ2—2nd folio vibration,SZ—Bevel vibration,DZ3—3rd folio vibration,DZ4—4th folio vibration,YZ—Circle vibration

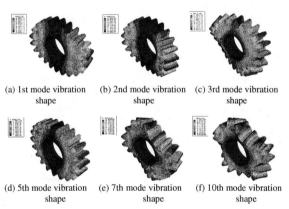

(a) 1st mode vibration shape   (b) 2nd mode vibration shape   (c) 3rd mode vibration shape

(d) 5th mode vibration shape   (e) 7th mode vibration shape   (f) 10th mode vibration shape

Fig. 6. Mode vibration shapes of the oval gear

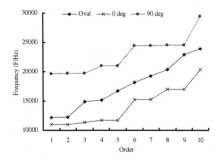

Fig. 7. Relation of frequencies between the oval gear and equivalent gear

DESIGN AND FINITE ELEMENT MODE ANALYSIS OF NONCIRCULAR GEAR

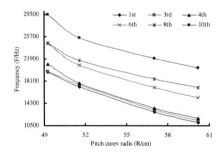

Fig. 8.   Relation between frequencies and radius

6.0   Conclusion

- In this paper, the design method of the noncircular gear is studied by using gear transmission technique, the mathematics software MathCAD, the 3D solid modeling software and the finite element software are combined to realize precise model of the oval gear, and a solid foundation is laid for analysis of the oval gear.
- The gear system dynamics principle is introduced to establish dynamics model for the noncircular gear.
- The basic theory of finite element and mode analysis method are applied, the finite element model for the noncircular gear is established, and natural vibration characteristic of the noncircular gear is studied.
- The finite element method is used, the natural vibration characteristic of the oval gear is studied, the main vibration shapes and natural frequencies of the oval gear and that of the equivalent cylindrical gears are analyzed and compared, the conclusions received reflect the dynamics performance of the oval gear, and solid foundation is laid for dynamics research and engineering application of the oval gear.

Acknowledgement

The authors wish to acknowledge the assistance and support of the National Science and Technology Planning Key Project of China (No. 2006BAF01B07-01).

References

[1] Wu Xutang, "Noncircular Gear and Variable Ratio Transmission" , Beijing: Machinery Industry Press, China, pp. 52~53, 1997.
[2] Li Fusheng, "Design of Noncircular Gear and Special Gear" , Beijing: Machinery Industry Press, China, pp. 57~59, 1983.
[3] Zhuang Qu, "Accidence Guide for ABAQUS Finite Element Software" , Beijing: Tsinghua University Press, China, pp. 49~80, 1999.
[4] Li Runfang, "Dynamics of Gear System" , Beijing: Science Press, China, pp. 69~96, 1996.

E – Manufacturing

The 6th International Conference on Manufacturing Research (ICMR08)
Brunel University, UK, 9-11th September 2008

RFID-ENABLED INFORMATION INFRASTRUCTURE FOR REAL-TIME DIGITAL MANUFACTURING

Yingfeng Zhang [1, 2], George Q. Huang [1], Xin Chen [3], Pingyu Jiang [2], Frank J. Xu [4]

1. **Department of Industrial and Manufacturing Systems Engineering, The University of Hong Kong**

2. **The State Key Laboratory for Manufacturing Systems Engineering, Xi'an Jiaotong University, China**

3. **Faculty of Mechanical Engineering, Guangdong University of Technology, China**

4. **E-Business Institute, The University of Hong Kong**

Abstract

This paper has presented an easy-to-deploy and simple-to-use gateway framework with which advanced applications can be developed to achieve real-time and reconfigurable manufacturing. Three key enabling technologies including shopfloor gateway, work-cell gateway and RFID-enabled smart objects are integrated into the framework to implement real-time manufacturing data collection, visibility and traceability. The methodologies and technologies proposed in this paper will enable manufacturing enterprises to improve shop-floor productivity and quality, reduce the wastes of manufacturing resources, cut the costs in manufacturing logistics, reduce the risk and improve the efficiency in cross-border customs logistics and online supervision.

Keywords: RFID / Auto ID, Reconfigurable Manufacturing, Agent, Real-Time Manufacturing.

1.0 Introduction

With the increasing competitiveness and globalization of today's business environment, enterprises have to face a new economic objective: manufacturing responsiveness, i.e. the ability of a production system to respond to disturbances which impact upon production goals, and consequently, its ability to adapt to changing production conditions of shop floor level. Even if the manufacturing companies have implemented sophisticated ERP (Enterprise Resource Planning) systems, they are also suffering from the following typical problems:

- Customer orders, process plans, production orders and production scheduling are conducted in separate systems which are not integrated.

- Shop-floor disturbances such as machine breakdowns and maintenance are not fed back and considered when plan the production order, resulting in unbalanced lines.

- The loading level of work orders at specific machine is unknown to the scheduler and production planner, leading to further line unbalances.

- WIP (Work-in-progress) inventory levels are extremely high and varieties are large.

- Weak ability to track the production order due to the tough production environment, e.g., vibration, humidity, and lack of line of sight.

Therefore, it is essential to adapt advanced manufacturing technologies and approaches (both software and hardware) to cope with the highly dynamic manufacturing requirements. In the recent decades, rapid developments in wireless sensors, communication and information network technologies (e.g. radio frequency identification - RFID or Auto-ID, Bluetooth, Wi-Fi, GSM, and infrared) have nurtured the emergence of Wireless Manufacturing (WM), Real-time manufacturing system (RTM) as core Advanced Manufacturing Technology (AMT) in next-generation manufacturing systems (NGMS).

Real-time visibility and interoperability have been considered core characteristics of next-generation manufacturing systems as in [1]. Pilot projects have recently been implemented and reported (see various whitepapers and reports at http://www.autoidlabs.com/ research archive/ for more descriptions). The progress of Wireless Technologies such as RFID and AutoID applications in the "manufacturing scenario" has been noticeable although limited. As early as in early 1990s, Reference [2] has discussed the roles of Auto ID as a real-time data capture tool in a computer integrated manufacturing (CIM) environment. Early RFID manufacturing applications have been briefly quoted as in [3] and further promoted as in [4]. Reference [5] provides a general overview on how Auto ID technology can be applied in manufacturing. Several relevant whitepapers have been prepared to provide roadmap for developing and adopting Auto ID-based manufacturing technologies as in [6] and [7]. More recently, the Cambridge Auto ID Lab has launched an RFID in Manufacturing Special Interest Group (SIG) (http://www.aero-id.org/).

The concept of agent has been widely accepted and developed in manufacturing applications because of its flexibility, reconfigurability, and scalability as in [8] and [9]. An agent based concurrent design environment as in [10] has been proposed to integrate design, manufacturing and shop-floor control activities. Some mobile agent-based systems as in [11] have been applied to the real-time monitoring and information exchange for manufacturing control. Reference [12] proposed an architecture where many facilitator agents coordinate the activities of manufacturing resources in a parallel manner. Reference [13] applied the MAS (Multi-Agent System) paradigm for collaborative negotiation in a global manufacturing supply chain network. Besides, in various kinds of applications such as distributed resource allocation as in [14], online task coordination and monitoring as in [15], or supply chain negotiation as in [16], the agent-based approach has played an important role to achieve outstanding performance with agility.

RFID-ENABLED INFORMATION INFRASTRUCTURE FOR REAL-TIME DIGITAL MANUFACTURING

It becomes particularly challenging to integrate the advantage of RFID, wireless technologies and agent based methods. On one hand, RFID, wirelessly networked sensors facilitate the automatic collection and processing of real-time field data in the manufacturing processes, and reduce and avoid the error-prone, tedious manual activities. On the other hand, agent-based system enables relevant activities more flexible, intelligent and collaborative especially in distributed networked environment for building RTM systems.

2.0   Infrastructure of Real-time Digital Manufacturing

To apply RFID technologies to develop an easy-to-deploy and simple-to-use shop-floor information infrastructure for manufacturing companies to achieve real-time and seamless dual-way connectivity and interoperability between application systems at enterprise, shop-floor, work-cell and device levels. The role of the proposed technology is shown in Fig.1. The proposed infrastructure is consistent with the manufacturing hierarchy. That is, a manufacturing factory hosts one or more shop-floor production lines. Each production line consists of work-cells and each work-cell is involved of a variety of manufacturing objects such as operators, machines, materials etc. and different production lines are often designed to enable different production processes.

According to the manufacturing hierarchical structure, the proposed RTM infrastructure includes the following core components: (1) Shop floor Gateway, (2) Work-cell gateways and (3) RFID-enabled smart objects, which will be discussed in the following section.

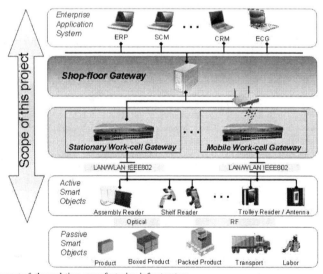

Fig. 1.   Deployment of the real-time manufacturing infrastructure

3.0   Key Enabling Technology

In order to make the RTM infrastructure runs well, sufficient enabling techniques are needed. Here, we only discuss three main key enabling techniques, i.e. shopfloor gateway, work-cell gateway and RFID-enabled smart objects.

3.1   Shopfloor Gateway

The shopfloor gateway (SF-Gateway) is at the centre of the overall Real-Time Manufacturing Gateway (RTM-Gateway). Following the Service-Oriented Architecture (SOA), Enterprise Application Systems (EASs), Shopfloor Application Systems (SASs), equipments and smart object services (SOSs) in a manufacturing company can all be considered as manufacturing services. Fig.2 shows the overview framework of the SF-Gateway. SF-Gateway is composed of five major components, namely (1) Manufacturing Service Definition Tool, (2) Manufacturing Process Configuration Tool, (3) Manufacturing Process Execution Engine, (4) Manufacturing Service Data Adaptors and (5) Registry and Repository. Detailed functions of these components are described in the following:

- Manufacturing Service Definition Tool: All the manufacturing services are defined through two main steps, namely installation and registration. The EASs and SASs are deployed and installed on their own servers and the general information is registered at the SF-Gateway. The low-level SOSs are directly plugged in SF-Gateway and the drivers are installed and registered.

- Manufacturing Process Configuration Tool: The deployed manufacturing services are configured to the workflow of a specific manufacturing process. Both the work-cells workflow (WC-workflow) in the shop-floor and the smart-objects workflow (SO-workflow) in the individual work-cell are configured simultaneously. This tool also performs a series of functions such as filtering, aggregation, and counting of tag data to reduce the volume of data prior to sending to the repository.

- Manufacturing Process Execution Engine: Nodes in a workflow are translated to smart objects and work-cells of the real manufacturing environment to enable their intelligent management of the manufacturing process. Smart objects, work-cells have different degree of intelligence for data filtering, and thus to ensure an appropriate execution process. Explorers are provided to operators, managers and supervisors for monitoring and controlling the workflow execution lifecycle, e.g. start, stop, suspend, resume, abort, etc.

- Manufacturing Service Data Adaptors: Enable the communication between EASs and legacy SASs. Real-time production data from shop-floor level is converted to standard data format (e.g. ISA95) and transmitted to EASs, so that the enterprise resource and supply chain information required in the production definition and scheduling process could be retrieved.

- Registry and Repository: Registry stores all the offline data for definition and configuration stages, e.g. the service description information and XML (eXtensible Markup Language) Process Definition Language (XPDL) file. Repository stores the online data for real-time execution of manufacturing process and thus provides visibility and traceability.

RFID-ENABLED INFORMATION INFRASTRUCTURE FOR REAL-TIME DIGITAL MANUFACTURING

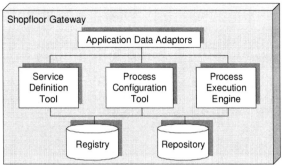

Fig. 2.   The Architecture of the shopfloor gateway

3.2   Work-cell Gateway

A Work-cell Gateway (WC-Gateway) has a hardware hub and a suite of software systems which acts as a server that hosts connects all RFID-enabled smart objects of the corresponding work-cell and provides work-cell Applications for operators to conduct, monitor and control their operations. A WC-Gateway is a physical hub that hosts and connects all smart objects of the corresponding work-cell via wired or wireless connection. Basically, there is a smart object manager (SOM) which is responsible for coordinating all smart objects in their life cycle, including definition, installation, and configuration. Apart from smart objects, the gateway also hosts the work-cell applications which are built-in services providing integrated real-time information of work cells (i.e. work-in-process (WIP), the status of workstation etc.) such that essential functions could be performed in the shop floor, such as WIP tracking, throughput tracking, capacity feedback, and status monitoring. Moreover, the gateway could be wired or wirelessly connected to the enterprise network and hence there are two types of work-cell gateway which are stationary WC-gateway and mobile WC-gateway existing and allowing to be configured in terms of the manufacturing environment. Also, there are variety channel provided for auto ID devices connect to WC-gateway computer. In general, provided means of wireless connection are Bluetooth, ZigBee, Wi-Fi etc. on the other hands, the means of wired connection are including USB, and serial ports etc. The overall architecture of WC-gateway has been shown in the Fig.3. The key components of WC-Gateway and Smart Object are described as follows:

- Smart Object: A smart object is a manufacturing object that is made "smart" by equipping them with certain degree of intelligence: memory, computing power, communicating ability, and task-specific logics. Therefore, smart objects are able to sense, reason, and interact. The Auto-ID approaches such as RFID and barcode will be deployed to create an intelligent ambience where smart object interact with each other.

- Agent-Based Smart Object Manager: A smart object manager (SOM) is to manage smart objects and facilitates their operation. Also, it manages all real-time events and related information from smart objects. The most important features of smart object manager is to allow smart objects to be "Universal Plug and Plays" (UPnP) and communicate with other objects. Since a number of smart agents work together, the WC-gateway becomes a multi-agent system (MAS) which is compliable with the standard of the Foundation for Intelligent, Physical Agents (FIPA), and hence smart agents in the gateway must be FIPA compliant. Therefore, SOM can directly manage the smart agent of smart objects without concern the problem of communication protocols or devices incompatible with the gateway during the lifecycle of smart objects.

- Real-Time Work-cell Applications: Operators at the work cell use the real-time application to accomplish, monitor and control their work tasks. It is considered as middle lower level manufacturing applications and designed and developed according to specific logic requirements form manufacturing processes. In the WC-gateway, a number of built-in functions designed and developed locally. There are included WIP tracking, throughput tracking, status of WC-gateway monitoring, and devices configuring etc.

- Work-Cell Agent DF: Work Cell Agent directory facilitator (WC-Agent DF) is a component under FIPA specification for agent management. It provides yellow pages for finding services provided by other internal agents in the WC-gateway. Typically, smart agents can register, deregister, modify and search services in WC-Agent DF and its actions would automatically update into UDDI (Universal Description, Discovery, and Integration , UDDI) by SOM. For instance, smart agent register a service for retrieving data from a RFID reader in agent DF, then such request will be given to the SOM and make it as tModel then register in UDDI repository. Therefore, other agents or applications would use this service for obtaining data of the particular RFID device by means of web services technology.

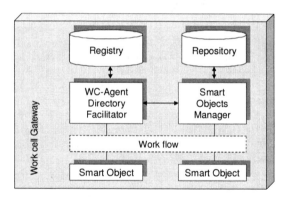

Fig. 3. The Architecture of the WC-gateway

3.3   RFID-enabled Smart Objects

There are four categories of physical resources or objects involved in manufacturing. They are so-called 4-M or 4-P: man (personnel), materials (products), machines (plant and equipment), and methods (processes). Each can be further divided hierarchically. All four types of physical objects are described in terms of their lifecycles, capabilities and capacities, schedules and performance metrics. They are the inputs and/or outputs of manufacturing enterprise application systems.

Typical objects at manufacturing shop-floors include Tools (e.g. jigs and fixtures, cutting tools), Mobile and Stationary Assets (e.g. machines, conveyors), Spaces and Locations, Work Centres, Human Resources (e.g.

operators), Materials (e.g. finished products, Work-In-Progress – WIP materials, raw materials including bought out components), passages and routes, doors and gates, and documents & reports (e.g. customer / sales orders, purchase orders, design specifications & drawings, process plans, production schedules, work / operation instructions, project reports, etc.).

In order to achieve shop-floor real-time visibility and interoperability, manufacturing objects can be equipped with various wireless devices and intelligent logics. Resulting objects become what are called smart or intelligent objects. Smart objects are able to achieve one or more functions: sense (detect), identify, interact, decide and act. Therefore, they are equipped with some or all of typical components. For example, sensing and identification can be achieved through one or more devices such as bar codes, smart cards, and RFID tags. I/O and feedback facilities such as display and keypads (e.g. User interface) are often required for them to interact with human operators. Interactions and communications with other devices are achieved through wired and/or wireless antennas in pair with access points or receivers equipped at other devices and smart objects. Smart objects accomplish their actions through PLC (Programmable Logic Controller). Integrated circuits and working memories are often necessary to support "Decide" and "Act" functions. More sophisticated intelligence is provided by the agents of the corresponding smart objects through further interactions with the WIPN and EAN.

Smart objects communication is based on agent technology since each object is represented by a smart agent in the gateway. The format of agent messages is standardized according to agent communication language (ACL). This format should be included the type of action (i.e. inform or propose), the ID of sender, the ID of receivers, the content and its used language etc. Each smart agent has a mail box to receive all messages sent from other smart agents. When one message is posted in a mail box the receiving smart agent would receive a notice, and it can select those related messages and process them based on business logic or rules.

Intelligent logic of smart object is based on the work flow of a work cell. It instructs the smart object what information should be submitted to the gateway. Typically, the simple logic of smart object is to filter those unwanted tag ID. For example, the location identification reader is to read the information of a location tag but sometime it may read other tags together such as pallet and carton tags. Therefore, the smart agent can filter out those tags which do not match the requirements from the logic and then submits to the gateway.

4.0   Case Study

According to the architectures and methodologies proposed above, a RFID-Enabled information infrastructure for real-time manufacturing system is developed. Fig.4 outlines an overview of the explorers of the WC-Gateway and SF-Gateway. At the WC-Gateway, the facilities are mainly responsible for both executing and controlling the operations taking place at their corresponding work cell or workstations as seen in the bottom of Fig.4. In contrast, the shop-floor manager or line supervisor is responsible for monitoring and controlling the assembly operations at the SF-Gateway. The facilities of SF-Gateway are to organize the real-time information captured from the WC-Gateway to serve different purposes. E.g. the explorer provides facilities for the manager/supervisor to monitor production status of a selected shift, inventories of WIP materials, conditions of critical tools and equipment process reliability and quality records etc. of the overall shop floor as seen in the top of Fig.4.

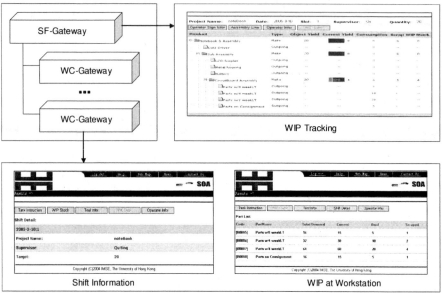

Fig. 4.   Sample screens of the WC-Gateway and SF-Gateway

5.0   Conclusion

This paper has presented an easy-to-deploy and simple-to-use gateway framework with which advanced applications can be developed to achieve real-time manufacturing. The gateway uses RFID technologies for real-time manufacturing data collection, and enables the dual-way connectivity and interoperability between high-level EASs and SASs, and creates real-time visibility and traceability throughout the entire enterprise. The vertical and lateral connectivity, transparency and traceability between applications deployed at different levels of enterprise decisions would lead to substantial benefits such as faster response time to market, better-balanced production plans / schedules, stabilized labour and material flows, reduced inventories, optimized space/resource/operator utilization, low scrap and rework, improved productivity, and records for continuous process improvement.

Based on insights gained through initial studies and proof-of-the-concept developments, the gateway framework is under further development along two key dimensions. Firstly, the shop-floor gateway (SF-Gateway) will be fully extended to manage the lifecycle (definition, configuration and execution) of manufacturing services of all levels (EASs, SASs, WASs, and SOSs). The SF-Gateway provides central intelligence services for WASs and SOSs. Secondly, a WC-Gateway provides tools for managing manufacturing operations taking place with devices and operators at an individual work-cell. Objects within a work-cell such as machines, materials (and/or their containers), operators, and tools are converted into so-called smart objects by combining different wireless devices such as RFID and barcodes, computing power and memory, and operational logics. Smart objects within a work-cell form an intelligent ambience where they interoperate with each other in an UPnP (Universal Plug and Play) fashion. Such interoperations are traced and tracked, thus realizing the collection and processing real-time shop-floor data.

Acknowledgement

We are most grateful to various companies who provide technical and financial supports to this research. Financial supports from the HKU Teaching Development Grants (TGD), Seed Fund for Applied Research, and HKSAR ITF grant are also gratefully acknowledged.

References

[1]   Huang, G.Q., Zhang, Y.F., Jiang.: "RFID-based wireless manufacturing for real-time management of job shop WIP inventories", International Journal of Advanced Manufacturing Technology. In press.

[2]   Udoka S. J., : "The role of automatic identification (Auto ID) in the computer integrated manufacturing (CIM) architecture," Computers and Industrial Engineering, 23 (1-4), pp. 1-51, 992.

[3]   Brewer, A., Sloan, N., and Landers, T.: "Intelligent tracking in manufacturing", Journal of Intelligent Manufacturing, 10 (3-4), pp. 245-250, 1999.

[4]   Li, Z.K., Gadh, R., Prabhu, B.S., : "Applications Of RFID Technology And Smart Parts In Manufacturing", Proceedings of DETC'04: ASME 2004 Design Engineering Technical Conferences and Computers and Information in Engineering Conference September 28-October 2, Salt Lake City, Utah USA DETC2004-57662, 2004.

[5]   Chappell, G., Ginsburg, L., Schmidt, P., Smith, J., and Tobolski, J. : "Auto ID on the Line: The Value of Auto ID Technology in Manufacturing", Auto ID Center, CAN-AutoID-BC-005, 2003.

[6]   Harrison, M., McFarlane, D.: Whitepaper on "Development of a Prototype PML Server for an Auto ID Enabled Robotic Manufacturing Environment", http://www.ifm.eng.cam.ac.uk/automation/publications/w_papers/cam-autoid-wh010.pdf, 2003.

[7]   Chang, Y., McFarlane, D., Koh, R.: Whitepaper on "Methodologies for integrating Auto ID data with existing manufacturing business information systems", http://www.ifm.eng.cam.ac.uk/automation/publications/w_papers/cam-autoid-wh009.pdf, 2003.

[8]   Sikora, R. and Shaw, M.J.: "A multi-agent framework for the coordination and integration of information systems", Management Science, 44 (11), pp.65–78, 1998.

[9]   Macchiaroli R. and Riemma S.,: "A negotiation scheme for autonomous agents in job shop scheduling", International Journal of Computer Integrated Manufacturing, 15 (3), pp.222–232, 2002.

[10] Tan, G.W., Hayes, C.C. and Shaw, M. : "An intelligent-agent framework for concurrent product design and planning", IEEE Transactions on Engineering Manufacturing Management, 43 (3), pp.297–306, 1996.

[11] Shin, M. and Jung, M. : "MANPro: mobile agent-based negotiation process for distributed intelligent manufacturing", Int. J. of Production Research, 42 (2), pp.303–320, 2004.

[12] Jia, H.Z., Ong, S.K., Fuh, J.Y.H., Zhang, Y.F. and Nee, A.Y.C.: "An adaptive upgradable agent-based system for collaborative product design and manufacture", Robotics and Computer-Integrated Manufacturing, 20 (2), pp.79–90, 2004.

[13] Jiao, J.R., You, X. and Kumar, A.: "An agent-based framework for collaborative negotiation in the global manufacturing supply chain network", Robotics and Computer Integrated Manufacturing, 22 (3), pp.239–255, 2006.

[14] Bastos R.M., Oliveira F.M. and Oliveira J.P.: "Autonomic computing approach for resource allocation", Expert Systems with Applications, 28 (1), pp. 9–19, 2005.

[15] Lee W.B. and Lau H.C.W., : "Multi-agent modelling of dispersed manufacturing networks", Expert Systems with Applications, 16 (3), pp. 297–306, 1999.

[16] Wu D.J,: "Software agents for knowledge management: Coordination in multi-agent supply chains and auctions", Expert Systems with Applications, 20 (1), pp. 51–64, 2001.

RFID-ENABLED INFORMATION INFRASTRUCTURE FOR REAL-TIME DIGITAL MANUFACTURING

The 6th International Conference on Manufacturing Research (ICMR08)
Brunel University, UK, 9-11th September 2008

A SOFTWARE CONCEPT FOR PLANNING IN NON-HIERARCHICAL PRODUCTION NETWORKS

Sebastian Horbach, Egon Müller

Department of Factory Planning and Factory Management, Chemnitz University of Technology

Abstract

Autonomous, elementary units of production, co-operating in temporary networks, are viewed as a key organisational form of enterprise in the 21st century. A scientific approach is provided by non-hierarchical networks based on customer-oriented, directly linked, smallest autonomous service units called Competence Cells. Simultaneously, this concept, which is researched at Chemnitz University of Technology, points out perspectives for present-day small and medium-sized enterprises (SME) to face ever-changing economic conditions.

A modular planning concept for networks – PlaNet – is developed in order to support the Competence Cells in meeting the special requirements on the planning of logistics structures and production plants in competence cell-based networks. With PlaNet, the Competence Cells are enabled to process different planning cases. For this purpose, they are provided with pre-configured procedures. These procedures consist of sequences of planning functions which are completed through proper planning methods supported by adequate software solutions.

One of the components of PlaNet and at the same time the toolset providing software support for the other components is the Net Planning Assistant (NPA). This includes especially the implementation of the planning methods for the completion of the planning procedures. Like PlaNet, the NPA has a modular structure in response to the special requirements on the software environment in competence cell-based networks. In the centre of NPA the Production Database (PDB) is situated. The PDB is developed on the basis of the production data model. A number of commercial and self-developed software tools are connected through the PDB in order to solve the existing planning problems. Their interaction is organised through a uniform interface concept.

In this paper, first, the competence cell-based networking approach is briefly introduced. This is followed by a short overview of PlaNet and its components. In the

main part the requirements on a software concept for networks are defined. Different approaches for a possible software concept are discussed. The NPA is introduced as a suitable concept and its architecture is outlined. Thereafter, the components of NPA are looked at in detail. First, the PDB including the web interface for its maintenance is described. Secondly, the uniform interface concept is explained. Thirdly, a number of adequate software solutions and techniques are presented in short.

Finally, some aspects of the deployment of the NPA in competence cell-based networks are discussed.

Keywords: Competence cell-based Networks, Planning Concept for Networks, Net Planning Assistant, Production Database, Uniform Interface Concept.

1.0   Introduction

Autonomous, elementary units of production, co-operating in temporary networks, are viewed as a key organisational form of enterprise in the 21st century. A scientific approach is provided by non-hierarchical networks based on customer-oriented, directly linked, smallest autonomous service units called Competence Cells. Simultaneously, this concept, which is researched at Chemnitz University of Technology, points out perspectives for present-day small and medium-sized enterprises (SME) to face ever-changing economic conditions. [1]

The vision of the competence cell-based networking approach (Fig. 1) is the following:

Elementary business units – called Competence Cells – are co-operating in Non-hierarchical Regional Production Networks in a customer-oriented manner and thus are capable of facing global competition.

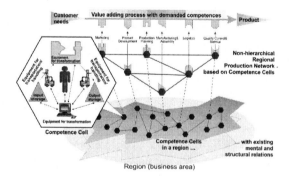

Fig. 1.   Vision of the competence cell-based networking approach

From the vision special requirements on the planning of logistics structures and production plants arise. The planning has to be supported by an appropriate software environment. This software environment also has to

A SOFTWARE CONCEPT FOR PLANNING IN NON-HIERARCHICAL PRODUCTION NETWORKS

satisfy special conditions caused by the approach. Therefore a suitable software concept will be introduced in this paper.

This short introduction is followed by a overview of PlaNet. In the main part the requirements on a software concept for networks are defined. Different approaches for a possible software concept are discussed. The NPA is introduced as a suitable concept and its architecture is outlined. Thereafter, the components of NPA are looked at in detail. First, the PDB including the web interface for its maintenance is described. Secondly, the uniform interface concept is explained. Thirdly, a number of adequate software techniques are presented in short. Finally, some aspects of the deployment of the NPA in competence cell-based networks are discussed.

2.0   Planning Concept for Networks - PlaNet

The competence-cell-based networking approach puts special requirements on the planning of logistics structures and production plants. Among them is the extended domain of planned objects in connection with an extended domain of planning methods, the greater responsibility of the autonomous units which on the other hand might lack planning competence and the participative way in which planning needs to be done due to the lack of hierarchies. Those requirements are only partly met by existing planning approaches.

Therefore a suitable framework for the planning of logistics structures and production plants in competence-cell-based networks needed to be produced. Such a framework has been developed with the Planning Concept for Networks „PlaNet" [2]. The Systems Engineering approach was identified as a suitable basis for PlaNet [3].

The components of PlaNet were derived from the components of the Systems Engineering approach. A structuring framework for the components of PlaNet is shown in Fig. 2.

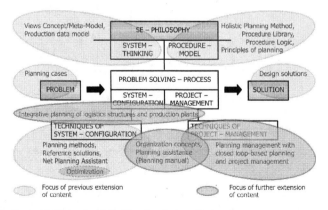

Fig. 2.   Planning Concept for Networks (PlaNet) based on Systems Engineering

A SOFTWARE CONCEPT FOR PLANNING IN NON-HIERARCHICAL PRODUCTION NETWORKS

With PlaNet, the Competence Cells are enabled to process different planning cases. For this purpose, they are provided with pre-configured procedures. These procedures consist of sequences of planning functions which are completed through proper planning methods supported by adequate software solutions.

3.0   Net Planning Assistant

The planning of logistics structures and production plants can not be effectively done without the supporting software. There are special requirements on a suitable software environment for the planning in competence cell-based networks. Such requirements are a holistic treatment, easy usability, interconnection of the Competence Cells, support of participative planning, extensibility and low costs.

One of the components of PlaNet and at the same time the toolset providing software support for the other components is the Net Planning Assistant (NPA) [4]. The NPA includes especially the implementation of the planning methods for the completion of the planning procedures. Like PlaNet, the NPA has a modular structure in response to the special requirements on the software environment in competence cell-based networks.

The concept of the NPA is illustrated in Fig. 3. In the centre of the NPA is the production database (PDB). Through a uniform interface concept the PDB associates commercial and self-developed software for the corporate realisation of complex planning processes.

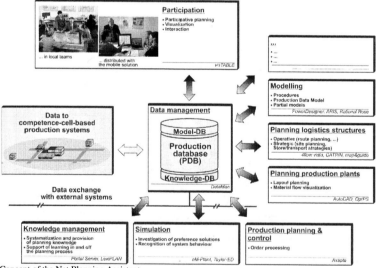

Fig. 3.   Concept of the Net Planning Assistant

In the sections of this chapter the components of NPA, i.e. the production database, the interface concept and the connected software tools, are introduced.

A SOFTWARE CONCEPT FOR PLANNING IN NON-HIERARCHICAL PRODUCTION NETWORKS

3.1   Production Database

The Production Database (PDB) is the central data storage place of NPA. The PDB is developed on the basis of the production data model. The elicitation and the processing of the data are mainly done by the associated software. PDB provides the input information to the planning tools and stores their output information. This output can again be used as input for planning tools which realise succeeding processes. PDB bases on a conceptual data model from which different types of relational databases can be created, as well as an XML-scheme.

In some cases a direct access on the production data is necessary. To make this comfortable a prototypical web-based user interface is under creation (Fig. 4 shows a screenshot). It enables the Competence Cells to access the PDB with their internet browser, thus avoiding the installation of special software.

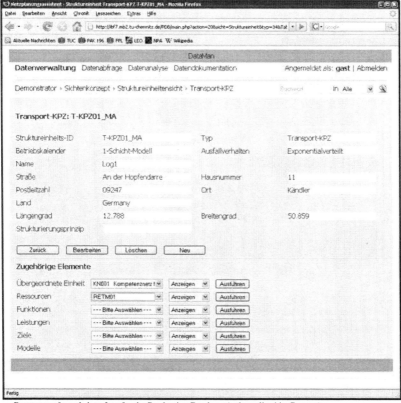

Fig. 4.   Prototype of a web-interface for the Production Database (only realised in German)

3.2   Uniform Interface Concept

**A SOFTWARE CONCEPT FOR PLANNING IN NON-HIERARCHICAL PRODUCTION
NETWORKS**

Their interaction is organised through a uniform interface concept. Thereby the exchange of data can take place in three different ways (Fig. 5)

1. Direct access to the PDB without transformation. The data access is realised by ActiveX Data Objects (ADO) or if this is not possible by Open Database Connectivity (ODBC).
2. Transformation through intermediate files or tables. An emerging standard for this is the eXtensible Markup Language (XML). Many applications use Microsoft Excel files (.xls) for the exchange of data. A similar approach is to use intermediate tables for transferring data between two databases.
3. Transformation without intermediate files or tables. This usually is realised through access of the database which is used by the application, provided the data structure is disclosed.

The way which has to be chosen depends on the associated software. Methods 2 and 3 require the use of adapters which realise the transformation. The generation of the adapters should be supported by proper software, which helps to automate the process. A solution for the creation of interfaces is under development. The generation of interfaces requires expert knowledge of the data structure.

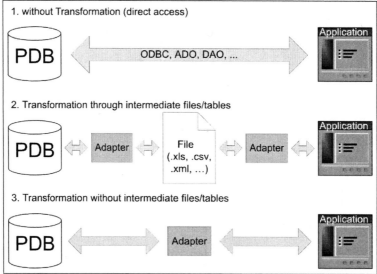

Fig. 5.   Uniform Interface Concept

3.3   Connected Software Tools

A number of commercial and proprietary software tools are connected through the PDB in order to solve the existing planning problems. Typical assignments of connected software together with examples of particular solutions are shown in Fig. 3. They realise the different functions of the planning process. Some of the software solutions realise components of PlaNet. The empty box in Fig. 3 suggests that NPA can be extended to yet unconsidered or unknown fields of application.

The incorporation of a software solution into the NPA usually requires the generation of two interfaces.

There are different types of applications which are especially qualified for the NPA. In the past (windows) applications, which have to be installed on every client, were used. Alternatively scripting environments, which are offered by a wide number of applications (the most popular being Visual Basic for Applications) can be deployed to integrate functions in commonly used software solutions.

Preferable are internet-based applications which support the interlinked planning and can be run through a web browser, ideally on all kinds of systems. Applications which don't demand any installation on the client's computer are programmed in languages like PHP or Python. The same is true, when Microsoft's Active Server Pages (ASP) can be used on the webserver.

While these techniques are good for rather simple solutions, applications which use a lot of graphics should be better run on the client computer. First choice for the development of such applications is Java which needs the Java Virtual Machine on the client but is independent from the operating system.

A promising emerging technology is the use of web services. That means that interfaces to functions are provided. Functions, which are implemented by a web service, can be easily called by most programming environments.

4.0   Deployment of the Net Planning Assistant

The configuration of the NPA for a particular Competence Cell should be adapted to the special needs of this Competence Cell. Especially the low budgets need to be taken into consideration. The processes, which have to be realised through the Competence Cell, determine which software is needed.

A distinction should be made especially between production or logistics Competence Cells with little planning competence and planning Competence Cells. The former might be given access only to some essential components of the Net Planning Assistant. The planning Competence Cells on the other hand could purchase a more costly specialised planning software and offer planning services with it not only to the Competence Cells in the Network but also to clients outside the competence-cell-based network as a service of this network. Additionally there might be Competence Cells with competences in Information and Communications Technology which host applications used by a number of Competence Cells at a hiring fee.

All Competence Cells need to have access to the PDB in which also their relevant data is stored. The Planning Manual provides the Competence Cells with the knowledge available in the network, especially the business processes connected to planning which have to be followed by all Competence Cells. Complementary to this also access to the Procedure and Method Libraries should be provided. For the controlling of orders it is desirable that all Competence Cell employ a kind of ERP system which also covers the PPC functions.

**A SOFTWARE CONCEPT FOR PLANNING IN NON-HIERARCHICAL PRODUCTION
NETWORKS**

Other components should be only employed by special planning Competence Cells since they demand special knowledge from the user and should be subject to a high degree of utilisation due to high purchasing costs. It might not be reasonable that some Competence Cells have all special tools at their disposal. They should rather specialise on some components gaining a high competence in employing them. Tools which qualify for this are visTABLE, simulation applications, or special tools for the planning of logistics structures or production plants. visTABLE was developed for the interaction and visualisation, especially of the plant layout, in order to the support participative planning process.

5.0   Conclusion and Outlook

The software support for the planning of logistics structures and production plants in competence cell-based networks is provided by the Net Planning Assistant. The modular concept of the NPA enables Competence Cell to acquire exactly the functions they need. Thus the concept of the NPA suits the requirements on a software environment for competence cell-based networks particularly well, meeting the restricted budgets of the competence cells.

The Production database has been used to store the data of industrial demonstrators in different research projects thus proving its suitability. The concept of the NPA was partly applied to industrial cases.

In the future the overall concept needs to be evaluated in industrial settings. Typical configurations need to be identified. The pool of connected software solution will be enhanced. Especially some components of PlaNet are planned to be implemented.

Acknowledgement

The work which is presented in this paper has been supported by the German Research Foundation (Deutsche Forschungsgemeinschaft – DFG).

References

[1]   E. Müller, S. Horbach, J. Ackermann, J. Schütze and H. Baum: "Production system planning in Competence-cell-based Networks", In: J. E. Middle (ed.): International Journal of Production Research, Special Issue: Selected papers from the 18th ICPR – "The networked enterprise: a challenge for a sustainable development", Vol. 44, Nos. 18-19, 15 September-1 October 2006, Taylor & Francis, pp. 3989-4009, 2006.
[2]   E. Müller, S. Horbach and J. Ackermann: "PlaNet – a Framework for Planning of Logistics Structures and Production Plants in Competence-cell-based Networks", Proceedings of the 15th International Conference on Flexible Automation and Intelligent Manufacturing – FAIM, pp. 786-793, Bilbao, Spain, 2005.
[3]   W. F. Daenzer and F. Huber (eds): Systems Engineering – Methodology and Practice, Systems Engineering – Methodik und Praxis, Industrielle Organisation, 2002.
[4]   S. Horbach and E. Müller: "The Net Planning Assistant – a Toolset to support Planning in Competence-cell-based Networks", Proceedings of the 16th International Conference on Flexible Automation and Intelligent Manufacturing – FAIM, pp. 949-956, Limerick, Ireland, 2006.

A SOFTWARE CONCEPT FOR PLANNING IN NON-HIERARCHICAL PRODUCTION
NETWORKS

The 6th International Conference on Manufacturing Research (ICMR08)
Brunel University, UK, 9-11th September 2008

AUTOMATIC IDENTIFICATION OF SEMANTIC RELATIONSHIPS FOR MANUFACTURING INFORMATION MANAGEMENT

Wei Yu, Ying Liu

Dept. of Industrial and Systems Engineering, The Hong Kong Polytechnic University

Abstract

Identifying the semantic relationships between different concepts in a domain knowledgebase is critical in information processing and knowledge management. Such information is often considered essential with respect to various tasks in manufacturing information and knowledge management, e.g. business intelligence, conceptual design, market segmentation, product recommendation, better customer understanding and so on. Previous studies of discovering semantic relationships, however, are mainly based on the manual information extraction or some predefined schemas which are tedious and inefficient. In this paper, we propose a new extraction method based on a novel document profile model and text clustering to automatically discover the semantic relationships between two different concepts from a domain knowledgebase. Through our method, the semantic relationships are mined at different granularities and the related documents containing such connections between two specific domain concepts are visualized in a ranked order through a user-friendly prototype. We exploited our method on a manufacturing enterprise corpus called manufacturing corpus version 1 (MCV1). The experimental results show that our method has provided an efficient and effective approach for the automatic discovery of semantic relationships in a domain knowledgebase.

Keywords: semantic relationship, ontology, manufacturing information management.

1.0   Introduction

Due to the vast development of IT & its application in manufacturing, e.g. product data management (PDM), enterprise resource planning systems (ERP) and customer relationship management (CRM), there is a dramatic increase of electronic manufacturing texts, including design documents, research papers, marketing analysis reports, etc. Documentation, as a linguistic form, provides the explicit representation of manufacturing ideas and concepts accumulated during the design and production process. Therefore, it describes manufacturing domain knowledge and is very important indeed to industry and research communities. How to make an efficient and effective indexing, retrieval, learning and reuse of these

1

manufacturing documents has created new challenges and opportunities for research. This is in contrast to manual document indexing using metadata of documents which has been accomplished by most existing manufacturing management systems and general document management tools [1]. One of the critical issues is to create a structured representation in indexing manufacturing documents which is able to record engineers' ideas and reasoning processes for a specific design. This representation should capture the important manufacturing concepts as well as their relationships explicitly and accurately so that engineers and researchers can quickly locate their documents of interest with less effort. It was found that engineers spent 20-30% of their time retrieving and discussing manufacturing information [2]. Therefore, it is important to minimize such overhead loadings using effective manufacturing information management (MIM).

MIM acts as "memory extension" for manufacturing engineers and enables information sharing among them [3]. Meanwhile, it's very useful to retrieve manufacturing knowledge concepts and identify their relationships in application contexts which help to better understand their implications. MIM can provide engineers and researchers with the capability of suggesting many candidate solutions to their problems. Although the benefits are obvious, an empirical study conducted by Marsh (1997) showed that engineers were reluctant to access documents to which they did not directly contribute or were not familiar [4]. Previous studies suggest that the performance of information management can be improved by using structured and semantics-based representations of documents [5]. To this concern, manufacturing ontology represents the semantic relations systematically among manufacturing decompositions [6-9]. The representation of domain concepts and their semantic relationships have made significant progress in establishing complex models as well as standardizing terminologies in describing the details of manufacturing process. Since the explicit representation of concepts and the semantics of domain knowledge improve information management greatly, domain ontology has been widely applied in manufacturing field [8, 9].

In many cases, however, either establishing the knowledge-sharing agreements or mapping the manufacturing decompositions is practically more time-consuming and tedious than ontology design itself, largely because domain ontology should be predefined by experts manually. Meanwhile, due to the different understanding and interpretations by editors and experts, it's difficult to reach a consensus on the ontology's structure and its comments. Hence, while describing the knowledge structure and semantics explicitly, a predefined ontology may introduce semantic ambiguity and disagreement at the same time. In contrast, a well-formed taxonomy, also known as concept hierarchy, can offer a comprehensive but concise form to reveal how information is interwoven. Taxonomies can be formed through clustering based on the dissimilarity of documents across categories and the similarity of documents within a category. The typical approach is that all documents are initially grouped into one big category, and subsequently subdivided into smaller clusters so that the concept hierarchy is formed. Various similarity measures, e.g. cosine similarity and Euclidean distance, are used in the taxonomy generation. A target number of clusters found or the similarity threshold between any two closest clusters are often chosen as the stopping criteria. These criteria are proposed based on the inherent properties of documents which reveal the nature of documents themselves, e.g. topics covered.

However, using taxonomy to facilitate information management possesses some limitations. For example, concept relations are not explicitly represented in taxonomy. In order to tackle this problem, we propose a new method to automatically identify the semantic relationship between concepts in manufacturing knowledgebase. The semantic relationships are extracted based on the joint approach of a document profile model we proposed and text clustering. Through our method, the semantic relationship is able to be mined at

2

different granularities and the related documents containing the connection between two specific domain concepts are visualized in a ranked order via a user-friendly way. We explored our method on an enterprise corpus, namely manufacturing corpus version 1 (MCV1) [10]. Experimental results show that our method is very cost-effective.

The rest of this paper is organized as follows. Related work is introduced in Section 2. Section 3 describes the method we proposed for information extraction and relationship identification. Section 4 reports the details of experimental study. Section 5 concludes.

2.0   Related Work

Li & Ramani (2007) used shallow natural language processing and domain-specific design ontology to construct a structured and semantics-based representation from unstructured design documents [9]. The design concepts and their relationship representation were recognized from documents based on the linguistic patterns identified and finally joined together to form a concept graph. The integration of these concept graphs led to an application-oriented design ontology, which was often considered as the structured content representation of corporate document repository as well as an automated approach to populate domain knowledge base from former design practices. However, in this approach, the ontology referred by the application-oriented design ontology must be manually predefined. Meanwhile, this approach could only process those queries containing the concepts and relationships already represented in the domain ontology and the application-oriented ones. YAGO, a light-weight and extensible ontology extracted through WordNet and Wikipedia was proposed for Semantic Web [11]. YAGO extracted the concepts' hierarchy and synonymy from WordNet and classified the entities and their semantic relationships in Wikipedia into a concept hierarchy. The entities and semantic relationships in Wikipedia were regarded as the instances of concepts described in WordNet. However, YAGO was intended as a general ontology and could not process domain specific queries, e.g. manufacturing.

Most existing studies on taxonomy generation were reported using a hierarchical clustering approach [13]. Hierarchical clustering algorithms aim to group data objects into a tree of clusters. Such methods are further classified into hierarchical agglomerative clustering (HAC) and hierarchical divisive clustering, depending on whether the hierarchy is formed in a bottom-up or top-down fashion [14]. Resnik (1999) presented a semantic similarity in an IS-A taxonomy based on the notion of information content and showed its effectiveness when compared to the traditional edge counting approach [15]. However, since no semantic relationships were represented in the taxonomy, the classification itself could hardly be used to address the queries related to semantic relationships proposed by engineers and researchers.

In literature, a few studies which aim to compute the semantic proximity of different concepts or instances using taxonomy knowledge have been reported. Ziegler et al. (2006) proposed a method using Google and the Open Directory Project (ODP) to construct semantic profiles for two different concepts [17]. Then, a topic vector was created to compute the semantic similarity of each topic in the semantic profiles of two concepts. The final semantic proximity was obtained using the Pearson's correlation coefficient to measure the similarity between two topic vectors of different concepts. Li et al. used a metric that combines shortest path

3

length and subsumer depth in a non-linear fashion and managed to outperform traditional taxonomy-based approaches [18]. WordNet was adopted as the concepts hierarchy in deriving the semantic similarity of two concepts. However, such methods only targeted on the semantic similarity of two different concepts without identifying their semantic relationships and could not answer queries intended to address such semantic relationships.

In our previous study, a new method of handling imbalanced text classification was proposed [12]. It focused on a novel representation of categorization relationship among concepts in a domain-specific taxonomy while the distribution of category examples was heavily imbalanced. However, although experimental studies over a wide range of classifiers and datasets showed its merits, the issue of identifying the semantic relationship between different concepts in knowledgebase was not resolved. Therefore, in this paper we propose an approach to automatically tackle this issue using taxonomy and information extraction techniques. Moreover, the queries intended are not limited to domain knowledgebase or application oriented ontology only.

3.0   Semantic Relationships Identification

In our approach, users are allowed to propose the keyword-based queries, which are often familiar to them, in seeking the semantic relationships between two domain concepts, K_i (i=1,2), in the domain knowledgebase. Firstly, texts are classified into a domain specific taxonomy or an application oriented concept hierarchy so that the semantic relationships at different granularities and various aspects can be discovered. Next, a new weighting scheme is proposed to find out the connecting terms that have captured the semantic relationships of interest. Finally, documents containing such connecting terms of K_1 and K_2 are returned in a ranked order so that users can quickly examine these documents in details. Detailed steps are given as follows.

3.1   Data Pre-processing

Firstly, texts in the knowledgebase are pre-processed in order to reduce the noisy information. A standard list of stopwords and Porter stemming algorithm [16] are used to obtain "clean" documents. Next, documents in the knowledgebase are classified into different hierarchical classifications to define the different aspects and granularities of the semantic relationships between two concepts. We use our previously proposed probably based learning approach to conduct the classification since it performed very well on imbalanced texts [12].

Secondly, we choose the query terms K_i submitted by end users to search relevant documents in the knowledgebase. A TF/IDF scheme and the vector space model are used in this documents retrieval task. Note that we submit K_1 and K_2 as different search queries to the knowledgebase in order to obtain the document sets W_1 and W_2 related to K_1 and K_2 respectively. The reason that we do not combine K_1 and K_2 to form one single query in searching documents relevant to both K_1 and K_2 is that although some connecting terms are both related to K_1 and K_2 and do capture the semantic relationships between K_1 and K_2, they may exist in the documents containing K_1 and K_2 only. To separate K_1 and K_2 in query formation prevents the loss of such important semantic relationships.

4

3.2   Extracting Connecting Terms

Through the classification, we obtain the hierarchical classification of the knowledgebase. Suppose C_m is one class in the classification, and there is a document set B_{mi}, $B_{mi} \subset \{C_m \cap W_i\}, i = 1, 2$, where W_i is the document set related to K_i. Since the connecting terms are those may capture the semantic relationship of interest between K_1 and K_2, they must be both related to K_1 and K_2. Hence, only those terms appeared in both W_1 and W_2 can be regarded as the potential connecting terms. We extract such connecting terms from different classes and at different hierarchical levels respectively to obtain various semantic relationships at different granularities. Suppose there is a term set T_m containing the terms appearing in both B_{m1} and B_{m2}, for one term t, $t \in T_m$, the theme relationship that term t captures with respect to class C_m can be computed below:

$$I_t = (P(t, C_m)/P(t, \overline{C_m})) \times (P(t, C_m)/P(\overline{t}, C_m)) \tag{1}$$

Here, $P(t, C_m)$ denotes the probability of documents from class C_m where term t occurs at least once; $P(t, \overline{C_m})$ denotes the probability of documents not from class C_m where term t occurs at least once; and $P(\overline{t}, C_m)$ denotes the probability of documents from class C_m where term t does not occur. If term t is highly relevant to class C_m only, which basically indicates that t is a good feature to represent class C_m, then the value of $P(t, C_m)/P(t, \overline{C_m})$ tends to be higher. Meanwhile, the higher the value of $P(t, C_m)/P(\overline{t}, C_m)$ is, the better the feature term t is to represent C_m, since a larger portion of it occurs in class C_m. Hence, I_t denotes the amount of particular information term t containing for the class C_m. A higher value of I_t means that the presence of t highly indicates the membership of document so that t is a good representative of C_m and can really differentiate C_m. We sort t, $t \in T_m$ in a descending order with respect to the value of I_t and return the top λ terms as the connecting terms to represent the semantic relationships between K_1 and K_2 in class C_m. Documents containing in class C_m are ranked according to the similarity with connecting terms and returned in a descending order. The ranking function of the web page c_{mi} is defined below:

$$w(t_\alpha, c_{mi}) = tf(t_\alpha, c_{mi}) \times \log(\frac{N}{N(t_\alpha)}) \tag{2}$$

$$F_{c_{mi}} = \sum_{t_\alpha \in T_m}^{\lambda} w(t_\alpha, c_{mi}) \times (\lambda - \alpha + 1) \tag{3}$$

Here, $c_{mi} \in C_m$, $t_\alpha \in T_m$, t_α is the α-th term in returned top λ connecting terms. In formula (2), $tf(t_\alpha, c_{mi})$ is the frequency of the term t_α appearing in the document c_{mi}; N is the total number of the document in the knowledgebase and $N(t_\alpha)$ is the number of the document in the knowledgebase where the term t_α appears at least once.

4.0   Experimental Study and Results

In our study, we chose manufacturing knowledgebase MCV1 [10] as the test bed largely because of its wide coverage of manufacturing knowledge structure. MCV1 is an archive of 1434 English language manufacturing related engineering papers which were gathered from the Society of Manufacturing Engineers (SME). It combines all engineering technical papers published by SME from year 1998 to year 2000.

5

The 6th International Conference on Manufacturing Research (ICMR08)
Brunel University, UK, 9-11th September 2008

Codes	Label Names
C01	1. Assembly & Joining
C0101	1. Adhesive Bonding
C0102	2. Assembly & Joining Fundamentals
C0103	3. Assembly Test & Inspection
C0104	4. Automated Assembly
C0105	5. Brazing
C0106	6. Composites Manufacturing
C0107	7. Fastening
C0108	8. Material & Part Handling for Assembly
C0109	9. Riveting
C0110	10. Soldering
C0111	11. Wire Processing
C01TH	12. Others
C02	2. Composites Manufacturing
C0201	1. Composites Manufacturing Fundamentals
C0202	2. Composites, Bonding & Joining
C0203	3. Composites, Part Sealing
C0204	4. Composites, Sheet Molding Compounds (SMC)
C0205	5. Composites, Tooling, Molds & Patterns
C0206	6. Composites Layup Processes
C020601	1. Filament Winding
C020602	2. Pultrusion

Fig. 1. A hierarchical taxonomy of MCV1

In data pre-pressing, we chose Support Vector Machines (SVM) as the supervised method for classification. The well known SVM implementation SVM^{light} [20] was applied on MCV1 and our proposed term weighting approach was also adopted [12]. The parameters in SVM are first tuned using one third of documents in order to obtain the best parameter settings. Next, we obtained a hierarchical taxonomy representation of MCV1 as shown in Figure 1. Note that MCV1 is classified into a three-level hierarchy. Frequent word sequences were extracted as the class labels using our document profile modeling method [19]. There are a total of 18 major categories in MCV1 after classification. The relationships between the parent classes and the child classes can be considered as IS-A relationships. Hence, the hierarchy relationship in this taxonomy is very close to the superclass and subclass relation in ontology. In this case, we regard the taxonomy of MCV1 as an instance of ontology without explicitly defining the semantic relationships between each class and domain concepts. In the end, the connecting terms, which capture the potential semantic relationships, are mined and returned as the results for user queries concerned about the semantic relationships.

Our method was implemented in Java and a friendly user interface was presented to end users. Figure 2 shows the final results which consist of three major parts: the control panel (top in the figure), the cluster results (left column in the figure), and the document ranked list (right column in the figure). End users can submit the domain concepts K_1 and K_2 in the control panel. Next, the information retrieval task based on the TF/IDF similarity scheme and the Vector Space model is performed so as to find out the documents related to K_1 and K_2 respectively from MCV1.

In Figure 2, note there are two concepts "joint" and "tube" submitted in the control panel and eleven first-level hierarchical classes in MCV1 are identified. If the related documents are also included in the subclasses of the super-classes, both the numbers and titles of subclasses will also be displayed. For different super-classes and subclasses, different connecting terms are mined and displayed in the brackets beside the class title describing various semantic relationships contained in these classes. To check the related documents in the classes, one needs only to click the class titles. Relevant documents will be extended in a descending order

6

in the document ranking list. When click the document title or document number, users can look through the details. In our experiment, we set $\lambda = 50$. However, due to the concern of simplicity, only the top three connecting terms will be displayed in user interface. Documents containing these connecting terms from the knowledgebase are distilled and displayed through the interface for users' information and endorsement.

As shown in Figure 2, there are totally eleven major classes (C02, C07, C08, C09, C10, C11, C13, C14, C16, C17, C18) bearing the semantic relationship between "joint" and "tube", seven of them (C09, C10, C11, C13, C14, C17, C18) also consist subclasses that contain such a semantic relationship of interest. The connecting terms in the brackets beside the class title mainly describe the prevailing semantic relationships between two different concepts in this class. For example, in C10 Materials class, the connecting terms are "specimens", "stress" and "constraint". In its subclass C1009 Metals, the connecting terms are "aluminum", "metal" and "result". Since the connecting terms intend to capture the semantic relationship in the class of two concepts, at the different level of hierarchy, the connecting terms are different and describe the semantic relationships at various granularities.

In the experiment, note that the connecting terms of a particular class may look similar to its class title. For instance, the connecting terms of Class "C1009 Metals" contain the word "metal", and the connecting terms of C100901 Aluminum also contain the word "aluminum". The reason is that when we first extract the class title, we use our document profile model [19] and select the most distinct words for its class content description. Since these connecting terms can also represent some particular semantic relationships being carried in the class, they may be overlapped with its class title to some extent.

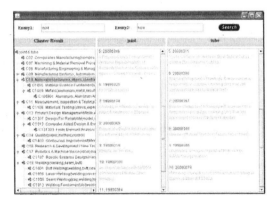

Fig. 2.   A user interface to mining the semantic relationships

5.0   CONCLUSION AND FUTURE WORK

The automated identification of semantic relationship has become an emerging challenge in manufacturing information management. In this paper, we introduce a new information extraction approach which is based on a classified knowledgebase to find out various semantic relationships between two different domain

7

concepts at various granularities. We have proposed a new information extraction scheme to filter documents in the knowledgebase and select those connecting terms that capture the semantic relationships between two concepts in a particular classification. A user-friendly prototype has been implemented and search queries are able to be submitted. Our experimental study based on a manufacturing centered corpus, i.e. MCV1, demonstrates that the method proposed is very effective in identifying the semantic relationships in a manufacturing oriented information scenario automatically. In the future, we aim to further expand our method and focus more on mining the complex semantic relationship of multi-concepts.

Acknowledgement

The work described in this paper was supported by a research grant from the Hong Kong Polytechnic University, Hong Kong Special Administrative Region, China (Project No. G-YF59)

References

[1] Weber, C., Werner, H., & Deubel, T. (2003). A different view on product data management/product life-cycle management and its future potentials. Journal of Engineering Design 14(4), 447-464.
[2] Court, A.W., Ullman, D.G., & Culley, S.J. (1998). A comparison between the provision of information to engineering designers in the UK and the USA. International Journal of Information Management 18(6), 409-425.
[3] Ullman, D.G. (1997). The Mechanical Design Process. New York: McGraw-Hill.
[4] Marsh, J.R. (1997). The capture and utilization of experience in engineering design. PhD. Thesis. University of Campbridge.
[5] Guarino, N., Masolo, C., & Vetere, G. (1999). Ontoseek: content-based access to the web. Ieee Intelligent Systems 14(3), 70-80.
[6] Olsen, G.R., Cutkosky, M., Tenenbaum, J.M., &Gruber, T.R. (1995). Collaborative engineering based on knowledge sharing agreements. Concurrent Engineering: Research and Applications 2(3), 145-159.
[7] Kim, J., Will, P., Ling, S.R., & Neches, B. (2003). Knowledge-rich catalog services for engineering design. Artificial Intelligence for Engineering Design, Analysis and Manufacturing 17(4), 349-366.
[8] Kitamura, Y., & Mizoguchi, R. (2004). Ontology-based systemization of functional knowledge. Journal of Engineering Design 15(4), 327-351.
[9] Li, Z., Ramani., K. (2007). Ontology-based design information extraction and retrieval. Artificial Intelligence for Engineering Design, Analysis and Manufacturing 21(2), 137-154.
[10] Liu, Y. Han, T.L. (2007). Corpus building for corporate knowledge discovery and management: a case study of manufacturing. KES (1) 2007: 542-550.
[11] Suchanek, Fabian M., Kasneci, G. & Weikum, G. (2007). YAGO: a core of semantic knowledge unifying wordnet and wikipedia. In Proc. of WWW 2007.
[12] Liu, Y. Han, T.L. & Sun, A. (2007). Imbalanced text classification: a term weighting approach. Expert Systems with Applications.
[13] Mirkin, B. (1996). Mathematical classification and clustering, Springer.
[14] Jain, A. K., Murty, M. N., & Flynn, P.J. (1999). Data clustering: A review. ACM Computing Surveys (CSUR), 31(3), 264-323.
[15] Resnik, P. (1999). Semantic similarity in a taxonomy: An information-based measure and its application to problems of ambiguity in natural language. Journal of Artificial Intelligence Research, 11, 95-130.
[16] Porter, M.F. (1980). An algorithm for suffix stripping. Program, 14(3), 130-137.
[17] Ziegler, C.N., Simon, K., Lausen, D. (2006). Automatic computation of semantic proximity using taxonomic knowledge. In Proc. of CIKM 2006.
[18] Li, Y., Bandar, Z., and Mclean, D. (2003). An approach for measuring semantic similarity between words using multiple information sources. IEEE Transactions on Knowledge and Data Engineering 15(4), 871-882.
[19] Liu, Y., Loh, H. T., & Lu, W. F. (2007). Deriving Taxonomy from Documents at Sentence Level. In H. A. d. Prado, & E. Ferneda, Emerging Technologies of Text Mining: Techniques and Applications (pp. 98-118). Idea Group Inc.
[20] Joachims, T. (1998). Text categorization with Support Vector Machines: Learning with many relevant features. *Machine Learning: ECML-98, Tenth European Conference on Machine Learning* (pp. 137-142). Berlin, Germany.

8

The 6th International Conference on Manufacturing Research (ICMR08)
Brunel University, UK, 9-11th September 2008

AN INVESTIGATION ON 3D DATA MINING OVER THE WEB AND WEB-BASED CAD DATA MANAGEMENT

Lei Li, David K. Harrison, John S. Lynn

School of Engineering Science & Design, Glasgow Caledonian University, Cowcaddens Road, Glasgow G4 0BA

Abstract

The research activities motivate onto the Internet which is a great innovation for information sharing as well as enhancing people's lives. Modern enterprises of manufacturing encounter dynamic market and produce a huge volume of computer-generated 3D models to demonstrate products' features over the webs in order to attract customers and occupy market share against time. Due to its versatile platform the Internet provides, designers and researchers with the option to make use of these existing designs and acquire them over the World Wide Web. Motivated by this fact, the customer-oriented applications will shift from "How is the information retrieved by key words?" to "How is the achievement of shape retrieval by customers specified?" Obviously, the existing Internet search engines like Google, MSN and Yahoo are not the solution to the tool desired and also not robust to clean the arising problems based on the data retrieval of models similarity, but these tools show us the different approach and push forward to developing a characteristic 3D model search tool. This paper presents the architecture of web-based system and technologies applied in design. The algorithms for 2D, 3D data mining are described and relevant equation is introduced.

Key words: Data Mining, 3D Model Search Engine, Web-Based Design.

1.0   Introduction

As new technologies are exploited and requirements of customer increase, reusing design deserves prior attention of modern enterprises in manufacturing to refine the components they devised and manufactured to achieve the requirement of customers. The reuse of optimized design predicates the descent of design times, improvement of design quality and reduces cost in product development process. Moreover, reusing design is also speeding up productivity because designers don't have to reinvent and less time is spent on large parts of the design. Design reuse already involves researches, methodologies and tools into variant domains and environments, and is rapidly becoming a market. Recent research of data management suggests high levels of design reuse achieves the average 75% of design content in common for each industry served and products for different customers in the company studied of ADAPT Automation, Inc [1]. However, the current traditional product data management exhibits the shortcoming in the variant design environment such as lack of collaborative design and information sharing with problems associated with location and distance. The increasing requirements and gap of collaborative product development affect the progress of product design and manufacturing. As a directly available means, the application of reuse concept is widely recognized within various environments of production. However, there is no efficient solution to gather appropriate designs in the massive volume of existing components [2]. Many companies established item libraries to control the indexing of common parts which hold the standard and description that they specify [3]. However, this approach is often ineffective and inelastic to survey the non-standard items, especially for gathering data and information among different organizations and companies. In order to overcome the defect of low data sharing and time-consuming design for new product, the usability could be improved via developing a new content-based search engine system to help in the processes of locating and reuse of existing components. The Internet is viewed as a common workspace and infrastructure to support a possible intelligent solution-making system, which is already enhanced to offer the powerful web-capable technologies for the arising of global electronic information sharing [4]. According to help overcome this, an integrated framework based on web and J2EE platform technologies is developed and the approach of efficient CAD document management, model retrieval and reuse design in this distributed web-based system is also put forward. Similar works and experiments being carried out so far are put online for user's testing and assessment by a few international famous universities and institutes, including Princeton University, National Research Council Canada, Ludwig Maximilians University of Munich, Greece Informatics and Telematics Institute and National Institute of Multimedia Education Japan etc. These recent researches are all based on the features similarity search and shape pattern recognition of 3D models. However, the implementing mechanism and strategy are different and grouped regarding to the system development. Basically, recent works can be outlined as three categories: query by keyword, query by sketch and query by paradigm. Keyword matching is a typical method and generally used for searching text-based model catalogues. Some systems are developed by viewing a 2D geometry-sketched shape as the query instance, which provide users with a graphic user interface to sketch by hand in real time. These systems can retrieve similar model shapes after submission of users. The acquisition by paradigm query method aims to provide an interface design which allows user uploading a 3D model file to conduct an automated similarity matching that focuses on the research of extracting invariant model features. This approach is associated with the modelling format, model topological structure, componential element division and sources storage issues. This paper aims to figure the importance and benefits of reusability in modern product design. The mechanism for promoting effective reuse of existing designs and proposed strategy of developing web-based model retrieval system are introduced. The algorithms hiding in system development are described and relevant equations are induced.

2.0   The Framework, Principle and Architecture

2.1   The Mode Deployed in the Development of Web Application

The key technologies and methods to achieve 3D models management are based on J2EE module technology and three-tiered B/S (Brower/Server) mode in which outlines as client layer, application layer and database layer. Aarsten et al. [5] presented the problems arising of applying the C/S (Client/Server) mode to large applications in particular regarding to the scalability and portability issues in 1996. As the two-tier software architecture was developed in1980s, the highest portion of processing in two-tier mode of designs invokes services and processes data in client side. That results in the heavy dependency on the platform adopted and system tools installed. The way reflects on enhancement of these issues above is to induce a new three-tier architecture for solving the increasing difficulty of applications maintenance such as application upgrades, platform upgrades and client hardware upgrades. The added tier provides effectively distributed client/server design and hides the complex processing from user and also avoids low portability and scalability of code, which enable to descend the dependency of client-side hardware customization. Furthermore, the one of great advantages is that it allows each tier to be built on different programming language in particular regarding to the trend of using object-oriented policy around the world now.

2.2   The Architecture of 3D CAD Document Retrieval System

Applying the B/S mode to the logical architecture of web-based 3D data searching system exhibits the benefits of reducing burden to the client machine, especially to promote the independence from user's platform and lower the quantity of code programmed simultaneously. The implementation of new architecture not only hides the narrowness of traditional structure but also abstracts the logical idea from the client side and then turns to the added middle tier which integrates the large portion of design from the application server. The system architecture of three-tier B/S mode is analyzed and illustrated in Fig.1.

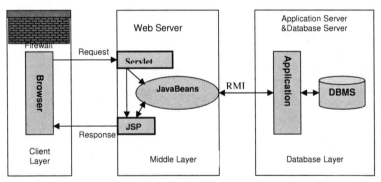

Fig.1.   The Structure of a Proposed Web Application System

The first layer is designed for users, which provides with an interface design to make conversation. Interface design acts as an important role of the suit of system development not only for human computer interaction but also take charge the query/response/data transmission and collaboration of separate modules with distinct jobs in system. The browser is running on the client layer as the distributed client application. It is easy to set up and already embedded into user's computer with the arising era of the Internet. It runs smoothly and allows user to easily navigate and to take a tour without heavy work on client. Moreover, browser doesn't directly make any call level request and service to interact with database. The second layer is the added middle tier which takes over the requests from client and fulfills the main tasks of web-based search engine system. The third layer is the database layer which takes up the storage and managing all the data and file used during implementation of web-based system. It contains DBMS (Database Management system) and application server which works together to verify query logic and achieve the storage.

**AN INVESTIGATION ON 3D DATA MINING OVER THE WEB AND
WEB-BASED CAD DATA MANAGEMENT**

2.3   Event Flow of the Web-based System

The search engine system has the capability of managing document storage and processing output and input data flows according to the request from user besides users' authority provides the secure access to system and information privacy. The functions embedded into web publishing are outlined below.

1) Operational entry for web-based system and database, which includes creating new entry by administrator, deleting entry specified, and modification of existing entries.
2) Secure control of users' information and web-based document storage includes:
  –   user's registration system and level authorized
  –   user's login system and loading pass process
  –   security operation of documents during the role verifying for authorization
3) Inner modules and interface design of search engine system are built into functionality-oriented Javabeans and associated conversation, collaboration and remote management.
4) Black board or message system deployed for communication among users to comment upon the system performance is obviously vital, effective way to gather feedback and criticisms; meanwhile it is also a necessary and important phase in software engineering.

The query of managing document browsing of web-based system is carried out and the event flow chart is shown as below.

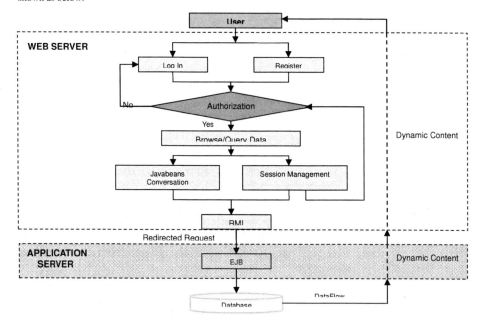

Fig.2.   A User Case of Accessing Search Engine System

3.0   Implementation of the Critical Design

**AN INVESTIGATION ON 3D DATA MINING OVER THE WEB AND
WEB-BASED CAD DATA MANAGEMENT**

The design of web-based search engine system is considered to develop through J2EE platform and adopt JBuilder as the design and debug tool. JBuilder is a java integrated design environment from Borland Software Corporation. It has won well known reputation and consecutive awards as the most powerful exploitation environment for new generation professional Java Programming. The web-based system is using Tomcat embedded into web server to test and achieve the dynamic connection jointing up the client browser to server. Tomcat serves as the reference implementation of the Java Servlet and JavaServer Pages (JSP) Specifications as well as even integrates into the Apache Web Server, which is proven to be stable and run stand alone [6]. The web-based system is created under the increasingly popular object-oriented design to take the place of traditional functionality design, which is realized by using modules design with the agreement of different technologies. Each module strictly designs as encapsulation and communicates one another with each appropriative interface.

3.1   Client-side Design

In the client-side design, the client invokes service through the web browser as explained in above section. In this phase, client-side design can be divided into the outer layer for layout design and inner layer that controls the data transfer and logic determination. JSP can be coded for the outer layer using template data, custom elements and server-side Java objects to return dynamic content to a client. In addition, the agile JavaScript programming is embedded to enrich and control resulting JSP pages. Servlet program works at server side as a controller by accessing the middle logic-optional modules (JavaBeans objects) and then reforming the resulted JSP pages according to the client request. The middle modules are designed regarding to deriving from the appropriative JavaBean object stored in web server, which is generating critical content and interacting with application server using a request-response paradigm. Fig.3 gives the idea of event flow diagram that shows the interaction between end users and server-side application, and the combination of web techniques applied in variant situations.

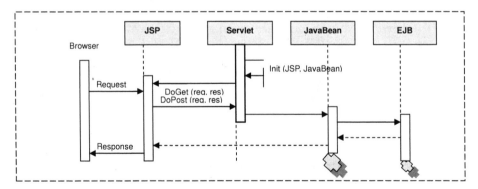

Fig.3.   Event Flow of Web Technologies APIs

3.2   Server-side Design

**AN INVESTIGATION ON 3D DATA MINING OVER THE WEB AND
WEB-BASED CAD DATA MANAGEMENT**

In the communication with the application server, the Servlet engine provides interface to identify Http client across to Http server. An HTTPSession is called and presents a session view of server [7]. Web server will be viewed as a client-side opposed to the application server waiting for conversation, which setups a second phase of client-server interface connection. The instance of JavaBean in application server takes over the conversation and obtains request from the session created, processes it, and returns results to the session through the interface of the JavaBean specified.

4.0 Data Mining and Similarity Search

The development phases are in four steps: user's query, data indexing, features matching and parts retrieval. The web-based system provides an interface to enable users to search interactively for 3D models. In order to retrieve models efficiently, the system supports query methods based on uploading 2D, 3D models, and then the new entry will be analyzed so that it will be submitted to an intelligent search agent for matching later on.

4.1 Implementation of the 2D Mesh Model Shape Matching

In the way to achieve matching 2D model, the web-based search engine system offers a multifunctional graphic user interface which provides the way to analyze 2D model. 2D models could be jpg, gif, png and 2D document etc. that any Java programming can support. Obviously, there is a demand to calculate vital invariants and features for a mesh model. The models can be transformed into volumetric representation and stored in a voxel space notated. The grids in the space are called voxels. 2D models are rasterized into voxels which enable a further voxel to voxel comparison. This approach of voxel to voxel comparison is computed accurate and intensive but time consuming according to the demand of memory [8] [9]. An accumulation of the denotation is applied in the web-based system. Some invariants can be clarified. For example, grids in the discrete space can be seen as an invariant and then every voxel detonated as Voli is being specified according to the rule of assigning value: reference a value of 1 to a voxel if the width of the chipped surface is encapsulated into a voxel, and reference it a value of 0 on the contrary. Equivalently, the accumulation of the values in voxels can be approximately represented as key access of the models. The total accumulation in the case is,

$$f_{acc}(i, g) = \sum_i Vol_i \bullet \{Vol_i \mid i \in N, i \le g - 1\} \tag{1}$$

Where i, g are variables, i indexes the pointer's location in the matrix and g for the constant of the grids. Java 2D and 3D API provides a powerful, flexible framework to handle arbitrary shapes, text, and graphics and provides a uniform mechanism for performing transformations, such as rotation and scaling, on these objects. The Java APIs make benefits to developers who want to incorporate 2D, 3D graphics into their applications and applets. The classes used for graphic presentation such as dataBuffer, rewritable Raster, Buffered Image etc. and their subclasses abstracted (rewritten) by designers is concentrated on. The following small fragment of selected methods in classes shows how it implements and makes sense to the code development. This list is not exhaustive.

Table I: Selected methods for system implementation

Methods	Description
ModelAnalysis(): ModelAnalysis	Main implementation function for model transmission
ObjectRead(): ModelFormatsParser	Handler of object arriving, schedule next packet arriving and service involving in Math class.
ObjectClone(): ModelFileLoader	Handler of returning a copy
Compute(): ModelFormatsParser	Provide the function of marking packet with calculated bands
WriteAccumulation(): ModelAnalysis	A function with fair mechanism to write stream using methods derived from Math class
getSampleModel(): ModelInfo	To get how the array elements managed by the class DataBuffer are translated into the samples of a particular packet
getFrequency(): ModelInfo	Provide functions to return frequency for the specified value
outputReport(): ModelInfo	Supply results processed after each implementation
DataBuffer	DataBuffer is a package for the array list or arrays used to store packet data

4.2   Implementation of the 3D Data Collection

The web-based system needs to index 2D and 3D models into a database for storage of model files by gathering over the World Wide Web. The 3D data of these models presents the capability of products, and will be indexed into a database as its own similarity features for future comparison. Although the standard and specification of 3D models exists, the data exchange is still an unstable factor for CAD systems. That motivates web-based system to adopt an output format compatible rather than exchangeable among different formats. STL is a rapid prototyping format which can describe objects as its mesh structure, and presents the parts and shapes with a number of triangles [10]. VRML is another choice due to using mesh models to represent the 3D contents as well. Furthermore, the great advantage of using these formats is that they can be used as a universal, interchangeable format among existing shape modelling systems [11].

4.2.1   Mesh Models and 3D Data Collection

As the adopting modelling formats are all meshed structure, this fact offers a way to develop the methods to collect features of 3D data and reform to index database. In the case, there is a math path to calculate the volume of 3D models. As mentioned in 4.1, models were rastered into voxels and then estimate the cumulative value in the volumetric space. The similar idea is to consider finding a basic element form and then dividing models into small pieces from inside. As we known, the meshed structure of STL and VRML, which presents the possible element form of triangle and tetrahedron. Thus the total volume depends on the accumulation of each element summed up. The preprocessing of calculation is to divide element form on the models. In the 3D case, that is divided into tetrahedron in mesh structure coding. In general, if it obtains a polyhedron describing as $(Vex_0, Vex_1, Vex_2, Vex_3)$ which has a $Vex = \{x, y, z\}$ existing in space, an algebra equation is held.

$$Volume\ (Vex_0, Vex_1, Vex_2, Vex_3) = Volume\ (Vex, Vex_0, Vex_1, Vex_2) + \ldots\ldots Volume\ (Vex, Vex_2, Vex_3, Vex0)\ (2)$$

**AN INVESTIGATION ON 3D DATA MINING OVER THE WEB AND
WEB-BASED CAD DATA MANAGEMENT**

And the vertexes of each face F (triangle) in polyhedral space has the same direction, thus the normal is set to zero vector.

$$\text{Volume}(V) = \sum_F \text{Volume}(\vec{0}, F.V_0, F.V_1, F.V_2, F.V_3) \tag{3}$$

The calculus is induced to extend the equation (3) and show integral equation as below which holds the situation of extending the green theorem [12] to three dimensional instance.

$$\iiint_A \vec{\nabla} \cdot F dx dy dz = \iint_S F \cdot \hat{n} \cdot d\sigma = \frac{1}{3}\sum_{i=0}^{n-1} \iint_{S_i}(x,y,z) \cdot \hat{n}_i \cdot d\sigma \tag{4}$$

Where a polyhedron is described as S, A is a sample of closure area in it, if the polyhedron has the number of surface S_i denoted by n which i assign between $[0, n)$, every surface S_i has the normal n_i and vertex $V_{i,j}$ which j assign between $[0, v(i))$. $v(i)$ is the sum of vertexes in surface S_i. And the $d\sigma$ is the infinitesimal cell in S. Equation (5) the finial form after integral.

$$\text{Volume }(A) = \frac{1}{6}\sum_{i=0}^{n-1}\left((\hat{n}_i \cdot V_{0,i})\,\hat{n}_i \cdot \sum_{j=0}^{v(i)-1}(V_{i,j} \times V_{i,j+1})\right) \tag{5}$$

The different design of object gives different quantity of facets which make a key as feature to identity similar design. In the formats applying to the system, the mesh structure presents an advantage of gathering this kind of data. A parser in loader system is developed to read streams and extract helpful information including calculation of surface area; the number of facets, vertexes, holes and their relationship that is presented by Euler's equation [13]. The surface area is the cumulative value of the total meshed surface in models. The summation varies due to the contrast of design complexity in different shapes. Determinant is applied here to create square matrix of elements determined by the vertexes of combination and used to calculate surface area.

5.0   Implementation of Data Storage and Search Engine System

DBMS has been extensively applied in business and industry for efficient and secure storage and data management. Oracle9i continues previous edition that focuses on the Internet by providing capabilities and functional bundled tools targeted at e-Business environments. In addition, Oracle9i continues to add features and capabilities designed on certain development areas. These areas are [14]: Internet Content Management, E-Business Integration, Packaged Applications and Business Intelligence Platform. Oracle9i permits users to store, manage and integrate multimedia content into database. The web-based search engine system adopted Oracle to request service using the data generated by the analysis program. The system can return the resulting 3D models that are most similar to the query one. The screenshots of the search engine system is illustrated in Fig.4 and Fig.5.

Fig. 4   User access to the Web-based system   Fig. 5   The Interface Design of Search Engine

6.0   Conclusion

In this paper, it presents the architecture of a web-based search engine system and concept of implementing content-based searching. The adopted technologies for web publishing and modular design are outlined and detail the cooperation and interface design between them. It describes and analyzes the event flow of a user case, secure access to system and private information protection. The methods and algorithm is mentioned to make sense the development of web-based application. The paper proposes how to extract 2D, 3D information and introduce the management of multimedia data after gathering. The equations are supplied and induced for data collection as well. The more research on further improving accuracy of experiment and exploitation of new algorithm is assessed and looked forward. The approach of interface design is still required to refine and develop along with enrichment of the system.

References

[1] Jenkins, B. (2005) "Justifying and Implementing of Practical Data Management: Lessons from Three Leaders", Manufacturing Solutions, http://www.autodesk.com.au/adsk/servlet/index?siteID=1157326&id=6627439 [accessed at 09/12/ 2005].
[2] Cardone, A. Gupta, S.K. & Karnik, M. (2003) "A Survey of Shape Similarity Assessment Algorithms for Product Design and Manufacturing Applications", Journal of Computing and Information Science in Engineering, June, Vol.3 No.2, pp.109-118.
[3] Sharma, S.C. (1978) "A critical study of the classification and coding systems in manufacturing companies", Thesis, Lehigh University, US.
[4] Cheng, K., Pan P.Y. and Harrison, D.K. (2000) Internet as a tool with application to agile manufacturing: a web-based engineering approach and its implementation issues, International Journal of Production Research, Vol.38 No.12, pp.2743-2759.
[5] Aarsten, A. Brugali, D. & Menga, G. (1996) "Pattern for three-tier client/server application" In Proceedings of the Pattern Language of Programs Conference (PloP'96), Monticello, US.
[6] Eaves, J. Jones, R. & Godfery, W. (2003) Apache Tomcat Bible, Wiley Publishing, Indiana, CANADA. ISBN: 0-7645-2606-5.
[7] Deitel, H.M. Deitel, P.J. & Santry, S.E. (2003) Advanced Java2 Platform: How to program, John Wiley, New York. ISBN: 0-13-089560-1.
[8] Chen, H.H and Huang, T.S. (1988) "A Survey of Construction and Manipulation of Octrees", Computer Vision, Graphics, and Image Processing, Vol.43, pp.409-432.
[9] Kitamura, Y. & Kishino, K. (1996) "A Parallel Algorithm for Octree Generation from Polyhedral Shape Representation", In Proceedings of the 13th International Conference on Pattern Recognition, Vol.3, pp.303-309.
[10] Silicon Graphics Inc (2004) STL Programmer's Guide, http://www.sgi.com/tech/stl/, [accessed at 4/10/ 2003].
[11] CMP Media LLC (2003) Streaming Web 3D, http://www.3dgate.com/tools/ [accessed at 17/09/ 2003].
[12] Thomas Jr, G.B. & Finney, R.L. (1996) Calculus and Analytic Geometry 9th Edition, Addison-Wesley, Reading, MA.
[13] Foley, J.D. Dam, A.V. Feiner, S.K. & Hughes, J.F. (1993) Computer Graphics: Principles and Practice 2nd, Addison-Wesley, Reading, MA. ISBN: 0201609215.
[14] Oracle Corporation (2005) Oracle E-Business Suite, http://www.oracle.com/applications/e-business-suite.html, [accessed at 12/2005].

AN INVESTIGATION ON 3D DATA MINING OVER THE WEB AND WEB-BASED CAD DATA MANAGEMENT

SIMULTANEOUS SCHEDULING OF MACHINES AND AUTOMATED GUIDED VEHICLES USING ARTIFICIAL IMMUNE SYSTEM

Noorul Haq * A, Gnanavelbabu A, Jerald J, Asokan P, and Narendar K

Department of Production Engineering, National Institute of Technology, Tiruchirapalli – 620 015, India *anhaq@nitt.edu , Fax No +91(431) 250 0133.

Abstract

This paper exploits the interactions between the machine scheduling and the scheduling of the material handling system in an FMS by addressing them simultaneously. This problem is composed of two interrelated decision problems (ie) the scheduling of machines and the scheduling of Automated Guided Vehicle (AGVs). Both problems are known to be Non Polynomial hard problems, resulting in a more complicated NP-hard problem when they are considered simultaneously. In this work, an Artificial Immune System algorithm (AIS) is introduced. This algorithm is applied to a set of 82 test problems which were constructed by other researchers and the results are compared. The results indicate the good performance of AIS when compared to other algorithms developed by other researchers.

Key words: FMS scheduling, artificial immune system, machine and automated guided vehicles.

1.0   Introduction

A Flexible Manufacturing System (FMS) is a highly sophisticated manufacturing system now-a-days to meet customer's requirements. The FMS fills up the gap between the traditional job shops and highly automated transfer lines. This kind of system is very useful to achieve high productivity and flexibility. The problems in FMS are generally classified into Design, Planning, Scheduling and Control. This work is primarily concerned with the scheduling problems of FMS. Sabuncuoglu and Hommertzheim [1] have tested the different machine and AGV scheduling rules in FMS against the mean flow time criterion. Another off-line model for simultaneous scheduling of machines and material handling systems in an FMS for the makespan minimization is presented by Bilge and Ulusoy [2]. The problem was formulated as a non-linear mixed integer-programming model and was addressed using the sliding time window approach. Ulusoy et al [3] have addressed the same problem using genetic algorithms. In their approach the chromosome represents both the operation number and AGV assignment which requires development of special genetic operators. Lacomme et al [4] have addressed the simultaneous job input sequence and vehicle dispatching for a single AGV system. They solved the problem using the branch and bound technique coupled with a discrete event simulation model. Gobal and Kasilinga [5], developed a SIMAN based simulation model to determine the number of AGVs needed to meet the material handling requirements. That calculation was done based on the idle time of vehicle and machine and the waiting time of parts. Reddy and Rao [6], address the simultaneous scheduling problem as a multiobjective problem in scheduling with conflicting objectives and it is more complex and combinatorial in nature. They solved the problem by using a non- dominating sorting evolutionary algorithm. Wu and Wysk [7], described some scheduling algorithm which employs discrete simulation in combination with straightforward part dispatching rules in a dynamic fashion.

1.1   Scheduling and Routing of AGV

Bozer and Srinivasan [8] presented a concept of conflict free and shortest time AGV routing. The main advantage of this idea is its simplicity and disadvantage is its optimal solution. Tanchoco [9] proposed the time window method for routing of AGV. In this path networks are shared and are used more efficiently. The Main contribution of the time window approach is the enhancement of the path utilization. This algorithm generally takes a long time. A dynamic routing technique is proposed by Taghaboni and Tanchoco[10] and this approach routes AGV relatively quicker compared with some static algorithms. However this method cannot achieve a high efficiency when the number of tasks and the vehicles increases.

1.2   Scheduling of both Vehicles and Machines

Akturk and Yilmaz [11] proposed an algorithm to schedule vehicles and jobs in a decision making hierarchy based on the mixed integer programming. But this approach is applicable only for the problem with a small number of jobs and vehicles. Bilge and Ulusoz [2] proposed a time window approach to simultaneous scheduling of machines and material handling system in an FMS. Ulusoz et al [3] proposed a genetic algorithm for the simultaneous scheduling of machines and material handling devices. In this work ant colony optimization is used for scheduling both jobs and AGV simultaneously in FMS environment. Kusiaka [12] explains material handling in Flexible Manufacturing Systems. Orhan and Doyen [13] explains a new approach to solve hybrid flow shop scheduling problems by artificial immune system. Lee and Jung [14] developed a multi-objective production planning model in a flexible manufacturing environment.

2.0   Problem Description and Assumptions

The environment within which the FMS under consideration operates can be described as follows:

(i) The types and number of machines are known. Operations are nonpreemptive. There is sufficient input/output buffer space at each machine. (ii) Processing, set-up, loading, unloading times are available and are deterministic. (iii) Number of AGVs is given and the AGVs are all identical in the sense that they have the same speed and load carrying characteristics. (iv) Flow path layout is given and travel times on each segment of the path are known. (v) A load/unload (L/U) station serves as a distribution centre for parts not yet processed and as a collection centre for parts finished. All vehicles start from the L/U station initially and return to thereafter accomplishing all their assignments. There is sufficient input/output buffer space at the

SIMULTANEOUS SCHEDULING OF MACHINES AND AUTOMATED GUIDED VEHICLES
USING ARTIFICIAL IMMUNE SYSTEM

(L/U) station. (vi) AGVs carry a single unit-load at a time. They move along predetermined shortest paths, with the assumption of no delay because of congestion. Pre-emption of trips is not allowed. The trips are called loaded or deadheading (empty) trips depending on whether a part is carded or no part is carded during that trip, respectively. The durations for the deadheading trips are sequence dependent and are not known until the vehicle route is specified. (vii) It is assumed that all the design and set-up issues within the hierarchy of OR/MS problems in an FMS as suggested by Stecke and Solberg [15] have already been resolved. Machine loading, i.e., the allocation of tools to machines and the assignment of operations to machines, is made. Pallets and other necessary equipment are allocated to parts. The set of part types to be produced during the planning period and the routing of each part type are available before making scheduling decisions. In other words, routing flexibility is not considered. The routing for a part type can be selected based on considerations of technological feasibility and processing efficiency, or by formulating the set-up phase problems in a manner that can also handle the routing decisions. (viii) Ready-times of all jobs are known. Initially, partially processed parts might be available at machines waiting for further processing, and they can be treated as jobs having zero ready times and their routing consists of the remaining operations. (ix) Such issues as traffic control, congestion, machine failure or downtime, scraps, rework, and vehicle dispatches for battery change are ignored here and left as issues to be considered during real-time control. (x) The speed of AGV 40m/min.

2.1   Vehicle Scheduling Methodology

Jobs are scheduled based on the operation sequence derived by the AIS algorithm. Initially AGVs carry jobs from the load/unload station to the respective workstations where the first operations are scheduled. AGVs perform two types of trips, a loaded trip where it carries a load and a deadheading trip where the vehicle moves to pick up a load. The deadheading trip can start immediately after the delivery and vehicle demand at different workstations are considered and the subsequent assignments are made. If both AGVs are available, assign the task to the earliest available vehicle. If no vehicle is available, compute the earliest available times of the AGVs and make the assignment. If the vehicle is idle and no job is ready, identify the operation that is going to be completed early and move the vehicle to pick up that job. This type of vehicle scheduling methodology helps in reducing the waiting times and thus helps in improving the resource utilization and the throughput. The flow chart of the vehicle assignment methodology is given in Figure 1.

3.0   Artificial Immune System (AIS)

Artificial immune systems are adaptive systems, inspired by theoretical immunology and observed immune functions, principles and models, which are applied for problem solving. The immune system is a complex of cells, molecules and organs which has proven to be capable of performing several tasks, like pattern recognition, learning, memory acquisition, generation of diversity, noise tolerance, generalization, distributed detection and optimization. Based on immunological principles, new computational techniques are being developed, aiming not only at a better understanding of the system, but also at solving engineering problems. Engin and Doyen [16] explained that the operative mechanisms of immune system are very efficient from a computational standpoint. Artificial immune systems were built on the following two principles:
a) Clonal selection principle and   b) Affinity maturation principle

The 6th International Conference on Manufacturing Research (ICMR08)
Brunel University, UK, 9-11th September 2008

3.1 Cloning Selection Principle

The clonal selection principle, or theory, is the algorithm used by the immune system to describe the basic features of an immune response to an antigenic stimulus. Each schedule has a makespan value that refers to the affinity value of that antibody. The affinity value of each schedule is calculated from the affinity function. The affinity function is defined as

$$\text{Affinity (p)} = 1/\text{makespan} \qquad (1)$$

From this relation, lower makespan value gives higher affinity value. Further the cloning of antibodies is done directly proportional to their affinity function values. Therefore, there will be more clones of antibodies that have lower makespan values than those with higher makespan values in the new generated clone population. Vargas et al [17] explains an immune-based approach to minimize makespan on parallel processors. Zheng et al [18] explains an affinity function based on makespan values of the schedules.

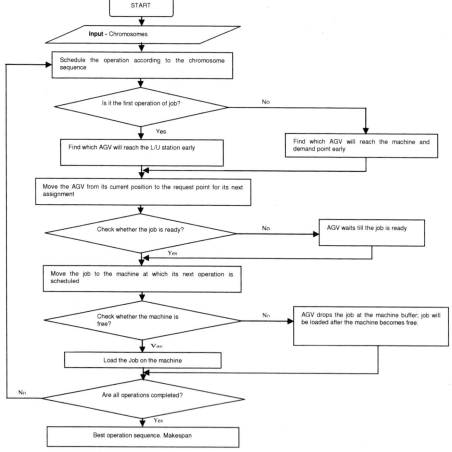

Fig. 1.   Flow chart of the vehicle assignment methodology

**SIMULTANEOUS SCHEDULING OF MACHINES AND AUTOMATED GUIDED VEHICLES
USING ARTIFICIAL IMMUNE SYSTEM**

752

3.2   Affinity Maturation Principle

It consists of two methods namely Mutation and Receptor editing.

Mutation: A two phased mutation procedure is used for the generated clones:

a) Inverse mutation b) Pairwise interchange mutation

a) Inverse mutation: For a sequence s, let i and j be randomly selected two positions in the sequences. A neighbour of s is obtained by inversing the sequence of jobs between i and j positions. If the makespan value of the mutated sequence is smaller than that of the original sequence then the mutated one is stored in the place of the original one. Otherwise, the sequence will be mutated again with random pair wise interchange mutation.

b) Pairwise interchange mutation: Given a sequence s, let i and j be randomly selected two positions in the sequence s. A neighbor of s is obtained by interchanging the jobs in positions i and j. If the makespan value of the mutated sequence is smaller than that of the original sequence, then store the mutated one in the place of the original one. In the case where the algorithm could not find a better sequence after the two-mutation procedure, then it stores the original sequence.

Receptor editing: After cloning and mutation processes, a percentage of the antibodies in the antibody population are eliminated and randomly created antibodies are replaced with them. This mechanism allows finding new schedules that correspond to new search regions in the total search space.

4.0   Implementation of Artificial Immune System (AIS) Algorithm

The artificial immune system algorithm is implemented for optimizing the sequences of parts into the machines and the AGVs sequence.

Generating Random Sequence: First initial populations of ten random sequences are generated and their respective Combined Objective Function (COF) values are calculated

Initial Population # 1

1.	4	7	12	1	13	2	10	11	8	3	5	6	9
2.	7	4	5	1	8	9	6	10	12	11	13	2	3
3.	4	5	10	1	7	6	8	11	12	9	13	2	3

Cloning the Sequences: An average of the COF is taken from the generated population and the affinity values are checked with the average, if the values of the affinities are greater than average values of COF of the population generated, then a clone is generated. A clone is nothing but a copy of the sequence.

Mutation: A two phased mutation procedure is used for the generated clones. Two mutations namely inverse mutation and pair-wise interchange mutations are carried out and the sequences corresponding to a lower COF than the original is chosen else the original sequence and its COF value is retained.

Example for Inverse mutation

Inverse mutation : i=1, j=4

Original Sequence

1)	**4**	7	12	**1**	13	2	10	11	8		3	5	6	9 **: COF = 122**

After mutation: I=1, j=4
2) **1** **12**   **7**   **4**   13 2   10   11   8   3   5   6   9   : COF = 199

Repair function: A repair function is developed that validates chromosomes with any precedence violations. Although some problem specific heuristics are incorporated, the repair function is not assigned to be too smart to prevent overly good repairs that lead to high performing children from poorly performing parents. When repairing, care is taken not to create other infeasibilities. Repair is used only to validate offspring generated by operation swap mutation. Find positions of the operations which violate the precedence relations. If the distance in between is smaller than half the chromosome length then swap violating operations else choose one of the operations randomly, lake it out and reinsert it right before/ after the other one depending on the precedence relations.

Example for Pair wise mutation:
Pair wise mutation : i=10, j=13
Original Sequence
3) 4   7 12   1   13   2   10   11   8   **<u>3</u>**   5   6   **<u>9</u>**   : COF = 122

After mutation
4) 4   7 12   1   13   2   10   11   8   9   5   6   3   : COF = 156

5.0   Results and Discussion

The scheduling procedure with AIS has been developed in the "C++" language. The processing times of the machines and also the AGV transportation times are given as input. The developed software gives optimal sequence of AGVs, the sequence of jobs and the optimized makespan values for the problems. The problems are designed at the ratio of travel times to processing times. The generation of example problems is based to a large extent on Bilge and Ulusoz [2]. The ratio of travel times to processing times (t/p) has been the main concern when generating the example problems. Table 1 Results gives comparison for t/p ratio >0.25

Table 1: Results comparison for t/p ratio >0.25

PROB.No	STW[2]	UGA[3]	AGA[6]	PGA[6]	AIS[proposed]
EX11	96	96	96	96	96
EX21	105	104	102	100	103
EX31	105	105	99	99	105
EX41	118	116	112	112	123
EX51	89	87	87	87	85
EX61	120	121	118	118	118
EX71	119	118	115	111	125
EX81	161	152	161	161	135
EX91	120	117	118	116	117
EX101	153	150	147	147	147
EX12	82	82	82	82	79
EX22	80	76	76	76	74
EX32	88	85	85	85	78
EX42	93	88	88	87	96
EX52	69	69	69	69	69
EX62	100	98	98	98	85
EX72	90	85	79	79	88

SIMULTANEOUS SCHEDULING OF MACHINES AND AUTOMATED GUIDED VEHICLES
USING ARTIFICIAL IMMUNE SYSTEM

EX82	151	142	151	151	128
EX92	104	102	104	102	90
EX102	139	137	136	135	131
EX13	84	84	84	84	78
EX23	86	86	86	86	77
EX33	86	86	86	86	80
EX43	95	91	89	89	99
EX53	76	75	74	74	67
EX63	104	104	104	103	78
EX73	91	88	86	83	94
EX83	153	143	153	153	130
EX93	110	105	106	105	92
EX103	143	143	141	139	132
EX14	108	103	103	103	103
EX24	116	113	108	108	111
EX34	116	113	111	111	121
EX44	126	126	126	126	134
EX54	99	97	96	96	98
EX64	120	123	120	120	125
EX74	136	128	127	126	140
EX84	163	163	163	163	146
EX94	125	123	122	122	123
EX104	171	164	159	158	172

Table 2: Results comparison for t/p ratio <0.25

PROB.No	STW	UGA	AGA	PGA	AIS
EX110	126	126	126	126	119
EX210	148	148	148	148	132
EX310	150	148	150	150	125
EX410	121	119	119	119	115
EX510	102	102	102	102	93
EX610	186	186	186	186	153
EX710	137	137	137	137	137
EX810	292	271	292	292	266
EX910	176	176	176	176	146
EX1010	238	236	238	238	188
EX120	123	123	123	123	118
EX220	143	143	143	143	129
EX320	148	145	145	145	124
EX420	116	114	114	114	111
EX520	100	100	100	100	92
EX620	183	181	181	181	141
EX720	136	136	136	136	136
EX820	287	268	287	287	248
EX920	174	173	173	173	145
EX1020	236	238	236	236	187
EX130	122	122	122	122	117
EX230	146	146	146	146	127
EX330	149	146	146	146	125
EX430	116	114	114	114	110
EX530	99	99	99	99	91
EX630	184	182	182	182	145
EX730	137	137	137	137	137

SIMULTANEOUS SCHEDULING OF MACHINES AND AUTOMATED GUIDED VEHICLES USING ARTIFICIAL IMMUNE SYSTEM

EX830	288	270	288	288	248
EX930	176	174	174	174	144
EX1030	237	241	237	237	186
EX140	124	124	124	124	118
EX241	217	217	217	217	189
EX340	151	151	151	151	125
EX341	222	221	221	221	184
EX441	179	172	172	172	166
EX541	154	148	148	148	139
EX640	185	184	184	184	141
EX740	138	137	137	137	137
EX741	203	203	203	203	203
EX840	293	273	293	293	247
EX940	177	175	175	175	146
EX1040	240	244	240	240	185

(STW: Sliding Time Window, UGA: Ulusoy Genetic Algorithm, AGA: Adaptive Genetic Algorithm, PGA: Proposed Genetic Algorithm, AIS: Artificial Immune System.)

Different combinations of these ten job sets and four layouts are used to generate 82 example problems. In all these problems there are two AGVs. Table 2 consists of problems whose t/p ratios are lower than 0.25. The digits that follow EX indicate the job set and the layout. In Table 2, another digit is appended to the code. Here, having a 0 or 1 as the last digit implies that the process times are doubled or tripled, respectively, where in both cases travel times are halved.

6.0   Conclusion

The purpose of this study is to make AGV scheduling an integral part of the scheduling activity, actively participating in the specification of the off-line schedule, rather than just reacting to it. The iterative algorithm created anticipates the complete set of flow requirements for a given machine schedule and makes vehicle assignments accordingly, as opposed to a real-time dispatching scheme that uses no information other than the move request queue. The iterative algorithm promises improvement in scheduling especially in environments where cycle times are short and travel times are comparable. In this research work, it is observed that artificial immune system algorithm performs better where travel times are very low when compared to processing times.

References

[1]   Sabuncuoglu I and Hommertzheim DL (1992) "Experimental investigation of FMS machine and AGV scheduling rules against the mean flow time criterion." *International Journal of Production Research*, Vol. 30, No. 7, pp. 1617-1635.

[2]   Bilge U and Ulusoy G (1995) "A time window approach to simultaneous scheduling of machines and material handling system in an FMS." *Operation Research* , Vol. 43, No. 6, pp. 1058–1070.

[3]   Ulusoy G, Sivrikayaserifoglus F and Bilge U (1997) "A genetic algorithm approach to the simultaneous scheduling of machines and automated guided vehicles." *Computer Operations Research*, Vol. 24, No. 4, pp. 335–351.

[4]   Lacomme .P, Moukrim.A and Tchernev.N, (2005) "Simultaneous job input sequencing and vehicle dispatching in a single-vehicle automated guided vehicle system: a heuristic branch-and-bound approach coupled with a discrete events simulation model." *International Journal of Production Research*, Vol. 43, No. 9, pp. 1911 – 1942.

[5]   Gobal,S.L. and Kasilingam R. G (1991) "A Simulation Model for Estimating Vehicle Requirements in Automated Guided Vehicle Systems." *Computer and Industrial Engineering*. Vol. 21, pp. 623-627.

SIMULTANEOUS SCHEDULING OF MACHINES AND AUTOMATED GUIDED VEHICLES
USING ARTIFICIAL IMMUNE SYSTEM

[6] Reddy,B.S.P and Rao,C.S.P (2006) "A hybrid multi-objective GA for simultaneous scheduling of machines and AGVs in FMS." *International Journal of Advanced Manufacturing Technology*, Vol. 31, pp. 602-613.

[7] Wu SYD and Wysk,RA (1988) "Multi-pass expert control system –a control/scheduling structure for flexible manufacturing cells." *Journal of Manufacturing Systems*, vol. 7, No. 2, pp. 107–120.

[8] Bozer, Y.A. and Srinivasan, M.M (1991) "Tandem Configurations for Automated Guided Vehicle Systems and the Analysis of Single-Vehicle Loops." *IIE Transactions*, Vol. 23, No. 1, pp. 72-82.

[9] Tanchoco JMA, Co C (1994) "Real time control strategies for multiple load AGVs." In: Tanchoco JMA (ed) Material Flow Systems in Manufacturing, Chapman and Hall, London, pp 300–331.

[10] Taghaboni F and Tanchoco JMA (1995) "Comparison of dynamic routingtechniques for automated guided vehicle systems." *International Journal of Production Research*, Vol. 33, pp. 2653–2669.

[11] Akturk MS and Yilmaz H (1996) "Scheduling of automated guided vehicles in a decision making hierarchy." *International Journal of Production Research*, Vol. 32, pp. 577–591.

[12] Kusiaka (1985) "Material Handling in Flexible Manufacturing Systems." Material Flow, Vol. 2, pp. 79-95.

[13] Orhan Engin and Alper Doyen (2004) "A new approach to solve hybrid flow shop scheduling problems by artificial immune system." *Future Generation Computer Systems*, Vol. 20, pp. 1083–1095.

[14] Lee SM and Jung HJ (1989) "A multi-objective production planning model in a flexible manufacturing environment." *International Journal of Production Research*, Vol. 27, No. 11, pp. 1981–1992.

[15] Stecke, K.E. and J.J. Solberg (1981) "Loading and Control Policies for a Flexible Manufacturing System." *International Journal of Production Research*, Vol. 19, No. 5, pp. 481-490.

[16] Engin O and Alper Doyen (2004) "A new approach to solve hybrid flow shop scheduling problems by artificial immune system." *Future Generation Computer Systems*, Vol. 20, pp. 083.

[17] Vargas P.A , Costa A.M , Von F.J, Zuben and França P.M (2002) "Makespan minimization on parallel processors: an immune based approach" in: Proceedings of the Special Sessions on Artificial Immune Systems, IEEE World Congress on Computational Intelligence, Honolulu, Hawaii, pp. 115–123.

[18] Zheng. H, Jingxin Zhang and Saeid Nahavandi (2004) "Learning to detect texture objects by artificial immune approaches." *Future Generation Computer Systems*, Vol. 20, pp. 1197–1208.

SIMULTANEOUS SCHEDULING OF MACHINES AND AUTOMATED GUIDED VEHICLES USING ARTIFICIAL IMMUNE SYSTEM

Manufacturing Supply Chains

The 6th International Conference on Manufacturing Research (ICMR08)
Brunel University, UK, 9-11th September 2008

A COMPARISON OF SUPPLY CHAIN EFFECTIVENESS USING THE 'QUICK SCAN' AUDIT METHODOLOGY

Thomas A.J [1], Childerhouse P [2], Towill D [1], Phillips G[1]

1. **Cardiff Business School, Cardiff University, UK**

2. **Waikato Business School, Waikato University, New Zealand**

Abstract

This paper presents a comparative analysis of supply chain effectiveness using an audit method known as Quick Scan. The 'Quick Scan' Audit Methodology (QSAM) provides a systematic approach to the collection, synthesis and analysis of qualitative and quantitative data from a supply chain. The audit concentrates primarily upon analysing the four main elements of the 'Uncertainty Circle' and the interactions that exist between these elements. From this analysis, QSAM provides a company with a series of short, medium and long term improvement opportunities aimed at reducing the uncertainty in each of the main areas of the circle.

To date the number of audits undertaken in companies is rapidly approaching eighty world-wide. This paper initially describes the QSAM methodology and then goes on to compare the Quick Scan audit findings undertaken with four UK companies and four New Zealand companies of similar structure and size. The companies are analysed, compared and scored against the four uncertainty circle elements and the twelve simplicity rules which are an integral part of the QSAM audit.

A set of conclusions are presented from the analysis showing the similarities and differences that exist between the eight companies in relation to the QSAM audit findings.

Keywords: Supply Chains, Auditing, Uncertainty Circle, Simplicity Rules, Comparative Study.

1.0   Introduction

The Quick Scan Audit Methodology (QSAM) is a systematic approach to the collection and synthesis of qualitative and quantitative data from a supply chain [1]. The QSAM approach is the initial step in a generic methodology to identify the change management and improvement opportunities in a supply chain. As well as being of operational benefit to specific companies the QSAM may also be utilised to develop generic research models of supply chain performance. The results of the application of this methodology into four New Zealand companies and four UK companies of similar size and structure is evaluated in this paper.

Through analyzing the uncertainty, complexity and simplicity scores obtained form the QSAMs, it was seen that regardless of the products manufactured and the sophistication of the technologies used by each company, each supply chain system differed very little by way of their capabilities and performance. In general, all companies were still struggling to achieve a seamless supply chain capability and all exhibited a number of complex material flow symptoms which reduced supply chain effectiveness in each organisation. The QSAM is thus able to advise companies in terms of the direction and magnitude of change required in their supply chains.

2.0   The Quick Scan Audit Methodology (QSAM)

The QSAM was developed by Cardiff University's Logistics Systems Dynamics Group. The details of the audit methodology is ideally explained in the work by Naim *et al* [1]. The structure of QSAM is based primarily on control systems theory and can be traced back to the work of Paranaby (1979) [2]. The QSAM involves an in-depth analysis of the company's supply chain system by a specialist team made up of university staff and their industrial partners who have the knowledge of the supply chain under scrutiny. Once a suitable supply chain has been identified and commitment from the company has been achieved, on-site attendance by the QSAM team is required for a period of between 3-4 days where semi-structured interviews and questionnaire completion with key staff members of the company is undertaken. The complete audit can normally be undertaken in a ten day period. A detailed walk-through of company operations is also undertaken in order to contextualize the questionnaire information and interviews. This method of data gathering allows the QSAM team to triangulate the data which further validates the information obtained and provide a firm foundation for further analysis of the supply chain effectiveness to be made.

The scope of the QSAM can vary from company to company depending upon the supply chain issues encountered by each company and the relative complexity and size of their operations and associated supply chain capabilities. Therefore as a means of ensuring each supply chain system is analysed in a similar manner, a Supply Chain Optimisation Modelling Architecture called SCOMA [1] was developed by the QSAM team. This approach segregates the supply chain issues dependent on the breadth of supply chain investigation undertaken. SCOMA identifies the supply chain issues at four different levels within the architecture, these are:

Level 1 - Analysis of the structure of the supply chain (transportation systems, factory location …).
Level 2a - Analysis of the information and material flows from customers and suppliers
Level 2b - Analysis of the internal planning and control mechanisms within the production system
Level 3 - Analysis of the individual processes in relation to the company's material flow.

The QSAM diagnostic is based upon four sources of data; (i) attitudinal and qualitative questionnaires, (ii) process maps, (iii) semi-structured interviews and (iv) archival information [1]. Up to eleven qualitative attitudinal questionnaires are completed during the Quick Scan Audit. These questionnaires are undertaken with key members of the company ranging from; managing director, production manager, purchasing, supply chain managers, quality manager, HR manager etc.

The second format of data collection is process mapping, which provides a detailed understanding of the material and information flows for the business processes. The third type of data that is collected during the Quick Scan is from semi-structured interviews. These are conducted with a cross-section of the senior and middle management from all functions and include similar coverage of all the questionnaires as well as the process mapping. The final type of data collected during the Quick Scan is archival data. The archival data is segmented into four categories utilising a generic Uncertainty Circle model [3] shown in Figure 1. The Uncertainty Circle model is a convenient way to categorise the disturbances that may be encountered by a business in the supply chain. Thus, for example, a business may find uncertainties associated with; erratic, frequent and problematic downtime of its machinery and equipment thus affecting process performance, changing customer schedules due to poor Voice of the Customer data capture and erratic demand profiling which leads to increased demand disturbance in a system, poor supplier delivery performance which affects adversely supplier performance and inaccurate and distorted production plans, wrong and inaccurate process control features which inhibits the company's ability to control its manufacturing operations in the way it ideally should. By understanding which of the four areas causes the greatest uncertainty a business may prioritise its resources adequately and focus on improving the areas which provide the highest scope for business performance improvement . These four areas of uncertainty identified as Process, Demand, Supply and Control (PDSO) are shown in Figure 1 in the form of an 'Uncertainty Circle. The elements of the circle are directly taken from the concept of a traditional manufacturing system.

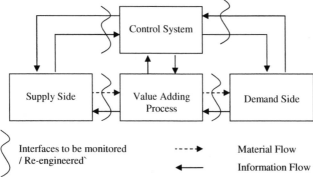

Fig. 1.   Uncertainty Circle based generic model utilised for collecting archival data during the Quick Scan Audit

The uncertainty circle method is based on the control of a company's internal process in responding to the effects of customer demand and in turn the ability of the company's internal processes to place orders on to their suppliers [4]. Uncertainty within the supply system can be significantly affected by the company's own process not yielding the required products on time. Supplier interface uncertainty results from the supply chain's inability to cope with the requested demand patterns (frequency and quantity of order profiles). Demand interface uncertainty is compounded by lack of accurate tracking of customer requirements by way of product features, volumes, frequency of delivery etc, players in the system generating 'rogue' orders for price leverage and so on. Finally, further uncertainty is induced by poor system controls based on the wrong decision rules and stale, noisy or incomplete information. As various business improvement programmes are successfully implemented into supply chains, it is expected that the corresponding uncertainty will reduce in size and the result can be a more effective and focused supply chain capable of moving towards a seamless supply performance [5].

In seeking to establish the degree of uncertainty in an individual value stream, complex material flow is a primary lead indicator [6]. Consequently, it is possible to produce checklists for supply chain analysts to use when monitoring the behaviour of their existing systems based around four groups of complex material flow symptoms. These groups are termed; (i) dynamic behaviour, (ii) physical situation, (iii) operational

A COMPARISON OF SUPPLY CHAIN EFFECTIVENESS USING THE 'QUICK SCAN' AUDIT METHODOLOGY

characteristics and (iv) organisational characteristics. Table 1 shows the groups and the elements contained in each group. The presence of uncertainty will result in a high frequency of these complex material flow symptoms occurring. This grouping of symptoms allows the analyst to work through individual checklists via a combination of data modeling, activity sampling, process mapping and structured questionnaires in order to clearly identify the symptoms and to attempt to provide solutions to these problems via the identification of a series of short, medium and long term improvement opportunities. Codification via Likert Scales allows the analysts to evaluate the statistical relationship between these four groups of uncertainty symptoms and the four uncertainty circle segments [7].

Table 1: Four classes of symptoms observed in comple material flow. Source: Towill [6]

Class of symptoms	Symptoms observed in complex material flow
Dynamic behaviour	Systems-induced behaviour observed in demand patterns
	System behaviour often unexpected and counter-intuitive
	Causal relationships often separated geographically
	Excessive demand amplifications as orders are passed upstream
	Rogue orders induced by system 'players'
	Poor and variable customer service levels
Physical situation	Large and increasing number of products per pound turnover
	High labour content
	Multiple production and distribution points
	Large pools of inventory throughout the system
	Complicated material flow patterns
	Poor stores control
Operational characteristics	Shop floor decisions based on batch-and-queue
	'Interference' between competing value streams
	Causal relationships often well separated in time
	Failure to synchronize all orders and acquisitions
	Failure to compress lead times
	Variable performance in response to similar order patterns
Organizational characteristics	Decision-making by functional groups
	Excessive quality inspection
	Multiple independent information systems
	Overheads and indirect costs allocated across product groups and not by activity
	Excessive layers of management between the CEO and the shop floor
	Bureaucratic and lengthy decision-making process

A smooth well controlled material flow system lies at the heart of best SCM design and practice [7] and is crucial if a company is to avoid the adverse impact of the bullwhip effect. By identifying the shortfall in smooth material flow it is possible to highlight those areas most in need of re-engineering to obtain significant performance improvement. To this end, a set of 12 rules shown in Table 3 has been devised. Together these rules point the way forward to smoothing material flow throughout the chain. They are an amalgam of the principles of planning and execution of good flow control. The philosophy associated with the 12 rules is simple yet effective, the analyst and systems designer must simplify the supply chain system by designing out problems at source rather than applying more complex control systems to an already complex system. This in

A COMPARISON OF SUPPLY CHAIN EFFECTIVENESS USING THE 'QUICK SCAN' AUDIT METHODOLOGY

turn limits the effectiveness, responsiveness and capability of the supply system. As a consequence of properly implementing good material flow control systems, it is found that all important business metrics are simultaneously improved since the supply chain system is tackled simultaneously in an holistic manner. Towill [6] explains that there is no downside to be traded against the enhanced bottom line.

Simplified material flow is a highly desirable feature of supply chain operations and can be achieved via innovative and thorough application of the 12 simplicity rules. Furthermore, these rules when correctly applied during BPR programmes produce a significant impact on 'bottom-line' performance metrics. Furthermore, if material flow is over complex, then numerous symptoms become clearly visible and result in ineffective product delivery process performance. Towill [6] identifies 24 detailed symptoms that can be categorized into dynamic, physical, organizational and process characteristics. All can be observed either physically or via analysing numerical data and/or written communication within the chain. Additionally, the 'digital nature' of the results obtained allows consistency to be built up between different analysts auditing the same value stream. Therefore the 12 simplicity rules have been designed as a complete set of guidelines by for practitioners to simplify their material flow, in the sense of developing the supply chain [6]. The following is a summary of each of the 12 rules that highlights why they have been included and when they are likely to be of particular importance. Table 2 shows the 12 simplicity rules

Table 2: The 12 Simplicity Rules. Source: Towill [6]

Rule 1	Only make products that can be quickly despatched and invoiced to customers
Rule 2	Only make in one time bucket those components needed for assembly in the next.
Rule 3	Streamline material flow and minimize throughput time
Rule 4	Reduce information lead times via the use of the shortest planning periods
Rule 5	Only take deliveries from suppliers in small batches as and when needed for processing and assembly
Rule 6	Synchronization of time buckets throughout the chain
Rule 7	Form natural clusters of products and designing processes appropriate to each value stream so that the requirements of diverse customer requirements can be best served.
Rule 8	Eliminate all uncertainties in all processes
Rule 9	Develop a structured approach to change. Understand, Document, Simply, Optimize (UDSO)
Rule 10	Highly visible and streamlined information flows
Rule 11	Use proven and robust decision support systems in the management of the supply chain
Rule 12	The operational target of the seamless supply chain needs to be commonly accepted and shared by all members of the change team

3.0   QSAM Audit and Findings

This section discusses the audit results of 8 value streams, (four from the UK and 4 from New Zealand) covering a wide range of market sectors including food, electronic, castings and precision engineering industries. Each of these value streams have been subject to a detailed team based on-site investigation using the Quick Scan approach. It is also worth noting here that the teams used for analysing the four New Zealand companies and the four UK companies were different and the results of each Quick Scan audit was not divulged to either party until the scores were entered onto a database and an analysis of the score was made. The companies identified for comparison were selected based on company size and volume of products manufactured. Table 4 shows a 2 x 2 matrix of the companies and shows the split between small and large company and high volume and low volume manufacture. Anonimity of the companies was assured with the companies being coded as NZ 1, NZ 2, NZ 3, NZ 4 for the New Zealand based companies and UK 1, UK 2, UK 3 and UK 4 for the UK based companies.

Table 3 shows the results of a comparison test undertaken with each of the companies and shows the analysis based on; geographical separation, company size and production volume capability. In Table 3 an analysis of supply chain uncertainty, supply chain complexity and supply chain simplicity was made. T-tests were conducted in order to see if there was any statistical significant factors present in the auditing system that may have skewed the results. The T-test results showed that there were no statistically significant issues with the audit process and that it could be assumed that each audit marked the companies in a consistent manner thus providing an initial benchmark for analysing the results.

Table 4: Company Breakdown based on Size and Volume

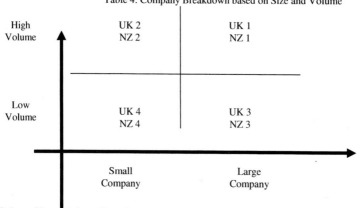

3.1 Uncertainty Results

Table 3 shows the average uncertainty scores based on company geography, size and volume throughput. A score closer to 1 shows low systems uncertainty and a greater robustness within the organisation to cope with externally induced uncertainty whereas a score approaching 4 shows that the company has high systems uncertainty and hence is less capable of controlling its supply chain system. In this case the results suggest that UK companies performed slightly better on average than New Zealand companies. UK companies showed a lower Uncertainty score (2.45 compared to 2.844 for New Zealand companies).

When comparing companies based on size, the uncertainty scores show that smaller companies performed less well against larger companies (3.125 small, 2.781 large) whereas the comparison of companies based on volume throughput showed that on average, high volume companies performed less well than low volume manufacturers (3.188 Low Volume, 2.719 High Volume).

Table 3: Average performance scores for geographic, size and volume comparisons

	Sample Size	Uncertainty	Simplicity	Complexity
Overall	8			
NZ	4	2.844	1.917	0.610
UK	4	2.450	1.367	0.558
t-test		0.68	0.60	0.64
Large Org	4	2.781	2.042	0.573
Small Org	4	3.125	1.583	0.735
t-test		0.55	0.31	0.42
High Vol	4	2.719	1.958	0.589
Low Vol	4	3.188	1.667	0.719
t-test		0.34	0.46	0.38

3.2   Complexity Results

The second analysis undertaken was that of comparing the complex material flow symptoms for each company. Table 3 shows the results of this analysis. Here a mark of 1 is awarded if a company shows a complex material flow symptom and a mark of zero given if it does not show the symptom. Therefore, the lower the average score then it is suggested the less complex the supply chain system is. In this case the results suggest that UK companies performed slightly better on average than New Zealand companies in that the average complexity score was closer to zero (lowest is best where complex symptom does not exist). UK companies showed a lower complexity score (0.558 compared to 0.610 for New Zealand companies).

When comparing companies based on size, the complexity scores show that smaller companies performed less well against larger companies (0.735 small, 0.573 large) whereas the comparison of companies based on volume throughput showed that on average, high volume companies performed better than low volume manufacturers (0.719 low volume, 0.589 high volume).

3.3   Simplicity Results

Finally an analysis of the 12 simplicity rules was undertaken. Table 3 again shows of each company's supply chain performance measured against the 12 simplicity rules. In this instance each rule is assessed and the company is given a mark of between 1 and 4 depending upon its adherence to each rule. Therefore a company is given a mark of 4 if they always adhere to the rule and is thus considered to be good. Alternatively a mark of 1 being awarded shows that the company never adheres to the rule and this is given a poor or bad rating. Therefore, the higher the value the more compliant the company is to following the 12 simplicity rules.

In this case the results suggest that NZ companies performed slightly better on average than UK companies in that the average simplicity score was higher. UK companies showed a lower simplicity score (0.1367 compared to 1.917 for New Zealand companies).

When comparing companies based on size, the simplicity scores show that smaller companies performed less well against larger companies (2.042 large, 1.583 small) whereas the comparison of companies based on volume throughput showed that on average, high volume companies performed better than low volume manufacturers (1.667 low volume, 1.958 high volume).

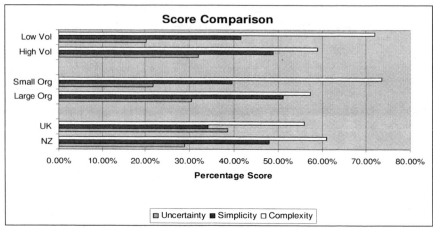

Fig. 2.   Comparison of Audit scores

4.0   General Conclusions

The results obtained from the QSAM audits are an initial set of findings aimed to identify trends and comparisons between companies split by; geography, size and volume. Figure 2 shows a comparison of the uncertainty, simplicity and complexity scores for each category analysed (volume, size, geography). The following conclusions can be made

- The average complexity score for all cases was 0.63 (1.0 = poor, 0 = good). This indicates that the companies regardless of size, location and volume throughput show a number of symptoms of complex material flow.

- The average simplicity score for all cases was 1.76 (4.0 = good, 0 = poor). This indicates that the companies regardless of size, location and volume throughput do not apply, practice and implement the simplicity rules.

- The average uncertainty score for all cases was 2.85 (4.0 = poor, 1.0 = good). This indicates that the companies regardless of size, location and volume throughput show that their supply chain systems are not moving towards a seamless and integrated approach and are susceptible to both external and internal influences affecting supply chain uncertainty and performance.

- A good general correlation exists between the three scores. In general when complexity scores are poor, the simplicity score and uncertainty scores show similar trends.

5.0   Further Work

It is recommended that further in-depth studies are undertaken on these initial set of results to confirm the findings and to develop a greater understanding of company performance. The creation of a detailed set of

A COMPARISON OF SUPPLY CHAIN EFFECTIVENESS USING THE 'QUICK SCAN' AUDIT
METHODOLOGY

guidelines aimed at enhancing the supply chain performance of these companies through the identification of good and bad supply chain practice will be developed in a similar manner to previous work within the automotive sector [8]

References

[1] Naim .M. M, Childerhouse. P, Disney,.S, and Towill.D (2002) "A Supply Chain Diagnostic Methodology: Determining the Vector of Change". Computers and Industrial Engineering, 42, pp 135-147.

[2] Parnaby, J. (1979) "Concept of a Manufacturing System" International Journal of Production Research, 17, 2, pp 123-135.

[3] Mason-Jones.R, Towill, D.R, (1998) "Shrinking the Supply Chain Uncertainty Circle". IOM Control September, pp. 17–22.

[4] Towill, D.R (2006), "Fadotomy – Anatomy of the Transformation of a Fad into a Management Paradigm", Journal of Management History, 12, 3, pp 319 – 338

[5] Childerhouse. P, Disney, S.M, Towill, D,R.(2004) "Tailored Toolkit to Enable Seamless Supply Chains", International Journal of Production Research, 42, 17, pp 3627 - 3646

[6] Towill, D. R. (1999) "Simplicity wins: Twelve Rules for Designing Fffective Supply Chains". Control the Journal of the Institute of Operations Management 25 , pp. 9-13.

[7] Childerhouse, P. and Towill, D. R. (2003) "Simplified Material Flow holds the key to Supply Chain Integration". OMEGA, The International Journal of Management Science 31 , pp. 17-27

[8] Childerhouse, P. and Towill, D. R. (2004) "Reducing Uncertainty in European Supply Chains" Journal of Manufacturing Technology Management. 15,7,pp585-598

The 6th International Conference on Manufacturing Research (ICMR08)
Brunel University, UK, 9-11th September 2008

BUSINESS PROCESS VALUE ANALYSIS USING AN ANALYTICAL HIERARCHICAL PROCESS

S. Rashid, K. Agyapong-Kodua and R.H Weston

MSI Research Institute, Loughborough University, Loughborough, Leics., UK

Abstract

To remain competitive and profitable, most Manufacturing Enterprises (MEs) need business processes with enhanced capability to realise high values at minimal cost. The drive to achieve this has generated several engineering and enterprise methodologies which in essence capture current state business processes and based on expected outcomes, derive alternative processes to help meet customer and enterprise requirements. In order to cope with this situation, a systematic decision-support approach is required which eases the decision making process and prioritizes performance indicators such as productivity, flexibility, cost, value, inventory, customer satisfaction, among others. Also for an enterprise deciding to bench-mark any of its functional aspects, a tool to support decision making is very important.

Whichever process an enterprise wants to adopt, it is required that scientific analysis in terms of its potential value generation be determined before implementation. This will save industries from adopting methods and implementing decisions which they are not clear of their benefits. In support of this, the research has focussed on conducting value analysis on some aspects of the business processes of a make to order pump manufacturing company located in Pakistan. The authors have demonstrated in the paper how analytical hierarchical process (AHP), a flexible and excellent decision making tool, is used in support of value engineering to measure performance indicators related to value, importance and cost.

Key words: Manufacturing Enterprise (ME), Value Analysis (VA), Make to Order (MTO), Analytical Hierarchical Process (AHP).

1.0   Introduction

The concept of value generation and cost reduction is featuring well in most MEs. The drive has become intense because MEs need to remain competitive and maintain larger market shares throughout their life time. To provide support to Industries which desire to enhance the value of their products, many researchers have propounded theories related to value generation. Key among these are a broad group of theories termed objectivity and subjectivity theories of value [1]-[3]. Another approach for measuring and improving performances was proposed through lean thinking in the form of value stream mapping [4]-[7]. Other approaches, based on the customer's perspective of value has been proposed [8] and instrumented with concepts of value engineering [9]-[10].

Although research is ongoing in this area to provide a fuller understanding of how value can be created or added to manufacturing processes, it is required that systems and their processes are designed taking into consideration existing knowledge about value enhancement and cost reduction. In attempt to achieve this objective, it is necessary that scientific methods capable of quantifying benefits derived from the deployment of alternative manufacturing scenarios are utilised.

In this paper the authors have identified with the value engineering definition of value and demonstrated how AHP can be used to support the derivation of values generated along specific process segments in a make to order pump manufacturing company located in Pakistan. During the research, data was collected through observation of activities at the shop floor and interviewing of key people related to the processes under consideration. The validated results provided a strong foundation in recommending changes in the operations required in company.

2.0   Value Analysis through the Application of AHP

The origin of value analysis, also known as value engineering, is closely associated with the Industrial community in the United States who in the 1940s needed to identify alternatives to raw materials that were in short supply as a result of the devastating effects of the World War II [11]. It was traditionally applied to reduce cost of projects, processes and services, with the view of improving performances which will ensure competitiveness and profitability [12]. The basic goal over here was to improve value realization. Initial work in this area defined value as a ratio of output (function) to the input (cost) [13]. This means that value can be enhanced essentially by increasing functionalities of products, processes or services at the expense of cost, although it is practically difficult to achieve. A clear limitation with this approach was that it was difficult to quantify functionalities in financial terms hence making value a subjective measure. An alternative approach recommended by value engineering is to define value as a ratio of importance to cost, where importance refers to fulfilment of product design specifications, product functionality and reliability, customer requirements, aesthetics etc.

Hence

Value of business process = (Importance of business process) / (cost of business process)   (1)

Analytical Hierarchical Process (AHP) has proven to be an effective technique for complex decision making and measuring relative importance of one process (decision) over the other [14]. The outcome of AHP is a prioritized ranking or weighting of each decision alternative. Three steps often feature in the application of AHP. These are:

- constructing hierarchies,
- comparative judgment;
- synthesis of priorities.

'Constructing hierarchies' requires that complex decisions are structured into a hierarchy descending from the overall objective to various 'criteria', 'sub-criteria', and so on until the lowest level. During the comparative judgment stage, prioritization of elements at each level ('elements' means number of the hierarchy) is done. A set of comparison matrices of all elements in a level of the hierarchy with respect to an element of the immediately higher level are constructed so as to prioritize and convert individual comparative judgments into ration scale measurements. The preferences are then quantified by using a nine-point scale as described by Table 1.

Table 1: Scale of preference between two elements

Preference weights/ level of importance	Definition	Explanation
1	Equally preferred	Two activities contribute equally to the objective.
3	Moderately preferred	Experience & judgment slightly favour one activity over another.
5	Strongly preferred	Experience & judgment strongly or essentially favour one activity over another.
7	Very strongly preferred	An activity is strongly favoured over another and its dominance demonstrated in practice.
9	Extremely preferred	The evidence favouring one activity over another is of the highest degree possible of affirmation.
2,4,6,8	Intermediates values	Used to represent compromise between the preferences listed above.
Reciprocals	Reciprocals for inverse comparison	

During the synthesis of priorities, the pair-wise comparisons generate a matrix of relative rankings for each level of hierarchy. The number of matrices depends on the number of elements at each level whilst the order of the matrix at each level depends on the number of elements at the lowest level that links it. After all matrices are developed and all pair-wise comparisons are obtained, eigenvectors or the relative weights (the maximum eigen value (λmax)) for each matrix are calculated. The λmax value is an important validating parameter in AHP. It is used as a reference index to screen information by calculating the consistency ratio CR of the estimated vector in order to validate whether the pair-wise comparison matrix provides a completely consistent evaluation. The consistency ratio is estimated as a ratio of consistency index (CI) to random consistency index (RI) as expressed in equations 2 and 3.

i) The consistency index for each matrix of order n is derived by the formulae:

$$CI = (\lambda max - N)/ (N-1) \qquad (2)$$

ii) The consistency ratio is calculated using the formulae:

$$R = CI/RI \qquad (3)$$

R1, random consistency index is obtained from a large number of simulation runs and varies depending upon the order of matrix.

3.0   Case Study Application of Methodology

3.1   Background of Company

The case study application relates to a Make to Order (MTO) pump manufacturing enterprise (herein referred to as 'ABC') located in Pakistan. ABC has been producing pumps of various makes in batches for its commercial customers since the past four decades. During the last three decades, the company has rapidly expanded its production range to include a large variety of pumps to serve various sectors of the economy. The new pumps for local production have been selected to particularly meet the requirements of sugar, paper and other process and chemical industries whilst meeting the requirements of drinking water supply, sewage disposal and surface drainage schemes.

ABC employs over 400 people and has many sales offices across the country. ABC is ISO 9001 certified with a progressive management team. In addition ABC has enacted a Business Process Reengineering (BPR) team to device improvements techniques to support their business processes so that cost of production may be reduced whilst improving productivity and quality. It is in support of this objective that the research was conducted.

3.2   Description of Manufacturing Process

In practice raw castings of pump flanges are produced by the foundry unit and allowed to undergo six other manufacturing operations. The initial process requires 'roughing' of the piece on a manual lathe machine, which is followed by further cutting and face turning operations. Activities like milling, drilling and deburring are also performed on the metal piece before final quality control is done. Figure 1 shows a simplified activity diagram based on the state of the art computer integrated manufacturing open systems architecture (CIMOSA), for the manufacture of flanges for a specific type of pump.

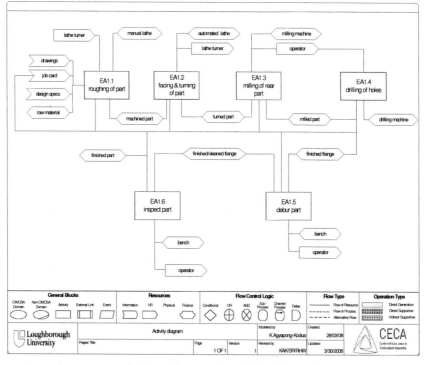

Fig. 1. CIMOSA activity diagram for the manufacture of flanges (simplified)

3.3   Data Collection and Results

BUSINESS PROCESS VALUE ANALYSIS USING AN ANALYTICAL HIERARCHICAL PROCESS

During the research data was collected through the interview of managers and other key staff associated with the process of interest. Data related to :

1. process cost for selected manufacturing operations;
2. quality and inspection history for products within research scope and
3. importance of selected manufacturing operations.

The latter was obtained through questionnaires and interviews whilst the others were based on existing data in the company. Typical figures related to processing times and cost associated with the six different operations are shown in Table 2.

Table 2: Cost and Time Data

Operation	Operation Time (hr)	Cost (Pak. Rupees)	Cost (%)
1 (roughing of part – manual lathe)	4	1,600/-	14.16%
2 (facing-automatic lathe)	6	3,600/-	31.86%
3 (milling)	8	4,200/-	37.17%
4 (drilling of holes)	2.5	1,500/-	13.27%
5 (deburring/cleaning)	0.5	150/-	1.33%
6 (quality checks)	0.5	250/-	2.21%
Total	21.5	11,300/-	100%

Further to this data collection, interviews were conducted from five relevant staff of the company regarding the relative importance of the six manufacturing processes. Four out of the five interviews were found consistent. One was rejected because its CR was outside the acceptable range of 0 to 0.20 (see Table 3).

Table 3: Example interview data sheet for case company

Interview Number	Interviewee's Designation	Interviewee's Department	Consistency Ratio (CR) For Interview	Interview Result (Accept/Reject)
1	Manager	Production	0.109	Accept
2	Manager	BPR	0.026	Accept
3	Asst. Manager	Production	0.090	Accept
4	Asst. Manager	Quality	0.280	Reject
5	Foreman	Production	0.016	Accept

An excel based approach demonstrating how a sample eigen value and pair-wise comparisons was performed is shown in figure 2

BUSINESS PROCESS VALUE ANALYSIS USING AN ANALYTICAL HIERARCHICAL PROCESS

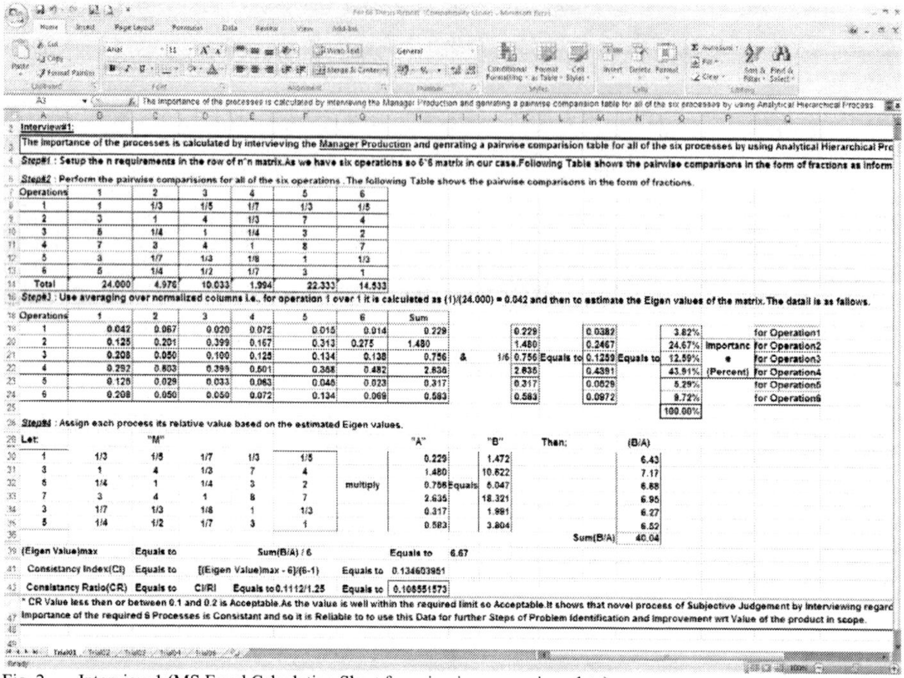

Fig. 2.   Interview 1 (MS Excel Calculation Sheet for pair wise comparison data).

Similar analysis was done for the four results gathered and the results shown in Table 4. A graph of importance against cost was also plotted to illustrate the processes or operations which needed improvement should the quest for process improvement be maintained (see figure 3).

Table 4: Value Table for Case Study 1

Opt .#	Importance of Operations (in percent) as mentioned by Interviewee (interview #)					Average Value of Importance	Cost (in Percent)	Imp. v/s Cost result (+ve/-ve)
	1	2	3	4	5			
1	3.82	3.29	5.16		4.22	4.12	14.16	-ve
2	24.67	32.41	24.84	Interview Not	35.62 (2')	29.39	31.86	-ve
3	12.59	15.35	13.45	Consistent	10.47	12.97	37.17	-ve
4	43.91	29.75	43.50	(interview	35.62	38.19	13.27	+ve
5	5.29	6.09	3.31	rejected)	4.22	4.73	1.33	+ve
6	9.72	13.11	9.73		9.86	10.61	2.21	+ve

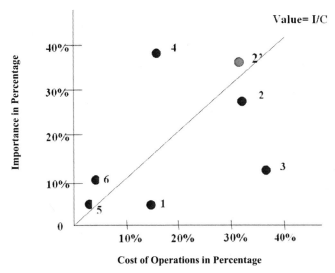

Fig. 3.   Cost – Importance Graph based on average value

From the foregoing results, it was imperative to admit that operations 4, 5 & 6 created more value in relative terms than operations 1, 2 and 3. Operations 5 and 6 are close to the limit and may require improvement to enhance the values. Also for profitability and sustainability, operations 1 and 3 may need to be improved.

4.0   Observations and Recommendations

Throughout the research it was observed that adequate time was necessary for interviews and data collection. The key challenge was appropriately selecting the human resource for interviews. Their objectivity was critical in ensuring that the rating of relative importance was accurate.

A study of the results shown in Table 4 indicated that for the company to remain profitable and competitive in its life time, most of the flange making operations are to be improved. Operation 1 (flange roughing) is done at a high cost whilst its importance is relatively low. This can be improved through casting the machine part to precision so that less machining will be required during roughing. When the time associated with machining is reduce, the cost associated with the operation will reduce whilst its importance is maintained, this will ensure an increase in value of the operation.

It was observed that 40% of the total time for operation 2 was used for setting up the work piece on the automatic lathe machine. It is therefore recommended that specially designed fixtures would be made introduced to reduce setup time. This approach may increase the tooling cost but the economics of mass production will ensure that the cost per unit of product is marginal.

Operation 3 can be improved by avoiding the milling of complicated contours on the rear side of the flange. This activity is functionally not very important. It was introduced to reduce the weight but on the other hand it ended up being expensive. A separate study may be required to investigate alternative materials that could be used.

Training of staff involved in the deburring and cleaning operations is required to improve the utilization of materials such as thinner, cotton cloth, safety gloves and shoes. The quality inspection was necessary hence exceeded the value requirements. However operators may be trained to be quality conscious which will improve the level of quality flanges that are manufactured.

It was observed that the AHP method assisted in measuring 'relative importance' of processes and hence in a way value could be quantified and plotted on a graph to determine which operations generated less value yet cost more. This verification assisted the company to benchmark which operations to improve in terms of 'importance and cost'.

References

[1]   Sraffa, P. and D. Maurice (1951). "The works and correspondence of David Ricardo." Cambridge University Press **1**.

[2]   Ramsay, D. (1992). "From Marx to Misses: Post-capitalist society and the challenge of economic calculation." La Salle: Open Court.

[3]   Shaikh, A. (1998). The empirical strength of the labour theory of value. Conference proceedings of Marxian economics, Macmillan, London.

[4]   Bicheno, J. (2000). The Lean Toolbox. Buckingham, England, PICSIE Books.

[5]   Hines, P. and R. Nick (1997). "The seven value stream mapping tools." International Journal of Operations and Production Management **17**(1): 46-64.

[6]   Jones, D. and J. Womack (2003). Seeing the Whole. Brookline, Massachusetts, USA

[7]   Womack, J. P., D. Jones, et al. (1990). The Machine that Changed the World: The Story of Lean Production. New York, Rawson Associates.

[8]   Agyapong-Kodua, K. and R. H. Weston (2007). "Towards the derivation of working definition of value." Internal paper: MSI Research Institute, Loughborough University, UK.

[9]   Park, R. (1998). "Value Engineering: A Plan for Invention ".

[10]   Miles, L. D. (2000). "Techniques of Value Analysis and Engineering."

[11]   Miles, L. D. and H. Erlicher (1947). "Value Engineering."

[12]   Tantawy, M. A. (2003). "Systematically optimizing the functions and values of goods and services."

[13]   Al-Yousefi, A. (1996). "Value management: concept & techniques."

[14]   Saaty, T. L. (1980). The Analytic Hierarchy Process: Planning, Priority Setting, Resource Allocation, McGraw-Hill.

The 6th International Conference on Manufacturing Research (ICMR08)
Brunel University, UK, 9-11th September 2008

MULTI – CRITERIA DECISION MAKING IN SUPPLIER SELECTION USING VIKOR AND ELECTRE METHODS

P.Parthiban [1], Y.R.K.Chowdary [2], M.Punniyamoorthy [3], K.Ganesh [4]

1. Lecturer, Department of Production Engineering, National Institute of Technology, Tiruchirappalli-620 015, India.E-mail:parthee_p@yahoo.com

2. M.Tech Scholar, Department of Production Engineering, National Institute of Technology, Tiruchirappalli-620 015, India.E-mail:yrkc499@yahoo.com

3. Professor, Department of Management Studies, National Institute of Technology, Tiruchirapalli-620 015, India.E-mail:punniya@nitt.edu

4. Assistant Consultant, Manufacturing Industry Practice, Tata Consultancy Services Limited, Email: kog@iitm.ac.in

Abstract

Today's consumers demand cheaper, high quality products, on-time delivery and excellent after-sale services. Hence, companies are under intense pressure to cut product and material costs while maintaining a high level of quality and after-sale services. Achieving this starts with supplier selection. Therefore, an efficient supplier selection process needs to be in place and of paramount importance for successful supply chain management. It begins with the realization of the need for a new supplier; determination and formulation of decision criteria; pre-qualification; final supplier selection; and the monitoring of the suppliers selected. Hence, development of an effective and rational supplier selection model is naturally desirable. Several evaluation and selection models for supplier selection have been proposed and reported in the supply chain literature. Supplier selection is an important purchasing activity for many firms. Given the financial importance, utility function and the multi-criteria nature of supplier selection decision, in this research an effort is made to develop a compromise ranking method called VIKOR that highlight those aspects for evaluation and selection of suppliers. The contribution of VIKOR is investigated, together with the assessment of proposed methodology with the existing multi-criteria decision making technique such as ELECTRE. The developed methodology has been illustrated using a case study for a retailer supply chain with the consideration of entities such as distributors, retailers and customers.

Key Words: Supplier selection, MCDM, VIKOR Method, ELECTRE Method

1.0   Introduction

In today's highly competitive and global operating environment, due to the high variety of customer demands, advances in technologies and the increasing importance of communication and information systems companies have been forced to focus on supply chain management. A supply chain is "an integrated process where in a number of various business entities (i.e., suppliers, manufacturers, distributors, and retailers) work together in an effort to: (1) acquire raw materials/components, (2) convert these raw materials/ components into specified final products, and (3) deliver these final products to retailers". This chain is traditionally characterized by the flow of materials and information both within and between business entities. Supply chain management is the use of information technology to endow automated intelligence to the planning and control of the flow of supply chain to speed time to market, reduce inventory levels, lower overall costs and, ultimately, enhance customer service and satisfaction. The ultimate goal of supply chain management is to meet customer's demand more efficiently. Briefly speaking, for a manufacturing enterprise, it is to make the right product, for the right customer, in the right amount, at the right time.

In most industries the cost of raw materials and component parts constitutes the main cost of a product, such that in some cases it can account for up to 70%. In such circumstances the purchasing department can play a key role in cost reduction, and supplier selection is one of the important functions of purchasing management. Several factors affect a supplier's performance. Hence it is a multi-criteria problem and it is necessary to make a trade off between conflicting tangible and intangible factors to find the best suppliers. Supplier selection process begins with the realization of the need for a new supplier; determination and formulation of decision criteria; pre-qualification (initial screening and drawing up a shortlist of potential suppliers from a large list); final supplier selection; and the monitoring of the suppliers selected (i.e. continuous evaluation and assessment).It is generally agreed in the literature that the following makes the supplier selection decision making process difficult and/or complicated

Supplier selection is a multi-criteria problem which includes both qualitative and quantitative factors. In order to select the best suppliers it is necessary to make a tradeoff between these tangible and intangible factors some of which may conflict. MCDM techniques support the decision makers (DMs) in evaluating a set of supplier against set of criteria. Multi- Criteria Decision Making is the most well known branch of decision making. It is a branch of a general class of Operations Research (or OR) models which deal with decision problems under the presence of a number of decision criteria. According to many authors MCDM is divided into Multi-Objective Decision Making (or MODM) and Multi-Attribute Decision Making (or MADM).

MODM studies decision problems in which the decision space is continuous. A typical example is mathematical programming problems with multiple objective functions. On the other hand, MCDM concentrates on problems with discrete decision spaces. In these problems the set of decision alternatives has been predetermined. Although MCDM methods may be widely diverse, many of them have certain aspects in common.

An MCDM problem can be easily expressed in matrix format. A decision matrix $\mathbf{A}$ is an $(M \times N)$ matrix in which element a_{ij} indicates the performance of alternative Ai when it is evaluated in terms of decision criterion Cj, (for $i = 1,2,3,..., M$, and $j = 1,2,3,..., N$). It is also assumed that the decision maker has determined the weights of relative performance of the decision criteria (denoted as Wj, for $j = 1,2,3,..., N$).

**MULTI – CRITERIA DECISION MAKING IN SUPPLIER SELECTION USING VIKOR AND
ELECTRE METHODS**

2.0   Literature Review

Early in 1960s, Dickson [1] identified 23 criteria that ought to be considered by purchasing personnel in evaluating suppliers. A latter review by Weber et al. [2] reported that well over half of 74 research papers reviewed addressed the supplier selection problem with multiple criteria. Another comprehensive review by De Boer et al. [3] discussed a framework for supplier selection. The framework covers different phases of the supplier selection process, including pre-qualification, formulation of criteria, final evaluation, etc. In the final evaluation phase of suppliers, after pre-qualification, quantitative models incorporating multi-criteria were constructed.

Some of the simple techniques for vendor evaluation include categorical, weighted point, and cost ratio approaches. The categorical method is discussed widely by Zenz [4]. In the categorical method, buyer rates each vendor as being preferred, unsatisfactory, or neutral on all the attributes considered in the evaluation process. The limitation with this approach is that all the attributes are weighted equally. Timmerman [5] proposes the so-called cost-ratio method. The cost ratio method evaluates the cost of each factor as a percentage of total purchases for the vendor. However, this approach has difficulties in developing cost accounting systems for this purpose.

In linear weighting models weights are given to the criteria, the biggest weight indicating the highest importance. Ratings on the criteria are multiplied by their weights and summed in order to obtain a single figure for each supplier. The supplier with the highest overall rating can then be selected. The analytical hierarchy process (AHP) is another method which uses pairwise comparison and it was applied by Narasimhan [6] and Nydick [7]. This approach is more accurate than the other scoring methods. De Boer et al. [8] suggested Outranking approach in which pair wise comparisons are made among alternatives under each one of the criteria separately.

Mathematical Programming Models allows the decision-maker to formulate the decision problem in terms of a mathematical objective function that are to be maximized or minimized. Weber and Current [9] developed a multi- objective MIP for vendor selection and order allocation among the selected vendors. Ghodsypour and O'Brien [10] used an integrated AHP and LP model for the vendor selection and order allocation problem.

In a research paper published by Zeger Degraeve, Eva Labro , Filip Roodhooft, [11] the authors propose to use the concept of Total Cost of Ownership as a basis for comparing vendor selection models. The TCO quantifies all costs associated with the purchasing process throughout the entire value chain of the firm. The cost of the acquisition and subsequent use of an item or service that is to be purchased is determined The three components of the TCO, namely supplier level cost, order level cost and unit level cost in percentages are the final values in the TCO approach

Talluri, Narasimhan,[12] suggested max-min approach to vendor selection The concept behind Max–min approach is to maximize and minimize the performance of a vendor against the best target measures set by the buyer. The combination of models utilized in this approach provides two measures of performance for each vendor, where higher values indicate better levels of performance.

Manoj Kumar, Prem Vrat, R. Shankar[13] take up a hybrid approach to vendor selection. A fuzzy mixed integer goal programming vendor selection problem that includes three primary goals: minimizing the net cost

**MULTI – CRITERIA DECISION MAKING IN SUPPLIER SELECTION USING VIKOR AND
ELECTRE METHODS**

minimizing, minimizing the net rejections, minimizing the net late deliveries subject to realistic constraints regarding buyer's demand, vendors' capacity, vendors' quota flexibility purchase value of items, budget allocation to individual vendor, etc

3.0   Problem Definition

In real time, retailers have the problem in selecting the right brand or right company for each consumer product. So that the retailer faces problems of maintaining more inventories for the non moving products. And he needs each brand to give his product with quality, delivery in right time and etc. In overall the retailers view is to   minimize the total purchase cost, maximize the product quality by minimizing the number of defective items and to maximize the delivery reliability, by minimizing the number of items missing their target delivery time and minimizing the number of items missing their target quantity, subjected to the demand, production and shipping capacity, in order to determine the who are the vendors to be selected for a particular product so that the retailers may have more sales and increase in profit.

The factors to evaluate the suppliers were selected through Brain storming among guide and experts. Selection factors selected for the retailers point of view. In this work, two multi criteria decision making methods such as VIKOR Method and ELECTRE Method were proposed as solution methodology.

4.0   Methodology

4.1   VIKOR method

The VIKOR method was developed to solve MCDM problems with conflicting and noncommensurable (different units) criteria, assuming that compromising is acceptable for conflict resolution, the decision maker wants a solution that is the closest to the ideal, and the alternatives are evaluated according to all established criteria. This method focuses on ranking and selecting from a set of alternatives in the presence of conflicting criteria, and on proposing compromise solution (one or more).

The advantage of the VIKOR method, enabling it to be applied in situations with multiple criteria, follows from the use of the L_p metric in the compromising programming method. It can be described as follows:

$$L_{p,i} = \left\{ \sum_{j=1}^{n} [w_j (f_j^* - f_{i,j})/(f_j^* - f_j^-)]^p \right\}^{\frac{1}{p}}$$

(1)

Where $1 \leq p \leq \infty$; $i = 1, 2, \ldots\ldots, m$

The utility function of the VIKOR method is an aggregate of $L_{1,i}$ and $L_{\infty,i}$. $L_{1,i}$ is interpreted as 'concordance' and can provide decision makers with information about the maximum 'group utility' or 'majority'. Similarly, $L_{\infty,i}$ is interpreted as 'discordance' and provides decision makers with information about the minimum individual regret of the 'opponent'.

The VIKOR method includes the following steps.

MULTI – CRITERIA DECISION MAKING IN SUPPLIER SELECTION USING VIKOR AND ELECTRE METHODS

Step 1. Determine the normalized decision matrix

Let a_{ij} be the numerical score of alternative i on criterion j. The corresponding normalized value f_{ij} is defined:

$$f_{ij} = \frac{a_{ij}}{\sqrt{\sum_{i=1}^{m} a_{ij}^2}}, i = 1,2,...,m; j = 1,2,...,n. \tag{2}$$

Step 2. Determine Ideal Solution (A^*) & Negative Solution (A^-)

The ideal alternative and the negative ideal alternative, denoted as A^* and A^- respectively, are defined as:

$$A^* = \{(\max_i f_{ij} | j \in J),(\min_i f_{ij}| j \in J^{\cdot})|i=1,2,...,m\}$$
$$= \{f_1^*, f_2^*,...,f_j^*,...,f_n^*\} \tag{3}$$

$$A^- = \{(\min_i f_{ij} | j \in J),(\max_i f_{ij}| j \in J^{\cdot})|i=1,2,...,m\}$$
$$= \{f_1^-, f_2^-,...,f_j^-,...,f_n^-\} \tag{4}$$

Step 3. Calculate the utility measure and the regret measure

The utility measure and the regret measure for each alternative are given as

$$S_i = \sum_{j=1}^{n} w_j (f_j^* - f_{ij})/(f_j^* - f_j^-) \tag{5}$$

$$R_i = \max_j \left[w_j (f_j^* - f_{ij})/(f_j^* - f_j^-) \right] \tag{6}$$

where Si and Ri represent the utility measure and the regret measure, respectively, and wj is the weight of the jth criterion.

Step 4. Calculate the VIKOR index.

The VIKOR index can be expressed as follows:

$$Q_i = v(S_i - S^*)/(S^- - S^*) + (1 - v)(R_i - R^*)/(R^- - R^*) \tag{7}$$

where $S^* = \min_i S_i$, $S^- = \max_i S_i$, $R^* = \min_i R_i$, $R^-\ \max_i R_i$ $\tag{8}$

Step 5. Rank the order of preference

MULTI – CRITERIA DECISION MAKING IN SUPPLIER SELECTION USING VIKOR AND ELECTRE METHODS

The alternative with the smallest VIKOR value is determined to be the best value.

4.2   ELECTRE Method

The ELECTRE (for *Elimination and Choice Translating Reality*; English translation from the French original) method was first introduced in [Benayoun, *et al.*, 1966]. The basic concept of the ELECTRE method is to deal with *"outranking relations"* by using pairwise comparisons among alternatives under each one of the criteria separately. The ELECTRE methods are based on the evaluation of two indices, the concordance index and the discordance index, defined for each pair of alternatives. The concordance index for a pair of alternatives a and b measures the strength of the hypothesis that alternative a is at least as good as alternative b. The discordance index measures the strength of evidence against this hypothesis [Belton and Stewart, 2001]. There are no unique measures of concordance and discordance indices.

The ELECTRE Method includes the following steps

Step 1. Normalizing the Decision Matrix

Let a_{ij} be the numerical score of alternative i on criterion j. The corresponding normalised value f_{ij} is defined:

$$f_{ij} = \frac{a_{ij}}{\sqrt{\sum_{i=1}^{m} a_{ij}^2}}, i = 1,2,...,m; j = 1,2,...,n. \tag{9}$$

Step 2. Weighting the Normalized Decision Matrix

The column of the **F** matrix is then multiplied by its associated weights which were assigned to the criteria by the decision maker. Therefore, the weighted matrix, denoted as **Y**, is:

$$y_{ij} = w_j f_{ij}, i = 1,2,...,m; j = 1,2,...,n \tag{10}$$

Step 3. Determine the Concordance and Discordance Sets

The concordance set C_{kl} of two alternatives A_k and A_l, where $M.k, l \geq 1$, is defined as the set of all criteria for which A_k is preferred to A_l. That is, the following is true:

$$C_{kl} = \{j, \text{ such that: } y_{kj} \geq y_{lj}\}, \text{ for } j = 1, 2, 3, ..., N. \tag{11}$$

The complementary subset is called the discordance set and it is described as follows:

$$D_{kl} = \{j, \text{ such that: } y_{kj} < y_{lj}\}, \text{ for } j = 1, 2, 3, ..., N. \tag{12}$$

Step 4. Construct the Concordance and Discordance Matrices

MULTI – CRITERIA DECISION MAKING IN SUPPLIER SELECTION USING VIKOR AND
ELECTRE METHODS

The concordance index c_{kl} is the sum of the weights associated with the criteria contained in the concordance set.

That is, the following is true:

$$C_{kl} = \sum_{j \in C_{kl}} w_j, \quad for \; j = 1,2 \ldots , N$$

(13)

The concordance index indicates the relative importance of alternative A_k with respect to alternative A_l. The discordance matrix $\mathbf{D}$ expresses the degree that a certain alternative A_k is worse than a competing alternative A_l. The elements d_{kl} of the discordance matrix is defined as follows:

$$d_{kl} = \frac{\max_{j \in D_{kl}} |y_{kj} - y_{lj}|}{\max_j |y_{kj} - y_{lj}|}$$

(14)

Step 5. Building the outranking relations

After computing the concordance and discordance indices for each pair of alternatives, two types of outranking relations are built by comparing these indices with two pairs of threshold values: (C^*, D^*) and $(C^-$,$D^-)$. The pair (C^*, D^*) is defined as the concordance and discordance thresholds for the *strong* outranking relation and the pair (C^-, D^-) is defined as the thresholds for the *weak* outranking relation where $C^* > C^-$ and $D^* < D^-$.

Next the outranking relations are built according to the following two rules:

(1) If $C(a, b) \geq C^*$, $D(a, b) \leq D^*$ and $C(a, b) \geq C(b, a)$, then alternative a is regarded as strongly outranking alternative b.

(2) If $C(a, b) \geq C^-$, $D(a, b) \leq D^-$ and $C(a, b) \geq C(b, a)$, then alternative a is regarded as weakly outranking alternative b.

The values of (C^*, D^*) and (C^-, D^-) are decided by the decision makers for a particular outranking relation.

Step 5. Rank the alternatives using distillation process

On the basis of the outranking relations, next the descending and ascending distillation processes are applied to obtain two complete pre-orders of the alternatives. The descending pre-order is built up by starting with the set of "best" alternatives (those which outrank other alternatives) and going downward to the worse one. On the contrary, the ascending pre-order is built up by starting with the set of "worst" alternatives (those which are outranked by other alternatives) and going upward to the best one.

MULTI – CRITERIA DECISION MAKING IN SUPPLIER SELECTION USING VIKOR AND ELECTRE METHODS

5.0   Case Illustration

The developed methodology has been illustrated using a case study for a retailer supply chain with the consideration of entities such as distributors, retailers and customers. Data was collected from a computer retailer shop. Altogether three products that are sold in retailer outlet are chosen. They are

      1.   Business PC'S ....(Product 1)

      2.   Home PC'S ....(Product 2)

      3.   Networking PC'S ....(Product 3)

Altogether six brands are chosen for these three products. These six brands supply all the three products.

5.1   PRODUCT 1 (BUSINESS PC'S)

There are four modules in evaluating suppliers

      1.   Selecting the criteria

      2.   Weighting the criteria

      3.   Constructing the decision matrix

      4.   Solving the decision matrix using selected methodologies

Module 1: selecting the criteria

Criteria for selecting Supplier

      1.   Timely delivery   (TD)

      2.   Quality   **(QY)**

      3.   Profit   **(PR)**

      4.   Proactive service   **(PS)**

      5.   Replacement of unmoved stock   **(RS)**

Module 2 : Weighting the criteria

In this study we have used Pairwise Comparison method. The method involves pairwise comparisons to create a ratio matrix. It takes pairwise comparisons as input and produced relative weights as output.

Table 1. Criteria weights for the product 1

MULTI – CRITERIA DECISION MAKING IN SUPPLIER SELECTION USING VIKOR AND ELECTRE METHODS

Criteria	TD	QY	PR	PS	RS
Weights	0.1904	0.5410	0.1273	0.0407	0.1004

Module 3 : Constructing the decision matrix

Table 2. Decision matrix for the product 1

Supplier/Criteria	TD	QY	PR	PS	RS
A1	0.85	0.95	5000	0.8	0.8
A2	0.9	0.95	2500	0.95	0.9
A3	1	0.9	2000	0.95	0.95
A4	0.95	0.95	3000	0.9	0.85
A5	0.8	0.8	4000	0.85	0.7
A6	0.8	0.85	4500	0.8	0.75

Module 4 : Solving the decision matrix using selected methodologies

VIKOR Method

Utility measure, Regret measure and VIKOR index for each alternative

Table 3. Utility measure, Regret measure and VIKOR index for each alternative for the product 1

Suppliers	Utility measure (S_i)	Regret measure (R_i)	VIKOR index (Q_i) at $\mathcal{V} = 0.5$
A1	0.2437	0.1428	0.1036
A2	0.2214	0.1061	0.0478
A3	0.3077	0.1803	0.1895
A4	0.1862	0.0849	0
A5	0.9015	0.54104	1
A6	0.6934	0.3606	0.6568

Preference order using VIKOR Method.

A4 > A2 > A1 > A3 > A6 > A5

MULTI – CRITERIA DECISION MAKING IN SUPPLIER SELECTION USING VIKOR AND ELECTRE METHODS

ELECTRE Method

Outranking relations for the product 1

$C^* = 0.8$, $\qquad$ $D^* = 0.25$, $\qquad$ $\overline{C} = 0.65$, $\qquad$ $\overline{D} = 0.35$

Table 4. Strong and weak outranking relations for the product 1

	A1	A2	A3	A4	A5	A6
A1	X	–	S^f	–	S^F	S^F
A2	–	X	–	–	–	–
A3	–	–	X	–	–	–
A4	–	S^f	S^f	X	–	–
A5	–	–	–	–	X	–
A6	–	–	–	–	S^F	X

Preference order using ELECTRE Method.

The pre-order from the descending distillation is A1 > A4 > A6 > A2 = A3 = A5

The pre-order from the ascending distillation is A3 = A5 < A2 < A6 < A1 = A4.

The two pre-orders are combined to get final pre-order

$\qquad$ A1 > A4 > A6 > A2 > A3 = A5

5.2 PRODUCT 2 (HOME PC'S)

Decision matrix for the product 2

Table 5. Decision matrix for product 2

Supplier/Criteria	TD	QY	PR	PS	RS
A1	0.8	0.85	3000	0.9	0.8
A2	0.95	0.9	2500	0.9	0.9
A3	0.9	0.95	2150	0.95	0.85
A4	0.95	0.95	3500	0.95	0.95
A5	0.6	0.8	2000	0.8	0.75
A6	0.75	0.85	3450	0.85	0.75

Criteria weights for the product 2

Table 6. Criteria weights for product 2

Criteria	TD	QY	PR	PS	RS

MULTI – CRITERIA DECISION MAKING IN SUPPLIER SELECTION USING VIKOR AND ELECTRE METHODS

Weights	0.1748	0.4367	0.2943	0.0654	0.0285

Preference order using VIKOR Method

A4 > A2 > A3 > A6 > A1 > A5

Preference order using ELECTRE Method

A4 > A1 = A2 = A3 = A6 > A5

5.3. PRODUCT 3 (NETWORKING PC'S)

Decision matrix for the product 3

Table 7. Decision matrix for product 2

Supplier/Criteria	TD	QY	PR	PS	RS
A1	0.8	0.85	3000	0.9	0.8
A2	0.95	0.9	2500	0.9	0.9
A3	0.9	0.95	2150	0.95	0.85
A4	0.95	0.95	3500	0.95	0.95
A5	0.6	0.8	2000	0.8	0.75
A6	0.75	0.85	3450	0.85	0.75

Criteria weights for the product 3

Table 8. Criteria weights for product 3

Criteria	TD	QY	PR	PS	RS
Weights	0.1904	0.5410	0.1273	0.0407	0.1004

Preference order using VIKOR Method

A2> A4 > A3 > A6 > A1 > A5

Preference order using ELECTRE Method

A3 = A2 > A4 > A6 >A1 > A5

**MULTI – CRITERIA DECISION MAKING IN SUPPLIER SELECTION USING VIKOR AND
ELECTRE METHODS**

6.0   Results & Discussion

Ranking of suppliers

Table 9. Ranking of suppliers

S.NO	SUPPLIERS	PRODUCT 1 (BUSINESS PC'S)		PRODUCT 2 (HOME PC'S)		PRODUCT 3 (NETWORKING PC'S)	
		VIKOR METHOD	ELECTRE METHOD	VIKOR METHOD	ELECTRE METHOD	VIKOR METHOD	ELECTRE METHOD
1	A1	3	1	5	2	5	5
2	A2	2	4	2	2	1	1
3	A3	4	5	3	2	3	1
4	A4	1	2	1	1	2	3
5	A5	6	5	6	6	6	6
6	A6	5	3	4	2	4	4

From the results it is found out that in case of PRODUCT 1, best alternative suggested by VIKOR method is A4, and best alternative suggested by ELECTRE method is A1. In case of PRODUCT 2, best and worst alternatives suggested by two methods are same but for the remaining alternatives these methods are giving different ranking. In case of PRODUCT 3, there is no difference in outputs from the three methods.

7.0   Conclusion

Supplier selection is one of the most important processes in supply chain and must be systematically considered from the decision makers. For this reason, supplier selection is evaluated by researchers for many years in a large framework consisting of various techniques from the experimental to the analytical ones and its successful applications were performed in numerous sectors.

This project proposed a unique approach called VIKOR Method for supplier selection by considering the concordance, discordance and maximum group utility. The VIKOR method for supplier selection presented in this research allows for comprehensive evaluation of supplier performance by estimating ideal, negative solution, utility and regret measures. A statistical data was used to exemplify the performance of two methods. From the results, it is observed that ELECTRE method is not giving complete pre order in some cases.

References

[1]   G.W. Dickson, (1966) An analysis of vendor selection systems and decisions, Journal of Purchasing 2 (1) 5–17.

**MULTI – CRITERIA DECISION MAKING IN SUPPLIER SELECTION USING VIKOR AND
ELECTRE METHODS**

[2] C.A. Weber, J.R. Current, W.C. Benton, (1991) Vendor selection criteria and methods, European Journal of Operational Research 50 ,2–18.

[3] L. De Boer, E. Labro, P. Morlacchi,(2001) A review of methods supporting supplier selection, European Journal of Purchasing & Supply Management 7 ,75–89

[4] Zenz, G., (1981). Purchasing and the Management of Materials. Wiley, New York.

[5] Timmerman, E., (1986). An approach to vendor performance evaluation. Journal of Purchasing and Supply Management 1, 27-32

[6] Narasimhan, R., (1983). An analytic approach to supplier selection. Journal of Purchasing and Supply Management 1, 27-32.

[7] Nydick, R.L., Hill, R.P., (1992). Using the Analytic Hierarchy Process to structure the supplier selection procedure. International Journal of Purchasing and Materials Management 28 (2), 31-36.

[8] De Boer et al. (1998), Van der Wegen, L. and Telgen, J. (1998) Outranking methods in support of supplier selection. European Journal of Purchasing & Supply Management, 4: p. 109-118

[9] Weber, C.A., Current, J.R., (1993). A multiobjective approach to vendor selection. European Journal of Operational Research 68, 173-184.

[10] Ghoudsypour, S.H., O'Brien, C.O., (1998). A decision support system for supplier selection using an integrated analytic hierarchy process and linear programming. International Journal of Production Economics 56-57 (1-3), 199-212.

[11] Degraeve, Z., Labro,2., Roodhooft, F., (2000). An evaluation of supplier selection methods from a Total Cost of Ownership perspective. European Journal of Operational Research 125(1), 34-59.

[12] Srinivas Talluri , Ram Narasimhan, (2003). Vendor evaluation with performance variability:A max–min approach, European Journal of Operational Research 146, 543–552.

[13] Manoj Kumara, Prem Vratb, R. Shankar, (2004). A fuzzy goal programming approach for vendor selection problem in a supply chain, Computers & Industrial Engineering 46, 69–85.

[14] E. Triantaphyllou, B. Shu, S. Nieto Sanchez, and T. Ray, (1998). "Multi-Criteria Decision Making: An Operations Research Approach". Encyclopedia of Electrical and Electronics Engineering, (J.G. Webster, Ed.), John Wiley & Sons, New York, NY, Vol. 15, pp. 175-186.

[15] Lee-Ing Tong . Chi-Chan Chen . Chung-Ho Wang, (2007) Optimization of multi-response processes using the VIKOR method International Journal of Advanced Manufacturing Technology 31: 1049–1057

The 6th International Conference on Manufacturing Research (ICMR08)
Brunel University, UK, 9-11th September 2008

PRODUCTIVITY ENHANCEMENT IN A MANUFACTURING ENTERPRISE BY IMPROVING MANAGEMENT PROCESSES

S.Khalid, S. Rashid and R. H. Weston

MSI Research Institute, Loughborough University, Loughborough, Leics., UK

Abstract

This paper describes research findings when focussing on the key area of management in order to improve the productivity of a manufacturing enterprise. To quantify effects of alternate management policies on productivity, CIMOSA enterprise modelling principles are used in a unified way with those of simulation technologies. This is done by describing a case study 'Precision Parts' manufacturing enterprise working in Pakistan. In this case study models of most business processes of the company are documented. Also dynamic (simulation) models of key process segments have been developed. Also in this case study, outcomes from modelling have been new qualitative & quantitative understandings about (1) effects of different management policies on productivity, (2) testing and quantifying outcomes on productivity enhancement of alternative management functions (policies). These outcomes are useful particularly to the case company but also potentially to this business sector.

Key words: Productivity Improvement, Management Process, Enterprise Modelling(EM), Simulation Modelling(SM), Manufacturing Enterprise (ME).

1.0   Introduction

This paper illustrates a way of undertaking an analysis of how alternative management processes have causal impacts on the productivity of specific manufacturing enterprises. Often manufacturing enterprises are focusing on the physical and harder aspects of the system like technology and technical activities fulfilment. The design and implementation of suitable management processes will commonly get insufficient attention; bearing in mind the relative impacts that good and bad management policies may have. One major reason for this is that conventional best practice when creating management policies is typically ad hoc, non systematic and seldom is justified in terms of quantifiable outcomes. In theory therefore the use of well structured modelling methods in support of management process design can lead to sufficient competitive advantage. When developing the use of a model driven approach to design management process, this paper address the notion that management processes can be decomposed into planning, organizing, leading and controlling processes [1]. Each of these four management processes has an important role in proper management process application in manufacturing organizations. It is observed by the prime author of the paper that in manufacturing enterprises seldom is any processes of management given appropriate attention. For instance the prime and second authors have experienced a lack of planning, organizing and to some extent control processes in a number of large public sector manufacturing enterprises and in small and medium sized manufacturing enterprises in the developing industrial country of Pakistan. This weakness results in low productivity of insufficient number of these enterprises and high cost of production.

2.0   Case Study Description

To exemplify benefits that can be gained by using a model driven approach to management process design this paper consider the application of such an approach in case study manufacturing enterprise which makes various high precision products. The case study company (referred to as 'ABC') is a public sector make to order enterprise working in Pakistan. ABC can be categorized as medium to large enterprise as it has approximately 2500 regular employees performing different product realisation activities in different departments; namely as design, manufacturing, chemical treatment, integration, qualification and project management departments. The current As-Is network of processes deployed by ABC was documented using the CIMOSA(Computer Integrated Manufacturing Open System Architecture) [2]. Here four modelling templates [3]; called 'Context Diagrams', 'Sub-Context Diagrams' and 'Interaction Diagrams' and 'Activity Diagrams' can be populated with case data. Figure 1 shows the context diagram for ABC.

Fig. 1.   Context Diagram of 'ABC' Make to Order Precision Manufacturing Realization Domain.

The project management department (DM3 in figure 1) holds the role of coordinating management activities within other departments at three decisional levels, namely strategic, tactical and operational decision making about product realization. In this paper DM3 focus of modelling is on using CIMOSA 'Sub-Context Diagrams' and 'Interaction Diagrams', (see figure 2 and figure 3).

Fig. 2.   Sub-Context Diagram of 'ABC' Project Management Domain – DM3.

**PRODUCTIVITY ENHANCEMENT IN A MANUFACTURING ENTERPRISE BY IMPROVING
MANAGEMENT PROCESSES**

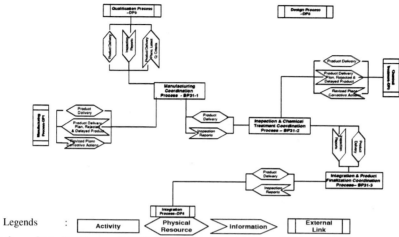

Legends :

| Activity | Physical Resource | Information | External Link |

Fig. 3   Interaction Diagram of 'ABC' Production Management Process – DP31.

ABC is facing significant problems because of having low productivity. Considering the above figure 3 which represent a portion of As-Is enterprise model of ABC, it is evident that no appropriate management process is in place. This lack of appropriate management process give a notion of low productivity.

Organizations generally operate in three hierarchical levels of management; top, middle and first line management (see figure 4).

i)   Top management – responsible for the entire organization having titles like CEO, president, executive director etc.

ii)   Middle management – located beneath the top level and are directly responsible for the work of first line management. Their titles include manager, director, chief, division head etc.

iii)   First line management – located at lower level of management and are directly responsible for operational work. Their titles include supervisors, group leaders, section in-charge etc.

The four management functions; planning, organizing, leading and controlling apply to all three hierarchical levels of management but there are some differences in emphasis [4].

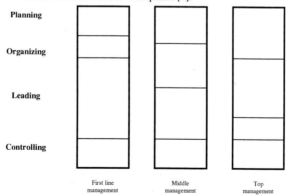

Fig. 4.   Management function at different hierarchical levels.

PRODUCTIVITY ENHANCEMENT IN A MANUFACTURING ENTERPRISE BY IMPROVING MANAGEMENT PROCESSES

To test the benefits of implementation of each of the management function described in figure 4 at different hierarchical levels a To-Be scenario is created for project management process DP31. In this scenario the effect of the "control" function of management process is introduced to the As-Is situation of the ABC (see figure 5).

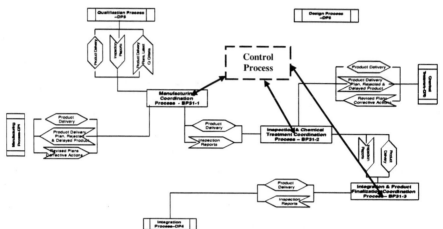

Figure 5.   Application of Control Process of Management on 'ABC' Production Management Process – DP31.

For instance in this paper only ABC's Manufacturing Coordination Process (BP31-1) is taken as an example to explain the effect of the control function and its results in terms of productivity. The Manufacturing Coordination Process is concerned primarily with coordination and transportation of mechanical products from the Mechanical Department to the Quality Department. After inspection accepted products are delivered to the Chemical Treatment Department for further processing. The configuration of ABC is such that the above mentioned departments; manufacturing, quality and chemical treatment department are not located in the same building or shop floor. The departments are at a distance of few kilometres apart from each other. In this case timely information about the readiness of the product and a better transportation support are of vital importance. Heavy work load on the quality department specially in the section of the bottleneck coordinate measuring machine (CMM) cause delays in communication regarding reporting inspected jobs ready to deliver. This is due to negligence of CMM operator busy in finishing the assigned jobs, busy phone lines, the responsible project manager to arrange the transport is not available on phone and large number of items inspected and in-process create a mess. Due to this communication failures and high work load the over all product completion times and hence productivity decrease. Although the procedure for reporting and communication are in place, they were considered to be a weak control that adds delays into the production process.

To test the effect of control process application on productivity an example item called as Top Flange is considered. Top flange products are manufactured in batches of ten by the manufacturing department. The Manufacturing Coordination Process (BP31-1) is required to communicate and provide transportation support to shift these items to the quality department for inspection. After 100% inspection acceptable items in the batches of top flanges are transported to the next process stage i.e., chemical treatment processing. As mentioned in the above paragraph due to loose control the communication delays cause production delays and hence decrease productivity. This situation was tested and analyzed using simulation technology. Simulation software SIMUL8 [5] is used which is a discrete event simulation tool. Initially the simulation model prepared and validated [6] replicated the 'As-Is' situation described above (see figure 6).

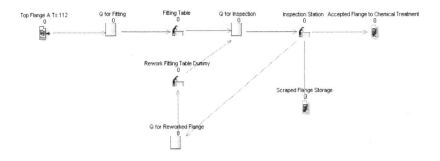

Fig. 6.   Application of Control Process of Management on 'ABC' Production Management Process – DP31

Effect of using better control and communication which is a To-Be scenario is then tested using the same simulation model with assignment of communication delays to zero. A results comparison is arranged in table 1.

Table 1: Effect of Control Process of Management for Manufacturing Coordination Process (BP31-1) on Productivity of ABC

Problems / Parameters	For Ideal System (To-Be scenario)	For System having weak Control Process (As-Is situation)
Average Time in System/job (hours)	6.35	8.45
Max. Time in System/job (hours)	8.05	12.20
Average Job Completed/week (Nos.)	6.10	4.10
Min. Job Completed/week (Nos.)	4.60	3.05

The results show that due to weak communication as part of the control function significant production delays are introduced which decreases the overall productivity in terms of more job's time in system and less job completion rate as described in table 1.

3.0   Conclusion

A systematic and unified application of CIMOSA and discrete event simulation modelling has illustrated how a selected management process has a vital impact on productivity in a case manufacturing enterprise. Better planning and organized leading to better designed control processes can significally increase the system output. The effect of better control process on productivity for a selected group of activities is the one to give rise of case company give rise to the need to apply better control on the whole value chain. Although only a control function of a management process has been tested, each and every function of management process like planning, organizing and leading has direct impact on the productivity of any organization whether private or public. Defining performance measures of each function and testing their effects on productivity in quantitative terms is an area of future studies for the authors. This will lead to design a better productive management system at all the hierarchical levels of enterprise while using unified modelling technique.

References

[1] **Antikainen, R.** (2006) Drivers of Knowledge Work Productivity, Tempere University of Technology, Finland.
[2] ESPIRIT CIMOSA Standards (1993) CIMOSA: Open System Architecture for CIM, Spinger-Verlag.
[3] **Monfared, R. P.** (2001) A component-based approach to design and construction of change capable manufacturing cell control systems. Ph.D. thesis, Manufacturing Engineering Department, Loughborough University.
[4] **Bartol, K. M. and Martin, D. C.** (1998) Management, McGraw Hill college div., ISBN9780073986548
[5] [Simul8 Corporation (2000), Simul8 User's Manual, ISBN: 0-97081-100-4.
[6] **Ramifarad, A.** and **Weston, R. H.,** (2006) The enhanced Use of Enterprise and Simulation Modelling Techniques to Support Factory Changeability, MSI Research Institute, Loughborough University, UK.

The 6th International Conference on Manufacturing Research (ICMR08)
Brunel University, UK, 9-11th September 2008

THE INCLUSION OF SHELF-LIFE EFFECTS INTO APIOBPCS INVENTORY MODELS

A.S.White, M.Censlive

School of Computing Science, Middlesex University

Abstract

The new e-business environment is concerned with rapid change. Principally we need rapid response to changes in customer requirements. The retailer of food and life-time limited products faces a costly dilemma to reduce wastage. In times of global warning it is essential to minimise excess production.

This paper describes a simple variant to the Towill/Disney models of inventory that includes the effects of shelf-life. We show here one method of reducing wastage of shelf-life limited products in a retail situation.

Keywords: Inventory, supply chain, shelf-life, deteriorating goods, APIOBPCS

1.0   Introduction

Supply Chains dominate the performance of modern Business. Many chains are at least imperfect or malfunctioning.

The new e-business environment is concerned with rapid change. Principally we need rapid response to changes in customer requirements. The retailer of food and life-time limited products faces a costly dilemma to reduce wastage. In times of global warning it is essential to minimise excess production.

In a supply chain we do not know the number of orders in advance. We only know the processes approximately. Several researchers have determined that the process of inventory control follows an automatic pipeline and order based production control system (APIOBPCS) (Riddalls and Bennett [1]) as observed by Sterman [2] in the playing of the 'Beer Game'.

Many problems exist in the chain, of which one, Bullwhip Wikner et al. [3]. is the amplification of disturbances to the demand/supply cycle the further down the chain the organisation is. A second problem is that if a product reaches the end of its' useful life before it can be sold then the retailer will lose money.

Developments in General Motors and Wal Mart show what business effectiveness can be gained from a better control of the supply chain. If the Bull whip effect can be reduced then safety stocks can be reduced at all levels in the chain, with subsequent cost savings.

1.1   Shelf-life Problems

Software designers have devised ERP software such as OMP planner that includes the problem of shelf life. These illustrate that it is an important problem for agricultural produces for example. National and International regulations are becoming much more important. In 2005 the European Union introduced the General Food law, which requires stringent quality assurance and traceability of food products. These elements of food safety and quality have caused food retailers and producers to examine all parts of their business much more carefully. Rapid growth of supermarkets in both developed and underdeveloped economies has transformed the whole are of food production and distribution. Supermarket share in Latin America and Asia is around 40-70% while in Africa it is around 10-25% (Vorst et al [4]). Procurement is shifting from wholesale markets to specialized wholesalers, using vast subcontracting chains. Many supermarkets have introduced Vendor Managed Inventory (VMI). This takes some of the susceptibility from the retailer to the supplier and will eventually provide gains for both sides if the economy is stable. Agrifood supply chains, as defined by Vorst, fall into two distinct classes:

- Chains for fresh products—these comprise growers, auction rooms, wholesalers, importers and exporters, retailers and specialty shops. All these stages leave the product essentially untouched. Main events are concerned with handling, storage, packing, transportation and trading of these goods.

- Chains for processed food products—portioned meats, juices, canned food, cooked food products
All the participants can experience quality decay because of delays in the other parts of the chain.

Table 1 Overview of Main characteristics of Food Supply Chain based on Vorst et al [5]

Supply chain stage	Product and process characteristics
overall	• Shelf life constraints • Recycling of materials
Growers and producers	• Long production times • Seasonality in production • Variability of quality and quantity of supply
Food processing industry	• High volume, low variety • Capital intensive machinery • Variable process • Storage buffer restricted
Auction/wholesalers/retailers	• Variability of quality • Seasonal supply • Requirements for conditioned transportation and storage • Shelf life problems

Table 1 shows the different aspects of differing components of the supply chain. The effect of these characteristics is to make the components of the supply chain be organized quite differently.

If we consider processed semi-finished poultry products, these are perishable and can only be held in stock for a limited time before they cannot be sold and must be discarded. There are health and contamination problems as well as costs associated with keeping this product in a fit state for consumption

THE INCLUSION OF SHELF LIFE EFFECTS INTO APIOBPCS INVENTORY MODELS

2.0   Modelling of Deteriorating Goods Supply Chains

Trends in modelling deteriorating inventory have been outlined by Goyal and Giri [6]. They classified models into three: those with a fixed lifetime; those with a random lifetime and those with an inventory corresponding to the proportional inventory decrease. The first two are generally treated using Markov techniques. The final division is split into uniform demand; time-varying demand; stock dependant demand or price dependant demand. These are generally treated using traditional OR methods.

.Arcelus et al [7] examines the effects of retailers pricing credit and inventory policies in response to temporary pricing incentives and provides schemes to deliver optimum price solutions. The system dynamics model of food chains from Georgiades et al [8] does not address the problem of shelf life at all. Chung-Yuan Dye et al [9] and Jian Li et al [10] both examine the use of an EOQ model to examine the effects of perishable items. The suggestion is that the retailer adds a percentage to their order for a cycle when there is no shortage or using a postponement strategy.

3.0   System Models

Conventional Operational Research models do not accurately represent the time variance of the supply chain. Two methods that do so are:
- System Dynamics
- Control-Theoretic Models

Both use similar features as the System is dominated by delays and feedback

In the control theoretic model the system can be simulated with SIMULINK® as it is here or described by transform methods.

The models described here are developed from the system dynamics models of Forrester [11] but are a good analytical basis to investigate control procedures (White [12]).

Delays due to production, for example, are described by a simple time constant Tp. The key to the way the inventory system behaves is the rate of ordering. The main structural system that has been investigated here is that a continuous model of APIOPBCS, the Automatic Pipeline, Inventory and Order Based Production Control System (APIOBPCS) within an inventory (Disney &Towill [13]).

The inventory error (EINV) is found as the difference between a fixed desired level of inventory (TINV) and the actual inventory (AINV). An averaging function is used to obtain the mean sales consumption (AVCON) as a function of the virtual consumption rate VCON or order from the retailer.

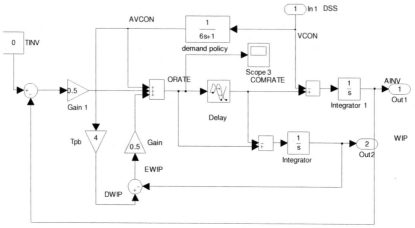

Fig. 1.   The APIOBPCS mode

This is used to obtain the order rate (ORATE) given to the production facility, wherever it is and whoever controls it. There is a delay in the production process. Disney and colleagues represent this production delay as a discrete delay. The stock-out problem is a direct result of this factory delay.

The sales smoothing was exponential in form, a good approximation to business practice of moving average smoothing (Towill [14]). Differing smoothing time constants were used for each stage.

3.1   The Shelf-life Model

The basic APIOBPCS of Towill and Disney is shown in Figure 1. This model has been modified to cater for the effects of shelf life by subtracting the produced inventory stock when it is positive and delaying it by a number of weeks. The best results from the tests conducted led to a model where variable inventory is targeted but not achieved.   A feed back of the amount of discarded items is subtracted from the required order rate.

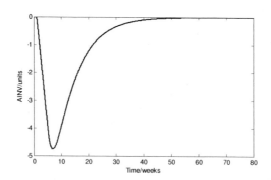

Fig. 2.   Inventory Response for APIOBPCS model

THE INCLUSION OF SHELF LIFE EFFECTS INTO APIOBPCS INVENTORY MODELS

This model reduces the amount of inventory still available and causes a larger order rate initially that for the regular model. Other models tested include the case with a constant target level, a model without WIP feedback and a model with a different delay model. All produced a worse set of results that the one illustrated here.

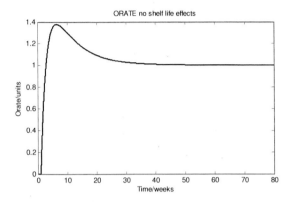

Fig. 3.   Order Rate for the APIOBPCS model

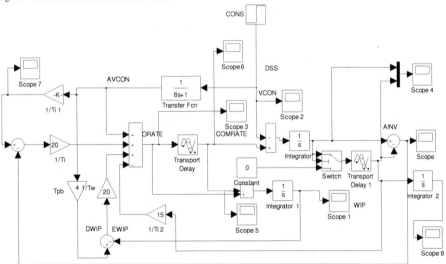

Fig. 4.   The modified model including shelf life effects

THE INCLUSION OF SHELF LIFE EFFECTS INTO APIOBPCS INVENTORY MODELS

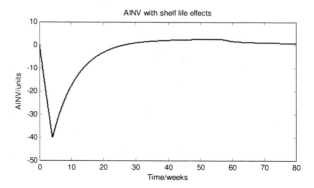

Fig. 5.   Inventory response with shelf-life effects

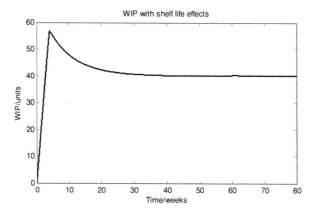

Fig.6 .   WIP with shelf life

4.0   Results of Shelf life Effects

The effects of shelf life are dominated by the value of the delay before goods need to be disposed of. The model shows that for a very large shelf life it tends to the values without shelf life being included as a check. The main effect on the inventory is to reduce the number of stored items after 55 weeks for a 30 week shelf life. The number of items that need to be discarded is less than 5% of the sales. For a shelf life of 5 weeks i.e. 1 week in the shop, the inventory oscillates and the number of goods disposed of breaches nearly 25% of sales. The feedback gain introduced, on the number of disposed items, has a dramatic effect on the number of items that cannot be sold.   The order rate and completion rate of delivered items settles more quickly than the simpler model would suggest.

4.1   Example

THE INCLUSION OF SHELF LIFE EFFECTS INTO APIOBPCS INVENTORY MODELS

We have made an initial comparison with the gross behaviour of blood supply within the National Blood service. If we use their figures of a target shelf life of 23 days and an in house time of 9 days. This is for blood rather than blood products, which have a longer shelf life. Data from the National Audit Office [15] indicates a wastage rate of 0.52 %. Our model gives a wastage rate of 1.36%. This may seem a poor comparison but we have not yet unentangled their precise ordering policy and these are average values not specific instances. The figure is within the same ballpark.

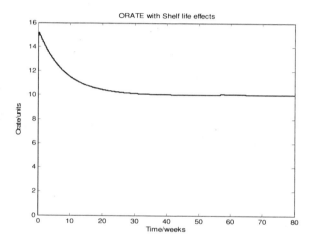

Fig. 7.   Order Rate with shelf life effects

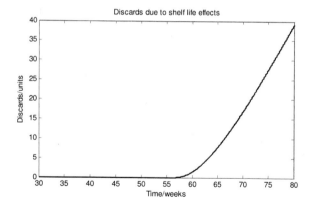

Fig. 8.   Discards for case with shelf life effects

THE INCLUSION OF SHELF LIFE EFFECTS INTO APIOBPCS INVENTORY MODELS

5.0 Conclusion

A model of an inventory system with the shelf life of products has been implemented in Simulink. This model shows that the excess inventory is reduced compared to the case without shelf life effects and that the disposed products can be reduced substantially to less than 5% for this data. Overall stockout tendency is also slightly reduced as is the time before responses settle down.

References

[1] Riddalls, C.E., Bennett, S. (2002) "Production-inventory system controller design and supply chain dynamics", Int. J. of Systems Science, Vol. 33, No3, pp.181-195.

[2] Sterman J.D., (1989) "Modelling managerial behaviour: Misperceptions of feedback in a dynamic decision making experiment", Management Science, Vol.35, No3, pp.321-339.

[3] Wikner, J., Naim, M. M., Towill, D.R. (1992) The system simplification approach in understanding the dynamic behaviour of a manufacturing supply chain, J. System Engineering., Vol. 2, No. 12, pp. 164-178.

[4] Vorst, van der, J, da Silva, CA, Trienekens JH, (2007) Agro-industrial supply chain management: concepts and applications, Food and agriculture organization of the United Nations, paper 17, Rome

[5] Vorst, van der, J.Dijk, SJ, Beulens, van, A, Beek, van, P (2005) Innovations in logistics and ICT in food supply chain networks, in Innovation in Agro-food Systems, (Eds)

[6] Goyal, SK, Giri, B C (2001) Recent Trends in modeling of deteriorating inventory, European Jnl of Operational Research, 134, 1-16.

[7] Arcelus, FJ, N H Shah, Srinivasan, G (2003), Retailers pricing, credit and inventory policies for deteriorating items in response to temporary price/credit incentives, Int.J Production Economics, 81-81=2, 153-162.

[8] Georgioades, P Vlachos, D, Iakovou, E (2005) A system dynamics modeling framework for the strategic supply chain management of food chains, J Food Engineering, 70, Iss 3, 351-364.

[9] Dye, C Y, Ouyang, L Y (2005) An EOQ model for perishable items under stock-dependent selling rate and time-dependent partial backlogging, European J, of Operational Research, 163, 776-783.

[10] Li, J, Cheng, TCE, Wang, S (2007) Analysis of postponement strategy for perishable items by EOQ – based models, Int.J of Production Economics, 107, 31-38.

[11]Forrester, J. (1961) Industrial Dynamics, MIT press, Boston

[12] White, A.S. (1999) "Management of Inventory using Control Systems", Int. J.Technology Management, Vol.17, No7/8, pp.847-860

[13] Disney, S.M., Towill, D.R. (2002) "A discrete transfer function model to determine the dynamic stability of a vendor managed inventory supply chain", Int. J. Prod. Res., Vol. 40, No1, pp.179-204.

[14] Towill, D.R. (1972) "Exponential smoothing of learning curve data", Int. J. Prod. Res., Vol.15, No.1, pp.1-15.

[15] Katsaliaki, K (2006) "Analysing the blood supply chain in the UK using Simulation", PhD Thesis University of Southampton.

Cost Engineering

The 6th International Conference on Manufacturing Research (ICMR08)
Brunel University, UK, 9-11th September 2008

IMPROVING THE SALES DEMAND FORECASTING PROCESS

Simon M. Miller, Riham Khalil and David Stockton

Centre for Manufacturing, De Montfort University, Leicester LE1 9BH, UK

Abstract

The paper reports on a Technology Strategy Board funded collaborative research project (Ref: H0254E) aimed at improving the demand forecasting process through the development of Artificial Intelligence tools. These tools are being developed to autonomously identify, search for, collect and analyse large amounts of data from a wide variety of disparate data sources and with this data generate improved demand forecasts. The development of these tools requires the selection, development and integration of individual Artificial Intelligence and knowledge elicitation methods that include Artificial Neural Networks, Fuzzy Logic and Genetic Algorithms.

Keywords: Demand forecasting, Artificial Intelligence, Artificial Neural Networks, Fuzzy Logic, Genetic Algorithms.

1.0   Introduction

This paper addresses the difficult problem of hierarchical forecasting of sales demand at individual nodes of complex supply chains (SCs). From an industrial perspective the focus on competing through SCs, increasing levels of off-shore manufacturing, and rapid adoption of new materials, processes and product technology are all increasing levels of complexity and variability in the SC demand forecasting process.

This will result in greater demands on the forecasting function to provide significantly improved forecasting techniques able to provide accurate estimates in more complex environments. These will improve customer service levels as well as help reduce non-added value inventory and capacity, thereby decreasing levels of operating capital required. The structure of the demand forecasting system to be developed is illustrated in Fig. 1.

The main Artificial Intelligence (AI) paradigms being employed include Fuzzy Logic (FL), Artificial Neural Networks (ANNs) and Genetic Algorithms (GAs) which are to be combined with knowledge elicitation processes. As shown in Fig. 1., the AI components are being used to develop four knowledge systems:

1. **Knowledge Identification System** - Supports knowledge collection by identifying potential variable types and the locations and navigation paths to sources containing knowledge and data for these variables.

2. **Knowledge Collection System** - Undertakes the actual navigation to the sources and collects relevant documents containing knowledge of variables

3. **Knowledge Extraction System** - Extracts items of information from documents that provide data representing sales demand predictor variables and/or dependent variables within the resulting forecasting models.

4. **Knowledge Analysis System** - Analyses the collected data in order to discover appropriate relationships from which demand forecasting models can be developed.

5. **A GA optimiser** - Using error value feedback from the four Knowledge systems, the GA will be used to improve the structure and content of each knowledge system to produce more accurate forecasts.

The demand forecast can further be used to optimise the planning of resources within the supply chain to meet the demand in the most efficient and effective way. Here again AI techniques can be used to generate realistic and intuitive models able to suggest optimal or near-optimal planning of the resources for each node of the supply chain.

The approach to the project is one of sharing knowledge between different sectors, with automotive, sustainable energy and general engineering being represented in the project partnership. The knowledge contained in these important sectors when forecasting operating resources is to be combined to produce a system most suited to this shared knowledge. The system will allow for a specification of generic concepts and relationships that will assist inventory and capacity forecasting.

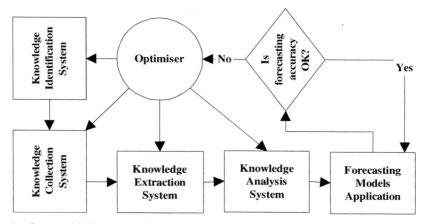

Fig. 1.   Structure of AI-Based Demand Forecasting System

2.0   Artificial Intelligence

An overview of how AI techniques are to be used is as follows:

Fuzzy Logic (FL) will be used to model the company, its supply chain and environment in a way that is representative of the uncertainty inherent in data, language and thought, i.e., it will allow us to represent and model vagueness, imprecision and uncertainty. In this way we can model human expertise using intuitive linguistic variables.

The approach taken, therefore, is to represent the uncertainty in values of each variable type using fuzzy sets, combine these fuzzy sets using rules, inference with those rules and then use defuzzification to produce a final value.

Artificial Neural Networks (ANNs) are a pattern recognition technique that will allow us to develop networks that take known inputs (i.e., observed values of predictor variables), to produce outputs representing the target variable (e.g., the demand forecast). Depending on the application the ANNs will be 'trained' using historical data to learn relationships between the predictor variables and the sales data. ANNs are particularly good at finding complex patterns and are able to discover non-linear relationships between data types.

Genetic Algorithms (GAs) are an evolutionary computing optimisation technique that borrows from the biological notions of genetics and natural selection. Essentially their probabilistic approach to searching large spaces will be used to optimise the FL and ANN modelling procedures, as well as the model forecasting relationships with the objective of optimising forecasting accuracy.

Natural Language Processing (NLP) techniques will be adopted for the development of processes for searching, collecting, aggregating and selecting appropriate data. These techniques include methods for parsing, annotating and extracting data from textual documents.

3.0   Knowledge Identification, Collection and Extraction

A flow diagram illustrating the structure of the knowledge elicitation system is shown in Fig. 2. The system to be developed is essentially an information retrieval system. For such a system to be useful Cordon, Moya and Zarco [4] state that it must be capable of "accessing relevant information" from a range of document types including text, images and tabulated data. This statement is pertinent to the proposed research as demand information is presented in a variety of formats.

As information will be collected from a wide range of sources it is essential that the work of Diamantopoulos and Winklhofer [6], who tested the accuracy of the wide range of forecasting methods used to predict export sales, is taken into consideration. Their results indicated that the "choice and the number of techniques" did not effect forecasting accuracy and suggested that "quality of data" was essential to consider.

Armstrong [1] was among the first researchers to identify and support the use of formal methods of forecasting and develop criteria for the selection of individual methods. Many organisations use multiple methods to produce individual forecasts of demand for a single sales item and then combine these forecasts into an overall estimate of demand. The system being developed must also take this approach since data from a variety of sources, including existing time series sales demand trends, must in some way be combined. Here Collopy and Armstrong [3], recognising the difficulty inherent in this process, make use of a rule base, consisting of 99 rules, to combine individual forecasts. Their method produced more accurate forecasts in situations where large trends, high uncertainty and unstable demand existed.

The level at which data is collected needs to be considered. For example when forecasting demand for automotive replacement parts the use of accident statistics should be taken into account. However, for each reported accident in the UK over 100 items of information are recorded in three main categories, i.e., in terms of the vehicles involved, the road conditions and the seriousness of injuries sustained. In order to identify the effects of non-recorded factors, aggregated or disaggregated data as identified by Garcia-Ferrer, de Juan and Poncela [7] should be kept in mind.

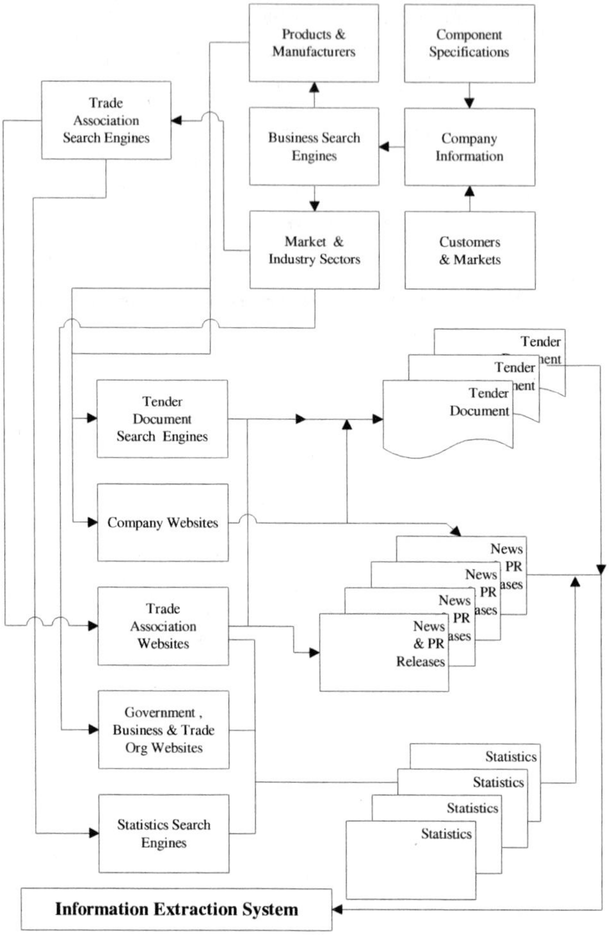

Fig. 2.   Structure of Knowledge Elicitation System

The proposed knowledge elicitation system is primarily focused on identifying the causal variables that affect sales demand. Armstrong [2] states that this is one of the most promising methods for improving forecasting accuracy. It requires methods to be developed for identifying the association types between potential predictor variables and the sales demand of the product.

4.0   Current Progress

To date, work has primarily focused on the identification, collection and extraction of demand information. A number of sources of different types were identified, including company websites containing press releases and news. As they contain mostly textual information, NLP techniques can be used for extracting useful information. For this purpose the General Architecture for Text Engineering (GATE) [5] framework developed at the University of Sheffield has been used. Preliminary experiments have been carried out with GATE to retrieve text from web pages using the Crawler plug-in, categorise retrieved documents using the Machine Learning API, and extract information from the collected pages with Gazetteers, Java Annotations Patterns Engine (JAPE) rules and the Machine Learning API. Fig. 3. illustrates the structure of the experimental system. Further potentially useful sources of information that are being currently investigated include tender documents, industry statistics, and others.

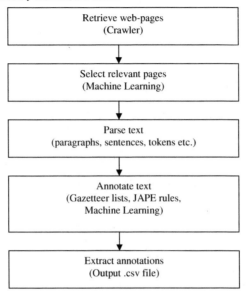

Fig. 3.   Structure of experimental GATE system

4.1   Optimiser

Other work in progress includes the construction of a representative SC model and optimiser for determining good inventory and capacity levels. In this case a preliminary model was constructed using Microsoft® Excel® and the AITrilogy™ tool, Genehunter®. The purpose of this was to illustrate the concept of GA optimisation. A simple SC was created with 5 manufacturer/distributors, 5 customers and 4 products over a period of 2 months. The customers and manufacturer/distributors are located in cities and towns in the UK. The manufacturers are located in Oxford, Leicester, Bristol, Coventry and London; customers are located in Exeter, Nottingham, Manchester, Birmingham and Reading. Any manufacturer can service any customer although it is economical to only service those closest to it.

To find a good solution for comparison, a customer demand forecast was created and entered into the inventory/capacity of nodes closest to customers. The result was a solution for the example forecast with an overall cost of £44,635.00. A GA was then setup to search for inventory plans that minimise overall cost; it was executed five times with seeds 1 to 5. Tab. 1. shows the outcome.

IMPROVING THE SALES DEMAND FORECASTING PROCESS

Tab. 1. Results of initial test run

Seed	Overall Cost (£s)
1	56,250.00
2	54,347.50
3	52,277.50
4	55,470.00
5	52.572.50

The GA never finds the optimal solution, but it does find good solutions. Looking at the suggested inventory it can be seen that it does not always pick the node closest to the customer for supply, also the GA solutions are inclined to make a surplus in the first month, and less than required in the second using all the carry over. The nature of the model means that it is penalised for carrying stock over after the second month, because of this it looks for solutions that leave it with no stock. In the real world this is not ideal, the final model should take this into account when deciding how much carry over is required for the final period of analysis.

It was thought that the GA may find better solutions if there were a heavier penalty for choosing nodes that are not closest to customers for supply. To do this a multiplier was used to produce a penalty on transportation; this worked by taking the product of the multiplier and the transport cost. Fitness is then judged on the overall cost plus the transport penalty. Adding the penalty provides a clearer gap in fitness for solutions with close or distant nodes. The seed was set to 3, the value providing the best result in the previous test.

The first test with the penalty increased the overall cost of the solution found, however by increasing the multiplier cheaper solutions were discovered. A multiplier of 8 gives the best result in this test, just £4510.00 from the ideal value found by selecting the best possible nodes for each customer.

The plans currently being produced could result in a situation where staff are paid overtime in the first period, and their hours cut in the second. Creating an even workload could make more efficient use of resources. In order to address this problem a second penalty was introduced on stock carried over from one period to the next. Obviously we would not want to completely eliminate carry over stock as safety stock can be beneficial, but carrying too much stock over creates peaks and troughs in production. The penalty is calculated by taking the product of the penalty multiplier and the total amount of stock carried over in both periods. Initially, only the carry over penalty was added to the fitness value, then both the transport and carry over penalties were added. Fig. 4. shows the best solution found in each test, Fig. 5. shows the discrepancies in operation costs between periods when the carry over penalty was added

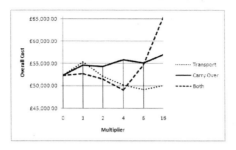

Fig. 4.   Effect of transport and carry over penalties on cost

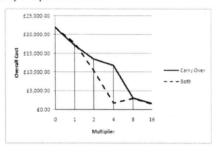

Fig. 5.   Effect of transport and carry over penalties on discrepancy in operating costs

The best solution was found when applying both transport and carry over penalties. With a multiplier of 4 a cost of £49,100.00 is achieved, and the discrepancy between period 1 and 2 is £1760.00. There is still room for improvement however, as often orders are not being satisfied by the node closest to the customer, but the overall cost shows that improvements have been made. In addition to this the discrepancy in workload over the two months is close to the best achieved.

A more complete model and optimiser are now being constructed using Matlab®. The final system should take the generated demand forecast as an input, and optimise the inventory and capacity to meet such demand.

5.0   Summary

The complexity and diversity of the demand forecasting domain knowledge and terminology is a major hurdle for the successful development of the AI methodologies. Fortunately, such hurdles have been overcome using NLP techniques; the establishment of an NLP system for demand forecasting will be the first step towards autonomously identifying the knowledge in this domain. The initial step in building the system will be to identify the purpose, scope, and requirements.

Based on these requirements, data and information about inventory and capacity forecasting will be collected using a variety of sources including published research, ontologies and, importantly, experts from industrial partners. The NLP system must maintain predictor-predictor variable and predictor-dependent variable relationships. Using these relationships the system will support knowledge collection by identifying potential data types and data sources and providing navigation paths during data collection. In doing so the Knowledge

Identification System must analyse users' requests in terms of model characteristics such as levels of forecasting accuracy required.

The purpose of the knowledge identification and collection systems will be to undertake the actual search, navigation and aggregation processes required to find appropriate data sources and extract from these sources the individual items of data that may represent predictor variables and/or dependent variables within the resulting forecasting models. FL will be used to undertake a 'rough cut' analysis of each data source as a means of reducing the amount of data moving on to the data analysis stage, i.e., it will make subjective decisions as to whether individual data types have causal relationships with demand.

The data and knowledge collected will be maintained in an appropriate database. Methods will then be developed for analyzing this data in order to discover appropriate relationships from which forecasting models can be developed. Models will be required at different decision making levels with organisations, i.e., strategic, tactical and operational, as well as for use in differing time periods, e.g., annually, monthly, daily.

The application of ANNs and FL will enable a wide range of models to be developed. For example, where strategic forecasting is required for new products and little data is available FL would be used. In complex situations, where there are large numbers of variables and large quantities of data then the system would automatically select an ANN approach.

In order to ensure the system is as autonomous as possible the knowledge elicitation and analysis systems will form part of a closed-loop control feedback system. The forecasting error generated by the models will be used to provide the fitness function values for a GA Optimiser. The optimiser will have full control over the structure and content of the knowledge elicitation and analysis systems such that they can be modified during the GA evolutionary optimisation processes.

The results of initial development work are promising and outline realistic solutions to the some of the problems that will be faced when creating the tools required. These experimental systems can now be used as a base upon which to build a more complete framework.

Acknowledgements

The research reported here has been funded by the Technology Strategy Board (Grant No. H0254E).

References

[1] Armstrong, J. S., 1983, "Strategic planning and forecasting fundamentals", The Strategic Management Handbook, McGraw Hill, New York, pp 2.1 - 2.32.
[2] Armstrong, J. S., 2006, "Findings from evidence-based forecasting: methods for reducing forecast error", International Journal of Forecasting, Vol 22, pp 583-598.
[3] Collopy, F. and Armstrong, J. S., 1992, "Rule-based forecasting: development and validation of an expert systems approach to combining time series extrapolations", Management Science, 38/10, pp1394-1414.
[4] Cordon,O., Moya, F. and Zarco,C., 2002, "A new evolutionary algorithm combining simulated annealing and genetic programming for relevance feedback in fuzzy information retrieval systems", Soft Computing, Vol.6, pp 308-319.
[5] Cunningham, H., Maynard, D., Bontcheva, K. and Tablan, V. GATE: A Framework and Graphical Development Environment for Robust NLP Tools and Applications. Proceedings of the 40th Anniversary Meeting of the Association for Computational Linguistics (ACL'02). Philadelphia, July 2002.
[6] Diamantopoulos, A. and Winklhofer, H., 2003, "Export sales forecasting by UK firms: Technique utlization and impact on forecast accuracy", Journal of Business Research, Vol 56, pp 45-54.
[7] Garcia-Ferrer, A., de Juan, A. and Poncela, P., 2006, "Forecasting traffic accidents using disaggregated data", International Journal of Forecasting, Vol 22, pp 203-222.

IMPROVING THE SALES DEMAND FORECASTING PROCESS

The 6th International Conference on Manufacturing Research (ICMR08)
Brunel University, UK, 9-11th September 2008

MANUFACTURING COST MODELING
FOR AIRCRAFT WING

Y. Xu[1], J. Wang[1], X. Tan[1], R. Curran[1], S. Raghunathan[1], J. Doherty[2], D. Gore[3]

1. School of Mechanical and Aerospace Engineering, Queen's University Belfast, Ashby Building, Stranmillis Road, Belfast, BT9 5AH, Northern Ireland, UK

2. QinetiQ, Cody Technology Park, Ively Road, Farnborough, Hants, GU14 0LX, England, UK

3. Airbus UK, New Filton House, Filton, Bristol, BS99 7AR, England, UK

Abstract

Life cycle cost (LCC) is truly representative to the total cost of a product through its life cycle. It is usually used for estimating the cost-effectiveness of a product design. Manufacturing cost is an important part of LCC. In order to meet the challenging environmental targets set by the Advisory Council for Aeronautics Research in Europe (ACARE), an Integrated Wing Advanced Technology Validation Programme was initiated in United Kingdom, to research, improve and validate aircraft wing design and integration techniques. The aircraft wing related technologies can be evaluated in different aspects, where Life Cycle Cost (LCC) is an important issue to evaluate. As an important part of LCC, manufacturing cost needs to be well estimated. So a manufacturing cost model for aircraft wing has been developed. Object-oriented and hierarchical approaches are used for manufacturing cost modelling. The developed cost model is generic, and can be customized and applied for estimating the costs of other aircraft systems, even the systems in other industrial sectors.

Keywords: Life Cycle Cost, Cost Engineering, Manufacturing Cost, Aircraft

1.0   Introduction

The life cycle cost (LCC) of a product includes all of the costs which are incurred during its life cycle, from research & development phase, through manufacturing and operation phases, to the eventual retirement and disposal phase[1]. LCC is usually used for estimating the cost-effectiveness of a product design. Manufacturing cost is an important part of LCC, and it is normally used to conduct trade-off study with operation cost, to minimize LCC. The aim of cost estimation should not be only for checking financial affordability of a product, but also for recognizing where and how cost can be reduced, and which design solution can give the best investment return.

There are three main types of costing methodologies generally accepted: analogous, parametric, and bottom-up [2]. The analogous method estimates the cost based on similarity of products, but its development, underlying rules, assumptions and repeatability are often difficult due to variations in the expertise of the user[2, 3, 4]. More commonly adopted in the aerospace industry is the parametric modeling technique, which typically utilizes linear regression for the development of Cost Estimating Relationships (CER)[2, 5, 6]. Their formulation is relatively easy, but the resulting accuracy is strongly dependent on the quality of the historically generated cost data. The final method, bottom-up estimating, relies on detailed engineering analysis, and the models are formulated in such a way that the costs associated with individual processes and assembly operations are accounted for[2, 7]. This methodology has been used in previous research[8, 9], in which the trade-off between aerodynamic tolerance and manufacturing cost was considered. Process-based cost models are usually more accurate than parametric models, but require a greater level detailed information at the beginning of the estimation process, which is generally not available[10].

2.0   Background

In order to achieve the challenging environmental targets set by the Advisory Council for Aeronautics Research in Europe (ACARE)[11], an Integrated Wing Aerospace Technology Validation Program (IWATVP)[9] was initiated in United Kingdom to research, improve and validate aircraft wing design and integration techniques. Normally there are likely to be a number of technologies available for an aircraft design meeting targets, so comparison and trade-off study between different technologies should be conducted. A tool called RETIVO[12] is used to conduct technology evaluation. Life Cycle Cost is an important part of RETIVO to evaluate technologies. Under the umbrella of IWATVP Program, a LCC model for aircraft wing is being developed[13-14], and manufacturing cost model is an important part of the LCC model, and is being developed.

3.0   Methodology

Manufacturing costs are incurred by both physical parts/systems and the related process/activities. Work breakdown structure (WBS) and/or cost breakdown structures (CBS) are established for cost estimation, e.g. material cost estimation, machining cost estimation, and assembling cost estimation. Some approaches are addressed in manufacturing cost estimation, in order to achieve some targets, e.g. to evaluate the impact of technology on cost.

3.1.   Architecture

The manufacturing cost model is designed into some functional modules, i.e. it has been modularized as a collection of functional modules for some reasons and aims:

- To enable to deliver each part of modelling separately and make it clear how it progresses
- To allow different levels of models to be integrated depending on the level of data available
- A single model would be a monster due to massive information related.

The manufacturing cost model's architecture is shown in Figure 1. It includes modules of Framework, Sizing Tool, Material, Machining, and Assembling. The core part of the manufacturing cost model is Framework module. It externally communicates with RETIVO, which conducts multi-disciplinary optimization for technologies in high level, to collect the wing design parameters, and return the desired manufacturing cost back to the RETIVO. The Framework module internally communicates with Sizing Tool module, and Materials, Machining, and Assembling Modules. It passes the wing design parameters to Sizing Tool, and gets a work breakdown structure of wing, and the quantity and attributes of each part. The Codes module is used to implement the cost estimation within the modules, and the communication between modules. The function of each module in the Figure 1 and their interfaces are described in Table 1.

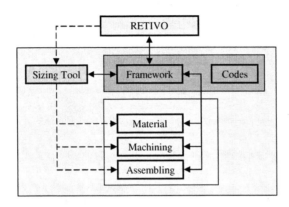

Fig. 1.   Architecture of the Manufacturing Cost Model

Table 1: Overview of modules in Manufacturing Cost Model

Module	Functions	Inputs	Outputs
Framework	Get and populate inputs and assumptions to other modules; Conduct trade-off study and produce graphical outputs.	Design parameters from RETIVO, User inputs	Manufacturing cost breakdown
Sizing Tool	Generate work breakdwon structure of wing with given design parameters	Design parameters of wing from Sizing Tool via Framework	Part size and attributes
Material	Estimate the raw material cost needed for wing parts	Part quantity, size and attributes from Sizing Tool via Framework	Raw material cost of each part
Machining	Estimate the machining cost for wing parts	Part quantity, size and attributes from Sizing Tool via Framework	Machining cost of each part
Assembling	Estimate the assembling cost for wing parts/systems	Part/subsystem quantity, and class; Fastener quantity, and class	Assembling cost of each part

3.2.   Object-oriented Approach

Due to the consideration of aircraft life cycle cost, the manufacturing cost model is developed using object-oriented approach. By using this approach, some or most cost elements are not wing specific, but rather common, and they can be customized to represent new cost elements in new cost models, e.g. the fuselage cost models. This approach is proved to be cost effective and efficient model development approach, especially in the software development.

The manufacturing cost model is founded on a series of objects, which are modularized and have specific attributes, operations and boundary conditions. Each object is described by attributes, e.g. the geometric and material information etc. for the wing parts. The object can be inherited, and it encapsulates the attributes and relationships to other objects. The operations are functions of the attributes and input parameters; they deliver the outputs of interest to users. In the manufacturing cost modeling for aircraft wing, wing parts and manufacturing related activities are classified to suitable objects by switching on/off the appropriate describing attributes. New objects can be evolved through adding new attributes and operations. The object may have more attributes and operations than needed for a specific part or activity, but these can be "switched off" if they are not required. On the other hand, new customized attributes and operations can also be added into objects. In addition to the wing part and manufacturing activities, a WBS and CBS element, and the functional modules are also represented by objects. All of the objects are organized in a hierarchical structure. The object-oriented model allows users to develop a new cost model for other aircraft systems quickly and easily.

3.3. Hierarchical Approach

The manufacturing cost model is developed based upon hierarchical structures, e.g. the hierarchical work breakdown structure and cost breakdown structure. This approach provides some advantages:

- To enable cost estimation at all development stage.
- To provide better fidelity of cost estimation.

At the early design stage, only a few design parameters are available for wing design, then Sizing Tool are used to provide WBS. As the design process goes, more system/parts design information become available at the later design stage, then the updated system/parts information are used for cost estimation, which consequently provides better fidelity of cost estimation.

Similar to the application of a hierarchical work breakdown structure, a hierarchical cost breakdown structure is also used in the cost estimation depending on the requirements and information available. E.g. manufacturing cost includes recurring cost and non-recurring cost (costs of tooling, jigs etc.), and recurring cost is more process related. Depending on the accuracy requirement, non-recurring cost can either be taken into account for cost estimation or not.

When the level at which to conduct cost estimation is selected, the standard time and unit cost for parts/systems at bottom level needs to be assumed. Assumption can either be done by using industrial standard, or using parametric models that are developed based on historical data. The data is classed by technologies, and technology factor is introduced in the parametric model, so the parametric model in this level is able to represent the impact of technology on cost.

4.0   Development of Manufacturing Cost Model

The manufacturing cost model is developed in Microsoft® Excel environment, The WBS is provided by Sizing Tool module based on the given wing design parameters, and CBS is built upon the WBS elements. Due to nature of each category of cost estimation, the WBS used for cost estimation and the substantial cost drivers are different. Learning curve effect has been taken into account for machining and assembling cost estimation.

4.1   Material Cost Module

Material cost module is responsible for estimating the cost of raw materials needed for either metal parts or composite parts. As metal materials are still the major material used for aircraft wing, there are more material types, part classes, and supply conditions for metal parts. Cost estimation will take all those information into account. For the structural parts of aircraft wing, the Table 2 shows some sample attributes and supply conditions used for cost estimation. The part class and attribute are provided by Sizing Tool. The final supply condition is determined by the Material cost module by comparing all supply conditions. Depending on the part class and supply condition, different part attributes, and different raw material allowance are used for cost estimation.

Table 2: Metal part attributes and supply condition used for cost estimation

Attributes		Supply condition
• Volume • Length • Width • Width Maximum • Width Minimum	• Thickness • Material Cross Sectional Area • Perimeter length • Area	• Rectangular Billet • Shaped Billet • Extrusion

For the composite parts, the raw material cost is estimated by the weight, which is provided by the Sizing Tool either directly or indirectly.

4.2   Machining Cost Module

Machining cost module mainly considers the cost of fabricating metal parts and composite parts. The metal parts are fabricated by milling process, while the composite parts are fabricated by laying up process.

4.2.1   Metal Parts

The machining costs of metal parts are mainly determined by the machining time, which is driven by the machining process parameters and part attributes. The machining time can be estimated by different methods, e.g. traditionally by the weight approach that is derived empirically from historical data. But the weight approach makes it difficult to take account of changes in machining technology as they are tied to historical data, also as a consequence of this they tend to lack transparency and therefore are difficult to validate.

In this paper, the machining time for metal parts are estimated by the volume removal ratio, which can be determined as a typical percentage of part volume to raw material volume. Due to the fact of milling process, the machining time is related to the machining speed, i.e. the revolution speed of cutting tool, feed rate and cut depth, standing time, as well as material properties, i.e.

$$T_m = C_f \cdot \frac{P \cdot V}{V_{rr}} + T_s \tag{1}$$

Where T_m is the total machining time for a spar or rib.

V is the volume of raw material billet for spar or ribs.

P is the volume percentage of raw materials to be removed during machining.

V_{rr} is the volume removal rate.

T_s is the machining standing time, which is unique for a specific part and determined by component properties, such as weight, shape etc.

C_f is the complexity coefficient, which is determined by geometric structures, component weight etc.

Here V_{rr} is determined by machining parameters, as shown in equation 2.

$$V_{rr} = R \cdot N \cdot F \cdot P_r \cdot D_r \cdot D_a \tag{2}$$

Where R is the revolution speed of cutting tool.

N is the number of tool teeth.

F is the tool feed rate per tooth.

P_r is the percentage of the cutter diameter engaged.

D_r is the diameter of cutting tool.

D_a is the axial cut depth of cutting tool.

Using above equations, the total machining time T_m can be estimated based on the milling process. Correspondingly, the machining cost can be estimated based on labor rate and machining time. The total machining cost for metal parts in aircraft wing will account each part by part.

4.2.2   Composite Parts

Similarly to the metal parts, the estimation of composite machining cost is conducted by estimating the fabricating time and raw material cost for composite parts. There are two basic types of composite materials used in aircraft wing: ATL Tape & Prepreg Sheet. The ATL Tape is fabricated by using Automated Tape Layer (ATL) process, and the Prepreg Sheet is fabricated by using Hand Lay-Up (HLU) process. The fabricating process for two types of composite materials are shown in Table 3. In addition to the ATL and HLU processes, both types of materials need curing, trimming and NDT checking processes. For each process, the drivers of fabricating time are also shown in Table 3. In addition to the main fabricating time, the setup time (loading parts, cleaning parts, CNC programming etc.) is also taken into account for the process time. Based on the estimated process time and labour rate, composite fabricating cost can be estimated.

Table 3: Composite manufacturing process and cost drivers

ATL Tape Composite		Prepreg Sheet Composite	
Process step	Drivers	Process step	Drivers
Automated Tape Layer	Length	Hand Lay-Up	Area, number of layers
Curing	Volume	Curing	Volume
Trimming	Profile length	Trimming	Profile length
NDT checking	Area	NDT checking	Area

MANUFACTURING COST MODELING FOR AIRCRAFT WING

4.3 Assembling Cost Module

The assembling cost mainly includes labour cost and material costs incurred by the assembling process. In the process of assembling aircraft wing, the material cost mainly includes the cost of fasteners. The labour cost is mainly determined by the assembling time, which is driven by the assembling process practice, typically the number and class of fasteners, and class of part/subsystems. The parts/subsystems included in and fasteners needed for assembling, are provided by the Sizing Tool. Based on the work breakdown structure of assembly, the assembling cost can be estimated. The material cost of parts included in assembly is not accounted. It is accounted in the Machining and Material cost modules instead. However, for fasteners, both material cost and labour cost are accounted. Technology factors are applied to the appropriate assembling process. The parts and fasteners are classified as below in Table 4, each class of parts/fasteners have their typical unit assembling time, and unit cost (for fastener only), which are determined by the industrial standard and practice.

Table 4: Examples of fastener and part classes in Assembling module

Fastener class	Part class
SmallBolt	InterSparRib
MediumBolt	TopSkin
LargeBolt	BottomSkin
RemovableBolt	Spars
FormableRivet	WingSkinStringer
MediumDeformableRivet	CompositeSparRibPost
	… …

5.0 Case Study

For demonstrating the capability of manufacturing cost model, a baseline aircraft is used as the basis for comparison, and a sample aircraft is used for estimating the manufacturing cost. Some parameters for these two aircrafts are shown in Table 5 below.

Table 5 Major parameters of wings

	Wing span	Wing Root Chord	Wing Tip Chord	Wing area	Semi span of wing
Sample wing	60.0000	1.8000	2.5000	360.0000	30.0000
Baseline wing	38.0000	6.5000	1.1000	140.0000	19.0000

Using above data, the manufacturing cost estimation is conducted, and the result is shown in Figure 2. Due to the confidentiality of costs, the cost result has been normalized.

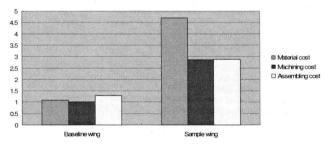

Fig. 2. Manufacturing cost comparison between two wings

MANUFACTURING COST MODELING FOR AIRCRAFT WING

6.0   Conclusion

A generic manufacturing cost model for aircraft wing has been developed based on bottom-up approach. The model is object-oriented and can be customized for other applications, e.g. to estimate the cost of other aircraft systems. The model developed using bottom-up approach allows the validation of technology impact on manufacturing cost.

Acknowledgments

The work described in this paper has been carried-out with the financial assistance of the Department for Business, Enterprise and Regulatory Reform (DBERR), under the Integrated Wing Aerospace Technology Validation Programme (IWATVP). The authors are very grateful to Michael Smith and Stuart Alexander of Airbus, Darren White, Andrew Eldridge and Paul Ellsmore of QinetiQ, for support and discussion of the work.

References

[1]   Asiedu Y, Gu P. Product life cycle cost analysis: state of the art review. Int J Prod Res 1998;36(4): 883–908.
[2]   R Curran, S Raghunathan, M Price, Review of Aerospace Engineering Cost Modelling: The Genetic Causal Approach, Progress in Aerospace Sciences, 2004, 40: 487-534.
[3]   Mukhopadhyay T, Vicinanza S, Prietula M. Examining the feasibility of a case-based reasoning model for software effort estimation. MIS Quart 1992;(June): 155-171.
[4]   Myrtveit I, Stensrud E. A controlled experiment to assess the benefits of estimating with analogy and regression models. IEEE Trans Software Eng 1999; 25(4): 510-525.
[5]   Tuer G. Integrated cost modelling at BAE SYSTEMS. SSCAG's 69th meeting, European Space Agency, Noordwijk, etherlands, 11-12 May 2000.
[6]   Taylor I. Cost engineering: a feature based approach. 85th Meeting of the AGARD structures and material panel, Aalborg, Denmark, 1998. pp.1-9.
[7]   Rand Corporation. Military jet acquisition: technology basics & cost-estimating methodology. MR-1596, 2002.
[8]   Sanchez, M., Kundu, A.,K., and Raghunathan, S..A methodology for assessing manufacturing cost due to tolerance of aerodynamic surface features on turbofan nacelles, International journal, advanced manufacturing technology 1998, vol. 14, no12, pp. 894-900
[9]   Kundu, A., Raghunathan, S., and Cooper, R.K., "Effect of Aircraft Smoothness Requirements on Cost", Aeronautical Journal, Vol. 104, No. 1039, Paper 2389, Dec 2000, pp.415-420.
[10]   K. Gantois, A. J. Morris, The multi-disciplinary design of a large-scale civil aircraft wing taking account of manufacturing costs. Structural and Multidisciplinary Optimization, 2004, 28: 31-46.
[11]   William J. Marx, Dimitri N. Mavris, Daniel P. Schrage, A hierarchical aircraft life cycle cost analysis model, AIAA-95-3861.
[12]   Paul D. Ellsmorel and Kevin E. Restrick, Application of RETIVO to Civil Aircraft, AIAA-2007-7808, 7th AIAA Aviation Technology, Integration and Operations Conference (ATIO), Belfast, September 2007.
[13]   Tan, X., Xu, Y., Early, J., Wang, J., Curran, R., and Raghunathan, S., A Framework for Systematically Estimating Life Cycle Cost for an Integrated Wing, AIAA-2007-7809, 7th AIAA Aviation Technology, Integration and Operations Conference (ATIO), Belfast, September 2007.
[14]   Y. Xu, J. Wang, X. Tan, J. Early, R. Curran, S. Raghunathan, J. Doherty, D. Gore, Life Cycle Cost Modeling for Aircraft Wing Using Object-Oriented Systems Engineering Approach, AIAA-2008-1118

The 6th International Conference on Manufacturing Research (ICMR08)
Brunel University, UK, 9-11th September 2008

ENHANCED PROCESS COSTING METHODOLOGY FOR DYNAMIC MANUFACTURING ENTERPRISES

K. Agyapong-Kodua [1], Bilal Wahid [2] R H Weston [1]

1. MSI Research Institute, Loughborough University, Loughborough, Leics., UK

2. Centre of Excellence in Customized Assembly (CECA), Loughborough University, Loughborough, UK

Abstract

For any Manufacturing Enterprise (ME) to realize its set of goals, there must be the proper design and introduction of raw materials (inputs) through well defined processes capable of achieving expected outputs. The design and introduction of inputs at various stages of the process affect the resource requirements. Typically, machine and technological resource supports will be needed to enhance the operation of human resources to achieve timely and responsive results meeting customer requirements. For dynamic MEs processes have to be optimized to ensure competitiveness and longer 'enterprise life span'. This requires proper process and resource design centred on cost effectiveness and value enhancement, among other key performance indicators the ME might be interested in.

Due to the inherent complexities and dynamics associated with MEs, it is fairly difficult to estimate, control and monitor cost consumption appropriately and instantaneousness without incurring errors. Most often factors which induce cost in manufacturing systems are at the operational level and are difficult to capture by existing methods. However the ability to capture cost information at the point where they occur and the onward realization of their effect on the total cost incurred by the ME is necessary if the ME has to survive in a dynamic and global market zone.

With this background, the authors have enacted a 'process-based approach to costing' which instruments the coherent application of enterprise and simulation modelling techniques, cost engineering methodologies and knowledge in manufacturing systems to derive an alternative costing methodology with the capability to capture salient manufacturing process dynamics which impact on cost. This has been demonstrated in a case study involving a bearing manufacturing company located in the United Kingdom.

Keywords: Manufacturing Enterprise (ME), cost engineering, enterprise modeling, system dynamics modeling (SDM)

1.0   Introduction

Cost accounting practices have recommended various means of estimating cost and using cost data as a basis for deriving profit, valuating inventory, performance measurements and decision making related to overall attainment of enterprise objectives [1, 2]. This has led to the adoption of many cost estimation models by Manufacturing Enterprises (MEs). Two examples of commonly used cost models were provided by Son [3], and Johnson [4]. A study of current cost accounting methods and their application in advanced MEs operating in dynamic business environments show that the actual 'step by step' processes involved in the manufacture of products are often neglected [3, 5]. This is partially as a result of lack of detailed understanding of processes and unavailability of cost data associated with complex manufacturing processes.

Most MEs are composed of complex process networks which are inter-related in a way that changes made to one process thread induce dynamics in the ME by having causal and temporal effects on other process threads [6], hence rendering the ME dynamic. Also literature in the area of business dynamics have confirmed that in general terms the problems faced by most MEs can be rooted to the phenomenon of complexity and dynamics which stem from the complexities involved in current markets [7]. The structural and dynamic complexity of the markets can be found in the structure and processes of the enterprise too [8]. Partly because MEs are highly organic (people-centred) and achieve their goals only through the integration of people, machines and technology. As a result of the interaction between these functional elements, changes related to any of the elements trigger effects on other elements which are causally related to other elements hence producing 'chains of reactions' in the ME. It is therefore required that decisions associated with these functional elements be made properly since they impact on cost and profitability of enterprises. Cost is one of the major key performance indicators for any ME operating in a dynamic market environment. This is due to its ability to ensure competitiveness and sustenance of the enterprise. It is therefore useful to adopt methods capable of modelling the dynamics that impact on their formation. When this is achieved scientifically, measures can be taken to reduce cost generation along process segments.

Literature in the domain of enterprise engineering have provided methods of capturing aspects of enterprises which partially create suitable platforms for developing models capable of mimicking real life dynamic instances [9-12]. The enterprise models created through these methods are themselves static and have not yet focused on the dynamic impacts of manufacturing processes on cost. Hence most cost information are displayed as static and requires manual updates and adjustment. On the other hand many cost accounting methods have also not considered the dynamic nature of MEs and therefore methods and approaches often deployed in this domain tend not to suitably represent the dynamic aspects in MEs. In view of this, the authors have demonstrated in this paper how knowledge from enterprise and cost engineering can conveniently be utilized to generate cost models which suitably represent the dynamic instances in MEs which impact on cost. With these background models, the effect of change on cost can be visualized and the ME organized in time to annex the effect of change on competition, price and sustainability.

2.0   Enhanced Process Costing Methodology

In the proposed process cost modelling methodology supported by the research team of the Manufacturing Systems Integration (MSI) Research Institute of Loughborough University, it is assumed that for any costing method to be suitable for a ME operating in a dynamic market environment:

ENHANCED PROCESS COSTING METHODOLOGY FOR DYNAMIC MANUFACTURING ENTERPRISES

1. The cost system should enable accurate and timely feedback schemes such that changes made to any segment of an enterprise process (especially at the operational level) can be reflected in financial terms.
2. The cost system should have an embedded state-of-the art decomposition technique such that process functionalities can thoroughly be modelled at suitable levels of granularity.
3. This cost system should be built upon state of the art IT systems integration capabilities, so that its operation is not constrained by software performance issues.
4. The cost system should also be sensitive to causal impacts of multiple activity realization on profit generation.
5. The cost system should enable enhanced traceability of costs to specific products and processes to enable improved management of cost distortions.

To achieve these requirements, the authors have recommended a four-staged approach to cost modelling. This involves:

1. Coherently representing the flows in a ME in the form of a graphic model based on state of the art enterprise modelling techniques. This ensures a thorough decomposition of aspects of MEs which would have otherwise not been captured through current methodologies. Also these models assist in recognizing the various relationships and interactions that exist between functional elements.
2. Cost information are embedded on the activity models to visually demonstrate how cost is generated along process segments. In effect cost is represented as a 'flow' from one activity to the other. This includes labour and machine cost, overhead, etc.
3. The third stage of the methodology adopts system dynamics modelling techniques to capture salient instances of dynamic impacts in the manufacturing process. This is illustrated in the form of causal loops representing dynamic models of specific areas within the enterprise where improvement or analysis is required. Essentially the causal loop models capture the cause and effect structure of the process, qualitatively.
4. At a latter stage, the qualitative causal loop models are converted to system dynamics simulation models to quantitatively analyze the impact of changes and dynamics in the manufacturing process on cost.

These steps have been illustrated in the case study application involving the sanding and sawing operations of a bearing manufacturing company in the United Kingdom.

3.0   Case Study Application of Modelling Methodology

3.1   Company Background

The case company is a rapidly growing ME with its main production and administrative base in the United Kingdom. It has global customers and stakeholders and employs over 35 regular workers in the UK site under study. Further production facilities are currently being developed in other parts of the world including the US with a view to increasing market share. At its current manufacturing site, the company manufactures a wide range of advanced composite bearings suitable for agricultural, marine, mechanical, pharmaceutical and food processing environments and applications. In general terms, bearings are made of reinforced plastic laminates composed of synthetic fabrics impregnated with thermosetting resins and solid lubricant fillers. The products exist in various shapes such as round, flat, strips and there are other fully finished components such as structural bearings, washers, wear rings, spherical, wear pads, wear strips, rollers, and bushes.

3.2   Enterprise Models of Case Company

A review of literature related to enterprise modelling showed that public domain architectural frameworks, methods, and tools for creating enterprise models existed with proven capability to model both large and small scale enterprise systems. Among them were CIMOSA[13], IDEF[14], PERA[15], and GRAI[16]. The CIMOSA approach was however observed to render unique decomposition ability which reflected the requirements of the case company. Based on the authors previous experience in modelling with CIMOSA, four main diagramming templates were used [17].

Normally, CIMOSA modelling commences by populating a context diagramming template which provides a high level (abstract) model of the contributing enterprise Domains (DMs) which can be viewed as actors that contribute to a common process under study. These are further decomposed into Domain Processes (DPs) and illustrated in the form of interaction diagrams to explicitly and graphically depict needed communication and physical exchanges between the DPs. DPs are further decomposed into Business Processes (BPs) which themselves comprise more elemental BPs and Enterprise Activities (EAs). EAs are considered to be the atomic building blocks of DMs and BPs and thus are modelled at the lowest level of abstraction

For the sake of simplicity and clarity, only the activity model of the section under consideration has been shown in this paper. The focus here is to illustrate how process-based thinking of cost can be used to inform decision makers on the financial impact of their decisions in the 'sand and saw' unit of the 'produce and deliver domain' of the case company. In real terms the 'operate and deliver process' comprises all the activities (processes) involved in the physical transformation of raw materials to finished goods. It includes the day to day manufacturing processes and resources involved in the fulfilment of customer orders. A CIMOSA activity model showing the various activities involved in the making of one of their product types, wear strips, in the sand and saw shop, is shown in fig 1.

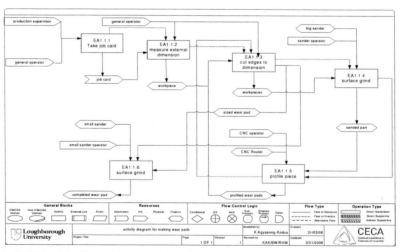

Fig. 1.   CIMOSA activity diagram for the manufacture of wear pads

ENHANCED PROCESS COSTING METHODOLOGY FOR DYNAMIC MANUFACTURING ENTERPRISES

After studying the activities involved in the production of wear pads in the shop, it was observed that there were three people involved in the processes with four different machines being utilized at different times. This information helped in embedding the activity models with cost information. Labour cost, Lc, was defined to be:

$$L_C = n_o tr f \{x\%C - \alpha\} \qquad (1)$$

where n_o is the number of operators; t is the time spent; r is the existing rate of pay or wages; f shows the functional relationships; x is a 'percentage of the operators competence, C', and α, a percentage availability factor. Also the machine cost, Mc, was defined as

$$Mc = t_o rx\%n\text{-}d \qquad (2)$$

where t_o refers to the total time for the operation; r is the rate per unit time; x is a fraction or factor of the efficiency, whilst d is an availability factor representing breakdowns, idle time and planned stoppages. Overheads and other forms of cost were assumed to be common to all the activities. Based on these realizations and understanding of the operations in the shop, a static cost model was generated as shown in fig 2.

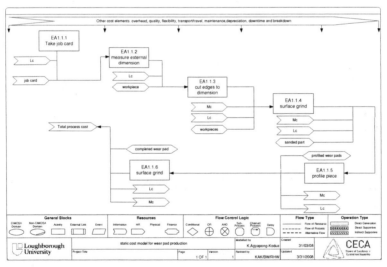

Fig. 2.   Static cost model for wear pad production

3.3   Dynamic Process Cost Models

At the next stage of modelling, system dynamics were deployed in the form of causal loop models to depict changes that were likely to occur and their impact on cost formation. It was observed through the study of fig 3, that for the company to fulfil their customer orders, there must be a close match up of expected production rate and actual production rate achieved. The actual production rate was dependent on a set of factors which included rate of supply of parts from the raw material shop to the 'sand and saw' shop and also the manufacturing capacity.. The set of factors which were found to influence the production capacity also affected the production cost.

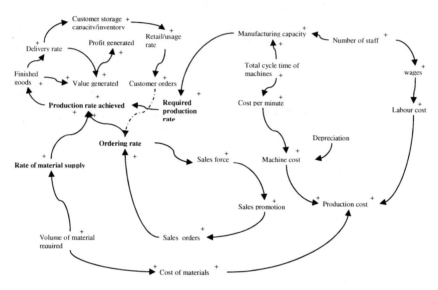

Fig.3.   Causal loop model

As could be observed from the causal loop models in fig 3, the models were adequate to qualitatively explain the influential factors on cost hence suggesting which 'levers could be pulled to enact required behavioural pattern of cost'. It was an important technique in commencing discussions on possible improvements with the Managers of the company. This model was further enhanced through the application of iThink/Stella system dynamics simulation software to quantify the effects of change on cost (see fig 4).

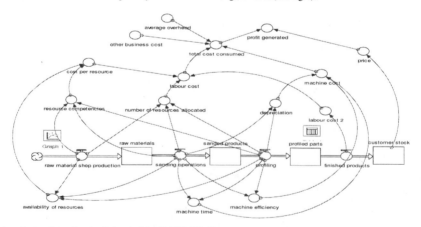

Fig. 4.   System dynamics simulation model with iThink/Stella

ENHANCED PROCESS COSTING METHODOLOGY FOR DYNAMIC MANUFACTURING ENTERPRISES

A snapshot of the model created with iThink/Stella software is shown in fig 4 whilst fig 5 shows a graph derived from the model to illustrate how a generalised trend of performance can be predicted based on changes in initial conditions under study. In the model shown in fig 4, cost elements for each of the activities were modelled and summed up. The example results shown in fig 5 relates to the increase in cost as a result of machining wrong parts. This was due to specification of wrong size on the job card. This affected the cutting size of the material and all other profiling operations.

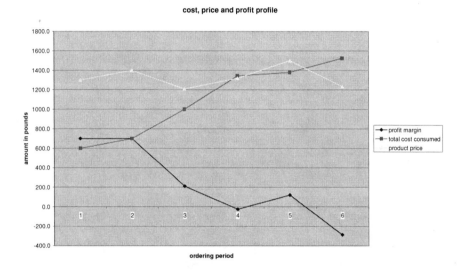

Fig. 5.   Graph depicting the impact of machining wrong parts

4.0   Observations and Conclusion

Throughout the research it was observed that the process of capturing elements impacting complexities and dynamics on cost demanded adequate data collection and thorough understanding of the processes being modelled. The close collaboration of the authors and the staff of the case company was necessary for the successful data collection, validation and analysis. In addition the following observations were made:

1. the application of enterprise modelling techniques in deriving cost models for manufacturing processes, provided an enhanced way of understanding of processes and activities involved in the company. By this approach cost was visualised as a flow and modelled to reflect how cost is incurred along process segments.

2. the support provided by the system dynamics modelling techniques were enormous. They allowed process dynamics to be modelled in granularity and also to observe how process elements impact on cost. The iThink software provided a complimentary support to the causal loop models in terms of quantifying the effect of changes on the models created, although the transformation of the causal

loops models to iThink was not straight forward. It required further understanding into the companies operations, hence modifying the original causal loops created.

3. it was observed that this approach exceeded current cost modelling techniques in the area of providing richer understanding of the processes to be modelled. It also provided a platform for modelling and analysing the impact of change and dynamics on cost.

4. the decision makers in the company were satisfied about the new level of understanding the models provided to them With these backbone models, experimentation of alternative business scenarios and their impacts on cost could be done.

It must however be emphasized here that, research is still ongoing in this area and further case study applications will be required to validate the enhanced modelling approach being recommended. Also research into specifying dynamic modelling requirements of cost in a complex and dynamic manufacturing environment is underway by the authors and their research colleagues.

References

1. Drury, C., *Management and Cost Accounting*. 6th ed. 1991, London: Thomson Learning.
2. Barfield, J.T., C.A. Raiborn, and M.R. Kinney, *Cost Accounting; Traditions and Innovations*. 1994, USA: West Publishing.
3. Son, Y.K., *A cost estimation model for advanced manufacturing systems*. International Journal of   Production Research, 1991. **29**(3): p. 441-452.
4. Johnson, H. and R. Kaplan, *Relevance Lost – The Rise and Fall of Management Accounting*. 1987, Boston, MA, : Harvard Business School Press.
5. Agyapong-Kodua, K. and R.H. Weston. *Process cost modelling in Manufacturing Enterprises*. in *4th International Conference on Digital Enterprise Technology*. 2007. Bath, United Kingdom.
6. Rahimifard, A. and R. Weston, *The enhanced Use of Enterprise and Simulation Modelling Techniques to Support Factory Changeability*. MSI Research Institute, Loughborough University, UK, 2006.
7. Wiendahl, H.P. and H. Scheffczyk. *Simulation based analysis of complex production systems with methods of nonlinear dynamics*. in *Institute of production systems, University of Hannover* 1999. Hannover, Germany: CIRP.
8. Rumelt, R.P., *Strategy, structure and Economic performance*. Harvard Business School, 1974.
9. Chatha, K.A., J.O. Ajaefobi, and R.H. Weston, *Enriched multi-process modelling in support of the life cycle engineering of business processes*. 2005.
10. CEN/ISO, *Enterprise integration - Constructs for modelling*. 19440.
11. P.Bernus, L.N., *Possibilities and Limitations of Reusing Enterprise Models (New Requirements for Enterprise Engineering Tools)*. Proceedings of IFAC workshop on Intelligent Manufacturing Systems. 1994, Vienna, Austria.
12. Vernadat, F.B., *Enterprise modelling and integration; Principles and Applications*. First edition ed. 1996: Chapman & Hall, London.
13. CIMOSA, *ESPIRIT CIMOSA Standards, CIMOSA: Open System Architecture for CIM*. 1994, Spinger-Verlag.
14. IDEF0, *Knowledge Based Systems, Inc,*. 2006.
15. Williams, T.J., *The Purdue Enterprise Reference Architecture*. Instrument Society of America. Research Triangle Park, North Carolina, USA, 1992.
16. Doumenigts, G., et al., *GIM- a GRAI integrated methodology. A method for designing CIM systems*. 1992, GARI/LAP, University of Bordeaux: France.
17. Monfared, R.P., *A Component Based Approach to Design and Construction of Change Capable Manufacturing Cell Control Systems*. PhD Thesis, Loughborough University, UK, 2000.

The 6th International Conference on Manufacturing Research (ICMR08)
Brunel University, UK, 9-11th September 2008

LAST ORDER COSTING – AN ITERATIVE METHOD TOWARDS MANUFACTURING COST REDUCTION

Davies A, John E [1], Thomas A.J, Worrall, B [2]

1. School of Engineering, Cardiff University, UK

2. Cardiff Business School, Cardiff University, UK

Abstract

In today's difficult business environment, where the selling price of a product is often dictated by the competitive forces which exist in the marketplace, it is vitally important that a company identifies and minimises the sources of costs generated within its manufacturing system. An active well structured 'cost / waste minimisation programme', in terms of labour, materials and overheads, should enable a company to maintain its competitive advantage in the longer term, by creating a wider margin between in-house costs and market prices.

In order to enable manufacturers to focus on the foregoing problem, a methodology has been developed which addresses the identification and minimisation of total production costs within the company. The methodology involves a detailed examination of each cost element within the organisational and manufacturing processes necessary to satisfactorily fulfil customer orders. The resulting analysis indicates the cost contribution of each element and highlights those where a more rigorous investigation may result in further financial reductions.

Included in the contribution is an outline and explanation of the methodology employed, together with an example of its application, within an organisation, to identify 'the cost of material waste' in the manufacturing process sequence of a representative product. The perceived advantages of the methodology, along with its iterative approach are also discussed, together with a consideration of its application in labour and overhead 'cost waste' reduction.

Keywords: Operations Management, Order Processing, System Design and Cost Reduction.

1.0   Introduction

The aim of this paper is to outline a cost reduction methodology the use of which can provide for an improvement in company operational costs. The scheme proposed is iterative in nature, which ensures that the cost data relating to individual products and used in the analysis is always current and not "an ideal value" or historical type information. As will be outlined in the explanation of the scheme methodology, the level of cost information currency or obsolescence is therefore dependent upon the frequency of product orders. This in itself is an important parameter and a valuable item of management information, highlighting as it does where managers should focus their attention during a product portfolio and profit contribution review. It should also be noted that, the scheme to be implemented at Wiltan provides for operational cost improvements via the use of various proven procedural elements to be found in operations management, process re-engineering, job or works order costing and variance analysis [1], [2].

In a financial sense therefore, it should be recognised at the outset that the cost associated with manufacturing individual products is often sub-divided into three distinct categories that is: - labour, materials and overheads. These initial sub-divisions are all capable of a further reduction, into the direct and indirect costs linked with the manufacture of a particular product. Traditionally however in costing system design, indirect labour and material costs are often recovered via a general factory wide overhead charge, this being applicable to all products in a company's portfolio and as a consequence, the overhead category itself may not be split into direct and indirect groups or associated with any particular product. The advantage or justification of this approach is often cited as being that there is a minimum cost involved in identifying and obtaining manufacturing cost information as direct labour and material costs are readily found.

The need to analyse overhead costs in more detail is important to any costing system. Niazi et al [3] describe a methodology which analyses current manufacturing cost estimation methodologies and ascertains the contribution of the three cost sub-elements of labour, materials and overheads to the overall manufacturing cost on a sample company. Their study revealed a need to implement an improved overhead estimation methodology based on dividing manufacturing overheads into time and material-related costs. A new mathematical model for estimating overhead for an individual product was proposed which allowed for the apportionment of total overheads based on both the product lead times and material quantities. The proposed methodology was found to be superior to existing methods as overheads were more accurately estimated.

An alternative is to sub-divide the cost categories and to identify the direct and indirect cost elements for each individual product / batch as they appear in both the administrative and production sequence. For each cost generated in the overall process, a linkage must be established to the individual product and its production batch, as this provides the incentive to reduce the cost or waste associated with subsequent batch production. Cost is often chosen as the analysis parameter in any manufacturing improvement scheme and was so in this case, because monetary units allow the process to be generic and is a common measure of either efficiency or effectiveness across many or all of a company's departments. When complete, the scheme to be implemented at Wiltan should provide a detailed cost analysis system that will be capable of interrogation, to indicate those products or processes that are more important than others in terms of their contribution to profit.

LAST ORDER COSTING – AN ITERATIVE METHOD TOWARDS MANUFACTURING COST REDUCTION

In turn this will point to where improvement activities should be focused to raise both efficiency and effectiveness within the manufacturing system and in addition, the scheme as designed will allow the preparation of interactive product quotations via scenario analysis, in the knowledge that the cost information used is both current and reliable. This avoids the situation where orders are accepted at a fixed cost based on ideal and possibly obsolete cost values and subsequently result in either a minimum profit or a loss being made on completion and delivery of the order to the customer. An additional feature of the implementation software is the prediction of the likely costs involved in the production of future products, this being based on the financial data currently held for similar items that already exist in the product portfolio.

2.0   Methodology

This type of complete product cost analysis had not been undertaken previously in the company and therefore no structure existed to identify or collect the required data. Accordingly, the first step was to map out the series of processes both administrative and production, that an order would go through before completion and dispatch to the customer. Experience has shown that this can be a very useful exercise, often illustrating unnecessary processes and complexity in the order processing system [1]. The unnecessary elements can subsequently be removed to streamline the system and effect an immediate cost saving. Once such a system map is available in its streamlined form, the financial data associated with each process can be collected and structured so that direct and indirect costs can be assigned to individual products and production orders. It should be noted that while the direct costs are fairly easy to assign, previous experience has shown that indirect costs are more challenging and need to be distributed in such a way that each finished product carries its own share of the total cost of operations to allow the individual product-order profit to be calculated [2].

By adopting the principle of value added, the direct and indirect costs associated with each step in the administrative and production process were recorded for each order passing through the system. In this way each step in the order completion process has an opening and closing balance which indicates the costs incurred and value added prior to the next step in the process chain, with the processes themselves being characterised in terms of the costs for labour, materials and overheads. Subsequently these cost groupings are re-categorised into the direct and indirect costs associated with each step in the order completion sequence. This method of standardising the expense of processing particular product orders allows for a direct comparison of current order cost with its immediate predecessor and thus provides a mechanism for continuous improvement.

If the current order processing cost is higher than its immediate predecessor then the processing step or steps generating the extra cost are readily identifiable along with the category of cost increase and the reason for it. Action can then be taken to correct the situation prior to processing the next order for the particular product. If the current order processing cost is lower than its immediate predecessor then the processing step or steps generating the reduced cost are again readily identifiable along with the category of cost reduction and the reason for it. This then becomes standard operating procedure and can be used as an example to the workforce of how to achieve improved efficiency and effectiveness within the order processing system. The staff involved in generating the improvement should be suitably rewarded for their initiative both to maintain workforce interest and to provide motivation to ensure a successful scheme.

Note that what is described above represents the initial iteration of the methodology and that when the system is in stable operation the current order cost is compared not only with its immediate predecessor, but also with the lowest previous order processing cost for that particular product. Care should be taken to ensure that a suitable cost correction factor is used with both these values to maintain their cost currency in relation to the current order itself. In this manner order processing costs are continually driven down with the cost datum used for comparison kept up to date and thereby dispensing with the often obsolete standard values used in such variance analysis. Further benefits which accrue from this methodology include a positive incentive for individuals in the workforce to innovate new methods of operation and effect cost reductions within their order processing step. Where such ideas are successful, as stated above, they become permanent changes in the operational method until displaced by new innovations, and in this way the order processing system is continually updated.

An additional benefit of the methodology is that new order quotation values are always based on the last order processed cost. This ensures that normally, any accepted customer orders should be profitable, as current costs are used to compile the quotation. However, this is not guaranteed as there is always a chance of the unexpected happening within the order processing sequence. Previous experience has shown that where the methodology has been implemented via a computerised database and thus the minimum profitable price known for individual products, it has been an invaluable aid in telephone sales negotiations where non-profitable orders have been refused by the company concerned [2].

3.0   Example

The example illustrated below, pertains to the implementation of the methodology outlined above in the material utilisation area, at company involved in the metal processing industry. Wiltan Ltd is a magnetic components manufacturing company which specialises in producing wound cores for transformer products. The cores are formed from cold rolled grain oriented silicon steel which is wound on specially designed machinery. They are subsequently annealed to relieve any work induced stresses, impregnated with insulation material and trimmed to size. The product range includes 'C' cores, 'E' cores, Toroidal cores, single and three phase power distribution cores, all having a number of different possible finishes such as natural, edge bonded, fully impregnated, polypropylene covered and epoxy resin coated, with or without end caps.

Because of the expense involved in using such specialised material to manufacture these products, and knowing the potential for cost savings to be realised, the initial work at Wiltan to implement the methodology of last order costing was therefore focused on material utilisation in product production. It was quite obvious that manufacturing any part or product in Witan at a competitive cost could only be accomplished when the materials and production processes were used both efficiently and effectively. In addition, as the waste material was only worth a fraction of its initial cost, there was a large incentive to improve material utilisation as a contribution to reducing overall manufacturing cost. As the product range has such a large variation of core types and finishes it should be noted that the material utilisation and cost analysis system has to take account of this, and to be adaptable enough to cope with each individual products manufacturing sequence.

A simple and straight forward scheme was adopted at Wiltan to define material utilisation within each step of the manufacturing sequence. It was based on the so called "weight model" ratio which defines material utilisation (m) as follows [4]: -

$$m \quad = \quad \frac{\text{Weight of the finished component}}{\text{Weight of the raw material used to make the component}}$$

As the value of 'm' tends towards one so material utilisation is improved and less scrap or waste is being produced. This leads to a consequential cost reduction in the overall manufacturing process cost for the product. Previously, this idea has only been applied as far as is known to individual components as part of a methodology to improve the design process. Here it has been adapted and applied to individual production processes, namely winding, annealing, impregnation, cutting, finishing and testing.

In the study conducted at Wiltan, the material utilisation values and costs for individual product orders and process sequence steps were recorded over a three month period and subsequently analysed and combined to yield a summary result table. This indicates an average material utilisation value for each manufacturing process step based on the orders included in the study and is reproduced as Table 1 below. It shows that the largest material utilisation improvement and consequent cost reduction in the manufacturing process sequence would be realised by improving the efficiency and effectiveness of the cutting process. Individual order cost analysis confirmed this result indicating that on average, a 2.6% improvement in material utilisation and consequent cost reduction was possible across the component range if the cutting process was improved over and above unavoidable material loss.

By modifying and improving the cutter used in the activity, some of the deficiencies in this particular manufacturing process were removed and an improvement in material utilisation achieved [5]. In addition, an improvement in quality of cutting was effected together with an extension in the life of the cutter used. Although the improvement in material utilisation was small in individual work-part terms, the multiplying factor of component throughput volume and the beneficial effect on the life cycle cost of the cutter ensured that the cost savings achieved were significant. It should be noted that the production costs per piece in the table are representative values which are used to maintain company confidentiality whilst still illustrating the usefulness of this technique.

Table I: Material Utilisation and Cost Values for a Product Production Sequence at Wiltan Ltd

Process	Material Utilisation (M)	Production Cost/Piece (£) (Y)	Relative Cost (X)	Partial Utilisation (MX)	(X-MX)
Winding	0.995	2.800	0.139	0.138	0.001
Annealing	1.000	2.800	0.139	0.139	0.000
Impregnation	1.000	6.990	0.347	0.347	0.000
Cutting	0.926	6.990	0.347	0.321	0.026
Finishing	0.506	0.580	0.028	0.015	0.013
Totals		20.160	1.000	0.960	

LAST ORDER COSTING – AN ITERATIVE METHOD TOWARDS MANUFACTURING COST REDUCTION

4.0   Conclusions

The technique of last order costing as outlined above is only in the initial stages of implementation at Wiltan and to date has focussed on the utilisation of material in the manufacturing sequence. As indicated by the representative example outlined in this paper, overall material utilisation in the production process is reasonably good. There are however specific processes within the manufacturing sequence which could be improved to provide a cost advantage to the company. The cutting stage for example is interrelated to the winding stage where the accuracy of winding determines the amount of material to be cut out of the core. Reducing waste at the winding stage by improving machine accuracy together with the use of standard coil sizes should therefore result in a higher material utilisation figure and a reduction in cost.

In the case of the finishing process, the losses here result from the size of the polypropylene sheets used. Whilst the physical material and cost losses are small, an improvement could be effected by matching the size of the sheets used to the batch quantity ordered, thus providing an improvement in this stage of the manufacturing sequence. In future, the further implementation of the methodology outlined above is expected to result in similar potential savings in other process areas. In particular, there are high expectations of cost reductions relating to the administrative tasks within the order processing chain.

References

[1] Thomas, P.V. & Davies, A; "Remodelling a Company via Systems Re-engineering", International Journal of Production Management, 1996, Vol 16, No 7, pp 14-26.
[2] Usener, M; "Re-engineering of a Thermoset Moulding Department", M.Phil Dissertation, University of Wales, Cardiff, December 1999.
[3] A. Niazi, J.S. Dai, S. Balabani and L.D. Seneviratne, A New Overhead Estimation Methodology: A Case Study in an Electrical Engineering Company, Journal of Engineering Manufacture, Proc. IMechE, 221(4): 699-710, 2007
[4] Robinson, S; "Material Utilisation in Component Design and Process Selection", Undergraduate Project Report No 0300966, Cardiff University, April 2007.
[5] Haslehurst, M. " Manufacturing Technology", 2nd Edition, English Universities Press, 1972, Chapter 1, pp 24-30.

The 6th International Conference on Manufacturing Research (ICMR08)
Brunel University, UK, 9-11th September 2008

APPLICATION OF LEAN TOOLS AND PRINCIPLES IN THE MANUFACTURING COST MODELLING PROCESS

Y. Delgado Arvelo, D. J. Stockton

Department of Engineering and Technology, De Montfort University, UK

Abstract

Cost models are built using a variety of approaches and methods which can classically be informal and decided on the judgement and experience of the product and manufacturing teams. During the New Product Development (NPD) process, cost data and information change along with its availability and can drive the selection of methods, including those for the identification and collection of data, as well as those for the analysis of the information gathered. These changes also have significant effect on the accuracy of the cost estimate and the total lead time for its production. As a result, current cost model development processes are yet described as often being time consuming and unresponsive to users needs; significantly lacking coherent and consistent approaches and very much depending on the use of process and product experts input to generate cost models. This paper explores two essential elements to the success of the cost model development process, namely the need for a coherent approach for developing cost models and the problem of long model development lead times, especially at the data identification and data collection stages. Industrial and academic experts in the fields of cost modelling and estimating from a variety of manufacturing sectors contributed to identify the steps involved in the development of cost models and their value adding contribution to the final estimate, and to explore the issues involved in the data collection and identification tasks and the potential application of new methods, such as Lean Manufacturing tools in the development of cost models.

Keywords: Cost modelling process, data collection tools, Lean manufacturing techniques.

1.0   Introduction

Expert opinion suggests that adding value is the key factor to gain and maintain competitive advantage [1]. The increasing market pressures generated by the race for reaching competitive advantage which affect the manufacturing sector, will have similar consequences on the cost model development process tasks and its final outcome, i.e. cost models [2]. Therefore, in order to effectively respond to spiralling increased market expectations, new cost models must be rapidly generated, and more accurate, comprehensible and accessible to a wide pool of users from a variety of business functions. As a consequence, emerging strategies and initiatives in support of enhancing cost estimation techniques and methods will ultimately result in improving the product development process and its outputs, especially if aiming to reduce the waiting times for cost estimates which ultimately cause delays in the product and process development times [3].

A major issue is the effect that the constraints placed on the cost estimating and modelling processes have on the main cost models' developing tasks, especially on the data identification and data collection tasks [4]. The appropriate selection of data sources and costing information, especially at the early stages of the cost modelling process, and later the use of the most appropriate data identification and collection tools and techniques are key elements for reducing the development times of models which represents one of the main types of waste in the process.

Increasing emphasis on minimising Overall Product Life Cycle costs and Product Development Cycle times will result in a greater need for more efficient and formalised data identification and collection methods available to cost engineers for reducing the development times of models [3]. In addition, the lack of costing data and the limited availability of process and product expertise at the concept stage of a new product development process, will significantly affect the tasks of data collection and data identification; hence the time, cost and accuracy of the cost modelling process and, the cost model itself will also be affected [2].

2.0   The Cost Modelling Process (CMP)

The objective of the Cost Modelling Process (CMP) is the identification and collection of product, process and cost information which is then analysed to estimate a cost or time [5]. The process essentially consists of a series of sequential data collection, data identification, data analysis and decision making tasks, whose main function is to identify the potential cost drivers or predictor variables for the construction of mathematical models (usually statistical regression equations), also known as CERs (cost estimating relationships) and TERs (time estimating relationships) that mathematically describe project, process or product costs [6].

Basically, cost models are the cost of an item or activity as a function of one or more independent/predictor variables. These equations are statistical relationships between cost or time and physical or performance characteristics of past designs such as process parameters and design variables. Sometimes those characteristics or parameters are called cost drivers [6]. Cost models are tools for cost estimation in the early stages of the product development process, when 80% to 85% of the product's whole life cycle costs are committed. They are also a main component and a starting point of product life cycle cost management. Nowadays, when knowledge of costs and cost behaviour are essential ingredient for effective decision making, cost models supporting product and process estimates have gained an important role since they are useful instruments to obtain process and cost information.

However, the increasing demand for cost models developed earlier in the product development process when there is limited or poor historical data and product and process expertise; the increasing complexity and availability of products and processes; and the increasingly reduced model development times will all make it difficult to undertake, efficiently and effectively, the tasks involved in the generation of cost models [7]. The market's pressure for breakthrough technologies and innovative products will increase the need to produce a greater number of cost models at different levels of detail, and will also increase the requirement for models containing a major number of independent (predictor) variables [8]. All these requirements will have to face the constraints of having less historical data available to generate cost models [1], and less process and product expertise to lead the cost model development process [7].

It is, therefore, imperative that the cost modelling process become more responsive and structured. To this end, changes are required in order to cope with the problem of data identification and data collection, essential tasks to the success of the cost model development process, particularly when cost models must be developed for production processes that are still under development [9].

3.0   Methodology and Work Undertaken

The main objective of this research investigation is to provide a step change on the speed and resources required to develop cost models by assessing the applicability and effectiveness of tools and methods used in the tasks of data collection and identification, including the potential use of Lean tools and techniques, and reviewing current model development practices. It builds on the work initially conducted as a major EPSRC funded research programme.

The contribution to knowledge includes building a more efficient and coherent cost modelling methodology, and developing a Model Scoping Framework integrated into the proposed development procedure. It is expected that these tools will assist cost model developers and users in defining the cost model purpose, and identifying the business objectives and functions the model is due to serve and support. They will also assist in identifying the relationship between the cost model characteristics (as established at the concept stage of the model development) and effective methods to select and collect the required cost data, in order to build a 'leaner' cost model, i.e. specific to the purpose, accuracy, resources and the development time available.

This is a data driven investigation where the initial research questions and enquiries on the issues being faced by the cost model developers where identified by an initial literature review, followed by survey questionnaires, and face to face interviews with academic and industrial experts in the area of cost modelling and estimating. In addition, given the current advances in communication technology, an electronic version of the survey was developed and distributed. Also, online resources, including professional discussion groups and special interest groups from a variety of industry sectors, contributed to identify and explore the applications of both traditional techniques and new tools for gathering cost data.

The initial scope of the project included the UK aerospace industry. However, the scope was later widened to include other industries as previous research have shown that existing costing methodologies and systems used in the aerospace industry, are not dissimilar to those used in the design and manufacture of other engineering products and services [10]. This paper focused on the work carried out by cost engineers and estimators when identifying the different elements and sources of data and information required for building cost models, and most importantly, on the identification of efficient tools and techniques for cost data collection and identification, including less traditional methods which fall under the category of Lean tools and techniques.

4.0   Applying Lean Principles and Tools in the Manufacturing Cost Modelling Process – Main Findings

The final objective of Lean principles results in the elimination or reduction of waste, more specifically, any activity that uses resources but does not add value, including rework and scrap, motion, inventory, over-production, waiting time, transportation, and resource under-utilisation [11]. Timely and reliable data sources play an important part on minimising the development time of cost models, and contribute to make the CMP more effective. In addition, the accuracy and validity of cost models depend to a great extent on their data sources, thus adding value. Data used in the development of cost models and estimates traditionally comes from a variety of sources [12]-[13]-[14]-[15], as described in table I.

Table I: Sources of Data

Information obtained from the expert knowledge of cost engineering practitioners, such as cost estimators, cost engineers, value engineers, project managers, and parametric analysts (combination of common sense, logic, skills, experience and judgement).
Information supplied by the model user (model purpose and characteristics),
Information acquired from previous costing estimating exercises generated for the same or similar projects, processes or products (historical cost information).
Information provided by the project or process owner, and members of the project team (manufacturing, design, procurement, sales)
Information obtained from customers and suppliers of the project or process (internal and external).
Other sources of information such as published literature, proposals, databases, Institutions and Associations, and Government Departments

Data sources (Table II) and data collection techniques (Table III) identified in the study were grouped into categories according to their nature, main features and their application within the CMP [3].

As expected, common data sources were identified, but also new sources of information appear to be gaining popularity in the past few decades. The World Wide Web, for instance, has made available a variety of online resources including electronic databases, specialist web sites, Professional Institutions, public bodies and the Government, patents and standards, special interest and discussion groups, electronic mailing.

In the CMP, extensive and complex research might take time and require specialist knowledge to reach the expected outcome. All these online sources allow having fast access to vast amount of information; and consequently, add value to the CMP as they simplify the data identification and collection tasks; promote using less effort by eliminating motion; and combine or simplify tasks in the process.

The applicability of data sources on the generation of cost models will depend not only on the characteristics of the data source itself [12], but also on the purpose and characteristics of the model and those of the process or product a cost model or estimate is required for [3]. According to the survey responses, data availability seems to be the main driver for the level of detail a cost model can be built at and the defining factor for the cost model characteristics, rather than those elements such as user requirements, model purpose and the business objectives the model aims to serve.

In the CMP, once the appropriate data sources have been identified, then the data collection tasks take place. Their function is to capture data relevant to the resource a cost model is required for. At this stage, issues such as time available to collect the data, what the data will be collected, resources, etc must be addressed [7].

Data collection in the CMP as a time consuming process, affected by the availability of data sources; data types and level of detail; amount of data to be gathered; frequency of data collection; and consistency in the data collection process [8]. These factors contribute to different types of waste throughout the Cost Modelling Process including waiting times, unnecessary motion and effort, processing and rework.

APPLICATION OF LEAN TOOLS AND PRINCIPLES IN THE MANUFACTURING COST MODELLING PROCESS

Table II: List of Data Sources by categories.

Category	Data Sources
1 - Process Sources	Actual Process Video of Process Process Expert Similar Processes Visual and Control Tools Computerised Planning Systems Process controllers
2 - Synthetic Sources	Synthetic Standards (Standard Data) PTMS Systems (MTM, MOST, MSD, MST)
3 - Product Sources	Costed Components CNC Programmes CAD Files Product Specification Bill of Materials (BOM) Engineering Drawings
4 - Equipment Sources	Equipment Specification Maintenance Manuals Operating Manuals Training Manuals Equipment performance records
5 - Model Based Sources	Process Models Empirical Laws Physical Models
6 - Paper/Internet Sources	Literature reviews Departmental records Operator's Black Book Quality manuals/reports Shopfloor Documentation, Planning/Control Sheets Patents World Wide Web (WWW)
7 - Heuristic Sources	Rules of Thumb Personal Judgment, Common sense, Logic Expert experience/opinion

Building a cost model requires the use of appropriate data collection methods for each particular data source. Information regarding the level of detail of input data, model accuracy, and cost drivers assists in identifying potential data sources and selecting the most effective data collection tools [3]. These methods must be able to eliminate some 'waste' and non-value added activities in the process by minimising the time and resources required to collect data and ensuring that the correct data is obtained when required and as required; and that the data is both accurate and valid. Table II shows the identified data collection methods and tools grouped into their respective categories.

APPLICATION OF LEAN TOOLS AND PRINCIPLES IN THE MANUFACTURING COST MODELLING PROCESS

Table III: Data Collection Tools and Techniques by categories

Categories	Data Collection Tools
Diagramming & Charting Techniques	2D & 3D Diagrams Flow diagram Flow process chart IDEF process chart Multiple activity chart Outline process chart Simultaneous motion cycle chart String diagram Travel chart Two-handed process chart Mind Mapping Tree Diagram
Motion & Time Study Techniques	Activity/Work Sampling Checklist Chronocyclegraphs Cyclegraphs Direct observation Video tape recording/Film analysis sheet Stopwatch Time Study Routing Sheet
Estimating Techniques	Analytical estimating Category estimating Comparative estimating Judgemental analysis technique
Team Working Techniques	Brainstorming Creative thought Decision modelling
Survey Techniques	Interview Questionnaires
Engineering Practices	Experimentation (operational experiments) Network analysis Program Evaluation and Review Technique (PERT) Critical Path Method (CPM) Value Stream Mapping

The study also identified particular preferences to use certain categories of data sources and collection methods (Figure 1). It was also revealed that, within the same category, there were differences in terms of the preference for certain data collection methods and sources of data.

In terms of data sources, Process and Product sources are the two most common providers of information. As expected, the primary and most important data sources identified were experienced cost engineers and

APPLICATION OF LEAN TOOLS AND PRINCIPLES IN THE MANUFACTURING COST
MODELLING PROCESS

manufacturing process experts. Data sources falling into the categories of Model based and Synthetic sources are also well known and used among the costing community.

As far as data collection methods is concerned, there is a predilection for the use of Estimating techniques, followed by Survey techniques and Engineering practices. This is among the whole range of data source categories.

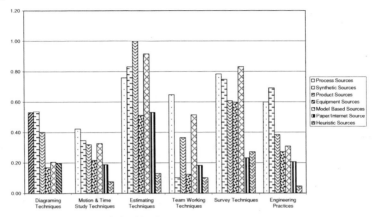

Fig. 1.   Results extracted from the analysis of the data.

Some data collection methods, on the other hand, which have not been used or encountered in the past despite their benefits, are attracting some interest. This is the case of Motion and Time study methods such as Activity/Work Sampling, Video tape recording/Film analysis sheet and Stopwatch Time Study. In the past, the use of these techniques was motive of preoccupation for trade unions [3]. However, a step change has occurred since the introduction of the Lean principles and techniques in the Western industry. The perception of these tools has started to change from being seen as intrusive and threatening control methods imposed by top management to techniques and procedures for improving working conditions and environment, increasing employees' motivation, and assist management in reducing unnecessary costs and root causes of waste while helping employees to 'understand the nature and true cost of work' throughout the business [11].

5.0   Conclusions

Two aspects of the cost model development process are essential to the success of the cost model development process, particularly when cost models must be developed for processes and products that are still under development: the need to develop a coherent model development methodology and the problem of data identification and collection. Identifying the right data sources, early in the development process, is the first step in the generation of accurate estimating models. The importance of adopting an effective model development process has been discussed, along with the contribution of the cost modelling tasks of data identification and data collection to improve the development process of cost models, by providing the first steps to make it a 'Leaner' process.

Data collection in the CMP as a time consuming process. The work described looks into the data collection process used within the CMP for the generation of cost models. Potential data sources and a range of data collection tools for data gathering were identified and categorised. Particular preferences were identified on the use of certain categories of data sources and collection methods. It was also revealed that there were differences in terms of the preference for certain data collection methods and data sources, within the same category. This work has also shown how new methods and tools are gaining importance especially since the introduction of the Lean principles in the Western industry, methods known as Lean Tools and Techniques.

A comprehensive life library of potential data sources and data collection tools and techniques has been developed and improved as new methods and sources are incorporated. This work also has been the basis for the development of a CMP methodology which includes a Model Scoping Framework. It is expected that the Library of Methods and Tools will support the data identification and collection tasks which are part of the proposed methodology adding visibility, value and efficiency to the task of generating cost models.

Acknowledgement

The authors wish to acknowledge the assistance and support of all those who gave freely of their time to make this work possible, not only by completing the survey questionnaires and participating in the focus groups, but also those who gave their time during the many interesting interviews. In particular, we would like to thank the engineers at Rolls-Royce plc in Derby and Bristol, BAE Systems Airbus in Bristol, and BAE Systems Military and Aerostructures in Preston, as well as the academic and research staff at the Centre for Manufacturing at De Montfort University in Leicester for their time and efforts. I would also like to express my thanks to the AACE's Cost Estimating Committee and the Institution of Engineering and Technology for their cooperation. Finally, I would like to acknowledge the funding received from ISES Consultants Ltd which enabled me to take part in this Conference. Thank you for your support.

References

[1] A Salas. "Cost estimation: more than an analytical tool". *IEEE Aerospace Conference Proceedings*, pp. 1053-1060, 2004.

[2] Q Wang, D J Stockton, P Baguley. "Using neural networks in cost model development process". *Proceedings of the Sixteenth National Conference on Manufacturing Research*, University of East London, pp. 59-63, September, 2000.

[3] Y. Delgado Arvelo, M. McNeill, D. Stockton. "Improving the Cost Model Development Procedure" *2002 International Transaction, 46th Annual Meeting of AACE International*, Portland, Oregon, June 23-26, pp. EST 14.1-14.11, 2002.

[4] D J Stockton, Y Delgado, M McNeill, P Baguley. "Improving the cost model development process". Deliverables Report No. 1. EPSRC Ref. No.: GR/M 58818, De Montfort University, UK, 2000.

[5] P. Ostwald. Engineering cost estimating. 3rd Edition, Prentice Hall, New Jersey, pp. 197-198, 1992.

[6] S O Ogunlana. Accuracy in Design Cost Estimating. PhD Thesis, Loughborough University, Loughborough, 1989.

[7] T Shaik. Automated Development of Process Time Estimating Models. PhD Thesis, De Montfort University, Leicester, UK, 2006.

[8] P Baguley. Improving the Cost Model Development Process using Fuzzy Logic. PhD Thesis, De Montfort University, Leicester (2004).

[9] D. J. Stockton, R. Forster, B. Messner. "Developing Time Estimating Models for Advanced Composite Manufacturing Processes". *Aircraft Engineering and Aerospace Technology*, 70, 6, pp. 445-450,1998.

[10] S Urkmez, D J Stockton, R Ziarati, E Bilgili. "Activity Based Costing for maritime enterprises". *Advances in Manufacturing Technology XXI Proceedings for the 5th International Conference on Manufacturing Research (ICMR 2007)*. De Montfort University, Leicester, UK, pp 83-87, 2007.

[11] F Meyers, J Stewart. Motion and Time Study for Lean Manufacturing. 3rd Edition. Prentice Hall, New Jersey, pp. 8-15, 2002.

[12] J K Hollmann, "What is Cost Engineering". *International Journal of Cost Engineering*, **48**, 3, pp. 8-9, March 2006.

[13] W R Park. Cost Engineering Analysis. A guide to the Economic Evaluation of Engineering Projects. John Wiley & Sons, New York, pp. 2-5, 1973.

[14] C Rush, R Roy. "Capturing quantitative and qualitative knowledge for cost modeling within a CE environment". *ISPE International Conference on Concurrent Engineering: Research and Applications*. Anaheim, Los Angeles, July 28th – August 1st, CETEAM, USA, pp. 209-218, 2001.

[15] W Winchell. Realistic Cost Estimating for Manufacturing. Second Edition. Society of Manufacturing Engineers. Michigan, USA, pp. 43-45, 1989.

APPLICATION OF LEAN TOOLS AND PRINCIPLES IN THE MANUFACTURING COST MODELLING PROCESS

Computer Aided Engineering (CAE)

SIMULATION SUPPORT OF LEAN LAYOUT CONSIDERATIONS FOR NEW PRODUCTS: A CASE FROM LARGE SCALE PRODUCTS

R. Darlington, B.Wahid, R. Weston, K. Case and R. Harrison

Wolfson School of Mechanical and Manufacturing Engineering, Loughborough University, Loughborough, Leics. LE113TU

Abstract

Planning a new production line for a product presents many opportunities to build best practice techniques into the new system. Set against the unknown quantities may be certain requirements for the production system to be lean, to have the flexibility to respond to market changes or make use of existing equipment of factory space. The unknown quantities can include: anticipated demand volumes, assembly and processing sequences, the specific production processes, lead-times of parts and components and even late changes to the product design after manufacturing/production decisions have been made. Simulations of a production system can be used to consider different scenarios and compare how well alternative approaches meet the defined requirements.

Uncertainties over production strategies, such as with a new production system, raises questions over which order to apply the use of simulation and layout optimization techniques. In addition, simulations of 'to-be' systems based on data from non-production prototypes and manufacturing estimates presents considerable challenges to the modeler to provide valuable decision support.

This paper considers the particular case study of simulation support for pre-production layout planning within significant cost and space constraints. The manufacturer in this case required that the production system remain lean while flexible enough to meet fluctuating demand volumes. While factory floor space was constrained, manufacturing equipment did not need to be fixed in place, allowing workspace flexibility. The paper describes the simulation issues overcome and the project structure used to produce various models for consideration of different manufacturing issues.

Keywords: Simulation, Lean manufacture, Layout planning, New product introductions.

1.0   Introduction

Simulation is a valuable tool for testing a wide range of manufacturing scenarios and potential changes to a system. The accuracy of the outputs of any simulation is driven by the data used to create the model, and as such when models are built using incomplete data or estimated values, the feedback that the simulation provides must be considered limited. When production has yet to begin for a particular set of processes it may be possible to estimate values or for the 'to-be' system or extrapolate test data for the purposes of building models, however this also leads to accuracy issues for the models concerned.

Lean manufacturing as a philosophy provides a basis for companies and supply chains to deliver value to customers through eliminating waste from production activities, and many tools exist for analyzing and improving existing production processes and facilities. Building lean concepts into a production system from it's first inception presents many opportunities for engineers to impact the levels of waste generated in the production process (however it must be noted that improvement activities should still take place once production begins). When presented with the opportunity to design a new production system, efforts to establish the best possible set-up and layout of the production system are made, and where feasible simulation tools can be used to support this process.

This paper considers how simulations can be used to support manufacturing layout planning in the face of incomplete 'to-be' data. A brief outline of the associated literature in the areas of lean manufacture and simulation is followed by a description of the methods that may be employed in modeling different manufacturing scenarios and some of the challenges that are faced in using estimates and test data for simulations. The paper closes with a case study manufacturer planning a new production system based on data from prototype products with cost and facility space constraints. Conclusions are drawn on how the authors supported the company's decisions on how the production system should be set-up using simulation tools.

2.0   Literature Survey

The following sections provide a brief outline as to the associated literature in the areas of lean manufacture and simulation.

2.1   Lean Manufacture

The concepts and mindset associated with lean manufacturing are now very familiar as a philosophy first conceived within the Toyota Production System (TPS) [1]. Many lean implementations fail, as the philosophy requires a mindset change and for cultural underpinnings of the company to be sympathetic to the changes that lean manufacture demands. Although there have been suggestions [2] of the application of 'fractal' lean

SIMULATION SUPPORT OF LEAN LAYOUT CONSIDERATIONS FOR NEW PRODUCTS: A CASE FROM LARGE SCALE PRODUCTS

concepts to points of production where flow and waste reduction can be most benefited without entire production systems undergoing the move towards lean manufacture.

The many tools used to highlight lean manufacture may be considered as largely related to analysis and mapping, one of the most simple analysis tools is lead-time mapping, which tracks, quantifies and prioritises the cumulative steps which contribute the total lead time. The concept behind the mapping is to highlight the main causes of delay in the products lead time by arranging the production steps which are commonly displayed chronologically in a Gantt chart format, into a Pareto format [3]. By severing the process step dependencies and focusing on the lead-times, those process steps which may contribute the greatest time savings can be focused upon. Process activity mapping is a name given to the process analysis style of mapping which originated in industrial engineering [4] which may be summarised thus:

- The study of the flow of processes
- The identification of waste
- Consideration of whether the process can be rearranged in a more efficient sequence
- Consideration of a better flow pattern, involving different flow layout or routing
- Consideration of whether everything happening at each stage is necessary and the result should superfluous tasks be removed

Value Stream Mapping (VSM) is a lean tool, and like all lean tools has the underlying motive of eliminating waste, it provides a visualisation of the physical and information flows through a particular value chain [5] and is very widely recognized in industry.

2.2   Simulation Support

Simulation projects generally follow a common set of steps [6] – [9]. The case for building simpler models allowing for easier changes and disposal of models in favour of newly released technology is a compelling one [10]. Sources that indicate that most simulation projects follow a similar form are generally in agreement in terms of the major steps that define the work. These key elements are outlined below [7]-[9], [11], [12] the approximate proportions indicated for each element of individual projects having been described [11].

Problem Definition and Analysis ~ 10% each
A written statement of the problem-solving objectives, understood by all involved, and it is *the* problem that needs solving.
Data Gathering and Validation ~ 10 to 40%
The models input parameters are specified and data collected relative to the model detail. The data is checked to ensure it is both appropriate and representative.
Model Construction ~ 10 to 40%
The model is built from either a simulation language or a simulator, it should be a simplified representation of reality, though including enough detail to provide a good approximation remembering that this will be used for problem solving.
Verification and Validation ~ 10%
Verification determines whether a model correctly performs as intended, and validation establishes the credibility of the model, ensuring there is a correspondence between the real system and the model- typically by collecting and comparing data from both.
Experimentation ~ 10 to 20%

Experiments are planned to efficiently produce meaningful output data from experimental test runs. The conditions that produce a change in results can be altered and contrasts between alternatives highlighted.

Analysis of Results ~ 10%

Statistical procedures should be implemented to measure performance, including estimates of errors where possible.

Recommendations ~ 5%

Documentation of the model is good practice to avoid any duplication of effort, assumptions made in the model should be noted and if suitable, the model should be implemented.

There are several forms of simulation that differ depending on the modeling focus and the processes under study. Discrete events are instantaneous actions that occur at points in time, while dynamic simulations are models that are influenced by time [7]. Discrete event simulations can however be used to describe a system as it progresses through time, and is widely used for manufacturing applications [13]. More effective communications between the user and the simulation analyst, so that both have an improved understanding of the problem, was a key reason in developing visual simulation tools [14]. This communication aid being recognised [15] as crucial when dealing with large teams or when presenting a concept. Simulating the system and using this tool to assist in the determination of the new layout (as opposed to determining layouts first) has been described [16] as preferable when operational policies are not predetermined, such as with a new production system.

3.0   Modeling Manufacturing Scenarios

Any simulation is at some level an abstraction of reality. Recognising this and understanding the level of detail that is appropriate to the system under consideration are key to successful simulation projects. A straightforward method to drive the modeling process to meet these objectives comes from a clear problem definition to establish exactly what it is the simulation sets out to achieve.

Too often modelers are asked to provide models of a system without clearly defined and agreed aims, objectives, and deliverables. The intention is that the models created may be used in a variety of different "what-if" scenarios to deliver many answers regarding changes in the production system. Such a tool would be invaluable to a company, however the difficulties in creating such a model, are often too much to overcome. A model capable of reflecting many different aspects of the business whilst exhibiting robustness to change would invariably involve vast quantities of data to be available or collected Additionally, construction of such a complex model would be time consuming to the extent of becoming obsolete.

The case for simple models, focusing on a particular set of problems is clear. In such instances, models can be quickly updated when fresh data becomes available or a new modeling technology comes to market. By making the models as simple as possible, validation of the outputs of the model is simplified and management decisions can be swiftly supported. A portfolio of models that reflect the issues that the manufacturer wishes to address, driven by clear definitions of problem areas, allows complex manufacturing systems to be represented by relatively straightforward models. Working from multiple models presents different working issues that must be considered.

The goals that the simulation sets out to achieve must be clearly structured and ideally broken down so as to assist in dividing the problem up into workable modeling areas. For greatest consistency, the model building activity should be undertaken by an individual, however given time, resource and practicality constraints, often the simulation process will involve a number of people or even multiple teams. In such instances great efforts must be made to clarify the stated aims of the simulation, and that all the modelers have a clear understanding of the methods by which the models will be built. The assumptions made in creating the model should be clearly documented and be consistent with assumptions made for all the models built for the system, likewise the variables that form the basis for the simulation should be explicitly outlined and consistent with the set aims of that particular model. Experiments using various models can contrast different scenarios where appropriate with a limited number of pre-selected variables driving the differences between the models. Assumptions should be kept consistent between models for this form of experiment in order to keep results meaningful, while competing manufacturing strategies (where the assumptions may be different) can be compared provided the differences between each model's construction are explicitly outlined alongside the results.

4.0   Challenges in Modeling 'to-be' Systems

Most commonly, modeling is undertaken on existing systems, in manufacturing particularly as part of Value Stream Mapping (VSM) processes, the incumbent system is referred to as the "as-is" system. When considering what the production system will become after a change is frequently termed the "to-be" system. As with any process which forecasts future systems or events, there are many difficulties associated with establishing the facts that will accompany a "to-be" system. Even more challenging cases exist where rather than improve upon an existing system, an entirely new production system is planned, with no opportunity to compare against previous operations or process data. As such, modeling a 'to-be' system means that risks associated with inadequate, incomplete or unavailable data threaten the success of the simulation project. Some approaches to reducing these data availability risks may be described as:

- **Use of comparison data**
  Where available, the use of data from similar processes or systems should be considered and substituted if given appropriate weighting and noted as an assumption of the proposed system performance.
- **Limiting the effect/impact of the data shortfall**
  In some instances it may be feasible to reduce the effect of the shortage of data through how the problem considered is framed. In limiting the impact on simulation accuracy, this practice will accordingly limit the benefits of the modeling undertaken by impacting the scope of what issues are explored.
- **Updating models as data becomes available**
  As the project progresses, information relating to equipment testing, product trialing, prototyping etc. may become available. By changing the models to reflect the most up-to-date information available risks to the simulation accuracy incrementally reduce, however risks to the overall manufacturing project may not be improved depending on when in the project the data becomes available!

The authors assert that there is no straightforward method to compensate for a lack of data when building models. However the value to be gained from undertaking simulation means that when it is possible to mitigate for the shortfalls in data availability then efforts should be made to make best use of what information *is* available to deliver useful decision support for developing the new or improved system.

5.0   Case Study

The issues previously outlined that surround simulation support of manufacturing activities based on 'to-be' data are illustrated further through the consideration of the following case study. The particular product considered is sensitive, therefore this paper has focused on the generic manufacturing aspects and no reference is made to any specific product or company details.

5.1   Background

Company X has a long established track record in manufacturing a wide variety of products, however current market conditions have caused the company to consider a new product as a potential revenue stream for the business. Several prototypes of the product have been created and the final design specifications are being finalized. The prototyping of two of the products have also been used to provide baseline processing times for the individual operations. A number of issues exist in using this data faithfully, through considerations such as operations that occur for prototypes may not happen during production and delays for parts that were not available as the supply chain was not yet adequately in place.

Estimates have also been made regarding anticipated demand and the production volumes (<10 / month) that will be required and space within the manufacturing facility earmarked for production. One of the key features of this new production system is that it requires no dedicated tooling equipment to be installed within the factory. The product will not require any transfer lines or dedicated machines so that the separate workstations will have a reasonably high degree of flexibility, however the production system will be required to have volume and product flexibility [17] to cope with changes in the initial period. A number of the operations do not have a fixed precedence and so the sequence of those operations can be altered to balance the production system.

Priority constraints for the company have been identified as production costs, as the product targets a new market there is some uncertainty as to pricing and profit margins. This uncertainty means that the company is keen to learn as much as possible about the costs associated with each potential manufacturing strategy. From a practicality point of view, the product itself is reasonably large and so the movement of the product and its constituent parts through the assembly system presents some issues, in addition to limiting the physical space available for workstations within the facility. The factory floor space outlined for production consists of half of an existing facility, with the possibility to expand to fill the whole factory should the business case and demand for the new product deem it necessary.

5.2   Project Structure

The modeling for this project was undertaken principally by staff at Loughborough University's Centre of Excellence in Customised Assembly (CECA), supported by other modelers from the university's Manufacturing Systems Integration (MSI) research group. The project had around 10 engineers with different backgrounds in modeling techniques and tools working with the company, and a considerable amount of coordination and time dedicated to clear communication between these modelers of the manufacturing issues was required. The modeling activity was broken down as described previously into a range of "problem areas" with small focused simulations being undertaken to address particular issues. Deconstructing the manufacturing issues began with consideration of the overall space limitations, with three scenarios drawn up; firstly the production system being implemented into half the factory (as initially intended), an alternative where the full factory is utilized and a blue skies comparison where no space limitations were placed on the system. Each of these scenarios had alternative workstation configurations suggested to present 9 alternative production layouts. These models formed the basis upon which experiments were performed to establish assembly sequences, capacity constraints, resource issues etc. An outline overview of the modeling areas and the structure of the simulation project is provided in Figure 1, below.

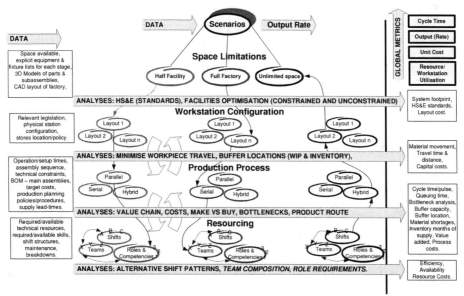

Fig. 1.   Outline of simulation project structure.

The different modeling areas were undertaken by those members of the CECA and MSI teams that had expertise within those manufacturing fields, and regular consistency meetings and cross checks were undertaken to ensure the models were built in a compatible and comparable manner. The output metrics from each of the models outlined in figure 1 were kept consistent and as a baseline included cycle times, the system output rate, unit costs and resource utilization. Each of the models was subject to a range of analyses which included lean tools to assess how well the layout and assembly scenario performed for that model's given assumptions (e.g. half factory floor, with layout configuration 1 etc.) In addition, 3D models were generated from product CAD and factory layout plans to compare workstation configurations suggested from the modeling efforts and to establish how the production layout would fit within the space available.

SIMULATION SUPPORT OF LEAN LAYOUT CONSIDERATIONS FOR NEW PRODUCTS: A CASE FROM LARGE SCALE PRODUCTS

5.3   Management of Simulation Issues

As anticipated with a project of this size and nature a wide variety of complexities had to be overcome. Data availability was a particularly constraining factor, with insufficient operation timings etc. recorded from the prototyping process. Collection of data from within the facility was also problematic, given the sensitive nature of the company's other products and restrictions on the time modelers could spend on site. These information issues caused significant concerns when it came to the accuracy of data that was used to drive the models, which identified where inadequate data was being incorporated into the simulation and flagged this next to the output results to remind the modelers of the confidence in the data. Fortunately, a final round of pre-production prototypes has been scheduled which presents opportunity to gather specific information relating to each operation as it is trialed. A program of data collection and information capture has been prepared and will provide improvements to the initial models created. Difficulties persist in the data not reflecting production information that could be collected were the full working system in place, however this updated information will be incorporated into the existing models to build greater confidence in those areas flagged as being subject to uncertainty.

Updating models as new information becomes available enables the modeling team to provide the most accurate simulation support possible as changes occur as the production system is prepared. Unfortunately this means that decision support early in the project was largely strategic and detailed feedback of the working of the system was necessarily broader than hoped. Additional problems to overcome updating of models were compounded through the distributed nature of the model building in this project. With each update in available information, the new data had to be analysed, disseminated and changes to modeling constructs agreed amongst the teams prior to undertaking the required changes. Communication is a key element to the success of this project and a close collaborative working environment has been established between the teams. Most of the personnel have worked together in the past, however working meetings and the overall project environment have been structured to allow open and clear communication of modeling issues as any member of the teams raise them.

A selection of analysis tools have been used to feedback information in conjunction with the various modeling scenarios. Each scenario (as indicated in figure 1) has in addition to the accompanying model, five analysis methods applied to the proposed production layout to assist in decision support for the company. These methods consist of mappings of the layout (through spaghetti or string diagrams), detailed consideration of the processes (through lead-time maps, process activity mapping and estimated value stream maps as described in section 2) and cumulative costs (through creation of a cost time profile [18] accumulated through production). Examining the processes in this way further confirms the assumptions that have been made accompanying each model, where processing times or resources have been estimated or appear dubious then they can easily be flagged here for future reference to explain any particular results of the modeling activity. Finally a matrix approach (as with Pugh's concept screening [19], [20]) is to be applied iteratively to compare the various layout scenarios. Selection criteria (such as layout cost, flexibility or system throughput) are set, against which the proposed layouts are scored by the team until a consensus is reached as to best alternative. Before discarding any layouts, improvement processes may be used to generate a hybrid design, which is modeled analysed and submitted for the next round of selection.

6.0   Conclusion

This paper has highlighted the wide range of issues faced when simulation is employed to support the launch of a new production system. Limitations from the lack of available reliable data relating to the proposed processes are significant, and while there are ways of mitigating against the impact of such shortfalls of data (notably in the case study presented by acknowledging the shortfall exists and building models flexibly to be updated as new information becomes available) there can be no replacement for comprehensive information available early in the project timescale. CECA and MSI's engineers continue supporting the company's decisions on how the production system should be set-up through the analysis of the proposed layout scenarios using simulation tools. Final examination of the selected layout and the extent to which the analysis methods and models assisted the company will be forthcoming in mid 2009 once the production system has been realised.

Acknowledgement

The authors wish to acknowledge the assistance and support of, CECA, HEIF and Company X.

References

[1]   Womack, J.P., Jones, D.T., Roos, D., *The machine that changed the world.* New York, Rawson Associates, 1990.

[2]   Womack, J.P., 'Take the lead in lean'. Institute of Electrical Engineers, *Manufacturing Engineer*, April/May 2005, 3.

[3]   Bicheno, J., *The Lean Toolbox.* Buckingham England: Moreton Press, 2000.

[4]   Hines, P., Rich, N., 'The seven value stream mapping tools'. *International Journal of Operations & Production Management*, 17, 46-64, 1997.

[5]   Tapping, D., Luyster, T., Shuker, T., *Value Stream Management: Eight steps to planning mapping and sustaining lean improvements.* New York, Productivity Press, 2002.

[6]   Askin, R. G., Standridge, C.R., *Modelling and Analysis of Manufacturing Systems.* New York, Wiley & Sons Inc 1993.

[7]   Gogg, T. J., Mott, J.R.A., 'Introduction to simulation'. *In:* M. M. G. Evans, E. Russell, W. Biles ed. *Proceedings of the 25th conference on Winter Simulation 1993,* 9-17, 1993.

[8]   Lung, A. W. M., 'Benefits of a systematic approach for problem analysis on manufacturing simulation modelling', *Proceedings of IEE international conference, Simulation 98: Innovation through Simulation,* 271-276, Herts, UK, Omega Print and Design publishers, 1998.

[9]   Seila, A. F., 'Introduction to simulation'. *In:* K. K. C. Alexopoulos, W. Lilegdon and D. Goldsman ed. *Proceedings of the 27th conference on Winter Simulation 1995,* 7-14, 1995.

[10]   Salt, J. D., Keynote address: 'simulation should be easy and fun'. *In:* M. M. G. Evans, E. Russell, W. Biles ed. *Proceedings of the 25th conference on Winter Simulation 1993.* 1-4, 1993.

[11]   Liyanage, K., Perera, T., 'Design and development of a rapid data collection methodology', *Proceedings of IEE International Conference, Simulation 98: Innovation through Simulation,* 297-302, Herts, UK, Omega Print and Design publishers,1998.

[12]   Musselman, K. J., 'Guidelines for simulation project success'. *In:* M. M. G. Evans, E. Russell, W. Biles ed. *Proceedings of the 1993 Winter Simulation Conference.* 58-64, 1993.

[13]   Robinson, S., *Successful Simulation.* London, McGraw-Hill Book Company, 1994.

[14]   Hurrion, R.D., Visual interactive modelling. *In:* Hurrion, R.D. ed. *Simulation.* IFS Publications Ltd, 1986.

[15]   Alabastro, M. S., Beckmann, G., Gifford, G., Massey, A.P., Wallace, W.A., 'The use of visual modeling in designing a manufacturing process for advanced composite structures'. *IEEE Transactions on Engineering Management*, 42, 233-240, 1995.

[16]   Alesia, E., and Lin, Li., 'For effective facilities planning: layout optimization then simulation, or vice versa?', *Proceedings of the 2005 winter simulation conference.* pp 1381-1385, 2005.

[17]   Sethi, A.K. and Sethi, S.P. 'Flexibility in manufacturing: a survey'. *International Journal of Flexible Manufacturing Systems*, 2, 289-328, 1990.

SIMULATION SUPPORT OF LEAN LAYOUT CONSIDERATIONS FOR NEW PRODUCTS: A CASE FROM LARGE SCALE PRODUCTS

[18] Fooks, J.H., *Profiles for performance: Total Quality Methods for reducing cycle time*, Addison Wesley, Reading MA, 1993.
[19] Pugh, S*., Creating innovative products using total design*, Addison Wesley, 1996.
[20] Pugh, S., *Total design*, Addison Wesley Reading MA, 1990.

SIMULATION SUPPORT OF LEAN LAYOUT CONSIDERATIONS FOR NEW PRODUCTS: A CASE FROM LARGE SCALE PRODUCTS

The 6th International Conference on Manufacturing Research (ICMR08)
Brunel University, UK, 9-11th September 2008

MODEL DEVELOPMENT FOR TURNING PROCESS

Iwona Piotrowska, Christina Brandt, Hamid Reza Karimi, Peter Maass

University of Bremen, Center of Industrial Mathematics, Bibliothekstr. 1, 28359 Bremen, Germany. (e-mails: {iwona, cbrandt, hrkarimi, pmaass}@math.uni-bremen.de)

Abstract

In recent years, significant advances in turning process have been achieved due greatly to the emergent technologies for precision machining. Turning operations are common in the automotive and aerospace industries where large metal workpieces are reduced to a fraction of their original weight when creating complex thin structures. The analysis of forces plays an important role in characterizing the cutting process, as the tool wear and surface texture depending on the forces. In this paper, the objective is to show how our understanding of the turning process can be utilized to predict turning behaviour such as the real feed rate and the real cutting depth as well as the cutting and feed forces. We also study machine cutting processes by a different model compare to one has been recently introduced for grinding process by Malkin and Guo [6]. The developed two-degrees-of-freedom (2DOF) model includes the effects of the process kinematics and tool edge serration. In this model, the input infeed is changing because of current forces during turning process and the infeed rate will be reducing by elastic deflection of work tool in opposite direction. Besides, using the forces and material removal during turning, we calculate the effective cross-sectional area of cut to model material removal. With this model it is be possible for a machine operator, using the aforementioned turning process parameters, to obtain a cutting model at very small depths of cut. We present model that predict real position of the tool tip and predict the cutting and feed forces.

Keywords: Turning process, model analysis, and simulation.

1.0   Introduction

Turning is the one of the basic machining processes in manufacturing industry. With improvements in machine and spindle technology, an important and challenging issue in turning is the modeling of the process. Recently, many papers tackled that problem focusing on dynamical representation of turning processes; see for instance [2], [3] and the references therein. They present the dynamic modeling and simulation of the surface generation in turning process. In particular they investigate the dynamic machining tool structural response, cutting process variables, tooling geometry as well as dynamic cutting force model. The force model plays an important role in material removal operation and has to be in detail analyze. In [7] the authors present a model of the dynamic cutting force for the three – dimensional turning process. The start point to modeled forces is the Kienzle model which taking into account the material parameters. Similar approach one can find in [4]. Due to this concern, we present our recently enveloped concept of modeling in the turning process, i.e. a two-degrees-of-freedom (2DOF) model is given for actual feed rate of the tool. In his work we consider a single-point diamond turning process. Now we collect the classical notions and well known physic feature that will be needed in the sequel. We will denote by t the time. In the sequel, the symbol K_e stands for the effective system stiffness. For a giving feed f the speed of the tool and the workpiece velocity are given by v_f=nf and $v_w = 2\pi nr$, respectively. Moreover, it is assumed that the input depth of cut is smaller than the tool radius.

The rest of this paper is organized as follows. Section 2 includes the main results of the paper, that is, development of an 2DOF model for a turning process. Section 3 provides simulation results to illustrate the specifications of the process and Section 4 concludes the paper.

1.1   Notations:

f	The feed rate	b_e	The width of the tool
v_f	The feed velocity	l_h	The length of the tool holder
a	The actual feed rate	r	The work radius
v_a	The actual feed velocity	A_c	The cross-sectional area of cut
v_c	The cutting velocity	A_f	The cross-sectional area of feed
a_p	The depth of cut	K_{ey}	The machine stiffness in y - direction
n	The rotational work-speed	K_{ex}	The machine stiffness in x – direction

2.0   Model Description

We present the model for real position of the tool tip as well as the actual depth of cut. The basic idea is to investigate the forces which occur during process.

2.1   Process Kinematics

In this subsection we discuss in some detail the geometry of turning process. Recall that we consider the plane turning process with a single-point diamond tool restricted to orthogonal cutting. The cutting tool is moving along the radius to the center of the workpiece with a given feed rate f. In Figure 1 one can see a two-dimensional image of geometry and the movement of the turning tool on the workpiece surface. The geometry of the tool, vibrations and the elastic deformations affect on the surface roughness. Note that the surface roughness in turning is also influenced by the depth of cut a_p, the feed rate, the workpiece material and its hardness. These elements determine the kinematic roughness. The interested reader is referred to [1], [8] for further details.

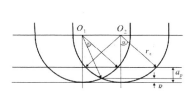 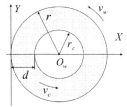

Fig. 1.   Geometry of turning process

Moreover for analyzing the forces we will need the definition of the cross-sectional area. Recall that the cross-sectional area of cut A_c can be approximated by product of the depth of cut a_p and the feed rate f, i.e. $A_c=a_pf$ [1], [8]. Similarly, the term $A_f=a_pb_e$ is defined as the cross-sectional area of feed. Moreover, for analyzing the forces we will need the following definitions of the cross sectional areas

$$A_c(t) = a_p^a(t)a(t)$$ (1)

$$A_f(t) = b_e a_p^a(t).$$ (2)

2.2   Forces Model

We start with consideration about force model for turning process. We confine attention to the feed force F_f and the cutting force F_c. The forces in machining operations are often found from empirical equations. The one type of the model of the cutting force is obtaining from the Kienzle diagram and taking into account the material parameters. For the model constant c_f the feed force is given by

$$F_f(t) = c_f A_f(t) v_a(t) = c_f b_e a_p^a(t) v_a(t).$$ (3)

The feed force has the main influence on the elastic deflection of work tool in opposite direction to the feed. The cutting force F_c affects on the work tool and is responsible for its elastic deflection in direction orthogonal to the feed. We define the cutting force by

$$F_c(t) = c_c A_c(t) v_c(t) = 2\pi c_c a_p^a(t) v_a(t)(r - d(t))$$ (4)

where c_c is a model constant and the displacement of the turning tool on the workpiece surface represented by d(t) is computed as

$$d(t) = \int_0^t v_a(s)ds = n \int_0^t a(t)dt . \tag{5}$$

The both forces F_f and F_c depend on the time and affect on actual feed and depth of cut.

2.3   Model

Our main task is to develop the 2DOF model that characterizes the displacement between command and actual position of the tool tip in turning process. We take the similar approach as in [6], which investigates the model for cylindrical plunge grinding process. In these the actual infeed rate is reduced by the elastic deflection and the radial wear rate of the wheel. For more details we refer the reader to [5]. Because of diamond construction and also diameter of cutting tool in turning case does not occur the last effect. We introduce two dimensional Cartesian coordinate system (X,Y) in such a way that the tool tip at the beginning is at the origin, see Figure 1. During the process, on the work-tool affect the feed force F_f and the cutting force F_c which led to the displacement at the X-, and Y- axes, respectively. We denote the deflection at the time t in x and y directions by $\delta_x(x)$ and $\delta_y(t)$, respectively. Then the actual position of the tool tip on the X axis is given by

$$P_x(t) = v_f t - \delta_x(t), \tag{6}$$

and the actual position on the Y axis is

$$P_y(t) = \delta_y(t) . \tag{7}$$

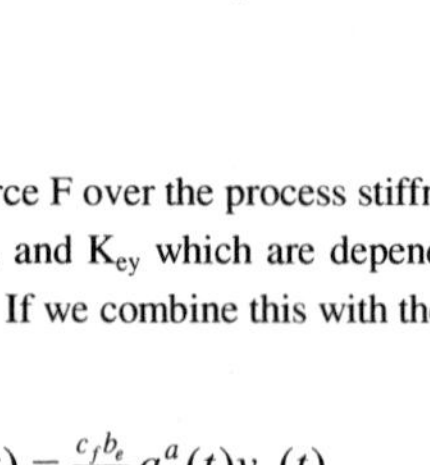

Fig. 2.   The actual depth of cut

The deflection is computed like usual i.e. the force F over the process stiffness K_e. In our model we distinguish two process stiffness for two directions i.e. K_{ex} and K_{ey} which are depending on height, width and length of tool holder as well as on the material properties. If we combine this with the equations (3) and (6), we obtain

$$\delta_x(t) = \frac{c_f b_e}{K_{ex}} a_p^a(t) v_a(t). \tag{8}$$

Eq. (7) combined with the relations (4) and (5) gives

$$\delta_y(t) = \frac{c_c 2\pi}{K_{ey}} a_p^a(t) v_a(t)(r - \int_0^t v_a(s)ds) \tag{9}$$

We simplify the writing by denoting two constants c_x and c_y in the equations (8) and (9) as $c_x = \frac{c_f b_e}{K_{ax}}$ and $c_y = \frac{c_c 2\pi}{K_{ey}}$, respectively. Furthermore, the total displacement of the tool is given by $\delta(t) = \sqrt{\delta_x(t)^2 + \delta_y(t)^2}$. Moreover the actual depth of cut shown in Figure 2 can be obtain with following expression

$$a_p^a(t) = a_p - (l_h - \sqrt{l_h^2 - \delta(t)^2}) \approx a_p - \frac{\delta(t)^2}{2l_h} \tag{10}$$

where l_h denotes the length of tool holder.

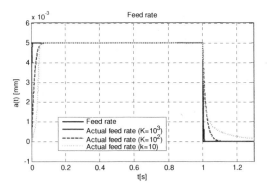

Fig. 3.   Curves of the feed rate and the actual feed rate signals.

The last term in (10) one can obtain by taking two first positions into account from Taylor series expansion. Computing the derivatives of (8), (9) and (10), and combining with equation (6) we obtain the following equations system

$$\begin{cases} \dot{d}(t) = v_a(t) \\ \dot{v}_a(t) = \dfrac{v_f - v_a(t)\left(1 + c_x \dot{a}_p^a(t)\right)}{c_x a_p^a(t)} \\ \dot{a}_p^a(t) = -\dfrac{1}{l_h}\left(\delta_x(t)\dot{\delta}_x(t) + \delta_y(t)\dot{\delta}_y(t)\right) \\ \dot{\delta}_x(t) = v_f - v_a(t) \\ \dot{\delta}_y(t) = \dfrac{c_y}{c_x}\left[\dot{\delta}_x(t)(r - d(t)) - \delta_x(t)v_a(t)\right] \end{cases} \tag{11}$$

MODEL DEVELOPMENT FOR TURNING PROCESS

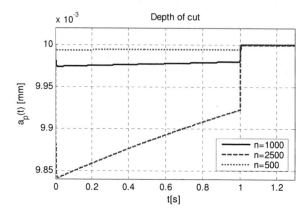

Fig. 4.   Time histories of the actual depth of cut.

Remark 1: The feed velocity $v_a(t)$ and actual depth of cut $a_p^a(t)$ are calculated by solving the nonlinear differential equations (11) by considering the boundary conditions $d(0) = 0$, $v_a(0) = 0$, $a_p^a(0) = a_p$ and $\delta_x(0) = \delta_y(0) = 0$. Moreover we can predict the feed and cutting forces using the equations (3) and (4), respectively as well as the actual feed a(t).

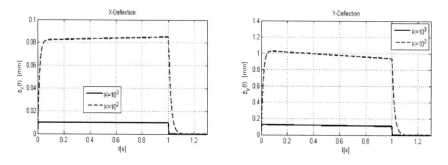

Fig. 5. Curves of deflections in both x and y directions.

3.0   Simulated Results and Discussion

For simulation of the turning process shown by the nonlinear equations system (11), the MATLAB software takes two-stage input information related to the workpiece properties, tool specification, and the process parameters. The developed model in (11) is then executed to predict turning behavior including feed rate, depth of cut, forces and deflections. The nonlinear differential equations of the system have been solved numerically for the nominal system parameters: $K := K_{ex} = K_{ey} = 10^3 \, ^N\!/_{mm}$, $r = 40 \, mm$, $r_e = 0.76 \, mm$, $b_e = 0.2 \, mm$, $l_h = 300 \, mm$, $f = 0.005 \, ^{mm}\!/_s$, $n = 1000 \, ^{rev}\!/_s$, $c_f = 10^3 \, ^{Ns}\!/_{mm^3}$ and $c_c = 10 \, ^{Ns}\!/_{mm^3}$.

MODEL DEVELOPMENT FOR TURNING PROCESS

To illustrate the simulation, consider a 2-stage feed rate as input shown in Figure 3 together with the predicted actual feed rate a(t) for the actual turning process in three different values of the machine stiffness. In Figure 4 we show time history of actual depth of cut $a_p^a(t)$ for various rotational work-speeds. Figure 4 also presents the results for cutting with n=500. Note that, this case corresponds to a relatively small workpiece velocity. One can see that the cutting process is very smooth with small fluctuations around the assumed cutting depth. In contrast to that Figure 4 (for a larger rotational work speed n=2500) shows cutting depth with large fluctuation of a cutting depth. The Figure 5 shows the deflections in x and y directions, respectively, for three different values of the machine stiffness. It is seen that during the cutting time corresponding to increase of $\delta_x(t)$, the deflection in y direction, i.e., $\delta_y(t)$ is decreased. Moreover, the curves of the feed force and cutting force are depicted in Figures 6 and 7, respectively, for three different values of the machine stiffness.

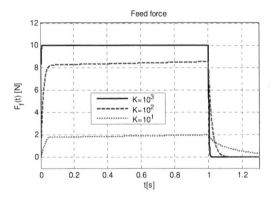

Fig. 6. Curve of the feed force.

4.0   Conclusion

We have developed a novel two-degrees-of-freedom (2DOF) model for turning processes to show how knowledge of the effects of the process kinematics and tool edge serration can be utilized to simulate the tool-workpiece system behavior. In this model, the input infeed is changing because of current forces during turning process and the infeed rate will be reducing by elastic deflection of work tool in opposite direction. It was shown that the model predicts real position of the tool tip and predicts the cutting and feed forces. Moreover, using the forces and material removal during turning, we calculated the effective cross-sectional area of cut to model material removal. One advantage of this model is that it makes possible for a machine operator to obtain a cutting model at very small depths of cut using the aforementioned turning process parameters.

The 2DOF model of the turning process presented in the paper can be extended to provide a better understanding on the multidimensional turning dynamics where the multidimensional modelling must be used for accurate predictions of the forces, the depth of cut and the surface of the final product. Therefore, this extension is a topic currently under study.

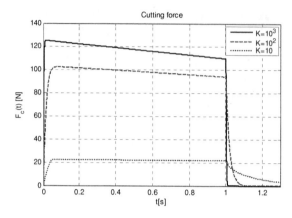

Fig. 7.   Curve of the cutting force.

Acknowledgement

The authors greatly acknowledge the financial support of this work provided by the German Research Foundation (DFG). The authors also wish to thank Dr.-Ing. Oltmann Riemer for his valuable remarks in performing this research work.

References

[1] Y. Altintas 'Manufacturing automation: metal cutting mechanics. Machine tool vibrations and CNC design', Cambridge University Press, Cambridge (2000).
[2] K. Cheng, X. Luo, R. Ward 'The effects of machining process variables and tooling characterization on the surface generation', *Int. J. Advanced Manufacturing Technology* (2005), **25**:1089 - 1097.
[3] K. Cheng, X. C. Luo, X. K. Luo, X. W. Liu 'A simulated investigatin on the machining instability and dynamic surface generation', *Int. J. Advanced Manufacturing Technology* (2005), **26** 718 - 725.
[4] A. V. Dassanayake, C. S. Suh, 'On nonlinear cutting response and tool chatter in turning operation', *Communications in Nonlinear Science and Numerical Simulation* (2008), **13**:979 – 1001.
[5] S. Malkin 'Grinding Technology: Theory and Application of Machining with Abrasives', Ellis Horwod Ltd., Chichester, and John Wiley & Sons, New York, (1989). Reprinted by SME (1996).
[6] S. Malkin, C. Guo 'Model based simulation of Grinding Processes',
 http://www.abrasivesmagazine.com/mtext/product/Model\%20Based\%20Simulation.p
[7] B. C. Rao, Y. C. Shin, 'A comprehensive dynamic cutting force model for chatter prediction in turning', *International Journal of Machine Tools and Manufacture* (1999), **39**:1631 – 1654.
[8] O. Riemer 'Trennmechanismen und Oberflächenfeingestalt bei der Mirozerspannung kristalliner und amorpher Werkstoffe', Aachen, Shaker (2001).

MODEL DEVELOPMENT FOR TURNING PROCESS

The 6th International Conference on Manufacturing Research (ICMR08)
Brunel University, UK, 9-11th September 2008

COMPUTER WORKSTATION EVALUATION APPROACH BY NEURAL NETWORK (NN)

N. Phaoharuhansa [1], K. Krishnamra [1], S. Nanthavanij [2], and W. Kongprawechnon [1]

1. Electronics and Communication Program, School of Communications, Instrumentations & Control

2. Engineering Management Program, School of Management Technology, Sirindhorn International, Institute of Technology, Thammasat University, Thailand

Phone: (+662) 501-3505 Ext. 1804, Fax: (+662) 501-3505 Ext. 1801, E-mail: waree@siit.tu.ac.th

Abstract

In developing countries such as Thailand, the application of ergonomics to enhance safety in business offices is still not a common practice. Office employees have been mistakenly assumed to be safe from ergonomics, health, and safety hazards that are common in industrial facilities. Thus, they tend to receive inadequate training, education, and protection regarding hazard conditions and practices in their workplaces. Musculoskeletal disorders are commonly found in office employees who work with computers on a prolonged basis, especially those using inappropriate workstation, assuming poor work posture, or performing improper work practice. This paper discusses a neural network based expert system for evaluating desktop computer workstations according to ergonomics principles. Initially, an ergonomics assessment form is used as a survey tool to evaluate the appropriateness of workstations and desktop computer accessories. The survey forms are then assessed by an ergonomics expert to determine the level of appropriateness. A neural network application program for computer workstation evaluation is constructed. The survey data are then divided into two parts, one part for training the neural network program and the other part for testing it. The test results show that the neural network based computer workstation evaluation program can satisfactorily generate the assessment results which are comparable to those performed by the real ergonomics expert.

Keywords: Neural Network, Ergonomics, Computer Workstation Evaluation, Expert System.

1.0   Introduction

Most office employees feel that they are working in a safe workplace and appropriate work environment. In fact, they are exposed to a certain ergonomics hazard on a daily basis. This hazard is induced by the computer work that the office employees perform nearly eight hours each day. Base on the statistics in 2006, in Bangkok there are 511,382 employees who use computers regularly in their normal work routine. However, virtually all employees are not aware of the effects of poorly designed computer workstation and inappropriate arrangement of computer accessories on their work posture, which will, subsequently, cause work-related musculoskeletal disorders (WMSDs) such as low back pain, tension neck syndrome, and carpal tunnel syndrome.[4] Typically, ergonomics experts can conduct a workplace survey to evaluate office equipment and workstation, and to indicate a risk level of developing WMSDs. Very often, the outcome of the evaluation is determined subjectively. This process makes it difficult for any safety officers who do not have much knowledge and experience in ergonomics to perform such workplace survey. [2]

In order to enable inexperienced safety officers to perform the workplace survey and evaluate the appropriateness of workstation and equipment effectively, a knowledge-based computer program can be developed to assist them. There are many algorithms (e.g., mathematical programming, data recognition) that can compute or generate solutions based on the given data. However, most of them are inflexible algorithms because the values in their solution-deriving process are set with certain values. The knowledge-based program for compute workstation evaluation discussed in this paper is a neural network based program. The neural network is a learning system that emulates the nervous system of human brain. The neural network structure is extremely complex. It can adapt and model the complex relation between inputs and outputs or to find the pattern in data.[7] The organization of this paper is as follows. In Section 2, the Artificial Neural Network is discussed. Ergonomic factors will be explained in Section 3. Consequently, Data and numerical results are provided in Section 4. Finally, Conclusion will be described.

2.0   Artificial Neural Network

A neural network is a system of interconnecting neurons in a network working together to produce an output function. The output of a neural network relies on the cooperation of the individual neurons within the network to operate [1].

Gradient descent is analogous to an error minimization process. Error minimization is an attempt to fit a closed-form solution to a set of empirical data points, such that the solution deviates from the exact value by a minimal amount. In Fig. 1, the diagram illustrates the process of minimizing the error of a function through the set of empirical data [6]. The learning process begins with the presentation of an input pattern to Backpropagation Network (BPN). The input pattern is propagated through the entire network, until an output pattern is produced. BPN then makes use of what is called the generalized delta rule to determine the error for the current pattern contributed by slightly in a direction that reduces its error, and the process is repeated for the next pattern. In this study, backpropagation neural network is adapted for the identification in term of lending decision system.

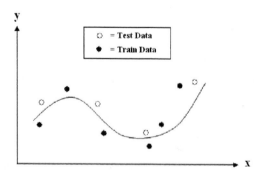

Fig. 1.   The diagram illustrates the process of minimizing the error of a function through the set of empirical data

COMPUTER WORKSTATION EVALUATION APPROACH BY NEURAL NETWORK (NN)

Fig. 2 shows the typical three-layer backpropagation neural network: the input layer with 1 node, the hidden layer with m nodes and the out put layer with n nodes. Between layers there are W_h weights, and W_{oh} represent the strength of connection of the nodes in the network [5].

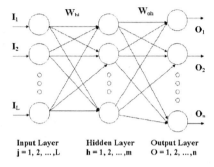

Fig. 2.   Typical three-layer Backpropagation neural network.

The first type of operation of backpropagation neural network is called feed forward and is shown as solid lines with arrows in Fig 2. During this operation, the output vector $O(t)$ is calculated by feeding the input vector $I(t)$ through the hidden layer of the neural network. For the given input vector $I(t)$, the output of the node h in the hidden layer $H(t)$ is

$$H_h(t) = F(Net_h(T)) \tag{1}$$

$$H_h(t) = F[\sum W_{hi}I_i(t)] \tag{2}$$

where Net_h represents the total input to the node h in the hidden layer; and $F(x)$ is the activation function, which has to be differentiable, for example the sigmoild function

$$F(x) = \frac{1}{1+e^{-x}} \tag{3}$$

The output of the node o in the output layer, $O_0(t)$ is,

$$O_0(t) = F(Net_0(t)) \tag{4}$$

$$O_0(t) = F(\sum_i W_{hi}I_i(t)) \tag{5}$$

where Net_0 represent the total input t_0 the node 0 in the output layer.

   The second type of backpropagation neural network is called error backpropagation, which is marked by dashed lines in Fig 2. The error function, defined by the sum of the square of the differences between the desired output T_0 and the net output $O_0(t)$ is

$$E = \frac{1}{2}\sum_{t,0}((T_0(t) - O_0(t))^2 \tag{6}$$

COMPUTER WORKSTATION EVALUATION APPROACH BY NEURAL NETWORK (NN)

For the connection between the hidden layer and the output layer, the adaptive rule for the weight W_{Oh} can be determined as

$$W_{Oh}(t + \Delta t) = W_{Oh} + \Delta W_{Oh} \tag{7}$$

$$\Delta W_{Oh} = -\eta \frac{\partial E}{\partial W_{Oh}} \tag{8}$$

$$\Delta W_{Oh} = -\eta \sum_t \Delta_0(t) H_h(t) \tag{9}$$

$$\Delta_0(t) = \frac{dF(Net_0)}{dNet_0}(T_0(t) - O_0(t)) \tag{10}$$

Similar to the adaptive rule for connections between the input layer and the hidden layer W_{hi} can be written as

$$\Delta W_{hi} = -\eta \frac{\partial E}{\partial W_{hi}} \tag{11}$$

$$\Delta W_{hi} = -\eta \sum_t \Delta_h t(t) I_i(t) \tag{12}$$

$$\Delta_h(t) = \frac{dF(Net_h)}{dNet_h} \sum_0 W_{ho} \Delta_0(t) \tag{13}$$

where the coefficient in (8) and (11) is the learning rate. Applying the differentiation process successively, the error backpropagation rules shown in (8)-(13) can be expanded to the networks with any number of hidden layers. The weights in the network are continuously adjusted until the inputs and outputs reach the desired relationship [3]. Summary of backpropagation algorithm is shown in Fig 3.

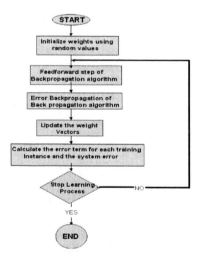

Fig. 3.   Backpropagation learning algorithm

3.0   Ergonomic Factors

Ergonomics is an interdisciplinary field that deals with the study of human data such as anthropometric data, physical capabilities and tolerances, expectation, etc. and how to apply such knowledge to help to design the equipment, workstation, work environment, and tasks that are suitable to humans. The objective of ergonomics is two-fold: (a) to maximize the human contribution to the integrated human-machine-environment work systems, and (2) to minimize the impact of other system components (i.e., equipment, work environment, and work procedure) on the well-being of humans.

Three ergonomics factors are considered to have significant effects on the appropriate of the computer workstation. They are: (1) equipment, (2) equipment arrangement, and (3) work environment. Specifically, the ergonomics factors for the computer workstation evaluation are grouped into three groups as follows:

Group 1: Workstation components and computer accessories information
Group 2: Computer accessories arrangement information
Group 3: Illumination information

Table I: Explanation of Ergonomic factors

Factors	Examples of Data
Workstation computer and computer accessories	Type of computer table, chair, keyboard, monitor, and mouse
Computer accessories arrangement	Positions of keyboard, mouse, monitor, and document
Illumination	Brightness and light direction

Using the workstation survey form, the survey data from 50 computer workstations were collected. Then, the data were converted into numerals in order to be represented in an appropriate form for the neural network. The numerical data were inputted through the designed Neural Network. The neural network was initially trained so that it can generate the evaluation results similar to the ergonomics expert. After that, it is tested with another set of data and the results were compared with the target to evaluate the error.

4.0 Data and Numerical Results

The data are numerated into an appropriate form to input in Neural Network. It is not common to have more than one hidden layer when solving a classification problem. The many layers also take a running time longer. The appropriate layer and neuron size must be design with concerning in time and error of the result. The Neural Network model consists of 3 inputs, 1 hidden layer with 5 neurons and 3 neurons respectively, and 1 output in the output layer.(as shown in Fig. 4)

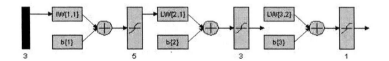

Fig. 4.   Designed neural network with 5-3-1 layers

First, training test was conducted by using backpropagation method. The algorithm of this method demonstrates in Fig. 3. The output in training set equals to "1" for selected case and "-1" for rejected case. The training test was conducted by using 35 cases. After the neural network is trained by using backpropagation method, the network was tested by using different of another 15 test data set from training part to ensure accuracy of the outcome. The estimations of output response for selected dataset are located to "1", and for rejected dataset are located close to "-1. Mostly, the estimations of output response in appropriate cases are located close to one, and for rejected cases are located close to negative one. The result over 0.75 indicates that the data is very appropriate. The data between 0.25 to 0.75 is an appropriate case. The acceptable case is placed between -0.25 to 0.25, the result between -0.25 to -0.75 tends to be inappropriate case, and the result below -0.75 indicates that the data is to be very inappropriate. The percentage of error was calculated from actually outputs compared to the ergonomist analysis. The percentage of error was 14 percents as show in Table II.

Table II: The Predictive accuracy of models

Neural network model	Percentage calculation
Very appropriate	0 percent
Appropriate	13.33 percent
Acceptable	0 percent
Inappropriate	59.94 percent
Very inappropriate	26.64 percent
Percentage of error	14 percent

5.0   Conclusion

In this study, Neural Network approach is applied for the desktop computer workstation evaluation. Normally, the evaluation is based on ergonomist and emotion judgment. Due to the lack of qualified and experienced ergonomist in Thailand, consequently, the expert system by using Neural Network approach has been simulated. The simulation results have shown that the neural network can outperform the ergonomist by employing a less time-consuming. Since a network of computing units self-organizes to implement the desired behavior by using a learning algorithm, neural network can make decisions with the same standard for all cases and takes less time to analyze compared to human analysis. The ergonomists can use this approach as a guideline for making judgments. Computer users can also use this approach as a first step evaluation to modify their applications so as to be able to improve their operations in workstation if the result is unfavorable.

References

[1] Demuth, H. and Beale, M. (1993), "Neural Network Toolbox for use with MATLAB", Foundation and Application, Mathworks Inc.
[2] Komolavanij, S. and Nanthavanij, S. (2007), "Developing a Neural Network based expert system for evaluating destop and notebook computer operations and workstations ", Proceeding of the 8th Pan-Pacific Conferrence on Occupational Ergronomics.
[3] Satish, K. (2005), "Neural Networks", a classroom approach, Mc-Grew Hill, International Edition.
[4] Asfah, C.R. (1995), Industrial Safety and Health Management, 3rd Edition, Mc-Grew Hill.
[5] Srakoopunth, L., Kittipatimakorn, P., Sakulphramana, R. (2001), "Auto tuning for computer numerical control (CNC) System by Using Neural Network Theory", Fianl Report of Senior Design project, Sirinhorn International Institute of Technology, Thammasat University.
[6] Laurence Fausett (1994), "Fundamentals of Neural Networks Architectures, algorithms, and applications", Prentice Hall International, Inc., pp. 11-44.
[7] K. Mingsakun, P. Piyapinyo, S. Komolavanij and W. Kongprawechnon (2007), "The Project Selection Model by Fuzzy Linear Programming", The International Conference on Engineering, Applied Sciences, and Technology, Bangkok, Thailand.

OPTIMAL DECISIONS IN PRODUCT MODULARITY DESIGN USING REAL OPTION APPROACH

Yile Wang, Ming Dong *, Dong Yang

Department of Industrial Engineering and Management, School of Mechanical Engineering, Shanghai Jiao Tong University, P.R. China *mdong@sjtu.edu.cn

Abstract

In the field of product modular design it is desirable to have a methodology leading to a dynamic product design responding to the changing market. "Dynamic" means that the design process can be controlled dynamically by the preference of customers. The product producer who is assumed to be rational should make his/her decisions based on current demands of the market. It is a kind of flexibility to adjust introduction of the different modules in the product life cycle. In this paper, option-pricing theory is applied to the module introduction decision-making in product modular design. Introduction of modules in product modular design is a portfolio of consecutive decisions. Two multi-stage stochastic models for product modular design are proposed in this paper. The models are used to simulate the process of introduction decision-making, in which the modular design configurations can be changed in a dynamic manner responding to changing demands. This paper illustrates how to control the process of adaptively selecting modules responding to the fluctuations of the market. The module introduction in the product design is a multi-stage process. At each stage the decision maker can decide to add, reject and merge modules to form different kinds of configurations. In the first model, we reevaluate the option value of mergence and the cost value at each stage according to the condition of the market to maximize the net present value of the profit through multiple stages. In the second model, the decision maker looks ahead one more stage and implements the optimization. At each stage, the model incorporates the demands of customers and the cost value of modular design in the option valuation. By modeling the demand uncertainties as stochastic processes, numerical simulation methods can be used to value flexible modular configurations. Simulation results demonstrate that effectively and timely exercising the options can significantly increase profit. Through real option analysis, a great value of embedded flexibilities in the product modular design can be revealed. Finally, we demonstrate the proposed approach through the design of mobile phones. The results show that the two models can dynamically respond to the customer demands and bring greater NPV for companies.

Keywords: Product modular design, Real option, Decision analysis, Stochastic simulation

1.0   Introduction

In the fast-changing world, a product producer may find itself in a situation that its products will be out of date quickly after they are launched (de Neufville [2004], Eckert C [2004]). The requirements of customers are changing quickly. So some components of these products must be updated as soon as possible to satisfy the requirements of customers. There are many methods by which products can have flexibilities such as product platform methodology (Konstantinos Kalligeros [2006], G. Yang [2004], Eun Suk Suh [2005], Gonzalez-Zugasti J [2000]), parameter design, modular product design and etc. These methods are not isolated, but interdependent and intercrossed with each other. Among the methods, modular product design is a flexible method to endow the product with a kind of flexibility that it can change with the evolving market (Eppinger S [1994]). The product designed by modular design method usually has a set of common design parameters which compose a base product with basic functions. Meanwhile other design parameters can form several modules to achieve different extended functions. However, how to identify a set of common parameters and a series of modules to is really a challenging task for a product designer. The whole product can be viewed as a configuration of these modules. If the product can somehow evolve adaptively with the changing market, then the producer can bring tremendous profit. In this paper, we adopt a real option approach to value such flexible configurations. The configurations involve the recursive decision-makings during the development process of the product. In this paper, Model 1 is presented to deal with the deterministic parameters of demands. While with the evolution of demands which are modeled by stochastic processes, Model 2 will be evaluated.

The concept of real options refers to flexibility embedded in real operational processes, activities, or module introduction opportunities, in the sense that the decision-maker has the right, but not the obligation to take a certain action (Hull [2002]). Combining product design with options thinking is really a new idea (Birgit Geppert [2003], de Weck O [2004]). Similar to the financial options case, where the decision-maker exercises the options contingent upon stock price movements, we consider a case that the decision-maker makes timely changes of the product configuration as the customer demands evolve. That is, we treat the new product development decision as an American-style real option. American-style option indicates that the option can be exercised at any time before the expiration of the option.

2.0   Literature Review

The concept of the modular product design was proposed by Meyer [1997]. He put forward a concept of the platform which is composed of a set of common design parameters. The platform can derive a series of modules that can be oriented to the different sections of the market. Baldwin and Clark [2000] defined three properties of the platforms: modular structures, interfaces that connect modules, design rules which designers should follow to make sure that module can be substituted by others. These concepts advance the development of the modular product design. But the key issue is how to value these methods. Simpson [2004] summarized the methodologies of design and optimization of the product platform. He pointed out that the product platform is the key factor of the success of the whole product family. Many companies utilized product platform strategies to diversify products, decrease the lead time of the development of products, and cut down

OPTIMAL DECISIONS IN PRODUCT MODULARITY DESIGN USING REAL OPTION
APPROACH

costs. Meyer [1997] stated that platform leveraging strategies can be applied to different segments of the market. These segments are corresponding to potential products. So companies can decide how to make decisions to design the platform. Kurtadikar et al [2004] introduced a methodology based on the demands of customers which can be applied in the concept design phase. The common modules (platform) and the individual modules can be identified by the frequency of the demands. The relationship between them is illustrated in the Figure 1. Otto et al [2005] also put forwards some methodologies of modular design based on functions. Their examples were based on the certain functions of physical products. These methodologies can validate the effectiveness of the modular product design. These valuations of modular product design have some disadvantages such as lack of dynamic updating and flexibility. Lack of dynamic updating means the valuation which is implemented at the very start only considered the current information of demands. So the product producer will find that his product cannot satisfy the requirements of customers any more some time later. At last this product producer has to quit the market. Lack of flexibility means that the configurations of products cannot be changed because of the product structure designed at first time. The modules of a product should have some kinds of flexibilities: merge, substitute, update and etc.

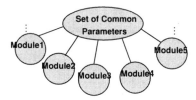

Fig. 1.   Modular product design

In this paper, we first introduce several kinds of flexibilities embedded in the product design. Uncertainty modeling is a key part of the decision-making process. Then two models are proposed to value the modular product design through multi-stage modeling procedure. Based on the models, an algorithm is designed to solve this optimal decision-making problem. Finally, a numerical simulation in which data sets are from mobile phone products is implemented to demonstrate the effectiveness of the models.

3.0   Problem Formulation

In this section, a product is viewed as a dynamic system, in which managerial flexibility is available for the decision maker to make contingent decisions. In order to maximize the expected profit, uncertainties, such as demands of different customers, must be considered. Some products, especially the digital products such as mobile phones, are renewed very quickly. Customers purchase new mobile phones because the old ones can not satisfy their changed preferences. With the managerial flexibility, the uncertainties may be turned to profitable opportunities. To demonstrate the value of flexible modular product design, we consider mobile phones as an example.

The multi-stage model with options is illustrated in Figure 2. At each stage, the product producer can exercise different kinds of options to form new configurations of the products responding to the new demands. The managerial flexibility considered here includes the following options:

1. Merge: the decision-maker can merge some modules to an integrated module to save cost.

2. Substitution: the decision-maker can replace an old module with a new module to respond to the new demands.

3. Reject: the decision-maker may reject an old module because of new demands.

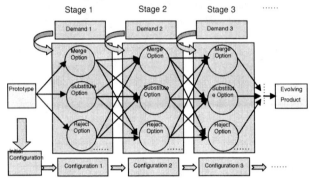

Fig.2.   Multi-stage modular product design with options

The modular product configuration means that the product is composed by a series of modules. In this model, the number of modules is assumed to be m. And the configuration decisions are made at the start point of each time period. At time t, some new demands for certain modules arrive. Meanwhile the decision-maker also decides which modules to be added into the product to satisfy the demands of customers. Upon receiving the information on the demands and current product configuration, the decision-maker maximizes the net profit by reconfiguring the product, including rejecting old modules, adding new modules and merging modules. If at a time period, there are two modules with interfaces in between, then they can be merged together to save a considerable cost. This process repeats at time t+1, and continues till time T which is the lifespan of this kind of product.

Two decision models are proposed in the following. Model 1 is deterministic and assumes that the decision-maker has the right, but not the obligations to merge modules in order to save cost. Model 2 is a two-stage optimization stochastic model. The decision-maker looks ahead one more period and performs the optimization with all available options. The following gives the notations of the models.

m: total number of modules

i, j: index of the modules

x_i^t : 0-1 decision variable indicating that whether the ith module will be added in time period t

y_{ij}^t : 0-1 variable indicating that whether modules i and j can be merged. If module i and j can be merged, then $y_{ij}^t =1$, otherwise $y_{ij}^t =0$

Dt: number of the modules in the time period t

R_i^t : ROI (Return of Investment) of the module i in the time period t

P_{ij}^t : profit of exercising the merging option between module i and j

C_i^t : cost of developing ith module in the time period t

ft: net revenue function in the period t

η_i^t : a standard normal random variable for ith module in the time period t

OPTIMAL DECISIONS IN PRODUCT MODULARITY DESIGN USING REAL OPTION APPROACH

μ_i^t : drift rate of the demand for the ith module in the time period t

σ_i^t : volatility rate of the demand for the ith module in the time period t

v_i^t : state variable indicating that how long the ith module has been adopted by the end of the time period t

r: discount rate for the demands between two consecutive periods

3.1 Uncertainties Modeling

The demand can be modeled as a stochastic process which is named Geometric Brownian Motion (GBM) which is used in the finance field to model stock price movement. Here, GBM is utilized to be analogous to the movement of demands. Stochastic variables can be defined as the following relation,

$$\frac{d^{t+1} - d^t}{d^t} = \mu_i^t \Delta t + \sigma_i^t \eta_i^t \sqrt{\Delta t}$$

(1)

where μ_i^t and σ_i^t represent the drift and the volatility rate of the demand for the ith module in the time period t. η_i^t is a standard normal random variable. The time step is denoted as by Δt, which is equal to 1 in this paper. The value of demands will be converted to an integer to represent the number of the modules.

$$D^t = \lfloor d^t \rfloor \quad t \in \{0, \ 1, \ 2, \ 3...T\}$$

(2)

The evolution of the GBM can be approximated by a binomial branch. Given the demand d^t at the stage t, at next stage t+1 the demand d^{t+1} has two states: the "up" state $d_{up}^{t+1} = upfactor \cdot d^t$ with probability p^t and the "down" state $d_{down}^{t+1} = downfactor \cdot d^t$ with probability $1 - p^t$. Here, $upfactor = \exp(\sigma_i^t \sqrt{\Delta t}) = \dfrac{1}{downfactor}$, $p^t = \dfrac{\exp(\mu_i^t \Delta t) - downfactor}{upfactor - downfactor}$. In Figure 3, an example of a binomial branching is given.

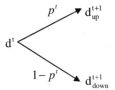

Fig.3   Binomial Branching

Therefore, in Model 2, which will be formulated in the following, the stochastic process of demands is described by a series of scenarios. Based on these scenarios, Model 2 can be converted to a deterministic ILP (Integer Linear Program).

3.2 Model 1: Deterministic Model with the Merging Option

In this model, the decision-maker only makes decision upon the information from the current time period. But he/she has the merging option in every time period. That means he/she can decide to merge the modules in a certain time period according to whether the exercising of the option can save cost. The integer program formulation is presented below. The objective function (Eq. (3)) consists of three parts. The first one is the profit introduced by adding new modules. The second one is the profit triggered by the exercising the merging options. The third one is the cost of introducing new modules. At each stage, the number of modules which product producer decides to add is no more than that required by customers. This is the constraint for the model. Meanwhile the parameters x_i^t and y_{ij}^t are 0-1 decision variables for the introduction of modules.

$$f_t = Max\left[\sum_{i=1}^{m} R_i^t x_i^t + \sum_{i=1}^{m}\sum_{j>i}^{m} P_{ij}^t y_{ij}^t \cdot max(x_i^t + x_j^t - 1,0) - \sum_{i=1}^{m} C_i^t x_i^t\right]$$
(3)

Subject to

$$\sum_{i=1}^{m} x_i^t \le D^t$$
(4)

$$x_i^t, y_{ij}^t \in \{0,1\}, \forall i, \forall j$$
(5)

After maximizing the objective function in time period t, the following variables are updated for the iteration of the next time period

$$v_i^t = \left(v_i^{t-1} + 1\right)x_i^t$$
(6)

3.3   Model 2: Two-stage Stochastic Optimization Model with the Merging Option

In this model, the decision maker looks ahead one more time period and performs the optimization. The decision-maker forecasts the demand for the next period. Based on the forecasting and current information of the demand, the decision-maker makes the decisions to maximize the expected profit. Let η_i^t be the demand of the ith module in time period t, r is the risk-adjusted discounted rate for each time period. The Model 2 is as follows:

$$Max[f_t + e^{-r}E_t(f_{t+1})]$$
(7)

Subject to

$$\sum_{i=1}^{m} x_i^t \le D^t$$
(8)

$$\sum_{i=1}^{m} x_i^{t+1} \le D^{t+1}$$
(9)

$x_i^t, y_{ij}^t \in \{0,1\}, \forall i, \forall j$

Note that the first model is an integer linear program (ILP), while the second model is an integer nonlinear program (INLP). If the scenario tree method is introduced to model the demands, a stochastic process of demands can be represented by a series of deterministic processes. So the INLP problem can be converted into ILP problem. In the section of numerical simulation, we will demonstrate the solutions given by optimization software CPLEX.

4.0   Simulation Algorithm

Following the proposed algorithm in below, the product producer can obtain NPV value of his/her decision process in a certain time period. In step 3, if model 2 is used, then scenarios for the next stage must be generated for the two-stage optimization procedure.

Notations:

K: the number of iterations

k: the index of the iteration

n: the index of the model, $n \in \{1,2\}$

Qn: expected ROI of the modular product design for model n

Fn(k): NPV of the kth simulation of model n

The algorithm procedure is as follows:

Step 0: $k \leftarrow 1$.

Step 1: If k>K, go to step 7, otherwise $F(k) \leftarrow 0$.

Step 2: Set t=0 and all variables to be zero.

Step 3: Generate the demand variable Dt (and generate scenarios for Dt-1). Find the optimal value of the objective function. Solve the decision variable and the objective value I_t

Step 4: Update the variable v_i^t

Step 5: If $t \geq T$, go to Step 6. Otherwise, $t \leftarrow t+1$, and go to the Step 3.

Step 6: $F_n(k) \leftarrow F_n(k) + e^{-rt} I_t$ and $k \leftarrow k+1$, go to step 1.

Step 7: $Q_n \leftarrow \left[1 \Big/ K \sum_{k=1}^{K} F_n(k) \right]$.

5.0 Application in the Mobile Phone Design

In this section, an mobile phone example is used to illustrate the above proposed models.

Table 1: Parameters of Numerical Simulations

Parameter	Symbol	Value
Number of modules	m	6
Return of the module i in the time period t	R_i^t	Stochastic data
Profit of exercising the merging option between module i and j	P_{ij}^t	Stochastic data
Cost of developing ith module in the time period t	C_i^t	Stochastic data
Drift of the demand for the ith module in the time period t	μ_i^t	Stochastic data
Volatility of the demand for the ith module in the time period t	σ_i^t	Stochastic data
Discount rate	r	6%
Number of time periods	T	5

Nowadays the mobile phones have been developed very quickly, but people found that some basic modules are almost the same. The hardware includes digital camera, blue-tooth, radio, MP3 player and so on. The software includes the browser, games, network and so on. These can be treated as some functions or services. That means whether or not one of these functions can be applied in a certain time period is determined by the market situation of that period. But sometimes the mobile phone developer may add some new functions which may not be popular at the present according to the forecast of the market condition. Sometimes the developer may combine several functions in one product because the merged functions can save plenty of cost

OPTIMAL DECISIONS IN PRODUCT MODULARITY DESIGN USING REAL OPTION APPROACH

comparing to developing them one by one. Hence, how to select the right function at the right time to maximize the profit is a key problem. The models proposed above will be utilized to help the developer to make decisions. We summarize some data from the information on a typical mobile phone. It includes almost all the normal modules nowadays. The values of parameters are listed in Table 1.

5.1   Optimization of Model 1

Table 2: Optimization Results of Model 1

Period	Cost	Return	Demand	Decision variable	Obj. value
1	94.852160	26.112167	3	(0,0,1,0,0,0)	27.98769
	66.964854	64.012123			
	71.375369	99.363061			
	72.560523	58.346849			
	98.959052	15.190594			
	92.454657	57.225571			
2	4.6336544	39.332849	3	(1,0,0,0,0,0)	34.69920
	58.902682	66.253082			
	75.491598	21.604363			
	78.490688	60.688577			
	84.104859	10.268962			
	83.974624	8.3293288			
3	17.421703	59.184262	3	(1,0,1,1,0,0)	160.2870
	69.568874	25.359949			
	33.379155	77.320912			
	2.6804605	77.263151			
	99.006361	50.791307			
	39.934927	29.493411			
4	48.929357	68.739993	2	(1,0,0,1,0,0)	72.75043
	89.932481	2.9527307			
	92.270155	72.012307			
	1.6978937	54.637690			
	18.404692	90.235809			
	44.764397	43.509974			
5	67.297880	25.782968	3	(0,0,0,1,0,0)	21.80659
	65.632602	58.138088			
	49.603439	4.6606905			
	14.779763	36.586353			
	69.334812	27.352798			
	54.789037	29.806368			

The matrix of "merged profit" in Table 2 is composed of the profit values of mergence. The (i,j) element indicates that the profit created by the mergence of ith and jth modules. The matrix of "combination" is filled with y_{ij}^{t}, which indicates whether or not two modules can be merged. Here, we assume that the mergence has nothing to do with the sequence of the modules. Therefore, both of "merged profit" matrix and "combination" matrix are symmetric. We assume these values as follows (see Table 3):

Table 3: The Profit and Permission of Mergence

Merged profit= 0 40 50 35 45 56	Combination = 0 1 0 0 1 0
40 0 43 23 78 45	1 0 1 0 1 0
50 43 0 48 75 56	0 1 0 0 0 0
35 23 48 0 58 65	0 0 0 0 1 1
45 78 75 58 0 60	1 1 0 1 0 0
56 45 56 65 60 0	0 0 0 1 0 0;

The simulation results of Model 1 are given in Table 2. In the 'cost', 'Return' and 'Demand' columns list predetermined data. The decision results are listed in the 'decision variable' column. For example, (0,0,1,0,0,0) means that the third module will be added in the first stage. The values of objective function are listed in the 'Obj. value' column in Table 2.

The NPV for model 1 can be computed as follows:

$$Q_1 = e^{-r}F_1 + e^{-2r}F_2 + e^{-3r}F_3 + e^{-4r}F_4 + e^{-5r}F_5 = 264.3984$$

where Q1 indicates that the flexible configuration only considering current stage information to optimize can bring NPV to 264.3984.

5.2   Optimization of Model 2

The optimization of Model 2 is implemented to get the NPV to compare with that of Model 1.

Table 4: Optimization Results of Model 2

Period	1	2	3	4	5
Obj. value	132.8430	89.49175	114.2905	151.2796	215.9178
Decision variable	(1,0,0,0,0,1)	(0,0,1,0,1,0)	(0,1,0,0,0,0)	(0,1,0,0,0,0)	(0,0,1,0,1,0)

The NPV for model 2 is computed as follows:

$$Q_2 = e^{-r}F_1 + e^{-2r}F_2 + e^{-3r}F_3 + e^{-4r}F_4 + e^{-5r}F_5 = 578.90$$

This result indicates that if two-stage optimization is implemented, the NPV will be enhanced dramatically.

6.0   Conclusions

In this paper, the product modular design with real option approach has been explored and two decision models have been proposed to value the design configuration selections. The valuation of the two models has been implemented by a quantitative approach based on the numerical simulation and integer programming. Mobile phones are used to illustrate the application of proposed models. By comparing the two models, we can demonstrate that the two-stage optimization model can dynamically consider the demands and bring greater NPV for product producers.

Some other kinds of options have not been considered in the proposed models, such as the option that promotes the out-of-date products with discount and the option that divides one module into several sub-modules. These options can be valuable if they are exercised at the right time. On the other hand, if the market can be modeled into several segments, in which the demands can be analyzed more deeply, the proposed models can find themselves in more fields such as product development.

Acknowledgement

The work presented in this paper has been supported by grants from National Natural Science Foundation of China (70571050) and Program for New Century Excellent Talents in University of China.

References

[1]   M. Meyer & A. Lehnerd. The power of product platforms, building value and cost leadership, The Free Press, New York, NY, 1997
[2]   C. Baldwin & K. Clark. Design Rules I: The Power of Modularity, MIT Press, Cambridge, MA, 2000
[3]   T. Simpson. Product Platform design and customization: status and promise, Artificial Intelligence for Engineering Design, analysis and Manufacturing 18:3–20. 2004
[4]   K. Holtta-Otto and K. Otto. Product Platform and product family design, chap. 4, Platform concept evaluation, pp. 49–72. Springer, New York, NY, 2005
[5]   Kurtadikar, R.M., Stone, R.B., Van Wie, M., and McAdams, D.A. A Customer Needs Motivated Conceptual Design Methodology for Product Portfolios, Proceedings of DETC 2004, ASME Design Engineering and Technical Conference and Computers and Information in Engineering Conferences, Salt Lake City, Utah, Sept. 28-Oct.2, 2004.
[6]   Konstantinos Kalligeros. Platforms and Real Options in Large-Scale Engineering Systems, MIT Ph.D. Dissertation, June 2006
[7]   G. Yang Kurt A. Beiter Kosuke Ishii. Product platform development: considering product maturity and morphology, 2004
[8]   Birgit Geppert, Frank Roessler Avaya, Combining Product Line Engineering with Options Thinking, Labs-Software Technology Research, 2003
[9]   Eun Suk Suh. Flexible Product Platforms, MIT Ph.D. Dissertation, September 2005
[10] de Neufville, R et al. Uncertainty Management for Engineering Systems Planning and Design, The Second Engineering Systems Symposium, MIT, Cambridge, MA, March 2004
[11] de Weck O, de Neufville R, Chaize. M Staged Deployment of Communications Satellite Constellations in Low Earth Orbit, Journal of Aerospace Computing, Information and Communication, 1, 119-136, March 2004
[12] Eckert C, Clarkson P, Zanker W. Change and Customisation in Complex Engineering Domains, Research in Engineering Design, 15(1):1-21, 2004
[13] Eppinger S, Whitney D, Smith R. A Model-Based Method for Organizing Tasks in Product Development, Research in Engineering Design, 6(1):1-13. 1994
[14] Gonzalez-Zugasti J, Otto K, Baker J. A Method for Architecting Product Platforms, Research in Engineering Design, 12(2):61-72, 2000
[15] Hull, J, Options. Futures, and Other Derivative Securities, Prentice Hall, 2002

OPTIMAL DECISIONS IN PRODUCT MODULARITY DESIGN USING REAL OPTION APPROACH

The 6th International Conference on Manufacturing Research (ICMR08)
Brunel University, UK, 9-11th September 2008

DIELECTRIC CURING OF WEB MATERIAL A CONTINUOUS MANUFACTURING PROCESS

A.M.Hasna

Department of Chemical Engineering, Abu Dhabi Men's College, Higher College of Technology, Abu Dhabi, United Arab Emirates.

Abstract

Traditionally paperboard manufacturing is an energy-intensive industry, dominated by fossil fuels for energy supply. The shift away from the fossil fuel era due to rising costs and global environmental responsiveness has prompted manufacturers to search for alternative curing processes. An energy consuming production stage, curing is a unit operation realized by means of a hotplate heat exchanger extensively used in the corrugating process. This paper investigates the feasibility of a substitute to the conventional hotplate heat exchanger with a dielectric option. Consequently, any potential improvement in the overall process efficiency, has an influence indirectly on emission and pollutants. Whilst microwaves still apply electricity it can be possibly viewed as carbon neutral on the proviso that the electricity generation is a green option, i.e. wind, solar, biofuels or other renewable non-fossil fuel alternatives. In particular, the experimental study investigates the dielectric heating (microwave technology) parameters to the continuous manufacturing of web martial (corrugated paperboard).

Keywords curing, web material, microwave, dielectric, hotplate, continuous processing

1.0   Introduction

The principal of global trading lies in the transfer of commodities from the manufacture supply to the place of demand [1]-[3], this requires the service of a packaging method. The ability to build corrugated paperboard packaging to meet different and specific customer needs has resulted in corrugated board a dominant transport packaging method [4]. Despite increased penetration by plastics packaging, [5]-[7] corrugated paperboard packaging remains competitive; it represents the largest proportion of key packaging material globally accounting for 37 percent of the total tonnage of packaging materials [8]. In 1993, corrugated paperboard world production totaled 69.9 million tons [9]. According to [10] the general adhesive industry in 1994 in the USA was worth $5.6-billion industry, which usually grows faster than GDP, packaging related activity signifies a large segment. Paper is made from a mixture of fibers and water sprayed on a net that travels of a speed of 500-1800 m/min [11]. Due to the manufacturing process all the fibers but the shortest ones are oriented in the horizontal plane [12]. Paper is therefore an anisotropic material. For many reasons the principal axes of the material properties are functions of position in the cross-direction of the paper web. During the converting and end-use of paper and paperboard, the material is often subjected to complex loading situations [13]. The mechanical properties of the paper in corrugated board are comparable to other basic materials, illustrated in Fig. 1.Corrugated board strength per cost value is favorable, [14].

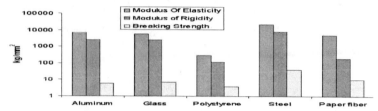

Fig.1.   Mechanical property values

2.0   Board Manufacturing Process

According to [15] speed versatility and consistency are essential to survival if you design and manufacture machine for the competitive packaging industry. At the time of this research, the process of forming corrugated board is to apply adhesive to the flute tips while the medium is contained in the corrugating roll. Followed by, flat paperboard, also referred to as liner; it is applied under both pressure and heat. The combination of heat from the corrugating and pressure rolls, and the mechanical pressure itself, forms the first liner to medium bond. Subsequently, the single face board is passed to a double facer or double backer where adhesive is applied to flute tips and the board applied to the flute tips and the board is then passed over a series of steam-heated platens to bond the second liner. Pressure is applied by a hold down transport belt on top of the board and a series of small rollers riding on that belt. Sandwich belts assist the travel of the double face board through the double-facer following the steam-heated platens [16] and [17].

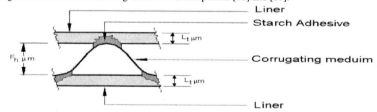

Fig. 2.   Cross section view of corrugated cardboard

2.1   Paperboard Structure

Industrialized paperboard conception in North America dates back to 1871, with the earliest registered US patent 122023 awarded to Albert L. Jones [18]. Material of basis weight greater than 200 g/m^2 is classified as paperboard, while lighter material is called paper, [19]. Cardboard is a common name given to various stiff paper or paperboard that is more than 0.1524 millimeters thick [20]. Corrugated cardboard structure consists of three layers; a central corrugated medium and two outer sheets, as demonstrated in fig.2. Starch adhesive is the second largest raw material used in the corrugated board manufacture, second only to the raw paper itself

DIELECTRIC CURING OF WEB MATERIAL A CONTINUOUS MANUFACTURING PROCESS

[21]-[23]. It provides both the quality, and strength of the finished product. The starch is used to glue together the paper components [24]. The central medium is a fluted thin board sandwiched in between flat paperboards. The flat paperboard, is adhered to the fluted section by starch adhesive. The starch type adhesive solution is placed at the peaks of the fluted section, which meet the flat paperboards. The feedstock for the fluting medium is waste paper and other additives with initial moisture content of an estimated 10 percent. Initially, the corrugated board structure contains a certain percentage of moisture.

2.2   Steam Platens Curing Process

The steam heated platens, or steam chests, are the most widely used curing apparatus in the corrugated board industry [25], The paperboard industry employs curing-dryers to adhere the various layers of the liners to produce the corrugated board structure. Curing machines are designed to match the board dimensions; wide web, narrow web, sheet feed, adhesive gel point, liner grade and flute type. The curing machine's capacity varies to accommodate enhanced quality and increased productivity. A diagram of the steam platen is shown in Fig. 3.

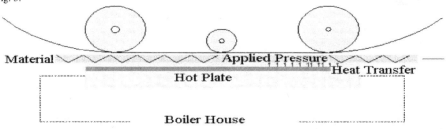

Fig. 3.   Schematic diagram of simple steam platen

The function of the hot-plate section is to furnish sufficient heat to set the starch. Reviewed literature [26], [27] indicates that there has been limited radical innovation in the steam hot plate drying systems in the last 50 years leading up to the research documented in this thesis. [28] stated, "if we are to compare a corrugated box made yesterday to one made 45 years ago, we can see no difference". Also, Crellin concluded that "drying of paper a hundred years ago was accomplished on a metal drying plate fed internally with steam condensing under pressure". Varying the steam pressure controlled the drying rate and hence the internal condensing steam temperature. This process is still the major part of the drying process in modern machines developed a hundred years later.

2.3   Patented Applications in Board Curing

Some of the most recent developments in the corrugated board curing are centred on the traditional hotplate method. Although the research approaches vary, the results still point towards the use of steam as the source of heat. As shown in fig.4. [29] Documented a description of a web drying patent, which comprised of two bands impermeable to liquid and having a smooth surface finish. [30] System consisted of a series of elongated heating chests positioned side-by-side and is defined by a series of laterally extending heating surfaces. Another attempt to improve upon the conventional steam heating chests is provided by [31] with an all copper construction hot plate. This system is able to enhance thermal conductivity and heat transfer efficiency, due to the high thermal conductivity and heat transfer rates of copper. Further developments were followed by [32] who employed a thermal radiant energy source. The radiant energy method uses an infrared source which was

DIELECTRIC CURING OF WEB MATERIAL A CONTINUOUS MANUFACTURING PROCESS

aligned parallel to the paperboard liner. Exposing the corrugated board medium and the adhesive to a thermal radiant energy ranging from 1100 to 2300 °C and emitting a dominant wavelength between 2.1 and 1.0 microns, sets the adhesive, whereby the speed of the bond development between the corrugated paperboard medium and the liner is improved and bonding is achieved at low mechanical pressure.

Fig. 4.   Boiler supplying steam to exchanger

The drawback of this method is that water and adhesive have a low co-efficient of absorption. It has also been documented that the infra-red absorption spectrum, for a typical paper sheet of 185gsm basis weight, shows 5% reflection in the 2.5 to 3.5 micron wavelength range. The reflection is increasing by decreasing the wavelength. Also, the temperature range of 1100°C to 2300°C, the radiant emittance of the source is sufficiently high to effectively bond the product components at the required commercially viable operating speeds and to make practicable use of small radiating areas. An improved method to control the heat in the steam chests was documented by [33] The system operates using an infrared heating lamp, positioned adjacent to a second surface, Electrical heated elements radiate heat to the heating plate having opposing first and second surfaces and the corrugated paperboard travels adjacent to the second surface of the heating plate so that the heat is transferred to the board. With no exceptions all of the designs mentioned in the above analysis have limitations associated with operation efficiency, hence energy conversion.

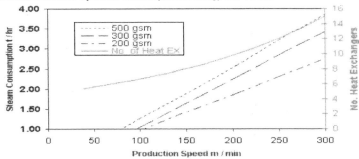

Fig.5.   Steam consumption vs. production speed

3.0   Microwave Heating Equation

Interaction of microwaves with materials depends on their dielectric properties, which determine the extent of heating of a material when subjected to electromagnetic fields. Therefore, knowledge of dielectric properties is important for the design of a continuous flow microwave heating system [34].Dielectric constant is a measure of the ability of a material to store electromagnetic energy, whereas dielectric loss factor is a measure of the

DIELECTRIC CURING OF WEB MATERIAL A CONTINUOUS MANUFACTURING PROCESS

ability of a material to convert electromagnetic energy to heat [35]. Dielectric properties can be defined in terms of complex permittivity and is given by the equation;

$$\varepsilon = \varepsilon_0(\varepsilon' - j\varepsilon'')$$ (1)

It is useful to list a few simple equations that are frequently used to describe microwave heat generation. [36] Described the equation governing microwave power absorption as;

$$P_v = 2\pi f \varepsilon_0 \varepsilon'' E^2$$ (2)

usually paper with values of ε'_r about 3–3.5 and tan δ (the loss tangent; the negative of the ratio of the imaginary part to the real part of the complex relative permittivity) about 2×10-3 at room temperature, rising to about 3×10^{-3} at 100°C (212°F) [37]. Considering a wave progressing into a dielectric-heating workload, its amplitude diminishes since absorbtion of power as heat takes place in the material. The measure of how opaque a material is in a microwave field is given by the penetration depth, that is the depth in the material at which the power flux has fallen to 1/e (= 0.368) of its surface value [38] and is given by;

$$D_p = \frac{\lambda_8 \sqrt{\varepsilon'}}{2\pi \varepsilon''}$$ (3)

Eqn (3) shows that the power penetration depth increases with larger wavelength or, in other words, with decreasing frequency. The penetration depth is a very important parameter for a specific workload because it gives an immediate first order indication of the heat distribution within it. [39] Described the electric size as a dimensionless number, L_E of a material as follows;

$$L_E = \frac{\lambda_c}{D_p}$$ (4)

Where L_c is the characteristic dimension of the material which is usually the smallest dimension across which a microwave field can penetrate, such as the diameter in a sphere or the depth of a tray ε'' dielectric loss and ε' dielectric constant are dependent on both frequency and temperature. The heat balance of a microwave drying system in which all the energy required is provided by a microwave source. The work load is assumed to start from an initial temperature, with moisture content m1 percent, and is required to be dried to a final moisture content m^2 percent. The moisture content is the percentage of water, by weight of the dry matter. The energy required is then the sensible heat initially required to raise the temperature of the work load to 100 °C, plus the energy required to evaporate the quantity of water implied by the reduction of moisture content from m_1 to m_2.

$$E = \frac{4.2}{60}\left(S_d(T_b - T_a) + \frac{m_1}{100} S_1(T_b - T_0)\left(\frac{m_1 - m_2}{100}\right)L\right)$$ (5)

s_d the specific heat of dry matter, s the specific heat of the liquid and L is the latent heat of vaporization. Eqn (5) provides the total heat input required to dry the workload through the moisture content specified (m_1-m_2), which in microwave curing is provided totally from the microwave source without any heat transfer to, or from the surroundings.

3.1   Applicator

The waveguide is one of the most used microwave transmission lines [40]. A transmission line is essentially like a track that steers the energy wave along a certain direction [41]. Among the many kinds of waveguides, the rectangular and circular waveguides are the most common, which vary in dimensions to accommodate the operating frequency. Waveguides serve an essential role in conveying power from the generator to the load [42]. In this research project, the heating applicator itself is based on waveguide principles and this is shown in Fig.6.

DIELECTRIC CURING OF WEB MATERIAL A CONTINUOUS MANUFACTURING PROCESS

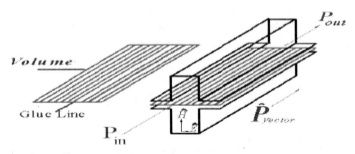

Fig.6   Applicator with a dielectric sheet

The imprinted glue line configuration in the corrugated board liner is shown in Fig.6, which happens to be perpendicular to the electric field. Coupling is limited to right angles and this is an advantage due to the sensitive nature of the adhesive. Excessive coupling can result in rapid cure, which compromises bond integrity. Fig.6 illustrates the directions of the electric and magnetic fields E and H respectively and the Poynting Vector P for plane wave propagation in the x-axis direction. The starch adhesive lines are perpendicular to the electric filed and are approximately account for ¼ of the treated surface area of the web material .

4.0   Experimental Setup

This experimental approach for curing the adhesive consisted of; generating the energy required to set the adhesive, controlling the coupling efficiency and mechanically conveying the product. A schematic of the experimental process equipment is shown in Fig.7. The set-up comprises of an applicator (sample chamber) made from aluminum rectangular tube see Fig.6. The microwave irradiation is generated by magnetron (with blower for the pre-heater) assisted by a circulator and a heat exchange dummy load. The impedance tuner was used to optimize, calibrate and standardize the transmission signal. The wet web material was introduced into the applicator via conveyor belt to be cured via microwave irradiation and it was also exposed to a pre heater from the recycled hot air. The cured material was collected and packaged in sealed bags in prepared for laboratory analysis.

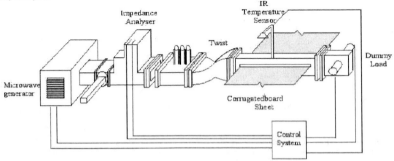

Fig.7   Microwave curing experimental apparatus, illustrating sheet feed orientation

DIELECTRIC CURING OF WEB MATERIAL A CONTINUOUS MANUFACTURING PROCESS

The purpose of the modified dummy load in this experiment were twofold; allowed transmitter attenuation adjustments; or termination for the applicator transmission line; heat transfer into the process through the circulating liquid where electrical energy was converted to heat energy. Dummy load heat exchanger, is the critical driver of overall experimental apparatus efficiency. The process overall efficiency was achieved by recycling all streams back into the heat exchanger to produced a closed fluid circuit. All streams were recovered into the top of the holding tank and pumped back into the line. Further, additional heat generated in the magnetron was transferred to the feed stream to the inlet manifold roller heat exchanger.

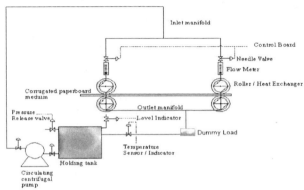

Fig.8   Rollers –holding tank pipe layout

4.1   Experimental Procedure

In the literature, several experimental set-up are used to for microwave heating described by [43]-[47]. However, the microwave heating conditions differed in this experiment due to the dielectric nature of the composite material, paper and starch slurry. A series of simultaneously operated equipment ran the curing pilot machine. For this start up, feedback procedures were included in the process control. This is demonstrated in a flow diagram Fig. 9, and the procedure is listed in Appendix 5. The concerned dielectric material was non-homogenous, whereas the liquid adhesive changed physical states during curing. The sample material travelled through the rectangular wave-guide applicator, WR340, as shown in Fig. 6, where the glue lines were parallel with the z-axis of the applicator. In order to evaluate the absorbed microwave power in the applicator by the corrugated paperboard, a six-port impedance analyzer (reflectometer) was used as an impedance analyzer. This measurement along with other parameters provided the tool to analyze the influence of process conditions to the overall response, that being the bond strength.

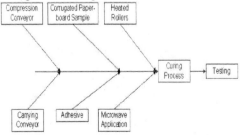

Fig.9   Adhesive curing experimental procedure

DIELECTRIC CURING OF WEB MATERIAL A CONTINUOUS MANUFACTURING PROCESS

4.2   Design of Experiments

Experimental design is a methodology of data collection in order to screen out insignificant factors and identify significant factors affecting the yield of a given response based on a sample taken at random. In addition, it indicates the existence of interaction effects between the factors. The method chosen for the design of experiment was a second-level factorial screening which was used to study the effects of applying simultaneously all possible combination levels of the given factors. Factorial experiments are more efficient than one factor at a time experiment, since all data are used for the computation of the effect and interactions between effects [48]-[50]. The most significant step in a successful design of experiment is to identify and quantify the response. The factorial design study identifies the vital factors that affect the process and provides estimation of main effects and interactions. The vital factors characterize the significance of factors that affect the responses. The experimental conditions are arranged in a matrix which contains replicates over blocks with centre points per block. Each replicate contains all treatment arrangements [51]. In addition, the experimental order or run is selected at random, so the observation may be explained in a statistical model. The total number of observations required depends on the factorial type, the number of factors, and the number of levels of each factor, i.e. the number of midpoint replicates and the number of blocks B. This is shown in the following relationship.

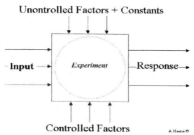

Fig.10   Experimental design schematic

$$N_{Experiment} = (2^{factors} \times Replicates) + (Center\ points \times Blocks)$$
(6)

Replicating the experimental design was used in order to run each combination of factor LN levels in the design more than once. This allowed an estimation of pure error in the Replicating, the experimental design was used in order to run each combination of factor LN levels in the design more than once. This allowed an estimation of pure error in the experiment. When replicating the design, one can compute the variability of measurements within each unique combination of factor levels. This variability gave an indication of the random error in the measurements (eg. due to uncontrolled factors, unreliability of the measurement instrument, etc.), because the replicated observations were taken under identical conditions (settings of factor levels). Such an estimate of the pure error was used to evaluate the size and statistical significance of the variability that can be attributed to the manipulated factors. In the corrugated paperboard production process, units were produced in natural "chunks" or blocks, i.e. paper reels, adhesive batch. Therefore, blocking was used in the experimental design to ensure that these blocks did not bias the estimates of the main effects. Adding centre points to the experimental design with factors that were set at two levels implicitly assumed that the effect of the factors on the dependent variable of interest (eg. Bond Strength) was linear. However, it was impossible to test whether or not there is a non linear relationship (eg. quadratic), if factors are only evaluated at two points (ie. at the low and high settings). Therefore, centre points were used in the analysis of variance.

DIELECTRIC CURING OF WEB MATERIAL A CONTINUOUS MANUFACTURING PROCESS

ANOVA (analysis of variance) determined exactly which of the factors significantly affected the dependent variable of interest. The controlled factors in this experiment were temperature of web, initial moisture content, incident power, treatment speed, and adhesive mass .The uncontrolled factors were ambient temperature, atmospheric pressure and the liner grade which were considered to be constants The response was, bond strength and globule size. The were modeled in a relationship between variables in the experiments. This was illustrated in an example of regression analysis, of a linear model, where y = response, Then, the following model;

$$y = a + b_1 x_1 + c_2 x_2 + E \tag{7}$$

Where, E = Error, was used as a representation of the relationship between the uncontrolled factors, which had been considered constants.

5.0   Discussion

According to [52] the mechanical behavior of the adhesive is mostly unknown. Whilst buckling behavior of corrugated paper packages was studied by [53], however there was no recognized data available in literature to compare our analysis with, perhaps due to the commercial sensitivity of the manufacturing process (intellectual property etc...). Hence a quantitative assessment of the concept of microwave curing was required. This was achieved by running a series of variable controlled experiments in order to determine the degree of effectiveness of proposed method of curing. The correlation between the experimental variables was described in two responses; $S\ (P,T\ ,m_s\ ,M,\ t)$, and G_s. In addition, the S of samples was measured at known positions in the applicator as indicated in fig.11.

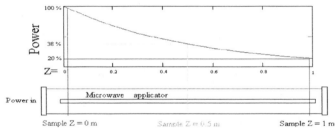

Fig. 11.   E field distribution along the test applicator

Fig.11shows the allocated zones of sample collection. The zone allocation was important due to the variation in electric field distribution along the applicator. For studies into the effect of electric field distribution along the applicator's axial direction refer to [54]-[56], bond strength was quantified using the adhesive joint globule size distribution. The experimental data was analyzed using an algorithm which is discussed in the next section.

DIELECTRIC CURING OF WEB MATERIAL A CONTINUOUS MANUFACTURING PROCESS

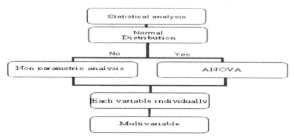

Fig.12   Statistical approach

5.1   Statistical Analysis of Results

Analysis of the experimental results was undertaken using the procedure outlined in fig. 12. Statistical analysis required data to be normally distributed; otherwise either a transformation or a non-parametric analysis would result. Experimental results were tested using a parametric and non-parametric analysis and stepwise procedure. As for the bubble size, G_s, data was analyzed both using the outliers and without. The value of the p-level represented a decreasing index of the reliability of the result. The higher the p-level, the less we believed that the observed relation between variables in the sample was a reliable indicator of the relation between the respective variables in the population. Specifically, the p-level represented the probability of error that was involved in accepting the observed result as valid; that being "representative" of the population. P-values <5% represented the probability that the relation between the variables found in the sample was a "coincidence."

5.2   Distribution

Data acquired from experimental were distributed in a normal probability plot of the studentized residuals to check for normality of these residuals. Studentized residual methods were used for detecting the outlying value observations with extreme values on the set of predictor variables or the dependent variables. The formula for studentized residual methods used was adopted from [57]–[59].

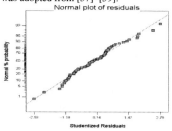

Fig.13   Normal probability plot of strength

To test the assumption that the standardized residuals were normally distributed, Standardized residuals were calculated using (SPSS) and plotted as per fig.13. as can be seen there was little significant outliers in the data. The studentized residual method was additionally confirmed by the frequency plot of the same data and this is shown in Figure 14. Frequency plot of the raw experimental data for bond strength Fig. 14 and Histograms were used to present a graphical representations of the frequency distribution of the granule size in which the columns were drawn over the class intervals and the heights of the columns were proportional to the class

DIELECTRIC CURING OF WEB MATERIAL A CONTINUOUS MANUFACTURING PROCESS

frequencies, as shown in Fig.15, and Fig. 14 Frequency plot of the raw experimental data for granule size Fig. 17 presents a graphical account of the experimental observations for both of strength and granule size. The plot of outlier t versus run was used in order to look for outliers, i.e. Influential values. Outliers were values which lay so far away from the mean that one may suspect the case in question was not representative of the population measure. This is shown in Fig.16.

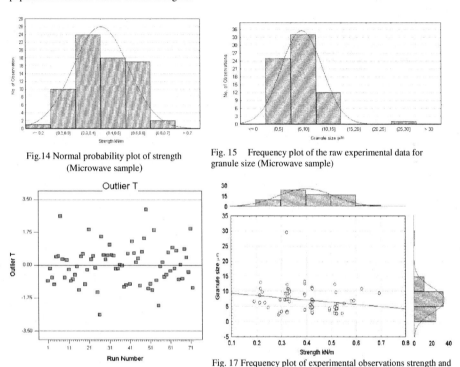

Fig.14 Normal probability plot of strength (Microwave sample)

Fig. 15   Frequency plot of the raw experimental data for granule size (Microwave sample)

Fig. 16   Strength outliers plot (Microwave)

Fig. 17 Frequency plot of experimental observations strength and granule size (Microwave)

5.3   Analysis of Variance (ANOVA)

A multiple linear regression stepwise analysis method was applied to fit an equation that described the strength in terms of power, temperature, mass of starch, moisture, and heating time, based on the experimental data S (P,T,M ,m_s,t). The predicted relationship was

$$S = \frac{58.4P - 6.72M - 3.9t}{1000} \qquad (7)$$

Therefore, for every one unit of strength, power increased by an order of magnitude. Mass of starch ms and preheat temperature T were statistically insignificant, with P values were found between 0.74 and 0.24. This was expected for mass starch, since the minimum amount to establish the bond was used in all runs.

5.4   Comparison with Conventional Drying Processes

DIELECTRIC CURING OF WEB MATERIAL A CONTINUOUS MANUFACTURING PROCESS

Descriptive statistics, including the mean, standard deviation, minimum and maximum values were calculated for each group. The statistical analysis of the bond strength values was performed by ANOVA with adhesion strength bonding analysis. This section established a comparative analysis of the bond strength bond strength characterization between microwave and conventionally cured wheat starch adhesive (35% solution). All references made to microwave heating also apply to microwave curing. However, in order to validate the present data, the bond adhesion strength and power levels were plotted vs. treatment time. Fig. 18 shows variation in strength was related to power level.

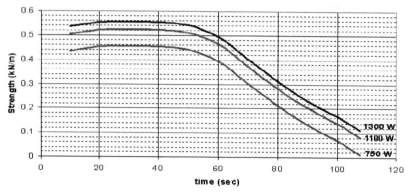

Fig.18   Bond strength over a range of microwave power levels

Bond strength measurements were made using a modified ASTM test [60] the bond strength results for microwave curing are represented in Fig. 18 and also for conventional curing in Fig. 19. The trend demonstrates that microwave curing reduces the curing time and marginally enhances the bond strength. The limits of the frequency distribution were based on the suggestion that 0.5kN/m is considered to be adequate industry standard for bond strength. Significance for all statistical tests was predetermined at $P \le .05$.

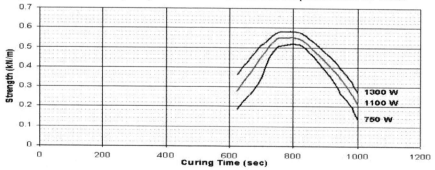

Fig. 19   Bond strength over a range of power levels conventional heating

The present findings indicated that the bond strengths of the curing modifications (power levels) used on three different trails were not significantly different. However it was noticed during the microscope observations of the spent microwave sample (Electron microscopic analysis of the dissected adhesive-fibers bond). That bond breakage had occurred along the paper fibrous interface rather than at the adhesion the starch bond. Hence,

DIELECTRIC CURING OF WEB MATERIAL A CONTINUOUS MANUFACTURING PROCESS

degradation occurred at the boundary and in the paper fibers, this was commonly noticed towards the larger bubble sizes were numerous minute rudimentary distribution occurred.

6.0   Conclusion

The conduct of dielectric curing of web material in a continuous manufacturing process has been tested on experimental data acquired; while the process still offers a potential for optimization the proposed method appears to offers an advantage, including fast cure time and potential for energy savings via faster curing. the experimental analysis established the following parameters in regards to the continuous dielectric processing (drying/curing) of web material; Power, moisture content and curing time were statistically significant in the analysis. However, mass of starch and preheat temperature were insignificant. It was also confirmed that the Bond strength was directly proportional to granule density, Size of starch granules decreased with higher strength values and Size of starch granules was proportional to input power.

Acknowledgement

The authors wish to acknowledge the assistance and support of the following organizations; Visy packaging Industries, the Department of Education Science and Technology and Training, Australian Federal Government, Australian Postgraduate Association Awards, Industry scholarship, Swinburne university of technology, Melbourne Australia for their financial assistance.

Nomenclature

ε''	dielectric loss factor	
ε'	dielectric constant	
M	moisture content of board	
ε_o	permittivity of free space ($8.854 \times 10-12$)	(F/m)
f	frequency	(Hz),
E	electric field strength	(V/m).
P	incident power,	(W)
Pv	power absorbed per unit volume	(W/m^3),
Dp	Depth of penetration	(m)
T	preheat temperature,	(^{o}C)
m_s	mass of starch,	(g)
t	treatment time	(sec)
Gs	granule size (bubble)	(μm)
S	bond strength	(kN/m),

References

[1] Gereffi, G, (1999), International trade and industrial upgrading in the apparel commodity chain, Journal of International Economics, Volume 48, Issue 1, June, Pages 37-70
[2] Kaplinsky R., (2000) Globalisation and Unequalisation, What Can Be Learned from Value Chain Analysis? , Journal of Development Studies, Volume 37, Issue 2 December, pages 117 - 146

DIELECTRIC CURING OF WEB MATERIAL A CONTINUOUS MANUFACTURING PROCESS

[3] Kaplinsky R, (2004), Spreading the Gains from Globalization, What Can Be Learned from Value-Chain Analysis?, Problems of Economic Transition Volume 47, Number 2 / June, p74 – 115.

[4] Jonson G, (1993), corrugated board packaging, UK, Pira international,

[5] Sandgren, K., (1996), Material flow analysis for an industry—A case study in packaging, Natural Resources Research, Volume 5, Number 4 / December, Springer Netherlands.

[6] Kirwan M J., (2005), Paper and Paperboard Packaging Technology, Blackwell Publishing Ltd

[7] Ramesh, C. Chandan, (2006) Manufacturing Yogurt and Fermented Milks, Fermented Dairy Packaging Materials, Chapter Author Aaron L. Brody, Blackwell Publishing.

[8] Moore G., (2001), Product sector technology trends to 2005, Pira International, United Kingdom.

[9] Ramo, K. M. A. (1995) New capacity Will it be virgin-fiber or recycled and where will it come from, PPI Packaging Board Conference 4, Nice, November.

[10] Breskin, I., (1995), adhesives and sealants, Chemical Week, Volume, 156, Issue 8.

[11] Norman, B., Fellers C., (1996), Pappersteknik, Stockholm, Paper. Tech, Royal Institute of technology.

[12] Akker, J. A. V. d. (1950),The elastic and rheological properties of papermaking fibers, Tappi Journal 33(8) p-398-402.

[13] Stenberg, N., (1999), Mechanical properties in the thickness direction of paper and paperboard, Licentiate Thesis no.69, Royal Institute of Technology, Stockholm, Sweden.

[14] Jonson G, (1993), corrugated board packaging, UK, Pira international,

[15] Schneider, R.T., (1999) Need vacuum on packaging equipment? Go with the flow, Hydraulics and Pneumatics, September, p 31-33.

[16] Hasna A.M. (2003), Curing starch based adhesives microwave or conventional, International Journal of Materials and Product Technology , Volume 19, Numbers 3-4,p 259 – 274.

[17] Kline J. E., (1991) Paper and Paperboard Manufacturing and Converting Fundamentals, 2d ed.,

[18] Daly.G.J, (1971), Fiber Containers, 20th Century Press, Chicago, USA, p206

[19] Biermann, CJ., (2007)"Paper", in Access Science, McGraw-Hill

[20] Aboura, Z., Talbi N., Allaoui S., Benzeggagh M. L., (2004), Elastic behavior of corrugated cardboard experiments and modeling, Composite Structures, Volume 63, Issue 1, January, Pages 53-62.

[21] Entwistle G., Bachelor S., Booth E., Walker K., (1998) Economics of starch production in the UK, Industrial Crops and Products , Volume 7, Issues 2-3, January 1998, Pages 175-186.

[22] Lawton Jr, J.W. (2004), Native starch, uses of Encyclopedia of Grain Science, 1-3, p195-202.

[23] Holik, H., (2006), Handbook of Paper and Board, Wiley, VCH.

[24] Bessen, A.H, (1999), The corrugator, Jelmar Publishing, New York.

[25] Harwood F. C, (1942), Chemical Engineering In The Laundry Industry, Journal of Chemical Engineering Research and Design - Volume 20a, Page(s) 44 - 54

[26] Boehm, R.M.,(1930), The Masonite Process, Journal of Industrial & Engineering Chemistry, American chemical society.

[27] Crellin, C. B., (1983), Drying in the Paper Industry, Drying and Curing, Institute of Energy, Melbourne, Australia.

[28] Bessen, A.H, (1999), The corrugator, Jelmar Publishing, New York. P 28.

[29] Rautakorpi, (1988), method and apparatus for drying paper, USA Patent, No 4887362.

[30] Sissons, A. J., (1993), Apparatus and Method For Enhancing Heating Uniformity For Setting Adhesives In Corrugated Paperboard Manufacturing, USA Patent, No5456783.

[31] Marschke, (1994), Heating device for corrugated paperboard production, USA. Patent, No 5495092

[32] Shaw, (1994), method of manufacturing corrugated board using a thermal radiant energy source, USA Patent, No5498304.

[33] Sissons, A. J., Thomas DA, (1998), corrugated paperboard manufacturing apparatus with controllable preheating, US Patent 5,788,803.

[34] Kumar P., Coronel P., Simunovic J., Truong V.D., Sandeep K.P., (2007), Measurement of Dielectric Properties of Pumpable Food Materials under Static and Continuous Flow Conditions., Journal of Food Science, Vol. 72, Nr. 4.

[35] Metaxas, A. C., Meredith R.J., (1983), Industrial Microwave Heating, Power engineering, Series 4 ed. London, England peter peregrines, page 109.

[36] Metaxas, A. C., Meredith R.J., (1983), Industrial Microwave Heating, Power engineering, Series 4 ed. London, England peter peregrines, page 115.

[37] [37] Calderwood, J. H., (2008), Dielectric materials, Access Science, McGraw-Hill,

[38] [38] Meredith R M. (1988), Engineers Hand Book of Industrial Microwave Heating, London, England The Institution of Electrical Engineers.

[39] Bows R.J. (2000), Microwave Heating, International Journal of Food Science &Technology, 35, p 417-30

[40] Ishii, T. K., (1989), Microwave engineering, 2nd edn, Harcourt Brace Jovanovich Publishers, USA, p-49.

[41] Laverghetta, T.S.,(1984), Practical microwaves. Indianapolis USA: Howard W. Sams and Co; P82.

[42] Sadiku M. N.O., (1989), Elements of Electromagnetic, Fortworth, USA, Saunders College.

[43] Metaxas, A. C., Meredith R.J., (1983), Industrial Microwave Heating, Power engineering, Series 4 ed. London, England peter peregrines, page 150.

DIELECTRIC CURING OF WEB MATERIAL A CONTINUOUS MANUFACTURING PROCESS

[44] Jones, P., Metaxas, R. (1988), International Microwave Power Journal, Vol., 23, No.4.

[45] Roussy, G., Thiebaut J. Charreyre-Neel M , (1984), A Chemical And Physical Model For Describing Paper Drying, Journal Of Microwave Power, 19, Vol 4, , P 243-250.

[46] Okress E.C. (Editor), Heenan, N.I. (1968), Travelling Wave Dryers, Microwave Power Engineering, Academic Press, New York, p. 126-144,

[47] Sutton, W.H., (1989), Microwave processing of ceramic material, ceramic bulletin, Vol.68, No. 2.

[48] Dixon, W. J., (1980), Efficient Analysis of Experimental Observations, Annual Review of Pharmacology and Toxicology, April, Vol. 20, p-441-462.

[49] Morris M. D., (1991), Factorial Sampling Plans for Preliminary Computational Experiments, Technometrics, Vol. 33, No. 2, May, pp. 161-174.

[50] Landgrebe, J., Bretz F., Brunner E., (2006) Efficient design and analysis of two color factorial microarray experiments, Computational Statistics and Data Analysis, Volume 50, Issue 2, Jan, p- 499-517.

[51] Montgomery, D. C., (1984), Design and Analysis of Experiments, 3rd edition, John Wiley, New York.

[52] Stenberg, N., (1999), Mechanical properties in the thickness direction of paper and paperboard, Licentiate Thesis no.69, Royal Institute of Technology, Stockholm, Sweden.

[53] Biancolini, E., Brutti C., (2003), Numerical and experimental investigation of the strength of corrugated board packages, Packaging Technology and Science, Volume 16, Issue 2, Pages 47 – 60.

[54] Hasna, A.M, (2001), Starch adhesive study, Boxboard Containers International, June.

[55] Metaxas A.C, (1996), foundations of electro heat, John Wiley.

[56] Metaxas, A.C, (1990) Rapid feasibility tests using a TE10 variable aperture resonant applicator, Journal of Microwave Power, Vol. 25, no.1, pp.16-24.

[57] Chistyakov, G. P., Gotze. F., (2004), Limit distributions of Studentized means, Annals Probably, Volume 32, Number 1A, 28-77.

[58] Hocking, R. R., (1996), Methods and Applications of Linear Models, John Wiley, New York.

[59] Ryan, T. P. (1997), Modern Regression Methods, John Wiley, New York.

[60] ASTM D903-98(2004), ASTM, D1974-98, Standard Practice for Methods of Closing, Sealing, and Reinforcing Fiberboard Boxes , ASTM International, West Conshohocken, PA.

DIELECTRIC CURING OF WEB MATERIAL A CONTINUOUS MANUFACTURING PROCESS

The 6th International Conference on Manufacturing Research (ICMR08)
Brunel University, UK, 9-11th September 2008

MICROCELLULAR INJECTION MOLDING: REVIEW AND LIMITATIONS OF CAE APPLICATION

P. Y. Chung [2], K. H. Lau [2], C. Y. Yip [1]

1. **General Electric Manufacturing Company**

2. **Department of Industrial and Systems Engineering, the Hong Kong Polytechnic University**

Abstract

Microcellular Injection Molding is an advanced foaming process which is capable of fabricating components with less material consumption, warpage, cycle time and clamping tonnage compared with its solid counterparts. However, because of the non-linearity of material properties, dynamic nature of injection process and incomplete process physics of foaming process, controlling the process parameters to maximize the potential benefits is challenging and essential to maximize the potential benefits. In our previous work, it has been proved that the use of deductive approach is one of the effective approaches for process parameters determination in injection molding process [1]. However, the availability of axioms/rules for all process parameters is critical for the deployment of deductive approach. Therefore, this paper is aimed to review the previous study to identify the axioms/rules governing the microcellular injection molding process and the parameters required further investigations. Furthermore, the last part of this paper discuss the limitations of using commercial CAE software for process parameters determination.

Keywords: Microcellular Injection Molding, Literature Review, Process Parameters Determination, CAE

1.0   Introduction

Microcellular Injection Molding (MuCell IM) is an advanced foaming technology which is capable of fabricating the microcellular plastics (MCPs) through the injection molding process by means of a supercritical physical blowing agent, usually nitrogen or carbon dioxide. The process chain of MuCell IM includes four steps, namely, (i) Gas dissolution, (ii) Nucleation, (iii) Cell Growth and (iv) Shaping [2]. The supercritical fluid (SCF) is injected into polymer melt to form a single-phase solution in rapid diffusion rate and constant high back pressure from 8 to 20MPa [3] to ensure complete dissolution. The single phase solution is then injected into a mold through the feeding system. Sudden pressure/solubility drop induces thermal instability and numerous nucleation sites simultaneously. Lastly, cell growth occurs during the mold fill stage. The cells growth subside until the strength of the polymer matrix is sufficiently high to resist the growth or the gas and polymer melt solution two-phase system reach their equilibrium state.

MCPs are the foamed plastics materials characterized by the cell density on the order of 10^9 cells /cm^3 or more and cell sizes on the order of 10 microns or less [4]. In the MuCell injection molding, the cell size produced is usually in the range of 10 to 100 microns [3], because the microstructure of MCPs varies greatly depending on the manufacturing methods and conditions [4]. By producing such tiny bubbles with material reduction, the bubbles serve as crack arrestors by blunting crack tips [4], thereby enhancing the part impact strength and fatigue life. The microcellular polystyrene (PS) has experienced five times the impact strength of its unfoamed counterpart [5]. And the fatigue life of microcellular polycarbonate (PC) with a relative foam density of 0.97 is four times that of its solid counterparts [6]. With the application of microcellular injection molding, it is claimed that the production efficiency can be enhanced through material saving (up to 35%), cycle time reduction (up to 50%), injection pressure or clamping force reduction (up to 60%). In addition, the product quality can be improved by warpage reduction (up to 50%), improved dimension stabilities (up to 30%) and elimination of sink marks [7] – [9]. However, there are certain limitations in microcellular injection molding process. Concerning with mechanical strength, inherent reduction in tensile strength/modulus [10] and weld line strength [11] was induced by reduction of material due to foaming, and tensile strength was found to be decrease almost linearly with the shot weight reduction [12]. Light scattering and swirling pattern on the part surface affecting the clarity and roughness hinder the deployment of the process in cosmetic part [3]. Xu had analyzed the formation of the swirling pattern is owing to broken bubble from the melt front and sheared bubble in the interface between mold wall and melt. Different methods to eliminate the swirl pattern and improve the surface roughness, such as Gas Counter Pressure, Co-Injection and Momentary Mold Surface Heating were also summarized [10,13]. More importantly, the processing know-how for microcellular injection molding has yet to be fully developed to enable the molding industry to maximize the potential process benefit. Further advancement of the fundamental understanding of the process physics is crucial so that the design and process can be optimized [11] [14]. The major challenges of the microcellular injection molding process included: (i) Continuous and efficient generation of single phased polymer gas solution with proper gas concentration and (ii) Control of the state of thermodynamic instability to create fine and uniform cells throughout the part. These two challenges are difficult in microcellular injection molding process because of the stop-and-flow molding behaviors in the most common reciprocating-screw type machine and the dynamic nature of thermodynamic profile in the mold cavity. Therefore, this paper was aimed at reviewing the development of the process and summarizing previous research result to identify the area require further investigation. In the last section, the limitations about the use of commercial CAE software for process parameters determinations were discussed.

2.0 Historical Development of Microcellular Injection Molding Machine

The concept of MCPs was initiated and successfully produced in batch process by Suh and his students at the Massachusetts Institute of Technology (MIT) in 1979. The length gas dissolution time (typically 2 to 3 days) in the batch process restrict the development of MCPs in continuous production process. Until Park was successfully modeled the relations of striation thickness and diffusion time, the dissolution time was shortened to industrial production level. The detailed historical development of the MCPs fabrication in batch and extrusion process was summarized in the work of Turng [2] and Suh [3]. Regarding microcellular injection molding, the exploration work was done by Wang [15] in 1995 followed by Shimbo who successfully produced MCPs in the inline screw molding machine [16] and pre-plasticizing type molding machine [17] in 1999 and 2000 respectively. The design modification by Shimbo was owing to instability of the polymer/gas mixing systems in the inline design, and it was solved by decoupling the plasticizing and injection process in the pre-plasticizing design. In 2001, microcellular foam molding process (MuCell Technology) was developed and patented by Massachusetts Institute of Technology and Trexel, Inc. The pressure restriction element provides the conditions for gas diffusion to create a uniform distribution of SCF [1] in the reciprocating-screw injection molding machine. After one year, Michaeli, from IKV Germany, develop a system with a specially designed injection nozzle mounted between the plasticizing unit and the shut off nozzle of a conventional injection molding machine for gas injection [18]. The ring shape die containing a torpedo and a static mixer elements were mounted between the gas injection nozzle and the shut off nozzle for the evenly distribution of SCF in the polymer melt. This technology was commercialized by Sulzer Chemtech as Optifoam in Switzerland. The other injection molding machine designed for MCP fabrication was developed by Park et al. in 2006, it was named as advanced structural foam molding technology, the design was based on a pre-plasticizing-type injection molding machine [19]. For the sake of the stop and flow molding behaviors induce inconsistent gas dosage; this technology can ensure uniform gas dispersion and complete dissolution in the polymer melt to prevent inconsistent gas dosing. The system comprises a positive displacement pump and an additional accumulator attached between the barrel and the two shut off valve. In 2007, Trexel has announced that they have developed the Series III MuCell System for small injection molding machine with screw diameters less than 40mm, and the air pump for gas compression was replaced by the electric drive motor [20].

3.0 Review of Process Parameters Investigations in Microcellular Injection Molding

Papers and books related to the investigation about the effect of processing parameters in microcellular injection molding on cell structure from 1995 to 2007 were reviewed, and the investigation results and rules were summarized in Table I.

Table I: Summary of Process Parameters Investigations in Microcellular Injection Molding from 1995 to 2007

Year	Author	Rules/Observations	Ref.
1995	Wang, C. et al.	• Packing pressure plays an important role in controlling foams density and the injection velocity and pressure are not critical. • Expansion ratio increase with decreasing packing pressure as high packing pressure may crush the foams or be large to resist foaming.	[15]
1999	Shimbo, M. et al.	• Expansion ratio decrease with increasing gas concentration because of unstable solubility of blowing agent, constant to the screw rotational speed and exist an optimum in resin saturation pressure. • Cell size become small when the screw rotational speed decreases, and he attributed it to lengthen of the retention time of resin in the barrel, and the solubility by diffusion is improved.	[16]
2000	Shimbo, M. et al.	• If the concentration of blowing agent is too much or too less , the cell size become too large or too small. • The cell size decrease with increasing injection velocity, because of the uniform cooling and pressure in the mold is released constantly. • The expansion ratio was doubled and cell size become bigger when mold	[17]

		temperature increase and it was owing to cell coalesce.	
2001	Pierick, D, Jacobsen K	• Cell size increase with melt temperature, because melt temperature reduce the melt strength of polymer and allow greater growth. • Cell size decrease with SCF level, because higher SCF level increased nucleation for smaller cell size. • Cell size is not significantly affected by injection velocity and mold temperature.	[9]
2001	Xu, J.	• The diffusion rate is depends on the state of blowing agent, melt temperature and the shear rate. • Constant back pressure in recovery and idle period of injection molding cycle and the melt pressure should be higher than the saturation pressure to prevent prefoaming. • The design of the plasticizing unit is to create uniform distribution of SCF, provides condition required for gas diffusion and dissolution and allows for a reasonable recovery rate. • A high injection rate to obtain better cell structures and maximize the weight reduction. • The pressure drop rate across the nozzle/gate should be higher than 1 GPa/s if the polymer is fully saturated with gas so as to produce the part with 10^9 cells/cm^3 cell density and 10µm cell size. Pressure drop rate = $dp/dt = \mu D^2 V^4/d^6$, D: Screw Diameter, V: Injection Velocity, d: nozzle diameters, µ:Material Viscosity. • Different injection velocity will be required at different saturation pressure to achieve microcellular structure. • The cell distribution along flow path was also investigated in this study, it was found that the slow injection speed induce non-uniform void fraction. Because slow injection speed fills the mold slowly, allowing thicker skin and narrower flow channel. This tends to create over packing near the gate area and under packing near the end of flow.	[2]
2002	Machaeli. et al.	• Higher injection velocity and melt temperature cause higher nucleation rate for higher cell density and finer cell .	[18]
2003 - 2004	Turng, L.S. et al.	• The process parameters: back pressure, SCF level, shot weight and injection speeds decrease with cell size, and melt temperature increase with cell size. According to the DOE result, the shot size and injection velocity are important parameters. • For the shot weight, it was founded that an optimal was exist for both cell density and cell size. It is postulated that a larger shot size leads to high molding pressure which hinder cell nucleation and less space for the cell to growth, whereas smaller shot size result in higher cooling rate and lower cell density and size. In this study, it is also stated that too high weight reduction would lead to uncontrollable structure and huge cell. • Back pressure will affect the rate and degree of mixing, and melt temperature, shot size and back pressure will affect the injection pressure and then the pressure drop rate.	[21] – [24]
2005	Kramchuster et al.	• SCF level and injection speed are the significant factor on warpage and shrinkage, and cooling time is not significant.	[8]
2005	Hwang, S. S. et al.	• Higher injection speed and back pressure increasing made the cell smaller and deteriorated the toughness.	[25]
2005	Lin, C. K. et. al.	• Increase in SCF level increased the foam density and cell density. • The increase in melt temperature caused bigger cells, therefore lower tensile and impact strength. • Increases in SCF level cause less warpage and shrinkage, and it is due to the increase in foam quantity lower the heat loss and cooling rate.	[26]
2006	Xu, J.	• High shear rate is the key process parameter for making single phase solution, and the residence time of shearing may not be important for gas dosing in the plasticizing stage	[28]

MICROCELLULAR INJECTION MOLDING: REVIEW AND LIMITATIONS OF CAE APPLICATION

		• About the pressure different between gas injector and barrel, he pointed out that the different should be low (50 psi) for smaller gas droplet size which will dramatically shorten gas dissolution time and stabilize the gas dosing process. • An optimum injection speed exist for the best cell structure of foams, because too high injection speed and shear cause material degradation, and too low injection speed cause low nucleation rate. • Shot size should be predetermined parameters as it determined weight reduction and mechanical strength.	
2006	Cui, H.W. et al.	• Increasing injection velocity decrease weight reduction and increase cell size, and the increase in SCF level decrease weight reduction and decrease cell size.	[27]
2006	Kanai T. et al.	• In lower injection velocity, the more number of cells are observed near the gate, on contrary, under higher injection velocity, more number of cells is observed at the end of the cavity. • The cell morphology is influenced by the mold pressure and pressure distribution and cell is formed easier at the low pressure. • The relative tensile modulus is proportional to the relative foam density.	[12]
2006	Brehravesh et al.	• Shot size has a dominant effect on foam structure, too low a shot size causes non uniform microstructure and uncompleted foam part, too high shot size yield no expansion and the injected gas will remains dissolved in the polymer matrix. • The amount of gas required is equal to gas lost, unexpanded gas and the foamed gas.	[29]
2007	Lee, J.W.S. et al.	• The use of variable injection speed profile to improve the non-uniform void fraction distribution along the melt flow direction.	[30]

4.0   Investigation on CAE Software for Microcellular Injection Molding

The CAE software used for the simulation of MuCell® IM was first launched as one of the module by Moldflow Corp. in 2003. The algorithm of the simulation was developed by Han et al. [31]. It is the first application of the unit cell model to the microcellular injection molding. The development of the unit cell models can be found in the work of Osorio [32]. About the final cells size simulation result, it is claimed that the model was able to predict the same phenomenon as the real case. But significant different, about 50%, of final cell size was reported in the region far from the gate [31]. In the following part of this work, an experiment was carried out to study the possibility of using the simulation software for process parameters determination.

4.1   Experimental

An oven handle with dimension 306.5mm (Length) X 33mm (Width) X 10mm (Height), with nominal thickness 2.5mm (Fig. 1) was evaluated. The parts were made of PA66 with 33% glass-fiber (Spectron: E0453) and nitrogen was used as the blowing agent and it was molded with the Toshiba EC220N injection molding machine retrofitted with the SCF control systems module SII-10 from Trexel® Inc. Specimens were then prepared by quenching in liquid nitrogen and freeze fractured in the region of investigation (Fig.1). The fractured surfaces were gold coated and micrograph was taken by scanning electrons microscope (Leica Stereoscan 440). The cell density can be calculated by the following equations [3]:

$$N = (n/A)^{3/2}(1/1-V_f) \tag{1}$$

$$V_f = 1 - \rho_f/\rho \qquad (2)$$

N: Cell Density, n: Number of cells observed under interested area, A: Area of the interested area, V_f: Volume faction of the cells, ρ_f: Density of the foamed sample, ρ: Density of the unfoamed sample. The resultant cell density, cell size and deflections were plotted and compared with the simulation result.

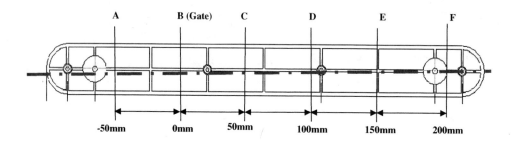

Fig. 1   The investigated sections in the oven handle assembly part

4.2   Result and Discussion

The cell densities at different location were plotted in Fig. 2, the cell density was ranged from 1.80E+07 to 3.51E+07cells/cm^3, and the average cell density in these six locations was 2.82E+07cells/cm^3. The lower cell density near the gate region could be owing to the lower pressure drop and pressure drop rate when the cavity pressure was build up [2], whereas the decreasing cell density after 100mm (position D) could be due to cell coalescence [3], the reasons behind required further investigation. The average cell density obtained from SEM

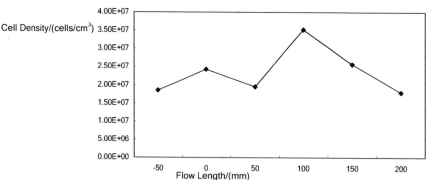

Fig. 2   The cell density distribution of the oven assembly part

micrograph was one of the input values in the software module, it should be worth pointing out that because the software algorithm was established through unit cells model which assume all the cells are already nucleated evenly and possess equal initial size [31], the parameters which control the gas dissolution and

MICROCELLULAR INJECTION MOLDING: REVIEW AND LIMITATIONS OF CAE APPLICATION

nucleation cannot be determined/optimized through simulations. On the other hand, the other input, initial bubbles radius was set at 1 micron in this case as suggested from the software manual and it is stated in the manual that too small initial bubbles radius will induce unstable result in the software [33]. However, in reality, the initial bubbles radius was not measurable even by high speed camera because of resolution problem, and it was believed to be in nano-scale [34].

The comparison of average cell size distribution from SEM micrographs and simulation was plotted in Fig. 3. From the figure, it is found that the cell size near the gate region was under-predicted in general, and the largest deviation was found in 0mm (position B – gate location) which is as high as 55%. The deviation could be owing to the assumption of uniform cell density in the simulation model [31]. From Fig. 2, the actual cell density was lower than the average, which leads to the under-predicted cell size. On the other hand, the software assume foaming was started at the end of filling [31], however, foaming should be start in filling stage when the cavity pressure was lower than the solubility pressure [2], which means the foaming time in the software was shorter and lead to under-predicted cell size. The deviation of material (PVT/viscosity) data can also contribute to the deviation [31].

5.0   Conclusion

In this paper, the development, challenges and investigations on effect of process parameters on cell structures were reviewed and summarized. It is found that the investigation of injection and injection profile on the mold/cavity pressure and result cell structure was just started in 2006 and no conclusive result was established. Therefore, rules/axioms establishment is required in injection and post-injection control through basic research. In additions, it is found that the use of CAE for process parameters determination may not be suitable because of its incapability to simulate gas dissolution and nucleation, variation of prediction of CAE and experiment could be as high as 50%.

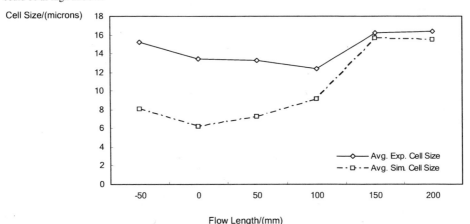

Fig. 3   The average cell size distribution from experiment and simulation

MICROCELLULAR INJECTION MOLDING: REVIEW AND LIMITATIONS OF CAE APPLICATION

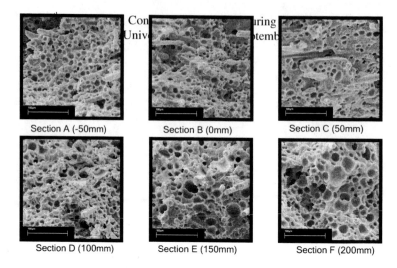

| Section A (-50mm) | Section B (0mm) | Section C (50mm) |
| Section D (100mm) | Section E (150mm) | Section F (200mm) |

Fig. 4   SEM micrograph showing different sections of the part

Acknowledgement

The authors wish to acknowledge the assistance and support of the Teaching Company Scheme of the Hong Kong Polytechnic University funded by the Industrial Support Fund (UIT/090) and the G.E.W. Corporation Limited.

References

[1]   Cheng K. P., Yip. D. C. Y.,, Lau K. H., Barnes S., "Development of a generic computer aided deductive algorithm for process design", *KES 2004*, LNAI 3214, p. 28 (2004).

[2]   Xu, J., Pierick D., "Microcellular foam processing in reciprocating-screw injection molding machine", *Journal of Injection Molding Technology*, vol. 5, p. 152 (2001).

[3]   Turng L. S., "Microcellular Injection Molding", *Journal of Injection Molding Technology*, vol. 5, p. 160 (2001).

[4]   Suh, N. P., in: *Innovation in Polymer Processing-Molding*. Stevenson, J. F. (Eds.), Hanser Publishers, Munich (1996).

[5]   Park C. B., Doroudiani S., and Kortschot M .T., "Microcellular sheet extrusion system process design models for shaping and cell growth control," *Polymer Engineering and Science*, vol. 38, p. 1205 (1998).

[6]   Seeler K. A. and Kumar V., *Journal of Reinforced Plastics and Composites*, vol. 12, 359 (1998).

[7]   Okamoto, K. T., in: *Microcellular Processing*, Hanser Publishers, Munich (2003).

[8]   Kramschuster, A., Cavitt, R., Ermer, D., Chen, Z. B., Turng L. S., "Quantitative study of shrinkage and warpage behaviour for microcellular and conventional injection molding", *Polymer Engineering and Science*, vol. 45, p. 1408 (2005).

[9]   Pierick D., and Jacobsen K., "Injection molding innovation: the microcellular foam process", *Plastic Engineering*, May, vol. 57, p. 46 (2001).

[10]   Yuan, M., Turng, L.S., Gong, S., Caulfield, D., Hunt, C., Spindler, R., "Study of Injection Molded Microcellular Polyamide-6 Nanocomposites", *Polymer Engineering and Science*, vol. 44, p. 673 (2004).

[11]   Turng, L.S., Khabra, H., "Effect of Process Conditions on the Weld-Line Strength and Microstructure of Microcellular Injection Molded Parts",*Polymer Engineering and Science*, vol. 43, p.157 (2003).

[12]   Kanai, T., Kawato, T., Goda, H., "Control factors of foam structure and properties in microcellular injection molding", PPS-19, Melbourne, Australia, June (2003).

[13]   Xu, J., "Methods to the smooth surface of microcellular foam in injection molding",*SPE ANTEC Tech. Papers*, p. 2087 (2006).

[14]   Sporrer A. N. J., Sandler, J. K. W., "Tailored structural foams by foam injection molding with a specialized mold", Mantey A. and Altstadt, V., SPE Foams (2006).

[15]   Wang, C., Cox, K., Campbell, G. A., "Microcellular foaming of polypropylene containing low glass transition

rubber particles in an injection molding process", *SPE ANTEC Tech. Papers*, p. 406 (1995).

[16] Shimbo, M., Nishida, K., Heraku, T., Iijima, K., Sekino, T., Terayama, T., "Foam processing technology of microcellular plastics by injection molding machine", *Paper presented at First Int. Conf. Thermoplast. Foam*, p. 132 (1999).

[17] Shimbo, M., Kawashima, H., Yoshitani, S., "Foam injection technology and influence factors of microcellular plastics", *Foams 2000*, p. 162 (2000).

[18] Michaeli, W., Habibi-Naini, S., "Foam injection molding – a new nozzle for fluid injection", *SPE ANTEC Tech. Papers*, p. 552 (2001).

[19] Park, C.B., Xu, X., Lee, J.W.S., and Zhu, X., "Advances in Structural Foam Molding Technology". *SPI Plastic parts Innovations Conference*, Columbus, Ohio, April 2-4 (2006).

[20] www.trexel.com.

[21] Turng, L.S., "Microcellular injection molding", *SPE ANTEC Tech. Papers*, p. 686 (2003).

[22] Kharbas, H., Nelson, P., Yuan, M., Gong, S., Turng, L.S., "Effects of Nano-Fillers and Process Conditions on the Microstructure and Mechanical Properties of Microcellular Injection Molded Polyamide Nanocomposites", *Polymer Composites*, vol. 24, p. 655 (2003).

[23] Chandra, A., Gong, S., Yuan, M., Turng, L.S., "Microstructure and crystallography in microcellular injection molded polyamide-6 nanocomposite and neat resin, *Polymer Engineering and Science*, vol. 45, p. 52 (2005).

[24] Yuan, M., Winardi, A., Gong, S., Turng, L.S., "Effects of nano-and micro-fillers and processing parameters on injection molded microcellular composite", *Polymer Engineering and Science*, vol. 45, p. 773 (2005).

[25] Hwang, S. S., Chen, S. C., Chung, M. H., "Study on the mechanical properties of microcellular injection molded part", *SPE ANTEC Tech. Papers*, 776-780 (2005).

[26] Lin, C. K., Chen, S. H., Liou, H.Y., Tian, C.C., "Study on mechanical properties of ABS parts in microcellular injection molding process". *SPE ANTEC Tech. Papers*, p. 708 (2005).

[27] Cui, H. W., Wang, C. Y., Zhu, S., "Application of neural networks in prediction of the microstructure and mechanical properties of microcellular injection molded polyamide nanocomposites", *SPE ANTEC Tech. Papers*, p. 338 (2006).

[28] Xu, J., "Effect of injection molding process parameters on the morphology and quality of microcellular foams", *SPE ANTEC Tech. Papers*, p. 2770-2774 (2006).

[29] Behravesh, A.H., Rajabpour, A., "Experimental study on filling stage of microcellular injection molding process", *Cellular Polymers*, vol. 25, p. 85 (2006).

[30] Lee, J. W. S., Wang, J., Park, C. B., Tao, G., "Use of injection speed profile to achieve a uniform void fraction distribution in injection molded structural foams", *SPE ANTEC Tech. Papers*, Paper #304236, Cincinnati, OH, May 6-10, (2007).

[31] Han. S., Zheng, R., Kennedy, P.., Xu, J., Kishbaugh, L., "Numerical analysis of microcellular injection molding", *SPE ANTEC Tech. Papers*, p. 696 (2003).

[32] Osorio, A., Turng, L.S., "Mathematical modeling and numerical simulation of cell growth in injection molding of microcellular plastics", *Polymer Engineering and Science*, vol. 24, p.2274 (2004).

[33] www.moldflow.com.

[34] Leung, S.N., Park, C.B. and Li, H., "Impact of approximating the initial bubble pressure on cell nucleation in polymeric foaming processes," *CSME 2006 Materials Technology Symposium*, Banff, Alberta, May 21-23, (2006).

MICROCELLULAR INJECTION MOLDING: REVIEW AND LIMITATIONS OF CAE APPLICATION

The 6th International Conference on Manufacturing Research (ICMR08)
Brunel University, UK, 9-11th September 2008

DEVELOPMENT OF A NEURAL-NETWORK MODELLING TOOL FOR ENGINE PERFORMANCE TESTED DATA MODELLING

Mian Hong Wu [1], Wanchang Lin [2], Shang Y Duan [3]

1. School of Technology, University of Derby, Markeaton St., Derby, DE22 3AW, UK

2. Inst. Of Biological Science, University of Wales Aberystwyth, Ceredigion, UK

3. Powertrain, Test Technology, Lander Rover Ltd, Gaydon Test Centre, Banbury Road, Warwick CV 35 0RG, UK

Abstract

It is clearly that the huge amount of the experiment data are required from engine test bed to analysis and optimise the engine performance as the different setting of the associated parameters. The process of data collection from engine test bed is a time consuming and costly tasks. As a result, the method to reduce the amount of the tested data from ETB is an important research work in the engine test area. To develop a model is the best way to do the data investigation. It only need few data to install the models and shows the continually variation between the input data.

The paper introduces a developed Neural-network tool for the engine performance model. In the paper, the structure of the optimisation system of the engine performance has to be introduced first and then the Neural-network modelling tool is discussed. In the paper, the neural networks are classified into three groups, MLP, RBF and BAR.

The details of the major functions are listed in the tool for the different group. Finally, the test results are provided in the paper.

Keywords: evolutionary neural networks, engine modelling, engine calibration

1.0   Introduction

Over last decade, more and more attention has pay on the individual neural network (NN) modelling in the engine research and development. the ideal instantaneous engine operating point by minimizing weighted sum of exhaust emissions and fuel consumption predicted by the MLP networks. They stated based on the experiment works that their approach allows the emissions and economy performance of the vehicle to be tailored to suit the particular requirements of the installation. Jocob et al. [5] and Gu et al. [6] proposed the use of the radial basis function (RBF) network in the task of reconstructing cylinder pressure based on easy-to-obtain measurements of instantaneous crankshaft angular velocity and cylinder head vibration. The experiments gave a number of promising results. Du et al. [7] applied the RBF neural network to establish the non-parametric mapping model between the cylinder pressure time series and the engine cylinder head vibration signal frequency series. The experimental result, based on a two-cylinder, four-stroke direct injection diesel engine, has shown that this approach can reconstruct the cylinder pressure from vibration signals. and differences between the MLP and RBF in the non-linear function approximation and pattern r

Although the MLP and RBF are both universal approximator [8, 9], it is difficult to say which one is better in the practical modelling. Bishop [10] and Hassoun [11] compared the similarities ecognition. Therefore it is necessary to provide an unified approach to deal with practical modelling problems. In this paper, the neural networks tool, part of the optimisation system of the engine performance on the Engine Test Bed, is investigated as an unified approach to model the non-linear, complex engine system in engine calibration.

2.0   Structure of the Optimisation System of The engine Performance

The Figure 1 shows that the structure of the optimisation system of the engine performance on the Engine Test Bed. When the tested data is ready, they will be sending into the NN Models Tool Box. In the NN tool box, there are three different types and totally ten NN structures. In it, the tested data will be divided into three groups. The first group data will take 50% out of the total tested data. The second and third groups will take 25% out of the total data respectively. The first group data will be used to train the neural network and second group data will used to validate the NN model. Final group data will be used to test the NN model.

After NN Tool Box, the best fitted NN structural model is selected and sends to optimization section to defined the optimization data for Engine Management Unit.

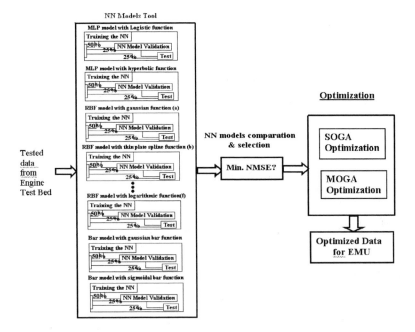

Fig. 1. The structure of the optimisation system of the engine performance

In the optimization section, there are two options for optimization purposes according to the different requirement. SOGA is the model for single objective optimization and MOGA is one for multi objectives optimization.

3.0   Neural Network Model Tool

As shown in Figure 1 the NN model tool is employed to select a best suitable NN model out of ten NN models for the subsequence operation of optimization.

Figure 2 shows the common structure of the neural network in NN model Tool and it is under the following assumptions:
- it is a three layers NN model
- the numbers of the hidden layer note is defined by 2n + 1: here n is the number of inputs.

The NN Model Tool includes three different type of neural networks, Multi-layer perceptron (MLP); radial basis functions (RBF) and bar function (BAR).

The 6th International Conference on Manufacturing Research (ICMR08)
Brunel University, UK, 9-11th September 2008

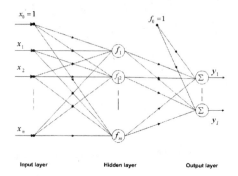

$x_0 = 1$

$f_0 = 1$

x_1

x_2

x_n

Input layer   Hidden layer   Output layer

Fig. 2.   Neural network structure

1.   MLP. The output of the MLP is denoted by

$$y_k(x) = \sum_{j=0}^{m} f(\sum_{i=0}^{n} x_i w_{ji}) w_{kj}$$

$$= \sum_{j=1}^{m} f(\sum_{i=1}^{n} x_i w_{ji} + w_{j0}) w_{kj} + w_{k0} \qquad (1)$$

$$k = 1, \cdots, l$$

where w_{ji} and w_{kj} are the input-hidden weight and hidden-output weight, respectively. f is the activation function which has two types:

(a) logistic function

$$f(\alpha) = \frac{1}{1 + e^{-\alpha}} \qquad (2)$$

(b) hyperbolic tangent function or *tanh*

$$f(\alpha) = \frac{e^{\alpha} - e^{-\alpha}}{e^{\alpha} + e^{-\alpha}} \qquad (3)$$

2.   RBF. The output of the RBF is calculated using the following form:

$$y_k(\mathbf{x}) = \sum_{j=1}^{m} \phi(\|\mathbf{x} - \mathbf{\mu}_j\|) w_{kj} + w_{i0}$$

$$= \sum_{j=0}^{m} \phi(\|\mathbf{x} - \mathbf{\mu}_j\|) w_{kj}, \qquad k = 1, \cdots, l \qquad (4)$$

where w_{kj} is the hidden-output weight and $\mathbf{\mu}_j$ is the centre of j-th hidden unit. ϕ is the kernel function. Defining a distance r from the input vector $\mathbf{x}$ to the RBF centre $\mathbf{\mu}_j$ scaled by the scale factor or width σ_j,

$$r = \frac{\|\mathbf{x} - \mathbf{\mu}_j\|}{\sigma_j} = \frac{1}{\sigma_j} \sqrt{\sum_{i=1}^{n} (x_i - \mu_{ji})^2} \qquad (5)$$

Within the RBF networks, six kernel functions are widely used:

(a) Gaussian function

$$\phi(r) = \exp(-r^2 / 2) \qquad (6)$$

(b) thin plate spline function

**DEVELOPMENT OF A NEURAL-NETWORK MODELLING TOOL FOR ENGINE
PERFORMANCE TESTED DATA MODELLING**

$$\phi(r) = r^2 \times \log(r) \tag{7}$$

(c) multiquadric function

$$\phi(r) = (r^2 + 1)^{1/2} \tag{8}$$

(d) inverse multiquadric function

$$\phi(r) = \frac{1}{(r^2 + 1)^{1/2}} \tag{9}$$

(e) pseudo cubic spline function

$$\phi(r) = r^3 \tag{10}$$

(f) logarithmic function

$$\phi(r) = \log(r^2 + 1) \tag{11}$$

3.   BAR. The BAR network has the same structure as the RBF network, but the kernel function is different. Two kernel function for the BAR network:

(a) Gaussian bar function

$$\phi(\mathbf{x}) = \sum_{i=1}^{n} \exp\left[-\frac{(x_i - \mu_{ji})^2}{2\sigma_{ji}^2} \right] \tag{12}$$

(b) sigmoidal bar function

$$\phi(\mathbf{x}) = \sum_{i=1}^{n} 1 / \left\{ 1 + \exp\left[-\frac{(x_i - \mu_{ji})^2}{2\sigma_{ji}^2} \right] \right\} \tag{13}$$

Table 1: lists the summery of the neural network structure used in the NN Model Tool.

Table 1: Nomenclature of neural network structures

NN Model	Activation Function	Abbreviation
RBF	Gaussian function	Rbf-Gaussian
	thin plate spline function	Rbf-TPS
	logarithmic function	Rbf-Logarithmic
	multi-quadric function	Rbf-Quadric
	inverse multi-quadric function	Rbf-InverseQuadric
	pseudo cubic spline function	Rbf-Cubic
BAR	Gaussian function	Bar-Gbar
	Sigmoidal function	Bar-Sbar
MLP	logistic function	Mlp-Logsig
	tangent function	Mlp-Tansig

4.0   Computational Example

In this section, a computational example for engine data modelling was carried out. The input data and output data are listed in Figure 3 and Figure 4.

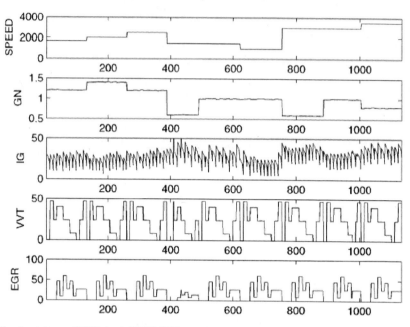

Fig. 3.   Input data set: SPEED (rpm), GN(%), IG(degree), VVT(degree) and EGR(%)

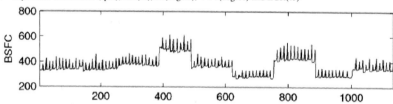

Fig. 4.   Output data set: BSFC (g/kWh)

Three NNs, MLP, RBF and BAR, with different activation functions, abbreviated in Table 1, were used throughout the example. The data was taken from engine test bed of the Lander Rover Group, plc. In order to assess the goodness of modelling, the normalized mean squared error (NMSE) over each output variable is used:

$$NMSE = \frac{\left(\dfrac{1}{N}\sum_{i=1}^{N}(y_i - t_i)^2\right)^{1/2}}{\left(\dfrac{1}{N}\sum_{i=1}^{N}(t_i - \bar{t})^2\right)^{1/2}} \tag{14}$$

where N is the number of total data points. y_i and t_i are respectively the model output and the target value, and $\bar{t}$ is the average value of the targets on the data set, defined as:

$$\bar{t} = \frac{1}{N}\sum_{i=1}^{N} t_i \tag{15}$$

NMSE has the value 0 for a perfect match between model and target, and the value 1 if the model just outputs

**DEVELOPMENT OF A NEURAL-NETWORK MODELLING TOOL FOR ENGINE
PERFORMANCE TESTED DATA MODELLING**

the target mean $\bar{t}$ .Table 2 shows the result of the example.

Table 2: Mean, standard (std. dev), minimum and maximum MSE over 10 runs for each model

	Mean	Std.dev.	Minimum	Maximum		Mean	Std.dev.	Minimum	Maximum
		Training					Test		
Rbf-Gaussian	278.83	34.82	233.46	330.88	Rbf-Gaussian	335.57	34.57	274.02	379.63
Rbf-TPS	283.34	32.02	237.32	308.40	Rbf-TPS	345.90	24.43	310.51	361.82
Rbf-Logarithmic	277.39	19.58	241.20	304.25	Rbf-Logarithmic	316.09	19.19	292.00	346.65
Rbf-Quadratic	292.43	7.45	288.74	313.35	Rbf-Quadratic	337.71	12.71	326.24	351.81
Rbf-InverseQuadratic	290.63	59.92	229.97	386.28	Rbf-InverseQuadratic	348.45	44.95	308.03	424.94
Rbf-Cubic spline	292.55	3.56	289.18	295.93	Rbf-Cubic	323.69	8.68	315.36	331.83
Bar-Gbar	66.75	11.82	56.47	84.41	Bar-Gbar	85.16	12.59	74.72	106.83
Bar-Sbar	68.65	14.98	54.77	88.86	Bar-Sbar	92.93	19.93	74.35	118.90
Mlp-Logsig	269.44	67.78	158.40	339.92	Mlp-Logsig	304.54	75.97	162.30	364.69
Mlp-Tansig	290.94	19.86	237.06	303.64	Mlp-Tansig	341.92	17.74	290.52	346.77
		Validation							
Rbf-Gaussian	289.49	27.02	230.97	327.41					
Rbf-TPS	301.45	17.05	282.35	323.80					
Rbf-Logarithmic	279.53	18.92	255.86	308.97					
Rbf-Quadratic	300.01	11.51	287.04	316.49					
Rbf-InverseQuadratic	301.84	35.50	263.44	353.18					
Rbf-Cubic spline	300.42	4.91	295.76	305.08					
Bar-Gbar	81.79	12.43	71.06	100.77					
Bar-Sbar	85.66	17.06	70.20	106.74					
Mlp-Logsig	281.66	74.78	145.68	341.73					
Mlp-Tansig	278.11	5.86	261.45	280.15					

It is clearly that the model structure which has the minimum MSE was the BAR model with sigmoidal bar function. The modelling result by Bar-Sbar is plotted in Figure 5.

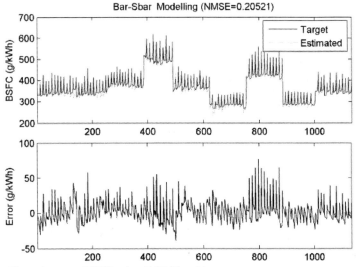

Fig. 5.   Modelling performance of BSFC by sigmoidal BAR model

5.0   Conclusion

In this paper, the structure of the Engine Test data modelling optimisation system is introduced. The details of the Neural Network Tool has been introduced. Finally the example shows that the NN model tool is running successfully to select the best NN model for Engine Data optimization.

References

[1]   M. Scaife, S. Charlton, and C. Mobley. A neural network for fault recognition. In SAEPaper930861, 1993.

[2]   S. P. Stevens, P. J. Shayler, and T. H. Ma., Experimental data processing techniques to map the performance of a spark ignition engine. Proc Instn Mech Engrs, Part D, Journal of Automobile Engineering, 209(D4):297 – 306, 1995.

[3]   P. Shayler, N. Darnton, and T. Ma. Predicting the fuel consumption of vehicles for drive cycles starting from cold ambient conditions. In SIA9506A27EAEC 275th International Congress, Strasbourg, 1995.

[4]   C. J. Brace, M. Deacon, N. D. Vaughan, R. W. Horrocks, and C. R. Burrows., An operating point optimizer for the design and calibration of an integrated diesel/continuously variable transmission powertrain. Proc Instn Mech Engrs, Part D, Journal of Automobile Engineering, 213(D3):215 – 226, 1999.

[5]   P. Jocob, F. Gu, and A. Ball. Non-parametric models in the monitoring of engine performance and condition, Part 1: modelling of non-linear engine processes. Proc Instn Mech Engrs, Part D, Journal of Automobile Engineering, 213(D1):73–81, 1999.

[6]   F. Gu, P. Jocob, and A. Ball. Non-parametric models in the monitoring of engine performance and condition, Part 2: non-intrusive estimation of diesel engine cylinder pressure and its use in fault detection. Proc Instn Mech Engrs, Part D, Journal of Automobile Engineering, 213(D2):135–143, 1999.

[7]   H. Du, L. Zhang, and X. Shi. Reconstructing cylinder pressure from vibration signals based on radial basis function networks. Proc Instn Mech Engrs, Part D, Journal of Automobile Engineering, 215(D6):761–767, 2001.

[8]   K. Hornick, M. Stinchcombe, and H. White. Multilayer feedforward networks are universal approximators. Neural Networks, 2:359–366, 1989.

[9]   E. J. Hartman, J. D. Keeler, and J. M. Kowalski. Layered neural networks with Gaussian hidden units as universal approximations. Neural Computation, 2(2): 210–215, 1990.

[10] C. M. Bishop. Neural Networks for Pattern Recognition. Oxford University Press, Oxford, 1995.

[11] M. H. Hassoun. Fundamentals of Artificial Neural Networks. MIT Press, Cambridge, MA, 1995.

The 6th International Conference on Manufacturing Research (ICMR08)
Brunel University, UK, 9-11th September 2008

EFFECTS OF THE PIPE-JOINTS ON ACOUSTIC EMISSION WAVE PROPAGATION VELOCITY

W Wichaidit [1] and Y H Joe Au [2]

1. **Industrial Metrology and Testing Service Centre, Thailand Institute of Scientific and Technological Research, Thailand** [1] wadee@tistr.or.th

2. **Advanced Manufacturing and Enterprise Engineering Group, School of Engineering and Design, Brunel University, UK** [2] Joe.Au@brunel.ac.uk

Abstract

In jointed-pipes, a variety of different acoustic emission (AE) waves can be generated by way of mode conversion, wave reflection and wave transmission from a joint. This can lead to interference waves as resulting complicated signals propagate along the pipe structure. To find out how the joint affects AE wave propagation in the jointed-pipes, experiments were conducted on a thin-walled copper pipes connected with two types of joint, compression and soldered. By using wavelet packet decomposition (WPD) analysis and the time-of-flight method, the apparent velocity of AE waves near the joints could be estimated as a narrow frequency band individually. Results confirmed that the wave velocities determined near a joint were influenced by not only the wave reflection but also the wave transmission. The measured wave velocity was least affected by those for the wave in the low frequency band (<125 kHz). It was also observed that a compression or soldered joint behaved like a low-pass filter to the transmitted AE signal.

Keywords: Acoustic emission, wave velocity, copper pipe, jointed-pipes, wavelet packet decomposition.

1.0   Introduction

Acoustic emission (AE) is the mechanical waves generated by rapid release of energy from a source within a material. They propagate through the material of the structure. One major application of the acoustic emission method is source location of defects in a structure using the arrival times of the signals at one or more sensors and this includes locating leaks in pipeline. Due to the fact that more than one AE wave mode is often produced at a source and that the different modes propagate at a different velocity, if the pipes connected with joints are now considered, complication occurs. When one of these modes interacts with the joint, reflected and transmitted waves of a variety of modes may be generated. This is because when a wave impinges an interface or boundary between two media, the wave energy is partly reflected and partly transmitted. The reflected waves might interfere with the original incident waves leading to more complex waves. Jin et al. [1] studied the wave reflection, conversion and transmission of Lamb wave mode propagating in a boundary plate. Hamstead et al. [2] studied the edge reflection using a small sample block superimposed on a large sample block with the lateral dimension sufficiently large to avoid the reflections from the sample edges. They reported that edge reflections, caused by the side edges of the small sample and also from the ends of the large sample, could superimpose on the direct signals when the source was an in-plane dipole located at a depth of 0.47 mm below the top surface. Rose [3] used the ultrasonic through-transmission approach for lap splice joint inspection to study the effects of the joint on wave propagation.

In this paper, the effects of joints on the wave propagation velocity were studied. Experiments were conducted on thin-walled copper pipes connected together with compression or soldered joints. The joints caused the pipe discontinuity in geometry due to the different thicknesses of the pipe wall and of the joints. Wave propagation was studied for this case where at the discontinuity, part of the incident wave energy is reflected and the rest is transmitted. If the AE sensor is positioned upstream of and close to the joint, the combined incident and reflected waves can make the accurate determination of the time of arrival of the signal at the sensor very difficult. This is because the cross-correlation method, which is used to obtain the time delay in the arrival of the signals at the two sensors, relies on the integrity of the wave shape of the signal.

If a signal from a given source position is detected at some other position after a time delay, Δt, and if the received signal comprises a swept sine wave plus extraneous noise, a cross-correlation between the two signals provides a signal which peaks at a time delay corresponding to the transmission delay. Given the wave propagating velocity, V, in the medium, the cross-correlation function thus allows an estimation of the distance, L, between the source and the receiver by the simple equation:

$$L = V \cdot \Delta t$$

(1)

2.0   Wavelet Packet Decomposition

It was reported that wavelet transform (WT) could improve the accuracy of AE source location on thin plates where the source was a transient AE signal [4]-[8]. However, for sources that produce a continuous AE signal, the accuracy seems to be less satisfactory. In the work by Shehadehand et al [9], they used wavelet packet decomposition combined with cross-correlation for determining the wave velocity in a long steel pipeline and they reported good estimates.

The work of Wichaidit and Au [10] shows that the idea of decomposing a dispersive wave component down to a single frequency or at least a narrow band of frequencies is a sensible alternative so that the wave velocity can be determined with greater accuracy. Wavelet packet decomposition (WPD) can offer that advantage because it separates a signal into narrow frequency bands. The number of bands depends on the level order of the WPD.

EFFECTS OF THE PIPE-JOINTS ON ACOUSTIC EMISSION WAVE PROPAGATION VELOCITY

In this paper, a third-level WPD with the fourth-order Daubechies wavelet was used. Consequently eight wavelet bands for each signal were created. The approximate frequency components for each band at each level are shown in Fig. 1

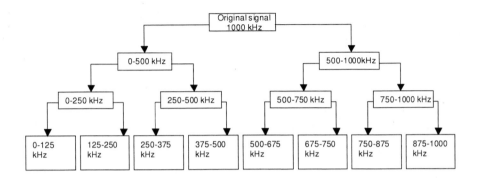

Fig. 1.   The frequency bands for the different levels of the 3rd-order Daubechies (db4) wavelets for a signal sampled at 2 MHz.

3.0   Experiment

The objective of this experiment was to investigate how the proximity of the sensor to the joint affected the measured wave propagation velocity. Experimental setups involved two pipe test rigs. One was a 5-metre run of copper pipe (BS 2871:1972), formed from a 3-metre and a 2-metre pipe joined with a compression joint. The copper pipe had an outer diameter of 22 mm with a wall thickness of 0.9 mm. Another one was a 6-metre run of copper pipe with the same diameter and wall thickness, formed from two of 3-metre pipes jointed with a soldered joint. The AE source S generated by pencil lead break was picked up with two broadband PAC-WD type AE sensors, T1 and T2, as shown in Fig. 2. The output from the sensor was fed to a preamplifier (60 dB gain) with a built-in band-pass filter (20 kHz – 1 MHz). The voltage output from the preamplifier was sampled at 2 MHz into a PC driven by LabVIEW™. The record length for each signal was 0.050 s. The acquired waveforms were stored for subsequent signal processing in MATLAB™. Ten trials were recorded for each experiment. The experimental procedure is described below:

a)   For both pipe test rigs (with compression joints and with soldered joints), sensors T1 and T2 were always placed 2-m apart and the pencil-lead source was always generated 0.2 m to the left of T1. The distance y measured from the middle joint to the sensor T2 was, however, variable, as shown Fig. 2. When T2 was to the left of the joint, y had a negative value and vice versa.

b)   For the compression-joint pipeline, y = -0.525, -0.425, -0.325, -0.225, -0.125, -0.075, -0.025, 0.025, 0.075, 0.175, 0.275, 0.375 or 0.575 m.

c)   For the soldered-joint pipeline, y = -0.507, -0.307, -0.107, -0.057, ±0.007, 0.207, 0.390 and 0.707 m.

EFFECTS OF THE PIPE-JOINTS ON ACOUSTIC EMISSION WAVE PROPAGATION VELOCITY

d) At each of these positions of *y*, the pencil-lead source was generated and AE signals were recorded at the sampling rate of 2 MHz for the duration of 0.05 s.

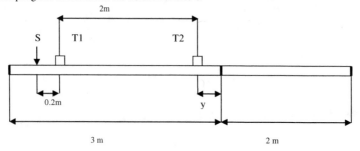

Fig. 2.   Schematic diagram of the joint reflection measurement

4.0   Results and Discussion

The effect of the compression joint to the transmitted signal is clearly demonstrated in Fig. 3. The diagrams on the left are the AE time signals and those on the right are the corresponding frequency spectra. The top pair shows the signal detected at the sensor T2 (Fig. 2) which was at the distance of 0.525 m upstream of the middle compression joint, the middle pair for T2 being 0.225 m downstream and the bottom pair for T2 0.575 downstream of the middle joint. It is noted that as the signal propagated past the joint, the higher frequency components were much more severely attenuated than the lower frequency components.

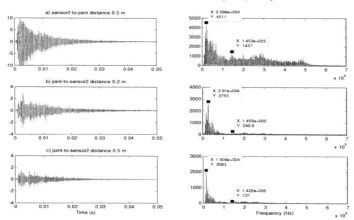

Fig. 3.   The typical waveforms and their spectrum of the detected signal at sensor2 positions away from the compression joint a) 0.525-m T2-to-joint distant, b) 0.225-m joint-to-T2 distant and c) 0.575-m joint-to-T2 distant

The wave velocity at each position of *y* in Fig. 2 was determined. Due to the fact that when *y* was small, the value of the wave velocity obtained would be affected by the wave reflection from the joint, the wave velocity is therefore called the *apparent wave velocity*. This velocity can be calculated by the equation (1) where the distance, *L*, in this case was 2 m and the time difference, Δt, obtained using WPD analysis. The process was

EFFECTS OF THE PIPE-JOINTS ON ACOUSTIC EMISSION WAVE PROPAGATION VELOCITY

that the pair of detected signals was first subjected to a WPD three-level wavelet (db 4) decomposition leading to eight components as shonw in Fig. 1 and corresponding component pairs then cross-correlated.

Plotting these apparent wave velocities against the distance y of the sensor T2 from the middle joint, with y being negative if T2 is to the left of the joint and positive if T2 is to the right, Fig. 4 for the pipeline with compression joints and Fig. 5 for the pipeline with soldered joints were obtained.

Referring to Figs. 4 to 5, it is possible to make the following observations with respect to apparent wave velocity:

1. That the joints had a stronger effect on the velocity of the higher frequency components (>125 kHz) than on the low frequency component (<125 kHz).
2. That the compression joint caused velocity fluctuations up to the distance of 0.8 m both upstream and downstream.
3. That the soldered joint caused velocity fluctuations up to the distance of 0.8 m downstream but considerably much greater distance upstream, up to 2 m.

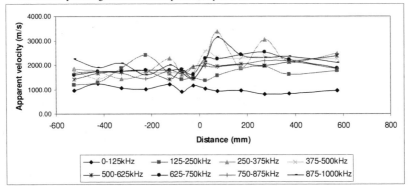

Fig. 4. Plots of the apparent velocities versus the distances of the sensor T2 from the compression joint distances ranging from -0.525 m to 0.575 m using WPD method

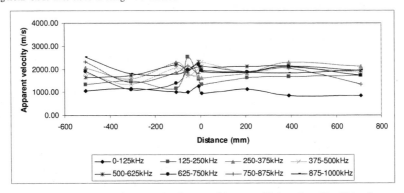

Fig. 5. Plots of the apparent velocities versus the distances of the sensor T2 from the soldered joint distances ranging from -0.507 m to 0.707 m using WPD method

EFFECTS OF THE PIPE-JOINTS ON ACOUSTIC EMISSION WAVE PROPAGATION VELOCITY

5.0   Conclusion

The reflected and transmitted AE signals from the compression and soldered joints were studied. The wave velocity measured using the time-of-flight method showed considerable variation as the sensor was placed at various distances away from the joint up to a range. Beyond this range, the measured wave velocity remained constant. The measured wave velocity was least affected by this phenomenon for the wave in the frequency band of 0 to 125 kHz. It was also found that the joint behaved like a low-pass frequency filter for the transmitted signal.

Acknowledgement

The authors wish to acknowledge the Royal Thai government and the Ministry of Science and Technology, Thailand for their support.

References

[1]. J Jin, S Quek, Q Wang, "Wave boundary element to study Lamb wave propagation in plates", *Journal of Sound and Vibration*, vol. 288, pp 195-213, 2005.
[2]. M A Hamstad, A O'Gallagher, J Gary, "Effects of lateral plate dimensions on acoustic emission signals from dipole sources", *Journal of Acoustic Emission*, vol. 19, pp 258-274, 2001.
[3]. J L Rose, "A baseline and vision of ultrasonic guided wave inspection potential", *Journal of Pressure Vessel Technology, Transactions of the ASME*, vol. 124, pp 273-282, August 2002.
[4]. Y Ding, R L Reuben, J A Steel, "A new method for waveform analysis for estimating AE wave arrival times using wavelet decomposition", *Journal of NDT&E International*, vol. 37, pp. 279-290, 2004.
[5]. M A Hamstad, A. O'Gallagher, J. Gary , "A wavelet transform applied to acoustic emission signals: part 2: source location", *Journal of Acoustic Emission*, vol. 20, pp. 62-82, 2002.
[6]. H Jeong, Y Jang, "Fracture source location in thin plates using the wavelet transform of dispersive waves", *IEEE Transactions on Ultrasonics, Ferroelectrics, and Frequency Controls*, vol. 47 No.3, pp. 612-619, 2000.
[7]. J Jiao, C He, B Wu, R Fei, X Wang, "Application of wavelet transform on modal acoustic emission source location in thin plates with one sensor", *International Journal of Pressure Vessels and Piping*, vol. 81, pp. 427-431, 2004.
[8]. J Jiao, C He, B Wu, R Fei, "A new technique for modal acoustic emission pipeline leak location with one sensor", *Insight*, vol.46 No.7, pp.392-95, 2004.
[9]. M Shehadeh, M Elghamry, J A Steel, R L Reuben "AE source location in long steel pipes using cross-correlation and wavelet transforms", *Proceedings of 17th Congress of Condition Monitoring and Diagnostic Engineering Management*, COMADEM, pp. 250-59, 2004.
[10].W Wichaidit, J Y H Au, "Comparison of acoustic emission signal-processing methods for sources location in copper pipes", *5th International Conference on Manufacturing Research*, pp 131-135, 2007.

EFFECTS OF THE PIPE-JOINTS ON ACOUSTIC EMISSION WAVE PROPAGATION VELOCITY

The 6th International Conference on Manufacturing Research (ICMR08)
Brunel University, UK, 9-11th September 2008

INVESTIGATION OF DESIGN AND MANUFACTURE OF CELLULAR-TYPE STRUCTURES FOR INJECTION MOULDING TOOLS

Mariana Dotcheva, Huw Millward, Richard Bibb

The National Centre for Product Design and Development Research (PDR), University of Wales Institute Cardiff (UWIC), Cardiff CF5 2YB, UK

Abstract

The work presented in the paper aims to investigate the capabilities of some cellular-type structures as fundamental elements for creating new internal material configurations for injection moulding tools. The idea is to design and manufacture cellular structures such as truss structures and honeycombs that have equivalent performance compared to parts with bulk material. These structures satisfy not only the mechanical and geometrical requirements of the injection tooling design but will also contribute to the thermal management of the moulding process. The versatility of layer-additive manufacturing allows fabrication of these complex unit cell structures which could provide design freedom for creating new micro and macro internal geometries. Selective Laser Melting (SLM) technology has been used for producing the experimental samples. Test samples have been designed with and without skin surface and then experimentally verified. Two different design and manufacturing solutions of a selected cellular structure are developed: open cellular material which allows the unprocessed metal powder to be removed, and closed cellular structure where the unprocessed metal powder stays inside the part but is not solid. These two experimental designs reflect one of the specifics of SLM technology that need to be considered during the design process. The SLM process capabilities, its advantages and disadvantages to produce such complex structures with required mechanical and geometrical characteristics were analysed.

Keywords: Injection moulding, cellular structures, Selective Laser Melting.

1.0 Introduction

The work presented in this paper explores the suitability of Selective Laser Melting (SLM) built cellular structures as a core material for injection moulding tools. Each year the number and complexity of plastic parts grows and the pressure to produce the injection moulding tools in shorter time and to achieve the required part quality increases. Injection moulding tools are expensive to manufacture and they are usually only used in mass production. Normally, several operations/machines are required, and it takes a long time, from several weeks to a few months, to produce them. Sometimes, mistakes in the design or in the mould machining can extend the production time. Any development that leads to reducing the production time of moulding tools or improving the moulding process and its efficiency has significant economic effect. The SLM process could be a key technology – providing cost and performance-efficient solutions for the mould making industry.

Using the SLM technology as a manufacturing process for producing injection moulding tools or inserts has been shown to be beneficial in three areas:

(1) the freedom of the part's geometry that SLM provides [1]-[2];

(2) the reduction of the production cycle time [3]-[5];

(3) the ability to build conformal cooling channels along with the 3D geometry of the tools [6]-[7].

Creating a conformal cooling system is restricted by the geometry of the injection moulding tools and inserts. In tools or tool areas where it is not possible to design conformal cooling channels, the cooling process depends mainly on the thermal conductivity of the mould's material. Alternative material or design solutions are needed to help in these cases for making the moulding process more efficient and accurate. The weakness of all laser-based freeform manufacturing processes is the huge consumption of time for building large solid parts, since only considerably small quantities of material can be processed per unit time. This can be improved significantly by employing the ability of the SLM technology to build cellular structures. SLM can create specific internal cellular structures simultaneously when producing moulding tools with complex external design and conformal cooling channels. A cellular type interior will reduce the production cycle and can contribute to the thermal management of the moulding process. The cooling portion of an injection moulding time can represent up to 75 % of the total cycle time. This number shows how important any reduction of the cooling time is. Better cooling also contributes to the quality improvement of the plastic parts. With SLM built skin/core structure, material is only used where the designer requires it in order to correspond to the load.

Cellular metal structures have been used in different industrial applications such as light constructions, heat exchangers, reconstructive surgery, chemical, automotive and aerospace industries. They possess valuable characteristics such as low density, high strength, good energy absorption, good thermal and acoustic properties [8]-[9]. These advantageous characteristics of the cellular structures make them desirable but the difficulties of producing them limit their applications. The new layer-additive technologies such as Direct Metal Additive Manufacturing technologies, Electron Beam Melting, Direct Metal Laser Sintering, and Selective Laser Melting (SLM), enable manufacturing free-form solid parts using laser technology and layers of metal powder. SLM gives the opportunity to produce complex parts from engineering materials (stainless steel, tool steel, titanium alloy, cobalt-chromium) in a short lead time, directly from 3D CAD data. This gives the designers freedom to use the cellular materials where they are needed creating better product functionality without sacrificing their mechanical quality.

The use of a cellular material for injection moulding tools is motivated by the desire to utilise the capabilities of SLM technology for fast building of 3D complex geometry and to improve the thermal management of the injection moulding process. This paper presents the preliminary results of the design and analysis of selected SLM built cellular structures, that are considered suitable as a core material for injection moulding tools.

INVESTIGATION OF DESIGN AND MANUFACTURE OF CELLULAR-TYPE STRUCTURES FOR INJECTION MOULDING TOOLS

2.0   Cellular Structures for Injection Moulding Tools

Solid cellular materials are classified as stochastic and ordered [8]. Stochastic materials, such as solid foams can have excellent heat- and sound- insulation properties and possess the ability to absorb a lot of energy. Ordered cellular materials, such as honeycombs and truss structures have great mechanical properties. They are widely used to enable the design of light structures, for creating unidirectional fluid flows, for absorbing the energy of impacts, to facilitate thermal transport across faces. The advantages of ordered cellular structures that make them desirable in injection moulding tools are their strength-to-mass ratio, and their high surface-to-mass ratio that defines their excellent heat transfer characteristics [9]-[10]. The ordered cellular structures provide consistent mechanical parameters of the part and can be implemented in moulding tool design.

Two types of ordered cellular structures were analysed in this research: honeycombs and truss. Honeycombs are often used because of their excellent compressive strength-to-weight ratio and high bending stiffness [8]. Truss structures or as they are also called lattice structures, appear to be mechanically competitive alternatives to prismatic honeycombs. It has been foreseen that these lattice structures could be of particular interest for injection moulding design because of their fully open interior structure which could assists multifunctional applications. The lattice core of injection moulding tools can be capable to supporting significant structural loads while also facilitating cross flow heat exchange. Fig. 1 illustrates parts with internal honeycomb or truss cellular structures.

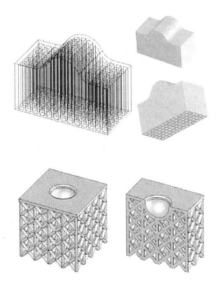

Fig.1.   Examples of parts with squire honeycomb and with truss cellular structures.

2.1   Cellular Structures Design Analysis

The design of cellular core structure for injection moulding tools have to combine the material mechanical properties and the functional requirements. This approach integrates design requirements and manufacturing capabilities. The chosen cellular structures have to correspond to three groups of requirements:

1. Geometry:
   - Cellular architecture: truss or honeycombs;
   - Low relative density;
2. Mechanical properties:
   - Adequate strength;
   - Maximum displacement of the pressure contact surfaces;
3. SLM Manufacturability:
   - Cellular elements not inclined at less than 45° [from PDR experience];
   - Diameter of the strut more than 0.1mm [11].

The geometry requirements have been defined from the general characteristics of cellular materials and from the desire to introduce the cellular structure as a thermal management element during the moulding process. The mechanical requirements are derived from the moulding process and from the quality requirements towards the tooling. The SLM limitations are derived from the capabilities of this layer-additive technology.

Rehme and Emmelmann [11] investigated the manufacturability and scaling laws for mechanical properties of periodic lattice structures. The layer-additive manufacturing process used in this work is SLM. Eight different unit cell types are presented that can be produced by SLM technology. Following the results reported in [11] we selected two designs that demonstrate the best compression stress results and that are SLM feasible. These two designs shown in Fig. 2 a) and b), posses low relative density, they response well to compressive load and they do not have struts that are orientated at an angle less than 45° with respect to the build plane. Lattice truss structures have several of these flow directions and very high specific surface area for contact with a coolant flow. As a result, they can provide efficient heat removal which is valuable for the injection moulding process. On the other hand honeycomb structures shown in Fig. 2 c) and d) although posses higher density than the truss cell structures, they have excellent mechanical characteristics under compression loading and high bending stiffness [8]. They are suitable for SLM production if they are vertically orientated as shown in Fig. 2. The four structures are named as follow: a) wall centred truss structure, b) half-wall centred truss structure, c) square honeycomb structure, and d) hexagonal honeycomb structure.

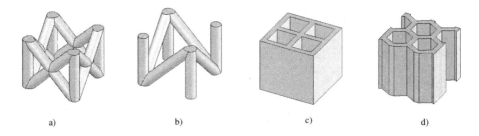

a)   b)   c)   d)

Fig. 2.   The selected cellular units.

INVESTIGATION OF DESIGN AND MANUFACTURE OF CELLULAR-TYPE STRUCTURES FOR INJECTION MOULDING TOOLS

2.2   Sample Design

The four selected designs (Fig.2) were analysed for their abilities to respond to the pressure during the moulding process. There were two recommendations to the preliminary design that has been generated for all four selected cellular structures. Firstly, the strut diameter or the honeycomb wall thickness has been defined as 2mm [11]. The second design recommendation concerns the width of the cellular units. In order to coordinate the width of the cells with the maximum diameter of a cylindrical surface that SLM can produce without support, it has been accepted that the cell size has to be smaller than 7 mm. The second recommendation has been introduced such that the cellular structure can accommodate additional design elements that do not require support for SLM production. Any additional support will significantly reduce the fluid flow trough the cellular structure.

Commercial CAD software was used for constructing the samples. The cellular structures were created by patterning a unit sell and the generated models can be combined with other models. The sample models are cubic shape featuring 3 cells in each direction as illustrated in Fig. 3 a). The overall sample dimensions are 23x23x23 mm. As the modelled cellular materials will be used as internal structures in injection moulding tools, a skin element has been introduced to each cellular sample as it is shown in Fig. 3. b). In order to investigate the influence of the depth of the skin on the mechanical behaviour of the skin-cellular structures several samples were modelled with skin depth of 2 mm, 3 mm, 4 mm, 5 mm and 6 mm. The cellular samples have same overall element cell dimensions, but different relative density.

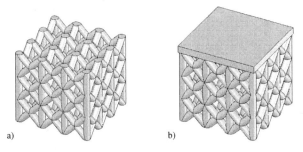

a)   b)

Fig. 3.   Models of wall centred samples without and with skin.

3.0   Mechanical Simulation and Results

After selecting the SLM manufacturable cellular structures, the second step for introduction of cellular structures in injection moulding applications requires mechanical analysis of the capabilities of the structure to satisfy injection moulding process demands. FEA is used for the structure analysis. The created cellular structures were analysed on compressive loading similar to the loading in injection moulding tools.

The average peak pressure that the contact surfaces experience is accepted in this study as 3.5 MPa. We applied a uniform pressure on the top surfaces of the samples. The samples are fixed in all 6 degrees of freedom. The material is Stainless Steel 316L with Modulus of Elasticity E=193 GPa, and yield strength 170 MPa. The FEA results of the four cellular structures were compared when applying the same boundary conditions. The clamped cellular samples were tested in compression using FEA simulation. For computational efficiency, due to the symmetry, only one-quarter of the samples need to be modelled. The maximum stress and the maximum displacement of the selected types of cellular structures are presented in Table I.

Table I: Comparison of the four cellular structures

	Solid	Wall-centered cells	Half wall-centered cells	Square honeycomb cells	Hexagonal honeycombs cells
Maximum stress (von Mises stress N/m³)	6.752×10^6	1.132×10^7	9.384×10^6	6.465×10^6	6.244×10^6
Maximum displacement (mm)	3.873×10^{-4}	3.698×10^{-4}	4.460×10^{-4}	3.918×10^{-4}	3.929×10^{-4}
Relative density	1	0.4302	0.2938	0.5664	0.5003

The FEA analysis results show that the maximum stress of the two lattice and two honeycomb structures are similar due to the close area size of the contact surfaces. The honeycombs maximum stress is similar to the stress in the solid body. The four structures have comparable maximum displacement which is low and demonstrates appropriateness of the chosen structures to support the compressive loading.

Then the skin element was introduced in the sample's design of the four types of cellular structures. Samples with 2mm, 3mm, 4mm, 5mm and 6mm horizontal skin have been analysed and the results for the maximum stress and displacement are presented in Fig. 4 with respect to the skin depth.

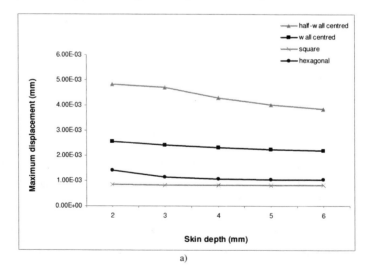

a)

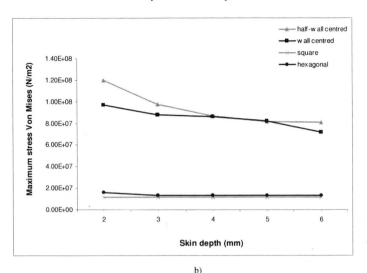

b)

Fig. 4.   Maximum stress and maximum displacement of the four structures with skin with respect to the skin depth

Although the stress and displacements levels shown in Fig. 4 of all four cellular structures are higher when applied skin compared to the same parameters in Table I when the structures are without skin, the trend is similar. Honeycomb structures demonstrate lower stress and displacement than the two truss structures. It is important to notice that all four structures show higher values of stress and displacements when thin skin is applied. After 4 mm skin depth the stress and displacement for each structure change a little. The FEA simulation with thicker skin up to 10mm was conducted and the trend is maintained. Taking this fact into consideration it could be concluded that there would not be a significant advantage for the mechanical characteristics of a part with cellular internal structure that has skin thicker than 4 mm. This fact is important for SLM produced parts, because the smaller quantity of solid part's areas means shorter machining time, less material, less energy.

In the second design of all four cellular structures it was required that their relative density would be the same. The relative density was set to 0.3, equal to the relative density of the half-wall centred structure. These equal mass structures were analysed under the same boundary conditions as the previous set. The results from FEA simulation are presented in Table II. Even with thinner walls in order to achieve the required relative density, the honeycomb cellular structures demonstrate better mechanical properties. However, the two truss structures also satisfy the mechanical requirements according the simulation. Which type of the cellular structure will be used in injection moulding tool design depends on the design ideas and on which of the structures will demonstrate better conditions for coolant flow during the injection moulding process.

Table II: Comparison of the four cellular structures with the same density.

		Wall-centered cells	Half wall-centered cells	Square honeycomb cells	Hexagonal honeycombs cells
Maximum stress (von Mises stress N/m³)		1.207×10^7	9.384×10^6	5.791×10^6	6.763×10^6
	With 2 mm skin	1.116×10^8	1.199×10^8	1.885×10^7	2.582×10^7
Maximum displacement (mm)		3.907×10^{-4}	4.460×10^{-4}	3.916×10^{-4}	3.835×10^{-4}
	With 2 mm skin	3.255×10^{-3}	5.258×10^{-3}	1.558×10^{-3}	1.997×10^{-3}
Relative density		0.3070	0.2938	0.3051	0.2981

These structures are uniform and capable of supporting the pressure that is experienced during the moulding process. They create repeatable and predictable parts characteristics. At the same time the density of the cellular material can contribute to the better cooling of the moulding. Some design optimisation approaches [12]-[13] create variable topology of the cellular structures in order to put material only in these positions where it is required from the load. This approach is efficient when the cellular structure is used only to correspond to certain loading. In our case the idea is to use the cellular structures as an active element of the cooling phase of the injection moulding process it is required that the cellular structure creates uniform coolant flow. If the density of the cellular material is variable it will create more material resistance in some areas and will slow the fluid flow.

4.0   Conclusion

The idea of applying the cellular material in injection moulding tools is motivated by the capabilities of SLM technology for fast building of 3D complex geometry and by the desire to improve the functionality of the moulding tools. Due to the limitations of the traditional manufacturing processes, the geometry and the applications of the cellular structures are restricted.

This study investigated selected cellular structures which are SLM manufacturable and satisfy the design requirements. The preliminary investigation highlights the feasibility of such cellular structures for the purpose of injection moulding tooling. Lattice cellular structures appear to be mechanically competitive alternatives to prismatic honeycombs structures. It has been illustrated that lattice core of injection moulding can be capable of supporting significant structural and process loads while also could facilitating cross flow heat exchange. Next steps of this research will be physical testing, thermal simulation and thermal physical testing [14].

The combination of structural strength with the potential for better thermal conductivity of the cellular core structure and the ability of SLM technology to build complex 3D shapes makes the proposed approach very desirable for injection moulding tooling. Future work will investigate the thermal characteristics of the cellular lattice structures and their application in injection moulding tools.

References

[1]   Regenfuss, P., Hartwig, L., Klötzer, S., Ebert, R., Brabant, Th., Petsch, T. and Exner, H., 2005. Industrial freeform generation of micro tools by laser micro sintering, *Rapid Prototyping Journal*, 11/1, pp. 18-25.

[2]   Santos, E. C., Shiomi, M. Osakada, K. and Laoui, T., 2006. Rapid manufacturing of metal components by laser forming, *Int. J. Mach. Tools & Manufact.*, Vol. 46, pp. 1459-1468.

[3]   Rehme, O. and Emmelmann, C. Rapid manufacturing of lattice structures with SLM, *Proceedings of SPIE*, Vol. 6107, February, 2006.

[4]   Mognol, P., Rivette, M., Jegou, L. and Lesprier, T., 2006. A first approach to choose between HSM, EDM and DMLS processes in hybrid rapid tooling, *Rapid Prototyping Journal*, 13/1, pp. 7-16.

[5]   Rännar, L-E., Glad, A. and Gustafson, C-G., 2007. Efficient cooling with tool inserts manufactured by electron beam melting, *Rapid Prototyping Journal*, 13/3, pp. 128-135.

[6]   Levy, G. N. and Schindel, R., 2002. Overview of layer manufacturing technologies, opportunities, options and applications for rapid tooling, *Proc. IMechE, Part B: Journal of Engineering Manufacture*, Vol. 216 (12), pp. 1621-1634.

[7]   Norwood, A.J., Dickens, P.M., Soar, R.C., Harris, R., Gibbons, G., and Hancel, H., 2004. Analysis of Cooling Channels Performance, *Int. J. Computer Integrated Manufacturing*, 17(8), pp.669-678.

[8]   Gibson, L.J. and Ashby, M.F., 1997. Cellular solids: Structure and properties, 2nd edition, Cambridge University Press, 1997.

[9]   Haydn, N. C. and Wadley G., 2006. Multifunctional periodic cellular metals, *Philosophical Transactions of the Royal Sosiety A*, 364, 31-68.

[10] Liu, C. Z., Sachlos, E., Wahl, D.A., Han, Z. W. and Czernuszka, J. T., 2007. On the manufacturability of scaffold mould using a 3D printing technology, Rapid Prototyping Journal, 13/3, 163-174.
      Kooistra, G.W. and Wadley, N.G.H., 2007. Lattice truss structures from expanded metal sheet, *Materials & Design*, 28, 507-514.

[11] Rehme, O. and Emmelmann, C., 2007. Cellular Design for Laser Freeform Fabrication, Proceedings of the Forth International WLT-Conference on Lasers in Manufacturing 2007, Munich, June 2007.

[12] Watts, D.M. and Hague, R. J., 2006. Exploting the design freedom of RM, *Solid Freeform Fabrication Proceedings, Solid, Freeform Fabrication Symposium*, Atlanta, Texas, August, 2006, p.656-667.

[13] Wang, H. V., Williams, C. and Rosen, D.W., 2006. Design synthesis of adaptive mesoscopic cellular structures with unit truss approach and particle swarm optimisation algorithm, *Solid Freeform Fabrication Proceedings, Solid Freeform Fabrication Symposium*, Atlanta, Texas, August, 2006, p.433-455.

[14] Tsopanos, S., Sutcliffe, C.J. and Owen, I., 2005. The manufacture of micro cross-flow heat exchangers by selective laser melting, Proceedings of Fifth International Conference on Enchanced, Compact and Ultra-Compact Heat Exchangers, NJ, USA, September, 2005, p. 410-417.

INVESTIGATION OF DESIGN AND MANUFACTURE OF CELLULAR-TYPE STRUCTURES FOR INJECTION MOULDING TOOLS

The 6th International Conference on Manufacturing Research (ICMR08)
Brunel University, UK, 9-11th September 2008

PROCESS OPTIMIZATION AND METAL FLOW ANALYSIS OF DIRECT AND INDIRECT EXTRUSION OF ALUMINIUM USING FEM SIMULATION

Longjiang Niu, Terry Sheppard, Xavier Velay

School of Design, Engineering and Computing, Bournemouth University, UK

Abstract

Extrusion is the normal process to transform a cast and homogenised billet into an intricate profile. Currently the design of extrusion dies and operation of the extrusion press is generally based on a process of educated trial and error. Understanding the way in which the material flow during hot extrusion of aluminium alloys is therefore essential if the process is to be intelligently controlled. Material flow is greatly affected by the friction between the tool and billet interface. In this paper both direct extrusion and indirect extrusion are simulated using the finite element method (FEM). The material behaviour is defined with a viscoplastic constitutive model and some of the tools are meshed in order to enhance the simulation of both friction and heat transfer between the work piece and the tooling. The simulated velocity fields for both direct and indirect extrusions are discussed and compared with experimental results. Advanced numerical techniques are used to trace backward and forward discrete particles of the workpiece. The effect of friction on the material flow is discussed. Back-end defects are simulated and practical methodologies are derived to minimize such defects using FEM. Peak loads, temperatures and strain rate distribution are also compared between direct and indirect extrusions. Numerical subroutines have been developed and integrated to the FEM software in order to introduce the possibility of prediction of microstructural evolution. The results of such numerical simulations to increase productivity within the extrusion industry are currently limited only by the lack of sufficient physical metallurgical detail and by obstacles preventing the FEM simulation to be directly applied. This aspect is discussed in some detail.

Keywords: Aluminium extrusion, FEM, Material flow, Microstructure.

1.0   Introduction

Although extrusion is a modern process (rolling and forging being much older) it precedes the development of aluminium which was only commercially available following the invention in 1886 [1, 2], concurrently by Hall and Heroult, of the electrolytic process to extract the metal from bauxite. The conventional extrusion process is complex. Among the industrial methods by which aluminium billets can be transformed to exceedingly complex shapes, extrusion has no rival and has firmly established itself as a major industrial process [3-5].We have noted that almost since the inception of the extrusion process there have been two modes of operation. The difference between the two modes is provided in great detail in previous studies [6, 7]. The major difference is that in the indirect mode there is no friction between the billet and container whereas in the direct mode the outer shell of the billet is assumed to move relative to the container as the extrusion proceeds [8, 9]. Thus in direct extrusion the surface of the billet is sheared at, or slides along, the container wall. In every case, part of the extrusion load, depending on the length of the billet, is expended in overcoming the friction between the billet and container, or in shearing the inner material from the slower-moving peripheral layer adjacent to the container wall. As one would expect, this results in considerable variation in flow behaviour which is discussed in this paper.

Metal flow in the extrusion process is an important factor controlling the mechanical properties of the extruded products. The description of material flow during the extrusion process has been the focus of much interest in aluminium alloys in general [10-14]. Studies of the material flow during extrusion are well documented in literature. The techniques range from commonly used ones such as gridded billets, introducing pins of an aluminium alloy into the as-cast billet and then grinding and etching the surface after the end of the extrusion[12, 13, 15], to marking grids within the initial billet [10, 11, 16, 17]. These techniques did achieve practical results describing metal flow. For a more comprehensive understanding of the extrusion process, numerical simulation with Finite Element Method (FEM) is now a powerful tool. The simulation of an extrusion sequence in an industrial environment consists principally of a thermo-mechanical analysis of the plastic deformation [18-20]. At present many researches show that with some commercial FEM codes, metal flow and other variables (such as temperature, pressure, strain, evolution of microstructure) could be well predicted. For instance , Deform 3D was employed to investigate the metal flow during the extrusion of AA7003 aluminium alloy with the influencing factors of billet temperature, extrusion load and surface quality [21]. Forge3 has been used to predict the required extrusion load, extrudate temperature and metal flow [10, 16]. Forge2 also successfully predicted, extrusion load, temperature, pressure, the evolution of the volume fraction recrystallised (Xv), subgrain size and internal dislocation density of the extrudate [22, 23].

Using Forge® (the latest version of Forge2 and Forge3), the present study investigated the flow of AA2024 aluminium alloy during both direct and indirect extrusion processes. Attention was paid mainly to the mechanism of formation of the surface of the extrudate. An advanced technique, called 'prior-sensors', was activated to show the back-end defects and practical ways to minimise undesired features were developed. A subroutine was coded and integrated into the code to visualise the change of the temperature compensated strain-rate (Z) during extrusion. Experimental extrusion data [15] agrees well with simulations result.

2.0   Simulation and Experimental Details

2.1   Finite Element Modelling Formulation

FEM simulation is used in the present study. Forge is implicit and fully thermo-mechanically coupled and with automatic meshing and remeshing capabilities. Material flow is based on Lagrangian descriptions. For hot extrusion, the elasticity effect can be ignored and hence the most economical constitutive laws are purely viscoplastic approximations [24]. The Zener-Hollomon parameter Z is used to describe the flow stress:

$$Z = \dot{\bar{\varepsilon}} \exp\left(\frac{\Delta H}{GT}\right) = \left[A\, Sinh\alpha\sigma\right]^n \tag{1}$$

where $\dot{\bar{\varepsilon}}$ is the mean equivalent strain rate and in practical terms is governed by the extrusion ram speed whilst ΔH is the activation energy for the material and is a function of alloy content, dispersoid and precipitate distribution. G is the universal gas constant and T is the temperature of the billet at the relevant location. The flow stress may then be written as follows where A, α, n are constants specific to each alloy:

$$\bar{\sigma} = \frac{1}{\alpha} Ln \left\{ \left(\frac{Z}{A} \right)^{1/n} + \sqrt{\left(\frac{Z}{A} \right)^{2/n} + 1} \right\} \qquad (2)$$

2.2   Material and FE Model

The aluminium alloy AA2024 was chosen as the material for all direct and indirect simulations. The alloy composition is given in Table 1. For the aluminium alloy AA2024, ΔH=148880J/mol, A=3.252x10^8, α =0.016, n =4.27 [25].

Table 1: Chemical composition of alloys (wt %)

alloy	Cu	Mn	Mg	Fe	Si	Zn	Ti	Cr	Al
AA2024	4.66	1.35	0.069	0.19	0.08	0.02	0.01	--	Balance

In direct extrusion, the ram pushes the billet downward through the die land to obtain the designed shape and properties. The container and die are fixed in this case (Fig.1). Whilst for indirect extrusion, the container and ram are fixed; the die moves vertically upwards in this configuration.

To reduce the computer analysis time, ram, container and die are assumed to be rigid, which means there is no elastic deformation of the tools and a single temperature value is assigned to each component during thermomechanical coupled computation. The radius of die corner is 1mm. The mesh size is a set value of 4mm with a meshing option of 'fine front' value of 2mm. This allows finer meshes near the surface of the billet or at the die corner (as shown in Fig. 1). Six-node triangle elements are adopted to discretise the billet. Each element side is described by a second order curve. The heat transfer coefficient between the billet and tools (die, ram and container) is set as 20000Wm^{-1}k^{-1}. The convective heat transfer coefficient is 10Wm^{-1}k^{-1}. The emissivity is chosen as 0.05. The Tresca friction law is adopted. The friction factor (0≤m≤1) on the ram/billet is 0.4, and 0.85 for the container/billet. For the die, according to Paterson's study [26], the friction factor on the die land contact region is much lower than that in other contact regions, in this study, the friction factor within the die land/billet interface is 0.1, and 0.8 for the remaining part of the die. Twenty eight sensors are used to easily visualise the metal flow. This is shown Fig. 4 for (a) direct extrusion and (b) indirect extrusion.

2.3   Extrusion Experiments

Experimental data are taken from Subramanian's experiments [15]. Extrusion was performed on a 5MN press operating with tooling set up for direct and indirect extrusions. Both extrusion ratios are 40:1, ram speed is 5mm/s and 3mm/s for direct and indirect extrusions respectively. The initial billet temperature was 400ºC and the temperature for tools is 350ºC. The billets were 75mm in diameter and 95mm long and were heated in an induction heater. The container was hydraulically lowered into position and the ram removed to its highest point. Two semi circular rings were placed on top of the container to prevent any damage to the main ram. The hot billet was transferred from the induction heater into the container. A pressure pad was dropped on top of the billet. The ram was then lowered. The procedure for indirect extrusion was essentially the same.

3.0   Results and Discussion

3.1   Evolution of Extrusion Pressure and Temperature

Fig. 2 compares the extrusion pressure/ram displacement diagrams obtained from the direct and indirect FEM simulations. The load loci differ for the direct and indirect extrusion but follow a similar pattern. As expected the indirect mode exhibits a pressure which is always lower than that in the direct case with a maximum difference of 0.63MN at the peak load. The difference is most pronounced during the period when the loads increase from zero to their peak loads; the 'steady state' region being attained earlier in the indirect case. Most certainly this is because the dislocation density will be lower in the indirect case. One interesting point is that the pressure rise at the finish of the ram stroke commences at 82mm for the direct case and is 87mm in indirect extrusion. This indicates that the discard depth should be 13mm for direct extrusion and 8mm if we are able to use an indirect press. This represents a small but significant increase in productivity. The reason for this would appear to be obscure since the direct billet will contain an undeformed dead metal zone which is potentially softer than material in the indirect billet at a similar location. However in direct extrusion the material will encounter greater friction along the die face than does the indirect billet.

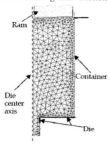

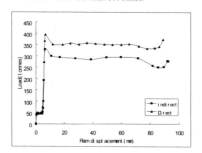

Fig. 1.   FEM model   Fig. 2.   Extrusion pressure/ram displacement

The predicted peak load for the direct extrusion load 394.43 tons is exactly the same as the load from experiment, 394 tons. Whilst the predicted peak load of the indirect extrusion exceeds the experimental measurement by 17%, this largely because of possible overestimation of the friction between the billet and tools and or an underestimation of the heat transferred across the die face.

The predicted temperatures at a ram displacement of 65mm are shown in Fig. 3. The results show that with the same initial temperature, extrudates in both direct and indirect extrusion experience a considerable temperature rise. This is greater and more acute for the case of direct extrusion. However the distributions have a similar pattern, the contours are almost the same if we turn the indirect extrusion map upside down, in which the temperature of the extrudate increased most, the farther it is from the die exit, the lower the temperature is, the lowest temperature appear at the corner farthest from the die exit in the billet. Critically the final temperature of the extrude appears to be determined by the die-entry radius. However the lower final temperature in the indirect case will result in fewer propensities for damage to the surface of the extrudate and/or the possibility to utilise greater extrusion speeds.

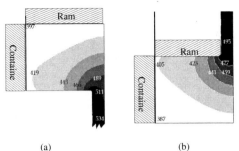

(a)   (b)

Fig. 3.   Temperature distribution for (a) direct and (b) indirect extrusions.

3.2   Metal Flow and Surface Formation

To clearly show the metal flow, a simulation technique termed 'prior-sensor' method is used in this study. The initial positions of the sensors are shown in Fig. 4 for both the direct and the indirect extrusions. For convenience, they are denoted according to their position in row and column. For example, sensor (3,2) implies the sensor at the intersection of row 3 and column 2.

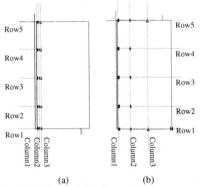

(a)   (b)

Fig. 4.   Sensors initial positions (a) for direct and (b) indirect extrusions.

Some frames are captured from the FE simulation and presented in Fig. 5. Fig. 5(a) and 5(b) demonstrate the material flow near the billet surface illustrated by the movement of the sensors. Fig. 5(a) shows that at a ram displacement of 61mm, sensor (4,3) has entered the extrudate and sensor (4,2) reached the die corner while little movement is observed for the sensors at row 1, 2 and 5. In Fig. 5(b), with an 85mm ram displacement, only the sensors at row 5 stay unmoved while two more sensors (sensor (3,3) and (3,2)) reach the extrudate and all the rest have been substantially displaced. Sensors of all three columns have entered the extrudate but they do not lie on the surface. Fig. 5(c) and 5(d) show the positions for all the sensors inside the billet at the ram displacement of 20mm and 54mm for indirect extrusion. In Fig. 5(c), it is clear that sensors (5,3) and (5,2) have already moved into the extrudate whilst those in column 5 remain on the billet/container interface. The surface of the billet at this stage can be seen to originate from row 5. After a ram travel of 55mm (Fig. 6(d)) sensors (4,2) and (4,3) have also entered the extrudate and those from column 1 are progressing along the die face and will form the surface of the extrudate. Clearly the indication is that as the ram proceeds to move downwards, sensors (5,1) and (4,2) will progress into the extrudate and the sensors which show least movement will be those four sensors in row 1.

**PROCESS OPTIMIZATION AND METAL FLOW ANALYSIS OF DIRECT AND INDIRECT
EXTRUSION OF ALUMINIUM USING FEM SIMULATION**

The 6th International Conference on Manufacturing Research (ICMR08)
Brunel University, UK, 9-11th September 2008

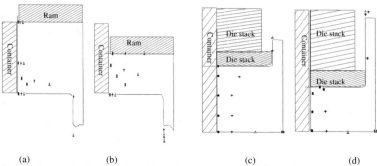

(a)   (b)   (c)   (d)

Fig. 5.   Position of sensors for direct extrusion at (a) ram displacement 61mm and (b) ram displacement 85mm; for indirect extrusion at (c) ram displacement 21mm and (d) ram displacement 55mm

Fig. 6 shows the sensors position in graphical form. For direct extrusion, in Fig. 6(a), it appears that none of the sensors become relocated to the surface of the extrudate. Column 1, the closest to the container, appears to be relocated to the ram face and hence will not appear in this depiction. It is thus clear that for direct extrusion those defects which are located on the billet surface (and in general are not removed by machining) will not harm the quality required in the finished extrude since their eventual location will be in the discard. Closest to the surface will be material originally located between the sensors 1 and 2. Reviewing both Fig. 5 and Fig. 6 leads to the conclusion that sensors from both columns 1 and 2 will also find their eventual location in the dead metal zone which is also destined for the discard of the extrusion process.

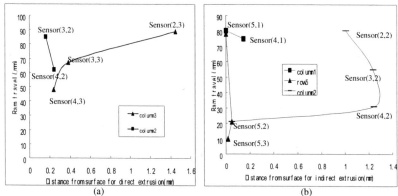

(a)   (b)

Fig. 6.   Relation between ram travel and sensor position from the extrudate surface (a) for direct extrusion and (b) for indirect extrusion

Fig. 6(b) clearly shows that the surface of the billet will most probably be formed from the material located in the designation of row 5. The figure indicates, however, that early in the ram stroke this material does not reach the surface of the billet which suggests that a 'dead metal zone' may be formed in the centre region of the die face as previously reported by Sheppard and Patterson [7]. This aspect clearly requires further definition which is currently ongoing. Combing information from both Fig. 5(b) and Fig. 6(b) indicates that in the indirect case material is also forced to the rear/billet interface and will form part of the discard. In this case, however, the feature is less critical since the billet is generally pre-machined. The fact that the surface appears

**PROCESS OPTIMIZATION AND METAL FLOW ANALYSIS OF DIRECT AND INDIRECT
EXTRUSION OF ALUMINIUM USING FEM SIMULATION**

to be largely formed from material located at the billet/die face interface indicates that careful machining may reduce production costs.

3.3   The Zener-Hollomon Parameter

The Zener-Hollmon parameter appears in many of the analyses necessary to determine the structure within the extrudate since it largely determines the subgrain size and by incorporating the 'Holt'[7] relationship may also predict the dislocation density. Fig.7 shows the distribution of this parameter throughout the extrude after 65mm ram travel. In direct extrusion in the vicinity of the die entry the parameter is at its maximum whilst in the dead metal zone the values are low. They are also of smaller magnitude at the rear of the billet. The fact that they exhibit a value above zero is a computer anomaly since the strain rate is very close to zero in these regions. The same comments apply to the indirect case where the die face and the material are the blocker/billet interface exhibit low values. This presents a problem in the incremental calculation of structural parameters (i.e. subgrain size, dislocation density, misorientation). This is thus one more fertile research area. Fig. 7 indicates substantial differences in the 'Z' parameter during direct versus indirect extrusion modes. Thus we may safely conclude that structure and properties resulting from the alternative processes will also vary.

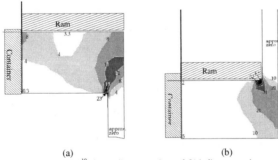

(a)   (b)

Fig. 7.   Distribution of parameter Z $(\times 10^{10})$ for (a) direct extrusion and (b) indirect extrusion

4.0   Conclusions

The pressure and temperature loci analysed for the alternative processes indicate that, for the indirect mode, productivity may be increased by utilising an extended ram stroke producing a slimmer discard. The values predicted for the predicted pressure necessary to produce the extrudate was very close to the experimental value. Predicted contours for iso-temperature are also very sensible.

For direct extrusion the original billet surface can be seen to reside either in the discard or in the dead metal zone at conclusion of the ram stroke. The surface is formed from the regions subcutaneous to the billet surface and located in a position between the experimental sensors defined by column 1 and 2. In indirect extrusion the surface is largely formed front the original billet face and not from the billet surface (which is most generally accepted). The authors consider that more thorough investigation is required on this particular point.

There are large differences between the origin of locations in the extrudate when comparing the two modes of extrusion.

The predicted distribution of the 'Z' parameter is acceptable and varies in the differing modes. It is concluded that incremental calculation of substructural parameters requires intensive study and at the present time there does not exist a suitable model.

Acknowledgement

The authors express their appreciation to the School of Design, Engineering and Computing at Bournemouth University for the provision of computing facilities. The experimental works performed by Dr. J. Subramanyan and Dr. S.J. Patterson is also gratefully acknowledged.

References

[1] Sheppard, T., *Extrusion of Aluminium Alloys*. 1999, Dordrecht, The Netherlands: Kluwer Academic Publishers.
[2] Castle, A.F., *Continuum and Structural Aspects of Aluminium Alloy Extrusion*, in *Imperial College*. 1974, University of London: London.
[3] Farag, M.M. and C.M. Sellars, *Flow-Stress in Hot Extrusion of Commercial-Purity Aluminum*. Journal of the Institute of Metals, 1973. **101**(May): p. 137-145.
[4] Sheppard, T. and P.J.M. Chare, *Extrusion of Atomized Aluminum Powders*. Powder Metallurgy, 1972. **15**(29): p. 17-41.
[5] Wood, E.P. and T. Sheppard, *Evaluation of shape factors for aluminium alloy extrusions*. Aluminium, 1975. **51**(12): p. 760-764.
[6] Mueller, K.M., M. Liu, and S.A. Burns, *Fully stressed design of frame structures and multiple load paths*. Journal of Structural Engineering-Asce, 2002. **128**(6): p. 806-814.
[7] Sheppard, T. and S.J. Paterson, *Direct and Indirect Extrusion of Aluminum-Alloys*. Metals Technology, 1982. **9**(Jul): p. 274-281.
[8] Chadwick, R., *The relevance of lubrication in extrusion* Metals and Materials, 1970. **4**(5): p. 201-207.
[9] Tuschy, E., *Differences in Flow Behaviour during Extrusion of Various Materials*. Zeitschrift Fur Metallkunde, 1971. **62**(7): p. 513-516.
[10] Flitta, I. and T. Sheppard, *Simulation of bridge die extrusion using the finite element method*. Materials Science and Technology, 2002. **18**(9): p. 987-994.
[11] Flitta, I. and T. Sheppard, *Nature of friction in extrusion process and its effect on material flow*. Materials Science and Technology, 2003. **19**(7): p. 837-846.
[12] Valberg, H. and T. Malvik, *Metal flow in die channels of extrusion investigated by an experimental grid pattern technique*, in *Extrusion Technology Seminar 96 II*. 1996: Chicago, IL, USA p. 17-28.
[13] Sheppard, T. and E.P. Wood, *Effect of Section Geometry on Extrudability of Al-Cu-Mn Alloy*. Metals Technology, 1980. **7**(Feb): p. 58-66.
[14] Clode, M.P. and T. Sheppard, *Formation of Die Lines during Extrusion of Aa 6063*. Materials Science and Technology, 1990. **6**(8): p. 755-763.
[15] Subramaniyan, J., *Extrusion of 2024 aluminium alloy sections*. 1989, Imperial College of Science and Technology.
[16] Flitta, I. and T. Sheppard, *On the mechanics of the friction druing the extrusion process*, in *7th international aluminium extrusion technology seminar*. 2000: Chicago. p. 197-201.
[17] Hou, J. and B. Bengtsson, *FE-analysis of inward flow of surface materials at the back end of billet during Al-extrusion*, in *7th international aluminium extrusion technology seminar*. 2000: Chicaco. p. 149-158.
[18] Dyja, H. and P. Korczak, *The thermal-mechanical and microstructural model for the FEM simulation of hot plate rolling*. Journal of Materials Processing Technology, 1999. **93**: p. 463-467.
[19] Kowalsky, U. and H. Ahrens, *FE-analysis of the recipient of an extrusion press applying microstructure-related material models*. Computers & Structures, 1997. **64**(1-4): p. 655-665.
[20] Meguid, S.A., G. Shagal, and J.C. Stranart, *3D FE analysis of peening of strain-rate sensitive materials using multiple impingement model*. International Journal of Impact Engineering, 2002. **27**(2): p. 119-134.
[21] Jo, H.H., et al., *Determination of welding pressure in the non-steady-state porthole die extrusion of improved Al7003 hollow section tubes*. Journal of Materials Processing Technology, 2003. **139**(1-3): p. 428-433.
[22] Flitta, I., T. Sheppard, and Z. Peng, *FEM analysis to predict development of structure during extrusion and subsequent solution soak cycle*. Materials Science and Technology, 2007. **23**(5): p. 582-592.
[23] Duan, X. and T. Sheppard, *Influence of forming parameters on static recrystallization behaviour during hot rolling aluminium alloy 5083*. Modelling and Simulation in Materials Science and Engineering, 2002. **10**(4): p. 363-380.
[24] *international conference on forging and related technology(ICFT'98)*. 1998: John Wiley & Sons Inc.
[25] Sheppard, T. and A. Jackson, *Constitutive equations for use in prediction of flow stress during extrusion of aluminium alloys*. Materials Science and Technology, 1997. **13**(3): p. 203-209.
[26] Paterson, S.J., *The direct and indirect extrusion of aluminium alloys*. 1981, Imperial College of Science and Technology: London.

**PROCESS OPTIMIZATION AND METAL FLOW ANALYSIS OF DIRECT AND INDIRECT
EXTRUSION OF ALUMINIUM USING FEM SIMULATION**

Product Life Cycle Management

The 6th International Conference on Manufacturing Research (ICMR08)
Brunel University, UK, 9-11th September 2008

DEVELOPMENT OF A CONSUMER END-OF-LIFE VEHICLE DATABASE SYSTEM

A. Sweetman, Q. Wang

School of Engineering, Durham University, Durham, U.K

Abstract

In this paper, different types of recovery technologies were identified and analyzed. An online database system has been constructed to store information on various vehicles and in particular information on vehicles 'green' credentials and has a secure area for editing and creation of vehicle models. The database system then utilises a comparison feature and a graphical interface to provide easy access for the consumer. This research will initially be wide ranging, but will then focus on any vehicle models that the consumer are using to aid the selection process. Where possible, information about components will be gathered from useful sources.

Keywords: End of life vehicles recovery techniques, online database system, green consumerism

1.0   Introduction

In the last few years environmental awareness has grown within society with increasing political debate and policies not only from the smaller political parties but also from the mainstream parties in the U.K. The Conservative, Labour and Liberal Democrats have taken more interest and are actively pursuing 'green' policies within their respective manifestoes.

As stated in Nourreddine's paper, there are over 14 million vehicles manufactured within the 15 original countries of the European Union (EU) [1]. Such high levels of production inevitably lead to a large volume of waste being produced with over 11 million vehicles reaching their End-of-Life (ELV) a year. The difference in the figures is primarily due to the exporting of high-end models to developing nations [2]. With an average recycling, reuse and recovery rate of ELVs of 75% this creates an estimated 2 Million Tones of potentially hazardous and toxic waste each year that is land filled in the EU [1, 3, 4].

2.0   The ELV Directive

In 1996 the European Commission began creating and researching legislation regarding a variety of waste streams, in particular ELVs [2]. This led in turn to the creation of the End-of-Life Vehicle (ELV) Directive

(2000/53/EC) in 2000 and the Reduction of Hazardous Substances (RoHS) and Waste Electrical and Electronic Equipment (WEEE) Directives in 2002 [5]. Even before the ELV Directive was created the automobile industry was one of the most heavily legislated industries in the EU with over 80 Directives affecting them [6]. Two further amendments were added to the ELV Directive by (2002/525/EC) and (2005/673/EC) in 2002 and 2005 respectively. These additions to the original proposals were the result of further investigation on the recovery of materials, hazardous materials and possible alternatives to the toxic and hazardous materials used in cars [7, 8].

Two Statutory Instruments implemented the ELV Directive into UK Law. Firstly Statutory Instrument (2003 No. 2635) laid down the original framework of legislation and was approved on October 10th 2003. Secondly Statutory Instrument (2005 No. 263) added the Extended Producer Responsibility (EPR) whereby the Original Equipment Manufacturer (OEM) has the financial and legal responsibility to carry out all ELV activities. The EPR came into force on January 1st 2007 for all vehicles [9, 10]. The ELV Directive created the following recycling targets:

Table 1: Reuse, Recycling and Recovery Targets Set Down in ELV Directive

Year	Reuse and Recovery	Reuse and Recycling
Pre Legislation		75%
2006	85%	80%
2015	95%	95%

The targets for vehicles produced before 1980 are lower than those shown in Table 1. The recycling and reuse target for such vehicles is set at 70% compared to 80% target for vehicles dismantled after the legislation came into force in 2006 [5]. The total reuse and recovery rate in for a vehicle produced pre-1980 is 75%, which is considerably lower than the 2006 and 2015 targets in the EU ELV Directive [5]. The figures for pre-1980 vehicles are lower as a large variety of materials were used in those vehicles and they suffered from the poor labeling on these parts, which makes recovery and recycling more difficult.

3.0   End-of-Life Vehicle Process

The main processes used for recycling are split into two distinct operations, which are dismantling and shredding. The components removed during dismantling are extracted for five main reasons: valuable materials; reusable; hazardous and toxic materials; damage shredding equipment; or a legal requirement. Examples of theses can be found in Table 2. The waste hierarchy of each operation is shown beside a diagram of the process in Figure 1.

Table 2: Components Typically Removed During Dismantling [11,12,13]

Category	Material
Valuable	Catalytic Converter & Battery
Reusable	Body Panels & Tyres
Hazardous & Toxic	Fluids and Oils
Damage Equipment	Air Bags
By Law	Tyres and Batteries

ELVs normally undergo a two-part process in the UK. Firstly an ELV is subjected to a dismantling operation at one of the UK's estimated 3,500 facilities [14]:

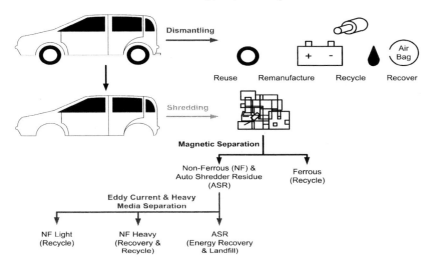

Fig. 1.   Diagram of ELV Process

On completion of the dismantling process the remainder normally referred to as a 'hulk' is delivered to one of the 38 automobile shredding facilities around the U.K. [14]. The vehicle is shredded and the chips are sorted using adapted mineral engineering techniques. The chips are sorted into firstly ferrous and non-ferrous fractions by magnetic separation. The ferrous fraction then undergoes a smelting operation where any impurities are removed.

After separation of the ferrous fraction, non-ferrous heavy metals and the auto shredder residue (ASR) are subjected to Eddy Current and Heavy Media Separation to split the different fractions. The light and heavy metals are sent to specialist recyclers for further processing. Historically the ASR was normally landfilled due to the complexity of composition and difficulties with cost effective recycling.

With higher targets being set in 2015 more novel and innovative techniques are surfacing to recycle and recover the ASR fraction. One method to reduce the volume landfilled is to undertake energy recovery. However there is considerable debate about its environmental credentials [11, 14, 15, 16]. The methods mentioned fit into the waste hierarchy as shown in Fig. 2.

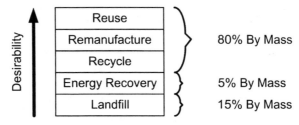

Fig.2.   Diagram of Waste Hierarchy (Adapted from 17)

DEVELOPMENT OF A CONSUMER END-OF-LIFE VEHICLE DATABASE SYSTEM

4.0 Online Database System Development

4.1 System Fields

From the literature review the following fields were included in the system. They can be roughly split into three main groups: basic vehicle information, vehicle performance and vehicle material composition. Although only the last category is critical to the ELV phase all the other fields are crucial to allowing a user to make important and reliable decisions.

Basic Vehicle Information: Make, Model, Version, Engine Size, Vehicle Dimensions, Cost, Country of Manufacture and Seats.

Vehicle Performance: Road Tax Band, MPG Urban, MPG Combined, and Grams of CO_2 per Kilometer.

Vehicle Material Composition: Vehicle Mass, Ferrous Metal, Non-Ferrous Light Metal, Non-Ferrous Heavy Metal, Glass, Tyres, Plastics, Fluids, Battery.

These categories were chosen as they contained information about the whole car and not just the end-of-life performance. Although the disposal of ELV is very important, the phase only lasts a few days and a car that performs well at the ELV stage but is environmentally unfriendly is undesirable hence the inclusion of the performance fields. The vehicle material composition is required to determine the ELV performance.

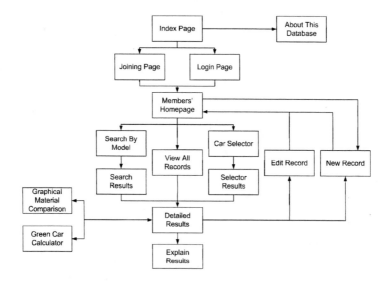

Fig.3.   Diagram of System Structure

4.2 System Structure

The basic site structure of the system is shown in Fig. 3. All the pages shown require a user to login for security and monitoring purposes except for the index page and about page on the top line of the diagram.

For this paper three main pages were highlighted. These were the member homepage, the car selector and the search results page.

The **member page** is the hub of the system. To access any area of the site a user must pass through this area. The screenshot in Figure 4 captures the members' page.

Fig.4.   Screenshot of Members' Homepage

The five main areas of the system that can be accessed from this page are:

Create New Record – This link begins a four page process dealing with each of the three basic categories on a separate page before allowing the user to review their information before submitting it to the online system on the final page.

Search for a Model – This link is designed for when the user has already decided on the vehicle that they wish to gather information on.

Car Selector – Is the subject of the Figure 5 and uses information from the user to enable the online system to select and recommend the most appropriate vehicles.

View All Records – This page displays all the vehicles held on the system for users who wish to see how much information is held on the system.

Edit Records – This page explains the procedure to edit records, which is currently limited to viewing the full detailed result of a vehicle and then selecting the editing feature.

The **car selector page** was developed to enable users to gather information about vehicles according to specifications that they have chosen. The screenshot of the car selector is shown in Figure 5. The fields that were chosen from the system to allow the user to select a vehicle were:

CO_2 per KM – This figure provides the in use environmental performance of a vehicle. This increasingly has become important for business users in the UK who are taxed depending on this figure. In the future Road Tax Bands are going to be reliant upon this figure and the best performing vehicles will be required to pay no road tax. An example of a vehicle that will pay no road tax is the new Volkswagen Polo Bluemotion, which just has a diesel engine. Lastly any users in the Congestion Charging Zone in London are required to pay extra amounts if the CO_2 per KM is too high and the vehicle does not have a hybrid facility on board.

Price Range – One of the most important factors in any new purchase is the cost of the vehicle as there is no point displaying vehicles that meet the other criteria but are too expensive for the user.

Engine Size – This feature for some users is important as some prefer more powerful vehicles and others prefer that their car has a smaller engine and is therefore slightly slower and more economic to run.

Fuel Source – Is an increasingly important factor in a new car purchase particularly in London where a hybrid vehicle may only attain 25 MPG and does not have to pay the congestion charge. Where, a non-hybrid vehicle that achieves 45 MPG does have to pay the congestion charge.

Seats – Users may be looking for large people carriers or small sports cars so this field enables the results to be narrowed down very simply.

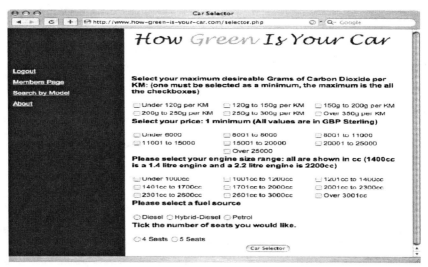

Fig.5.   Screenshot of the Car Selector Function

The **search results page** is very similar for the search by model, view all records and car selectors. The page screenshot in Fig. 6 shows the result of a research by model for Volkswagen Polo. The three different searches are required to be housed on three separate pages as the coding to retrieve the models from the database is very different. To keep the page as intuitive, simple and uncluttered as possible it does not show all the available options from the members' page.

Each view button on the right hand side contains hidden information regarding the model. There could be multiple makes and models on the system containing similar information. Each record is assigned an

DEVELOPMENT OF A CONSUMER END-OF-LIFE VEHICLE DATABASE SYSTEM

automatically incrementing catalogue number. The resultant unique catalogue number is the only information passed from the results page to the detailed results page. As this is a very small amount of information this improves the loading time of the search results page that, after commercialization, could contain a vast number of entries. When the view button is pressed the detailed results page of the designed model is displayed on a new page.

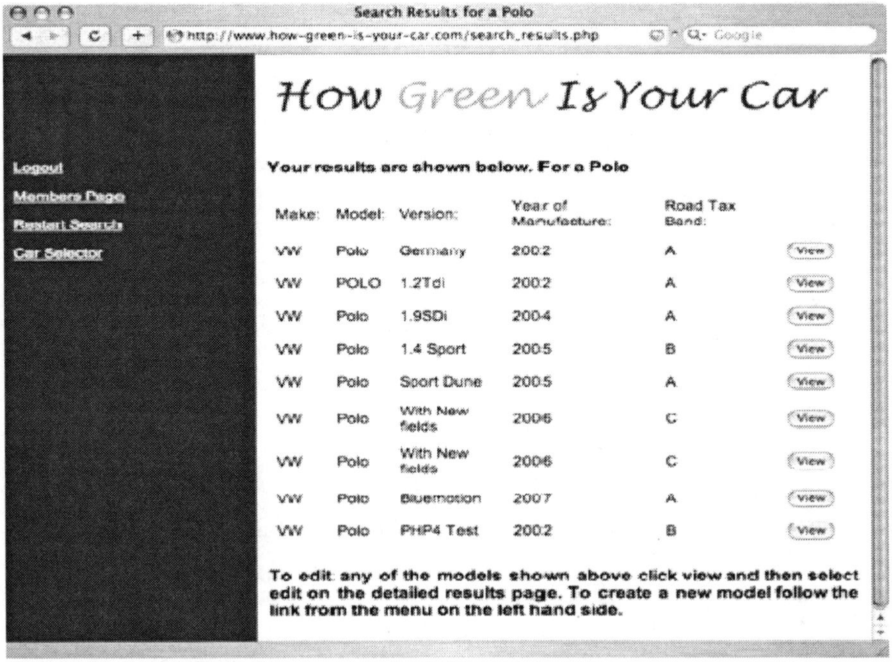

Fig.6.   Screenshot of Search Results Page

5.0   System Testing

Two types of testing were carried out on the system. These were compatibility testing and function testing. The compatibility testing was carried out to ensure that the website performed acceptably on the different web browsers on the market. This testing was required as the website was built using Mac OS X and Safari Web Browser. The compatibility tests prove that the system displays the same on four different web browsers that make up over 98% of web browsers used worldwide.

To prove the performance and capability of the system, the function testing was carried out to ensure that the results generated were accurate. Two separate programmes Microsoft Excel Spreadsheet and PHP were developed to check the values entered on the systems were the same. The only difference between the PHP and Excel programmes were the IF statements. In the PHP they were greater or equal to a number. In Excel it is not possible to create an IF statement with an equal statement within it as the software returns an error. This resulted in some errors when values entered into the system or excel checker programme were exactly equal to one of the various IF statement cut-off values. The online system performs the same as a separately created

Excel Programme. The information entered into the Excel Programme and the online system proved the system functioned correctly.

6.0   Conclusion

The main objective of the system was to provide the same level of information to car buyers as currently available to the dismantling industry. This was successfully achieved through the use of an online system and the various tools created to enable fact access and accurate information and intuitive displays and features.

The main problems that were encountered during the construction, development and propagation of the system were the difficulties of securing accurate and up to date information. It was hoped that increased variables and information entered by a user would lead to more accurate environmental assessment of the vehicles performance.

References

[1] M. Nourreddine., Recycling of auto shredder residue, *Journal of Hazardous Materials*, Vol 139, Issue 3, pp481-490, 2007.
[2] C. K. Smink, Vehicle recycling regulations: lessons from Denmark, *Journal of Cleaner Production*, Vol. 15, Issue 11-12, pp.1135-1146, 2007.
[3] W. A. Reinhardt., Drive towards compliance, *Waste Management World*, pp.55-62, July-August 2005.
[4] W.A. Reinhardt, Steer towards clarity, *Waste Management World*, pp. 63-72, November-December 2005.
[5] European Commission, End–of-life Vehicles 2000/53/EC
[6] E. J. Daniels, J. A. Carpenter Jr., C. Duranceau , et al., Sustainable end-of-life vehicle recycling, R&D collabration between Industry and the U.S. DOE, Journal of Management, Vol 56, No.8, pp28-32.
[7] European Commission, End-of-life-vehicles 2002/525/EC
[8] European Commission, End-of-life-vehicles 2005/673/EC
[9] UK Government, The end-of-life vehicles regulations 2003
[10] UK Government, The end-of-life vehicles regulations 2005
[11] T. E. Graedel & B. R. Allenby., Industrial Ecology and the Automobile, Prentice Hall, New Jersey, USA, 1998.
[12] DTI (now BERR) & DEFRA, Depolluting end-oflife vehicles, guidance for authorized treatment facilities, available from: http://www.defra.gov.uk/environment/waste/topics/pdf/elv-authorisedtreatment.pdf/ accessed 8 April 2008].
[13] Tyre Recovery Association, Used tyre management, available from: http://www.tyrerecovery.org.uk/page/used-tyre-management/ [accessed 8 April 2008]
[14] O. T. Forton, M.K. Harder & N. R. Moles., Value from shredder waste: Ongoing limitations in the U.K., *Resources Conservation & Recycling,* Vol. 46, pp104-113, 2006.
[15] D. Forelich., E. Maris., N. Haoues, et l., State of the art of plastic sorting and recycling: feedback to automobile design, *Minerals Engineering,* Vol. 20, Issue 9, pp902-912, 2007.
[16] M. R. Johnson & M. H. Wang., Evaluation policies and automotive recovery options according to the European Union Directive on end-of-life vehicles (ELV), *Proceedings of the Institution of Mechanical Engineers, Part D, Journal of Automobile Engineering,* Vol 216, No.9, pp723-739, 2002
[17] J. Gerrard. & M. Kandlikar., Is European end-of-life vehicle legislation living up to expectations? Assessing the impact of the ELV Directive on 'green' innovation and vehicle recover, Journal of Cleaner Production, Vol.15, pp.17-27, 2007.

"The 6th International Conference on Manufacturing Research (ICMR08),
Brunel University, UK, 9-11th September 2008"

INVESTIGATING FACTORS AFFECTING ERP IMPLEMENTATION IN MADE TO ORDER SME SECTOR — AN EXPERIENTIAL ACCOUNT

Aman Deep[2], Peter Guttridge [1], Dr. Samir Dani [2], Prof. Neil Burns [2]

1. **Guttridge Ltd.**

2. **Wolfson School of Mechanical and Manufacturing, Loughborough Univer**sity

Abstract

Over the past few years the number of large companies buying new ERP systems has reached saturation point. This has led to the ERP developers seeking instead other potential markets among Small to Medium Enterprises (SME). The Made to Order (MTO) scenario within the SME sector is one which is very capricious in terms of demand forecasting, lead times, routings etc. When selecting a system an organisation in such a segment needs a tailored methodology and a list of key target areas to consider.

This paper presents the findings of research carried out as part of an industrial project for selection and implementation of an Enterprise Resource Planning (ERP) system in a made to order Small to Medium Enterprise (SME) scenario. It presents an experiential account of the implementation process and highlights issues and recommendations for ERP implementation in SME's and specifically the MTO sector.

Keywords: ERP implementation, SME, Made to Order.

1.0   Introduction

ERP implementation is often the most significant and potentially amongst the most risky undertaking that any organisation faces [1]. Over the years it has become recognised as a process enabler and not just an IT function. Advancement in technology linking disparate functions of any organisation on an ERP platform offering increasingly luring functionality, steady reduction in software and hardware costs and better architecture platforms linking entire supply chains are often irresistible for Small to Medium Enterprises (SMEs) who are always on the lookout for competitive advantage to increase sales. However, it is easy to mistake these promises in thinking that ERP systems are a panacea for all SME maladies{ [2].

The Make to Order (MTO) sector within SMEs is one of specific interest for this study. The peculiarities of this niche have received little attention by research. MTO is an increasingly important sector within manufacturing, which is witnessing the change from mass production to mass customisation. Also SMEs are being forced to develop further in this sector as Make to stock (MTS) production models are either becoming leaner or are being offshored [3].

ERP adoption in this sector is riddled with uncertainties which make its implementation of an ERP system a very complicated task. Typical characteristics in MTO sector include an overall low volume of production including a higher variability in each product type, production schedules which need to be more predictive as well as flexible and are comparatively more unstable, a higher need for information sharing and higher local autonomy [4]. A lot of processes do not necessarily conform to the industry best practices and incorporating these practices often leads to, either extensive rebellion or otherwise to extensive customisation of software [5] which renders it difficult to upgrade or scale up at a later date. A prime example would be routings and operation times, which are absolute must for any ERP scheduling, are mostly unknown till very late in the cycle or just before it hits the shop floor when it is too late. This affects any schedules in the system and basically makes it near impossible for any sort of finite scheduling, available to promise and what-if calculations.

Indeed there are plenty of benefits to be had by a successful implementation as it offers a rare chance to revisit all the processes in the company, reengineer them if needed, identify areas and measures for improvement and essentially use technology to drive the growth envisioned by the management [6]. But it is also far from being a panacea as it is a tool and is needed to be run by individuals. SMEs lack well defined processes which is the basic premise on which all ERPs are based. Their skills shortage leads to the requirement of extensive conceptual training before any software training can begin [7]. Uncertainty in demand and multiple modes of operation make the process engineering all the more difficult.

This study investigates the peculiarities of this sector and highlights key concerns involved in an ERP implementation. This paper presents an experiential account of an implementation undertaken as a research project in this sector which may be useful to other companies in a similar situation and to ERP vendors venturing into this market.

2.0   Literature Review

ERP implementations have been studied in sufficient detail over the recent years particularly those relating to SAP R3 implementation. Various researchers [8],[9],[10],[4], [11], [12] have studied the entire process of selection and implementation in a case company but these are experiences of a large implementations which were managed (selection and implementation) by external consultancies. Other studies on the critical factors for ERP implementation are either focussed on large enterprises or are arguably generic in nature. [1] identifies the critical factors under the heading of strategic and tactical factors. Strategic factors include business vision, legacy systems, ERP strategy, management support and project plans. Technical factors include client consultation, personnel, communication, monitoring and trouble shooting.

With reference to ERP implementation in SMEs, the most noteworthy publication is by [2], who identified the main reasons for ERP implementation within SMEs . These were identified as being: (a) that the market for ERPs in large enterprises was saturated, (b) benefits accrued on account of electronic commerce, (c) as SMEs grow the ERP system can grow with them as they are more scalable and (d) growth is attributed to the fact that a majority of businesses are SMEs and therefore there is a huge market to be tapped. [5] has studied the factors affecting the adoption of ERP systems as a comparison between SMEs and Large organisations and lists the structural peculiarities of SMEs as the foremost obstacle to ERP implementations and also infers that the vendors addressing this segment lack strategy.

The work into studying peculiarities of SMEs includes identifying commonalities like leadership deficiency, financial restrictions, skills and expertise and organisational culture as barriers to process improvement techniques [3]. Although the study by [3] was focussed on process improvement through lean manufacturing these commonalities are equally applicable in implementing ERPs. Within SMEs, there is an increasing trend towards adoption of commercial packages but caution is directed towards ensuring the availability of special skills and project planning to conduct a successful implementation [13].

Although research has been conducted in ERP implementation a list of key target areas to be considered is missing. Further there is an absence of any research focusing on the Make to Order (MTO) sector. The twin concerns of SME and MTO pose concerns which are not yet covered in any depth. With due recognition to the available research referenced above, the author aims to focus only on the peculiarities of the SME MTO sector in this paper. Within SMEs, this research can be used as a check list to target areas of particular concern.

3.0   Research Methodology

This study compiles the experiential account of an action research methodology for case studies. [14] has suggested the use of single case study to study unique cases. The method employed for the study is one of action research defined as "studies where the author, usually a researcher, is a participant in the implementation of the system but simultaneously wants to evaluate a certain intervention technique....The strength is the in-depth and first hand understanding the researcher obtains. Conversely, a weakness is the potential lack of objectivity stemming from the researchers stake in effecting a successful outcome for the client organisation" [15].

Semi-structured interviews using open-ended questions to probe patterns, observations and documents related to change efforts were the main sources used for data. To ensure a wide scope of data all levels of the organisation and consultants were interviewed including top management, team members, consultants and end users. Also, a diary of daily events was maintained by the researcher over an eight month period to ensure accuracy of detail. All the data was analysed for recurrent themes, content analysis and triangulation techniques were used to prioritise themes. To expand on the experience secondary case studies were identified from available literature and participation in user forums and other web sources were used to combine the unique features.

This paper does not aim to prove or disprove any available research in the field of ERP implementation but to list down the factors identified requiring special attention from an actual experience of an implementation in the SME MTO sector.

4.0   Case Company and Background

The case company is a small sized manufacturing company (about 100 employees) located in the East Midlands region of the UK. Founded in 1962, they manufacture conveying equipment for moving bulk materials (eg wheat, flour, meals, pellets etc).Their turnover is approximately £10 million. Typical uses of the machines are in cereals storage plants, animal feed mills, pet food manufacturing plants, chemical factories and many other types of industries, both in the UK and abroad. The company operate out of a single manufacturing location.

About half of its production is based around standard range of machines, but each machine is customised to suit the client's needs (e.g length, outlets etc). Within additional extras the company is predominantly geared for a typical made to order scenario. But also comprises of a small but significant percentage of engineered to order machines. Also included in the portfolio is a strategic business unit (SBU) which offers the facility of laser cutting or subcontract operations for various customers to ensure best utilisation of spare capacity.

The company is representative of the section targeted in the study and conforms to the size and manufacturing processes of the market which has only recently opened up to the possibility of selecting ERP systems for achieving competitive advantage. Company A has witnessed a high and steady growth rate since 2000 and found themselves at a position where significant improvement was perceived by buying in/ upgrading their current MRP II system. The system in use at Company A was developed in house, initially on a DOS based platform. It was developed around the specific needs of the company and had been in use for the past 15 yrs. However lack of integration between systems and the increase in data resulting from the recent growth had challenged the company to investigate alternate options. The selection of the ERP system was conducted using a tailored methodology developed which is documented and at the time of writing this paper is awaiting publication [16].

5.0   ERP Implementation

For the Implementation the project owner was the company MD. The implementation was carried out using the Vendor specified implementation methodology. The implementation was led by a dedicated project manager and a team of eight senior users representing the different departments within the organisation. These members were responsible for mapping the requirements of their department to the functionality of the ERP system. All issues occurring throughout the duration were logged in an issues log. In SMEs it is difficult for team members to fully commit to the ERP implementation as resources are scarce and the team members have to multi-task in order to meet the requirements of their regular job functions and also the requirements of the ERP implementation. If this is not managed well it can lead to further issues with respect to meeting the implementation deadlines and objectives. Some of the key requirements to manage the implementation phase are summarised as:

1. Good communication between the implementation team members.

2. Adequate training for the team members with the new software.

3. Streamlining the business process in line with the requirements of the new system.

4. Adequate management support is critical, to permit team members to take time off from their regular activities for data analysis and user training.

5. Adequate time spent on Data cleansing, and Data migration to coincide with the requirements of the new systems. This may mean discarding some legacy processes. Creating the "Bill of Materials" as per the requirements of the new systems in a very important task.

6. Transferring the work-in-progress data to the new system in the correct format is crucial to get a successful "Go-Live" process.

7. One of the most important aspects of the implementation is sustaining the process once the initial implementation project is completed. This will require dedicated IT support to manage issues with the new

system. Most importantly, there is a requirement to have training for the users with trained user support and customised user manuals for the specific SME environment.

The following section presents an in-depth perspective on the requirements in each phase of the implementation process. These are primarily depicted for the SME MTO sector. For the purpose of analysis and identification the overall project has been subdivided into four generic stages with typical activities listed under each section. These are not specific for the vendor specified implementation methodology used, but represent typical stages of any implementation.

5.1   Stages (The Experiential Perspective)

Table I: Stage 1 — Plan

STAGE	ACTIVITIES	KEY CONCERNS SPECIFIC TO SME/MTO SECTOR
PLAN	Project Planning	• The Scope needs to be tightly defined as the chances of scope-creep are more likely as the organisation becomes familiar with capabilities of an ERP system during implementation. • Less likely to have experience of a formalised project management structure. • Less overall resources in terms of specialist people and time, • Presence of many variables and unknowns in procedures makes upfront budget planning base itself on many assumptions. • Special projects and strategic priorities are more likely to interfere in the allocation of time and resource.
	Communication Planning	• Management is more visible and have wider control. Needs a focussed communication channel specifically for implementation. • Less likely to have internal electronic communication channels like intranet.
	Theoretical Process optimisation	• Made to order scenario derives its advantage from offering flexibility of products. These gradually creep into existence of multiple process flow systems which would all need to be tied into the ERP system. • Difficulty in process mapping as there is an absence of standard times or routings. • Functional silos are more likely to exist. • Less evidence of standard operating procedures. • Difficulty in retrieving historical data for identifying common trends and analysis. • Some processes might differ from one customer to the other. • Information is more likely to be closely guarded.
	Data identification and initial mapping of headers	• Data mostly in disparate systems with little or no linkage. • Data might occur in databases which are out-dated and difficult to extract. • MTO scenario requires specialist fields and knowledge. The systems being replaced are either bespoke or have been customised over a long

STAGE	ACTIVITIES	KEY CONCERNS SPECIFIC TO SME/MTO SECTOR
		period which leads to a distinct difficulty in matching headers and finding fields pertaining to specialist knowledge, this eventually leads to customisation which needs to be properly documented and tracked in future releases. • More likely to have incomplete and insufficient data which need extensive reviewing and refining before it can be used.
	Designing new processes	• Often the introduction of a ERP system based on industrial best practices forces the organisation to implement new processes which were not mandatory before. • This can be a tricky process as it appears to require more work from the people and requires extensive training.
	Software installation	• SME organisations are less likely to have an elaborate IT infrastructure thereby incurring a significant hidden cost of implementation. • Lack of IT skills. • More risk involved with little backup systems for data and absence of a comprehensive risk assessment of the IT infrastructure.

Table II: Stage 2 — Design

STAGE	ACTIVITIES	KEY CONCERNS SPECIFIC TO SME/MTO SECTOR
Design	Implementation team training	• The requirement for senior users in resource allocation is extremely difficult due to individual dependant processes. • Make to order scenario usually lead to specialisations within a department therefore it becomes very crucial that every need of each end user is well understood by the department lead.
	GAP analysis and identifying modifications	• The gap between the theoretical optimum process and the offerings of the system can be difficult and being hasty can lead to mass modification. • SMEs are more likely to suffer from the "it's always been done like this" symptom. Therefore assessment of each process is often entails extensive brain storming and a clear vision.
	Business modelling (software based)	• Business modelling has to encompass a very broad range of product types, sales flow types, replenishment modes and production scenarios.
	KPI identification and reports modification	• SMEs are traditionally less reliant on information systems for improvement analysis and reports. • Little information is formally recorded or shared. • Less training on KPI identification and on the use of IS to generate these.
	Data Cleansing	• Data is more likely to lack a formal structure and may need more time and effort to cleanse. • Data is more likely to be redefined in a different manner for example

STAGE	ACTIVITIES	KEY CONCERNS SPECIFIC TO SME/MTO SECTOR
		sub assembly structures for parts, MRP replenishment details, price lists for purchase orders which can be both time consuming as well as a major change for the end users.

Table III: Stage 3 — Test

STAGE	ACTIVITIES	KEY CONCERNS SPECIFIC TO SME/MTO SECTOR
Test	Populate test database	• Less likely to have extensive IT skilled personnel to assist in populating database.
	Test data conversion	• Historical jobs, sales orders, BOM etc are crucial to the operation of made to order sector. These are not typically imported into ERPs as they require substantial import development time. • Data conversion needs to be tested for all subsequent downstream functions.
	Pilot	• Less familiar with integrated systems therefore pilots need to be more rigorous. • Issues like blank purchase orders, consignment stock, customer specific reporting are prevalent in SMEs and these need to be developed as an integrated system brings about its set of complexities which most SMEs are unfamiliar with. • In the make to order sector the prevalence of design changes, Bill of Material, warranty, job cancellations are more common. These changes can occur at any stage of the process and also after shipment.
	Print-off reports and forms for validation	• Report customisation also needs to be tailored to reflect unique fields and 'out of the box' reports are unlikely to be sufficient. • With little control over the demands of bigger organisations, reports and forms often need to be modified to suit the IS formats of clients.

Table IV: Stage 4 — Deployment

STAGE	ACTIVITIES	KEY CONCERNS SPECIFIC TO SME/MTO SECTOR
Deployment	End user training	• End user training involves both conceptual training and software training. Owing to lack of skills and trained workforce conceptual training can be extensive and consume a major portion of the training time. • Ease of use and general navigation need comparatively more attention to ensure easy flow through the system. • Often making a system tailored to suit the ease of use for a specific company entails a level of customisation albeit minor. These need to be tracked progressively as the system grows. • More likely to have same people across different functions. One person

INVESTIGATING FACTORS AFFECTING ERP IMPLEMENTATION IN MADE TO ORDER SME SECTOR — AN EXPERIENTIAL ACCOUNT

STAGE	ACTIVITIES	KEY CONCERNS SPECIFIC TO SME/MTO SECTOR
		wearing multiple hats. Therefore user training and assigning user privileges is more difficult
	Final pilot with full load	• Piloting with many users is more difficult within SMEs because of shortage of resources and backup procedures are not in place.
	Data cutover processes	• Transferring live orders, jobs, stock levels, balances needs to be carefully planned and involves a lot of preparation. These are tasks which again involves key users to be available full time on ensuring accuracy resulting in high dependence on backup roles to be in place.
	Go-Live	• Go live can lead to a sudden slowdown in business and teething issues which for an SME can pose as a major problem. • Internal and external support needs to be easily available on hand for a smooth transfer else it can lead to initial hostility towards the system. • The benefits may take longer to be visible as there is likely to be a longer period of familiarisation.

6.0   Conclusion

This paper provides valuable experiential insight into the details of ERP implementation, focussing on the peculiarities of the SME MTO sector. In particular it lists the experience gained from an action research, based on the foundations set by existing literature and identifies a list of key concerns for each section of the ERP implementation specific to a typical Made to Order SME. The major contribution from this study has been the identification of the key concerns specific to the MTO SME sector when embarking upon ERP implementation. The tables in the paper provide a ready reference of issues to consider throughout the 4 stages of implementation. The project has been successful in identifying the ERP system for the case company [16] and also implementing it. This paper hopes to provide a working guide for SMEs embarking on ERP selection [16] and implementation alongside the vendor specified implementation methodology.

Acknowledgement

The authors wish to acknowledge the assistance and support of the Knowledge Transfer Partnership scheme which is headed by the Technology Strategy Board, UK.

References

[1]   Holland, C. R. & Light, B. (1999). A critical success factors model for ERP implementation. IEEE Software, 16(3), 30-36.

[2]   Gable, G., (1999) "A conversation with Tom Davenport", *Journal if Global Information Management,* 8(2)

[3]   Achanga, P., Shehab, E., Roy, R. and Nelder, G. (2006), "Critical success factors for lean implementation within SMEs", *Journal of Manufacturing Technology Management,* 17(4), pp. 460-471.

[4]   Yen, H.R. and Sheu, C. (2004) "Aligning ERP implementation with competitive priorities of manufacturing firms: An exploratory study", *International Journal of Production Economics,* 92(3), pp. 207-220.

[5]   Buonanno, G., Faverio, P., Pigni, F., Ravarini, A., Sciuto, D. and Tagliavini, M. (2005) "Factors affecting ERP system adoption: A comparative analysis between SMEs and large companies", *Journal of Enterprise Information Management,* 18(4), pp. 384-426.

[6]   Beretta, S. (2002) "Unleashing the integration potential of ERP systems: The role of process-based performance measurement systems", *Business Process Management Journal,* 8(3), pp. 254-277.

[7]   Vinten, G. (1998) "Skills shortage and recruitment in the SME sector", *Career Development International,* 3(6), pp. 238-242.

[8]   Bingi, P., Sharma, M.K. and Godla, J.K. (1999) "Critical Issues Affecting an ERP Implementation", *Information Systems Management,* pp.7-14

[9]   AL-MASHARI, M. and AL-MUDIMIGH, A. (2003) "ERP implementation: lessons from a case study", *Information Technology & People,* 16(1), pp. 21-33.

[10] Braglia, M. , Petroni, A (1999) "Shortcomings and benefits associated with the implementation of MRP packages: a survey research", *Logistics Information Management,* 12 (6), pp 428-438

[11] Mandal, P. and Gunasekaran, A.,(2003) "Issues in implementing ERP: A case study", *European Journal of Operational Research,* 146(2), pp. 274-283.

[12] Gable, G. and Stewart, G., (1999) "SAP R/3 implementation issues for small to medium enterprises", *Proceedings of the 5th Americas Conference on Information Systems,* 1999, pp.779-81

[13] Koh, S. and Maguire, S., (2004) "Identifying the adoption of e-business and knowledge management within SMEs",. *Journal of Small Business and Enterprise Development,* 11(3), pp. 338-348.

[14] Yin, R.K. (1994), *Case Study Research, Design and Methods,* 2nd ed., Sage, Thousand Oaks, CA.

[15] Benbasat, I., Goldstein, D.K. & Mead, M.(1987), "The Case Research Strategy in Studies of Information Systems", *MIS Quarterly,* vol. 11, no. 3, pp. 369-386.

[16] Deep, A, Guttridge, P., Dani, S., Burns, N (2008) "Investigating factors affecting ERP selection in Made to Order SME Sector", *Journal of Manufacturing Technology Management,* Vol.19, No. 4

INVESTIGATING FACTORS AFFECTING ERP IMPLEMENTATION IN MADE TO ORDER SME
SECTOR — AN EXPERIENTIAL ACCOUNT

The 6th International Conference on Manufacturing Research (ICMR08)
Brunel University, UK, 9-11th September 2008

DECOMPOSITION OF AUTOMOTIVE MANUFACTURING MACHINES THROUGH A MECHANISM TAXONOMY WITHIN A PRODUCT LIFECYCLE MANAGEMENT FRAMEWORK

J F Darlington [2], R Darlington, R Harrison, L Lee[1], K Case and R H Weston

1. Ford Motor Co Ltd, Dunton Technical Centre, Basildon, Essex, SS15 6EE, UK

2. Wolfson School of Mechanical and Manufacturing Engineering, Loughborough University, Loughborough, Leicestershire, LE11 3TU, UK

Abstract

The automotive sector as with other manufacturing industries is under continual pressure from the consumer to deliver greater levels of product customisation at a higher quality and at reduced costs. Maintaining market position is therefore increasingly determined by a company's ability to innovate design changes quickly and produce greater numbers of product variants on leaner production lines with shorter times to market. In response manufacturers are attempting to accommodate product customisation and change through the use of reconfigurable production machines. Besides the need for flexibility, production facilities represent a significant investment for automotive manufacturers which is increasingly critical to commercial success; consequently the need to reduce costs through the reuse of assembly and manufacturing hardware on new product programs is becoming crucial.

The aim of this research is to enable production machines to be more easily and cost effectively built and subsequently reconfigurable through the adoption of a component-based approach to their implementation utilising virtual manufacturing tools such as Product Lifecycle Management (PLM). It is suggested that through the decomposition of manufacturing machines into standardised mechanisms and their associated data structures a revised business model can be defined. The mechanisms are classified and deployed as part of a consistent integrated data structure that encompasses product, process and plant information. An objective is to properly integrate manufacturing data with more established Product Data Management (PDM) processes. The main areas of research reported in this article are, (1) development of a method for identifying and mapping data producers, consumers and flow, (2) development of standardised data structures for the management of

DECOMPOSITION OF AUTOMOTIVE MANUFACTURING MACHINES THROUGH A
MECHANISM TAXONOMY WITHIN A PRODUCT LIFECYCLE MANAGEMENT FRAMEWO

961

manufacturing data within a PLM tool, (3) development of a taxonomy for the decomposition of manufacturing and assembly lines into a library of standard physical, logical and structural mechanisms and their associated interfaces. An automotive OEM case study is presented to illustrate the classification and management of production mechanisms focusing on an engine assembly line.

Keywords: data structure, component-based reconfiguration, Product Lifecycle Management, mechanism taxonomy.

1.0 Introduction

Product customisation is a principal theme of the modern manufacturing paradigm [1]. Companies aim to deliver a wider variety of products, while at the same time trying to use common product platforms to reduce component variations in order to realise the benefits of economies of scale. The nature of this dynamic environment increases the complexity of manufacturing systems [2]. The problems this creates can be clearly seen in the automotive sector where the exponentially increasing sophistication of vehicles is accompanied by greater complexity in product development, manufacturing, supply chain and logistics processes [3]. Manufacturers are striving to deliver product advances under the pressures of coordinating globally distributed networks of suppliers, production facilities and engineering teams is a considerable one. It is simply not the case that the most effective manufacturing plant or product designers will result in long term sector leadership [4]. Financial and organisational considerations are driving the leaders within the automotive sector to form influential and effective global partnerships [5]. Enabling the flow of information and material between distributed engineering teams, different engineering departments, computer systems and plants is of growing importance to the future success of the automotive sector.

At present automotive products are manufactured using well established engineering methods to high levels of quality and reliability. Development, design and operation management of manufacturing systems is similarly conducted using recognised methods, often paper based or through use of distributed heterogeneous tools, to manufacture production machines. Modern constructs in mechatronic engineering such as Flexible Manufacturing Systems (FMS) and Reconfigurable Manufacturing Systems (RMS) along with manufacturing methodologies such as Computer-Integrated Manufacturing (CIM), Concurrent Engineering (CE), Agile Manufacturing (AM) and Virtual Enterprises (VE) are all geared to enabling greater system agility. However the success of these methods depends on a shift in the manufacturing culture, greater integration of computer software to manage flexibility and a common model for representation and visualisation of machines for process engineers. It is also important that through the use of a Product Lifecycle Management (PLM) type approach, greater value can be gained from the growing 'toolbox' of digital manufacturing tools that have until now failed to provide the integrated solution required to model manufacturing systems.

The objective of this paper is to provide an insight how manufacturers are looking to exploit the growth of digital manufacturing technologies to realise commercial value. The paper goes on to explore the decomposition of manufacturing machines into base mechanisms; the resultant management of manufacturing

DECOMPOSITION OF AUTOMOTIVE MANUFACTURING MACHINES THROUGH A
MECHANISM TAXONOMY WITHIN A PRODUCT LIFECYCLE MANAGEMENT FRAMEWO

systems through use physical and information architectures and how these approaches can enable manufacturers to reconfigurable manufacturing facilities more quickly and reliably .

2.0   Reconfigurable Manufacturing Machines

Modularity is used to describe the use of encapsulated units to meet the dynamic changes being faced by their host system. It aims to identify independent, standardised, or interchangeable units to satisfy a variety of functions [6]. The term "modularity" indicates a high degree of independence among individual elements, excellent general usability, and seamless interfacing between elements. Separate element groups can be assembled into a hierarchical system, and the system can also be decomposed into the original element groups [2]. The challenge in developing reconfigurable systems is to incorporate system, software, control, machine and process factors into standard modules [7]. The potential benefits of modularity include: Economies of scale, increased feasibility of product/components change, Increased product variety, Reduced lead time, Decoupling tasks and the ease of product upgrade, maintenance, repair, and disposal.

3.0   The Role of PLM in a Manufacturing

Product Lifecycle Management (PLM) can be defined as the process of managing a product from its conception through design, manufacturing to service and end of life disposal, as shown in Fig. 1. Although the potential scope of PLM tool is very broad, in reality implementation within industry is more limited [8]. Most organisations utilise PLM software in its original PDM role at concept and product design stages for computer aided design (CAD) data management but there is limited use of PLM during manufacturing phases [9]. There have been a number of acronyms used by Product Data Management (PDM) vendors to describe lifecycle data management such as; Collaborative Product Development (cPDM), Collaborative Product Commerce (CPC), 3D Product Lifecycle Management (3D-PLM) and Product Knowledge Management (PKM) [9]. Although the term PLM is now considered standard terminology for engineering data management its applicability for manufacturing data management is not readily identified by process or manufacturing engineers as encompassing their data management needs, a better term may be Manufacturing Process Lifecycle Management (MPLM).

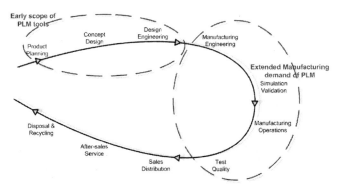

Fig. 1   Scope of PLM data management through product lifecycle [9].

**DECOMPOSITION OF AUTOMOTIVE MANUFACTURING MACHINES THROUGH A
MECHANISM TAXONOMY WITHIN A PRODUCT LIFECYCLE MANAGEMENT FRAMEWO**

The development of a production system is extremely complex and encompasses a wide variety of engineering activities ranging from machine design and control to operational management and plant services [5]. Consequently there are an equally diverse set of engineers, both internal and supplier based, to be integrated into the development process. The complexity of manufacturing tasks is a principal barrier that has limited the use of PLM tools in production environments. However, the emergence of Digital Manufacturing (DM) solutions delivering early stage benefits has resulted in increased interest in managing this data within a PLM environment. DM is defined as a set of tools that work with 3D data to support tool design, manufacturing process design, ergonomic design and other analyses types to optimise the production process [10,11]. The two best known providers of digital solution being Siemens with its suite of Teamcenter-(PLM) and Tecnomatix-(DM) and Dassault Systems with a corresponding set called Enovia/Smart-Team and Delmia respectively [13].

As the use of reconfigurable or flexible manufacturing systems is considered a key factor for the future success of manufacturing it is important that digital manufacturing tools are likewise reconfigurable. The use of a PLM tool to facilitate digital manufacturing and process development offers many benefits (1) both the real and digital realities work with the same data structures, such as a Bill of Process (BoP), (2) encourages collaboration between engineering departments at earlier development phases, (3) reuse of existing data and a tool to drive standardisation, (4) PLM is a mechanism for enabling the use of best practice information. PLM technology delivers high data consistency and transparency, which assists process and product quality [9].

4.0   Automotive OEM Case Study

The concept of reconfigurable machines can be extended to any level or domain of manufacturing system. The work conducted between Ford Motor Company engineers and the Loughborough University looked three distinct domains (1) the production and consumption of data from process, manufacturing and machine tool builder engineers, (2) the development of data structures for a PLM tool and its value in manufacturing and (3) the development of a mechanism taxonomy for the decomposition of manufacturing machines/facilities into reconfigurable elements.

4.1   Mapping Data Producers

Previous work had outlined the number of different software systems that are used as part of a new program and the movement of information between those platforms. In order to structure the many information flows into a PLM, the Loughborough team reviewed how data is created and communicated between departments as part of a program, and involved identification of the forms, standards, working documents that were used by engineers, external parties and other departments. Current data is managed through a wide range of different systems, with process engineers forming the links between different reference numbers, document types and storage locations. This current practice means that static reference information that is required when working on current live documents has to be identified, searched for, and retrieved to support engineering activity. A wide range of information types are currently associated with specific lines and machines. For example, specific tools and gauges are documented by means of CAD drawings that are stored alongside electrical drawings, hydraulics, and automation drawings associated with the same particular machine. The documents

DECOMPOSITION OF AUTOMOTIVE MANUFACTURING MACHINES THROUGH A
MECHANISM TAXONOMY WITHIN A PRODUCT LIFECYCLE MANAGEMENT FRAMEWO

used by a sample department were scrutinized to determine the particular information and relevant data that they contained. In analysing the documents in this way, a range of categories were identified that included strategy/guiding principle documents, working documents, (frequently used by the engineers to establish processes) specific data-sets and finalised production line associated drawings. The specific data that resided on these documents was frequently repeated, often in multiple locations. As part of the data collection activities efforts were made to establish the original source of these datasets, and which documents simply repeated the data for reference/convenience, cross referencing documents and data types against engineering departments.

4.2   Standardised Data Structures

The success of the move to distributed automotive production machinery and RMS relies on new manufacturing engineering business models that are able to couple physical and logical information at the machine level through many organisational boundaries both internally and with suppliers. A core element to this is the development of standardised data structures that decompose production lines into a BoP. Digitally managing a manufacturing facilities data from concept development to decommissioning, encompassing a large quantity of data from distributed departments, both technically and geographically, is highly complex. The scale of the automotive manufacturing data management task is in itself a significant barrier and consequently data is managed through loosely coupled databases and paper based systems that restrict rapid reconfiguration and often leads to data replication.

Developing data structures, such as that shown in Fig. 2 for the management of manufacturing lifecycle data has many potential direct and indirect cost savings. In the context of the work done in this project a common data structure for manufacturing is anticipated to achieve the following

- *Reusable process knowledge* – cloning of existing BoP structures for faster and more consistent manufacturing process planning, timely, accurate costing during the early stages (strategy/target setting phases) of the program

- *Provide closed-loop processes* – assuring that changes to BoP and other processes are effectively managed and implemented

- *Reusable mechanism(s)* – through classification of common manufacturing elements (i.e. tools, gauges, machines etc) and engineering best practice a reduction in engineering effort

- *Integrated digital manufacturing tools* – a digital repository and portal for digital manufacturing tools, leveraging more value from simulation and validation at earlier development phases

A global data management repository managed using standardised data management structures enables a more inclusive manufacturing engineering lifecycle. Engineers in different departments have increased access to monitor change, perceive impact of related engineering decisions and work collaboratively earlier in the development process. The structure shown in Fig. 2 decomposes manufacturing production lines in logical data layers where specific data resides ranging from CAD, documents, plans, safety or Programmable Control Logic (PLC).

**DECOMPOSITION OF AUTOMOTIVE MANUFACTURING MACHINES THROUGH A
MECHANISM TAXONOMY WITHIN A PRODUCT LIFECYCLE MANAGEMENT FRAMEWO**

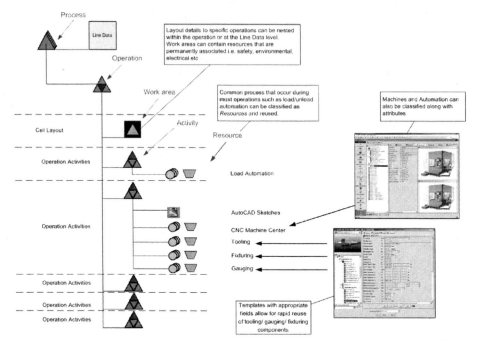

Fig. 2   Manufacturing PLM architecture for implementation into Teamcenter 2007.

The benefits of PLM are not just in the realm of information technology. PLM can be considered as part of the business model that a company uses to effectively support the full virtual/digital lifecycle of their products and accelerate business performance using a combination of process, organisation, methodology and technology [8].

3.3   Taxonomy for the Decomposition of Manufacturing and Assembly Lines

Reconfigurable manufacturing machines are designed to allow rapid adjustments not only in producing a variety of products but also in changing the system itself. Flexibility on this scale requires the classification of production machines into their lowest common denominator physically, logically or structurally both in the real world and in a digital environment. It is recognised that decomposing complete automotive production facilities into mechanisms has differing levels of granularity which related to the level of involvement in the manufacturing lifecycle as shown in Fig. 3. The finest granularity exists at the machine tool builder where machines may be decomposed into individual components; at the resource level decomposition is courser with mechanism being collections of components that provide a function.

DECOMPOSITION OF AUTOMOTIVE MANUFACTURING MACHINES THROUGH A
MECHANISM TAXONOMY WITHIN A PRODUCT LIFECYCLE MANAGEMENT FRAMEWO

966

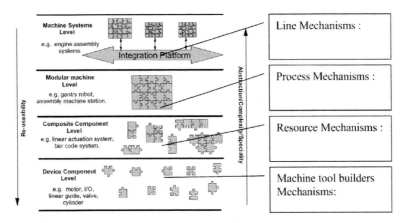

Fig. 3   Scope of PLM data management through product lifecycle [13].

The principal focus of the study looked at common machine mechanisms on the engine lines. To support the activities of engineering partners, largely ad hoc integration methods and mechanisms are currently employed [5]. A mechanism can be either physical (i.e. actuators, lifts, clamps), logical (i.e. RF data readers, position interrogation sensors) or structural (i.e. conveyance, fixturing). Mechanism decomposition can be viewed from three levels, firstly functionally: what is the physical operation to be performed by the mechanism? (i.e. translation, join, test etc), secondly process: what process steps does the mechanism perform to achieve the function? (i.e. grasp, rotate 180°, etc) and finally detail: considers mechanisms at a low level looking at the control logic, geometric, hydraulic, pneumatic, electrical requirements that combine to fulfil the mechanism function.

The scope for standardisation has also been considered, shown in Fig. 3 with the least mechanism commonality existing at present at the line level. The most detailed mechanism standardisation is at the machine tool builder OEM. This view is supported by Krause, they indicated the future direction is to utilise core modules/mechanisms where possible particularly on automatic and semi-auto stations. The greatest change can come at the process and Ford mechanism level in standardising station processes and the mechanisms that constitute a station.

5.0   Conclusion

A key factor in the success of automotive manufacturers is linked to their capacity to deliver greater product customisation through more flexible and reconfigurable manufacturing machines. Also to adapt and test existing facilities whilst they continue to make the current product. To quickly change to the new configuration and to launch with robustness and speed. Delivering increased flexibility while maintaining reliability, quality and volume will be aided by the growing folio of DM solutions available to manufacturing engineers to solve a wide range or problems from ergonomic analysis to real time machine simulation. The limitation has been that these tools offer point solutions that while being of high value only impact on specific technical challenges and

**DECOMPOSITION OF AUTOMOTIVE MANUFACTURING MACHINES THROUGH A
MECHANISM TAXONOMY WITHIN A PRODUCT LIFECYCLE MANAGEMENT FRAMEWO**

fail to offer global business benefits. There are major advances to be made in achieving integrated DM by utilising PLM tools, from the product design engineering world that facilitates cross commodity data management. This change in manufacturing engineering approach will require changes to business models and working practices, moving from manual process planning to computer based process planning. There is also a synergy between PLM and RMS, where resource libraries are a common feature of PLM tools which encourages engineers to build process plans from standard modules where possible. DM can help overcome many of the downstream issues that negatively impact manufacturing efficiencies [14]. However, some issues do arise that can be considered risks when making the investments required to take maximum advantage of DM. This is true, of course, with any major investment in technologies as they impact an organisation's processes and people's methods of working.

Acknowledgement

The authors wish to acknowledge the assistance and support of Ford Motor Company, CECA, HEIF and the IMRC.

References

[1] Ralston, D. and T, Munton, (1987) Computer integrated manufacturing. Computer-Aided Engineering Journal, August, pg 167-174.

[2] Bi, Z. M. and W. J. Zhang, (2001) Modularity Technology in Manufacturing: Taxonomy and Issues, Int J Adv Manuf Technol, Vol 18, pg381–390.

[3] Gusikhin, O, Rychtyckyj, N and Filev D, (2007) Intelligent systems in the automotive industry: applications and trends, Knowl Inf Syst, Vol 12:2 pg147-168.

[4] Harbers, W. O. (1966) Ford automation strategies and needs. In Automation Strategies Forum, Boston, Massachusetts, June (Automation Research Corporation).

[5] Harrison. R, A A West, R H Weston and R P Monfared, (2000) Distributed engineering of manufacturing machines, Proc Instn Mech Engrs Vol 215 Part B.

[6] Kusiak, A and Chun-CheHuang, (1996) Development of modular products, IEEE Transactions on Components Packaging, and Manufacturing Technology, Part A, 19(4), pg. 523–538.

[7] M. G. Meharabi, M.G, Ulsoy, A. G and Y. Koren, (2000), Reconfigurable manufacturing systems: Key to future manufacturing, Journal of Intelligent Manufacturing, Vol 11, pg. 403 – 419.

[8] CIMData, (2007), PLM-Automation Market Evolution, CIMdata White Paper, [Online]. Available: www.plm.automation.siemens.com/about_us/newsletter/images/jun2007/CIMdata_plmAutomationMarketEvolution.pdf, [2008, February 1]

[9] Abramovici, M and Sieg, O.C, (2002), Status and Development Trends of Product Lifecycle Management Systems, In: Proceedings of the IPPD 2002, Wroclaw.

[10] CIMData, (2006), Digital Manufacturing in PLM Environments, [Online]. Available: www.cimdata.com/publications/Delmia_White paper.pdf, [2008, February 1]

[11] Chrssolouris,G .D et al (2007) Digital Manufacturing: History, Perspectives and Outlook, Keynote Paper, Proceedings of the 4th International Conference on Digital Enterprise Technology (DET2001), Bath, UK,11 pp. 1-12.

[12] Forbes.com (2004), Digital manufacturing seen as high-growth PLM segment, [Online]. Available: http://www.forbes.com/technology/   feeds/infoimaging/2004/07/13/infoimagingcahners_2004_07_13_eng-cahners_eng-cahners_100223_37008762302 91254033.html?partner=yahoo&referrer, [2008, February 18]

[13] Moore, P.R (2003), Virtual engineering: an integrated approach to agile manufacturing machinery design and control, Mechatronics, Vol 13 Pg.1105 – 1121.

[14] Kuhn, W, (2006). Digital Factory – Simulation Enhancing the Product and Production Engineering Process, Proc Winter Simulation Conf, Florida USA

DECOMPOSITION OF AUTOMOTIVE MANUFACTURING MACHINES THROUGH A MECHANISM TAXONOMY WITHIN A PRODUCT LIFECYCLE MANAGEMENT FRAMEWO

The 6th International Conference on Manufacturing Research (ICMR08)
Brunel University, UK, 9-11th September 2008

A COMPARISON OF CONSULTANCY-ASSISTED AND IN-HOUSE NEW PRODUCT DEVELOPMENT STRATEGIES WITHIN A SMALL MEDICAL DEVICE COMPANY

Paul Chapman [1,2], Ian Corp [1], Huw Millward [2] and Julie Stephens [2]

1. Ultrawave Limited, Eastgate Business Park, Cardiff CF3 2EY. Tel: 0845 330 4236.

2. The National Centre for Product Design & Development Research (PDR), University of Wales Institute Cardiff (UWIC), Cardiff CF5 2YB. Tel: 029 2041 6725.

Abstract

A significant proportion of the UK medical device industry comprises of small and medium-sized enterprises (SMEs), and these companies typically specialise in high-technology, niche products. New product development (NPD) represents an important route for SMEs to harness their competitive advantage, and SMEs are in a prime position to identify new product opportunities due to their close working relationships with users, purchasers, suppliers and competitors. The culture within small, agile organisations with rapid decision-making pathways should be an asset for NPD, but SMEs frequently lack the staff with the experience necessary for high-risk NPD activities. SMEs in this scenario therefore face the choice of employing an external consultancy or expanding their in-house NPD knowledge and capabilities. The aim of this paper is to examine the advantages and disadvantages of these two NPD strategies, and provide a framework for SMEs to identify elements of best practice from each area. This paper employs a detailed case-study methodology to evaluate NPD outcomes within a company that has undertaken both types of strategy to improve their NPD effectiveness. Ultrawave are the UK's leading independent manufacturer of ultrasonic cleaning systems. They employed a local university-based product development consultancy (PDR) to assist in the redesign of one of their key medical products. The Hygea ultrasonic cleaner was launched at Medica04, and sales exceeded all initial targets. Ultrawave were keen to apply the lessons from this successful project to other products in development, and they established a Knowledge Transfer Partnership (KTP) with PDR in order to enhance their in-house NPD capabilities. The first major in-house development was the upgrade of the Q Series bench-top range, and this was launched at Medica07. Common elements across both the NPD strategies include concept design, rapid prototyping, and tooling design. The final manufacturing phase presented tooling issues for both projects, and their management and communication was critical to timely delivery of the production parts. The perceived advantages of the consultancy-assisted NPD project relate to the disciplined project management at design reviews and managing risk during transfer to manufacturing.

Keywords: NPD, SMEs, Consultancy, Knowledge Transfer

1.0   Introduction

There are approximately 11,000 medical technology companies within Europe, the largest share of these are based in the UK. The UK medical device industry therefore represents a significant sector due to its market size, well-developed infrastructure and exports levels (a positive balance of trade). Small and medium-sized enterprises (SMEs) make up more than 80% of this medical device industry [1]. In these high-technology sectors SMEs are at the forefront of innovation through their development of new products and novel processes. They are in a prime position to undertake new product development (NPD) activities due to their close working relationships with users, purchasers, suppliers and competitors. The nature of SMEs means that they have the flexibility to adapt technology and rapidly grasp emerging opportunities in order to maintain a competitive advantage over their competitors. Small agile companies, with horizontal structures and rapid decision-making pathways, should be an asset for the design and development of new products. However, SMEs frequently lack the stability, staff and resources necessary to handle the commercial and technical risks associated with NPD – this has been referred to as the paradox of the SME [2]. A notable study by Freel [3] shows that SMEs need to improve their internal design capabilities through staff development and/or engage external design consultants.

There are a vast number of publications in the area of product innovation and enhancing NPD activities. This work ranges from the early stage-gate process developed by Cooper [4] through to NPD best practices proposed by Kahn et al. [5]. This latter work allows NPD activities to be benchmarked across six areas: strategy, portfolio management, process, market research, people and metrics. In a more recent study [6], a design audit tool has been developed for SMEs, and a familiar finding was that small companies are wary of the expense of employing external design consultants, even though it is reported that external skills provide an opportunity to develop more radical product solutions. Clearly SMEs face the choice between consultancy-assisted NPD and expanding their in-house NPD capabilities, but there is little SME-based research that has been able to provide a direct comparison of these two strategies. The aim of this paper is to examine the advantages and disadvantages of these two NPD strategies, and provide a practical framework for SMEs to identify elements of best practice from each area.

A COMPARISON OF NPD STRATEGIES WITHIN A SMALL COMPANY

2.0   Case-Study Methodology

The National Centre for Product Design & Development Research (PDR) is based at the University of Wales Institute Cardiff (UWIC). PDR has a long-term commitment to collaborate with SMEs through a combination of commercial consultancy and research-based projects. PDR's commercial product development activities have provided realistic and timely design solutions across a broad spectrum of industry, but with particular expertise in the medical sector. PDR's applied consultancy work generates contacts with over 800 companies a year. In parallel to the consultancy projects, PDR's research knowledge has been harnessed to provide longer-term collaborations with industry in the form of Knowledge Transfer Partnerships (KTPs). KTP is a government-backed knowledge and technology transfer programme that has been successfully operated in the UK for approximately 30 years. PDR have completed over 25 KTPs, the majority of which have been with SMEs. PDR's consultancy work and wide range of KTP projects have generated a comprehensive portfolio of case-study material, and this provides the ideal opportunity to make a direct comparison of consultancy-assisted NPD and in-house NPD through two independent case studies based within a single company. The selection criteria for the company was as follows:

- A small company with between 10 and 50 employees, operating in the medical technology sector;
- Company engaged PDR to undertake product design consultancy work, and;
- Company established a two-year KTP with PDR in order to enhance their in-house NPD capabilities.

A number of companies met this selection criteria, but one company provided exemplar NPD projects, namely Ultrawave Ltd. Ultrawave are based in Cardiff, and are the UK's leading independent manufacturer of ultrasonic cleaning products and systems. Ultrawave have a staff of 35, and have approximately 50 core products, mainly serving the medical and precision cleaning industries. Their collaborative NPD projects are described in the next two sections.

3.0   Consultancy-Assisted NPD Project

In 2003 Ultrawave identified the growing need for process validation to be built into medical cleaning products. Satisfying this new requirement would provide the company with a clear advantage over their competitors. Ultrawave approached PDR to produce a new integral-validation cleaning product, with a brief to redesign an existing product to improve its manufacturability, reliability, aesthetics, ergonomics and functionality. This new product was named Hygea 1250, and the project had an aggressive works cost target and development timescale, which was dictated by a target launch at the world's major medical exhibition (Medica). Previously all new company design and development activities utilised stainless steel fabrication as the main production method, but Ultrawave appreciated that the new product might benefit from alternative manufacturing techniques. PDR had the appropriate knowledge of materials and manufacturing processes, especially as Design-for-Manufacture (DFM) and Design-for-Assembly (DFA) considerations were of prominent importance. Employing an external design consultancy eliminated the need to fully understand the design constraints required for new manufacturing processes, thereby minimising the project risk for the company.

PDR employ a stage-gate process for all new product development projects. This is a structured process that be can be adapted for each new development project. Benefits of using such a process include small stages with clear deliverables, and clear cost (or estimated cost) intentions. Client sign-off prior to proceeding to the

A COMPARISON OF NPD STRATEGIES WITHIN A SMALL COMPANY

next stage gives the client control of their project no matter what stage the project is at. The Hygea 1250 project consisted of four stages: (1) information and concept generation; (2) design development; (3) prototyping; and (4) manufacturing liaison. These stages were clearly presented to the client through a design proposal and project plan in the form of a Gantt chart. Ultrawave were happy with the intended approach, deliverables and cost, and raised the purchase order for stage one in February 2004, with an estimated completion date for the project in October 2004. The deliverables for stage one included a detailed product design specification (PDS) signed off by the company, basic visual construction of a number of concept solutions and a review meeting to present the strongest conceptual ideas for design development to the next stage. After initial discussions and the generation of a detailed product design specification (PDS), conceptual development began and this quickly identified a number of potential design directions. A total of three concept ideas were presented to Ultrawave: (a) a rotational moulded lid and front panel with a simple fabricated base; (b) a rotational moulded lid and base; and (c) a fabricated lid, base and tray holder with a vacuum formed baffle. To accompany these concepts a fourth idea was also generated as a blue sky opportunity. The alternate layouts, manufacturing technologies, assemblies and aesthetic approaches were presented, each based on a thorough understanding of the user, the market and commercial requirements of the project. Ultrawave selected their favoured elements of each of the concepts, and the project manager refined the design to capture and incorporate the changes, and project costings were reviewed in line with the outcome from stage one.

Proceeding to stage two (design development), the deliverables included a product design that fulfils all the criteria as defined by the design specification, a fully detailed CAD assembly of the unit, and a series of 3D models (IGES format) and drawings showing the final design in sufficient detail to allow prototype production and accurate tooling quotes. Ultrawave selected the design concept incorporating the rotationally moulded base and lid (containing the printer and user interface controls and electronics) and an injection moulded printer cover. PDR revisited the stage deliverables to incorporate the actual design concept into the plan. Deliverables changed slightly to include provision for five design review meetings at PDR and the creation of appropriate review documentation to allow accurate design reviews to be undertaken. The deliverables also included the graphics for a new interface membrane panel and liaison with the manufacturer. PDR on request of Ultrawave agreed to further investigate the detail design for the lifting mechanism in 3D CAD and generate the data for the production of an alpha prototype. The approach chosen utilised low-cost tooling technologies to minimise part count and assembly costs, and provided a new direction for the company in both aesthetics and manufacturing strategy.

Stage three (prototype production) utilised the CAD data to create a master prototype of the relevant design elements. All the models created were fully detailed to suit the relevant manufacturing process, with draft angles where applicable and accurate dimensions (within prototyping limitations). These prototypes were used to accurately assess fit and function, as well as to generate customer approval and confirm the overall quality of the design. A scale SLA of the base and lid were also produced to aid the rotational moulders and tool makers with regards to tool configuration and split lines. A blue foam model was used to assess the overall product aesthetic, the space envelope, and the new user interface. Metal work prototypes of the tank, lifting mechanism, front fascia panel, base plate and RF shielding were also produced.

Following prototype evaluation and design verification, stage four (manufacturing liaison) commenced. PDR assisted Ultrawave in the identification and subsequently liaison with an agreed list of third party manufacturers to get the product into production as quickly as possible to the appropriate standard. Where necessary, PDR visited potential suppliers to ensure their capabilities met the requirements of intended design. Manufacturing information including detailed 2D drawings, BOM's and material specifications. In addition, build and assembly instructions were generated, along with service and user manuals in collaboration with Ultrawave. Manufacturing liaison was an important part of this project in terms of ensuring design intent was maintained and managing timescales. PDR informed the company regularly in writing of the status of the work to ensure complete visibility and cost control at all times. The tooling was finalised, and this demanded close liaison and management to ensure the pre-production build program proceeded to schedule. The printer mechanism was designed and manufactured at PDR using low-cost injection mould tooling, offering an 80% saving over the originally planned bought-in module. Other mould tools were cut offshore for moulding by UK suppliers. The product was launched at Medica (November 2004) to a very positive response. Within two months of launch, the initial yearly sales projections had been exceeded three fold. This key product (shown in Fig. 1) helped to reposition the company as a modern, innovative and progressive enterprise, able to compete effectively with much larger competitors.

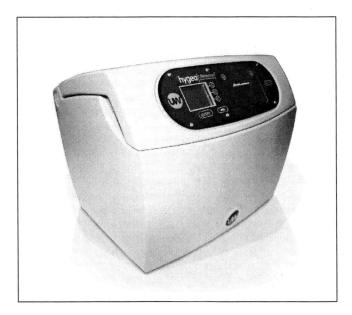

Fig. 1.   The final design of the new ultrasonic cleaner: Hygea 1250.

4.0   In-House NPD Project

This case study focuses on the use of an in-house design facility at Ultrawave for the design and development of a new range of products, namely the Q Series bench top cleaners. The project was formed in response to competition from Chinese low-cost cleaners that retail for less than half the price of an equivalent UK-manufactured product. However, the Chinese units have a limited product offering with one or two tank sizes, and minimal functionality – normally a set time limit or on/off button. A strategy was developed to keep Ultrawave competitive in the bench top market by developing a premium range of cleaners. The proposed new product line-up would feature a broad spectrum of tank sizes with an emphasis on quality and user-centric design. The range would feature an intuitive digital interface, state of the art cleaning activity and improved product aesthetics. The project demanded a swift development time, with a focus on modularity to ensure that the large product range could still be priced competitively.

At the end of 2006 Ultrawave established a KTP programme to introduce an in-house design facility, and the bench top development would be the first undertaking. Initially the upgrade focused on new electronics and software, and the addition of a new digital user interface. However when prototype units were reviewed at the beginning of 2007 it was clear that the improvements made to the electronics were undermined by a lack of overall product design. The Hygea 1250 project had already demonstrated the value of design thinking, so plans were made to rejuvenate the mechanical elements of the product and distinguish the product from the traditional 'metal box', and therefore position the new product range at the top end of the market.

During the early stages of the NPD project, communication between the sales and marketing department and the development team was enhanced through the presence of an in-house designer. A range of methods were employed to capitalise on the small size of the company, allowing for the user needs identified by the sales team to be rapidly converted into product features and solutions. Regular product development meetings were scheduled. These provided an opportunity for concepts to be communicated and risks to be managed. A key element in the new in-house design facility was the implementation of a SolidWorks 3D CAD system. The KTP equipment budget covered the initial hardware and software costs, and the premium bench top development provided an ideal opportunity to demonstrate its benefits. Initial sketches and brainstorming were narrowed down to three potential concepts. The key features and overall form of these ideas were then modelled and rendered in 3D CAD. This provided a clear demonstration of the potential of each solution. The renderings were then used to formulate rough costings, and the potential risks of each solution were assessed.

From the three concepts, a decision was made to develop an injection-moulded front panel. This was an entirely new undertaking for Ultrawave, and due to the number of different case variations the panel would need to be modular and customisable. Despite these complexities, clear benefits would come through the potential to embody the Ultrawave brand in product form. The mould would provide an ideal housing for the LCD user interface, and allow for fine details such as snap fit connections, the company logo and surface texturing. With the decision made on the manufacturing direction for the project, the original PDS was rewritten. A design brief was also introduced to complement the PDS; this captured the essence of the project in a few paragraphs to give clarity to the PDS and keep the primary objectives in focus.

There were to be a total of seven product variants in the range, based on different sizes of standard tank. The tanks range in size from three litres to 28 litres. In an ideal world a separate tool would have been commissioned for each tank size so that a front panel could be perfectly proportioned for each unit. The reality was that with estimated sales for each unit varying from between 50 to 300 a year, and with an estimated combined sales total for the range of between 1000 to 1500, a single re-configurable tool was the only feasible option. A front panel was designed that had two height configurations, and the seven products would be divided into two height groups. SolidWorks was used extensively at this stage to find the optimum position for the split in the tool so that the components could be accommodated in the smaller cases without the larger cases looking out of proportion. Changes could be made instantly, and Ultrawave were soon in a position to generate prototypes and get detailed quotations from tooling manufacturers.

Ultrawave are based next to their partner company Minerva Laboratories. Minerva specialise in bespoke hearing aids, and they have recently developed a rapid manufacturing element, comprising of 3D scanning

A COMPARISON OF NPD STRATEGIES WITHIN A SMALL COMPANY

equipment and a 3D printer (Objet 350) capable of producing precise, durable parts. Ultrawave took advantage of this opportunity to produce prototype front panels. The prototype panels were used to communicate with tooling manufacturers who were able to quickly evaluate the parts, suggest design improvements and put together costings and tooling development times. The prototype models were also used for marketing material and functional testing. The injection moulding project was discussed with a number of suppliers. Tooling and moulding lead times were now critical, and all of the moulders were concerned about achieving uniform material flow on the larger tooling configuration. There was potential to cause damage to the bottom section of the mould, and most of the suppliers elected to have a steel tool manufactured in China. Steel tooling would have increased development costs and Ultrawave had minimal in-house experience of injection moulding process. Therefore Ultrawave elected to use PDR for tooling fabrication and moulding liaison. This approach employed an aluminium tool with steel inserts, which reduced tooling costs (saving approximately £3000) but added a month's development time to the overall project.

To further enhance the visual and performance characteristics of the new bench top range, a custom lid was designed for each unit. A modular tool was not an option for this feature, therefore the challenge was to find an appropriate manufacturing process offering low-cost tooling and minimal part costs for the relatively low quantities required. With this in mind, a vacuum-formed lid was designed. Surface texture was an important consideration in order to achieve continuity between the relatively complex injection-moulded front panel and the vacuum-formed lid. The final design for the Q Series range is shown in Fig. 2. The new bench top range was successfully exhibited at Medica (November 2007), and the full product launch followed in December 2007.

Fig. 2.   The new Q Series range of premium bench top ultrasonic cleaners.

5.0   Conclusions

A COMPARISON OF NPD STRATEGIES WITHIN A SMALL COMPANY

The advantages and disadvantages of the two NPD strategies are best illustrated if we employ some of the elements of NPD best practice from Kahn et al. [5]. In terms of market research, Ultrawave has extensive knowledge of the ultrasonic-cleaning market, which in turn allowed them to identify new emerging customer needs. The up-front homework undertaken for the Hygea project with PDR was essential to its long-term success; this proactive data gathering was a clear advantage for the company, and could not have been accomplished by a design consultancy operating in isolation. In terms of people, the company have the core knowledge, and links with users and customers, whereas the typical design consultancy has the skills and experience of product design, development risks, and the time and costs associated with manufacturing. The advantages of consultancy-assisted NPD become more evident when there is a strong product definition and the product needs to be moved rapidly from concept stage through to manufacture. Furthermore, in order for consultancy-assisted NPD to succeed there must be a strong relationship between the consultant's project manager and the company point-of-contact. The one element that provides a clear contrast between the two NPD strategies is process. The consultancy-assisted project had a clear stage-gate process, with additional design reviews, such that inevitable design changes were accommodated and managed in a structured way. The result was that the company were happy to invest in managing the technical risks, and the project was delivered on time. The in-house project lacked the discipline of a stage-gate process; for consultancy projects someone has to sign a cheque before progressing to the next phase. The result was that it was possible to make late changes to the in-house NPD project, which increased both hidden costs and lead times. Managing change and uncertainty was handled in different ways across the two projects. The Hygea project had formal communication channels and key decisions were documented. The Q Series project may have had too many lines of communication, which indicates that even SMEs can have complex operating and reporting structures. The final element worth considering is portfolio management – the two projects indicate that a balance between consultancy-based and in-house NPD projects may be needed. The Hygea project produced a radical design solution because the design consultancy were given free reign to explore a number of concepts. The Q Series project was a development of an existing product, and therefore provided a lower risk for in-house product development but still provided key challenges in terms of modularity and re-configurable tooling.

References

[1] Eucomed (2007) 'Key facts and figures on the European medical technology industry'.
[2] Friedman, K. (2004) 'Design management for small and medium-sized enterprises', *Proceedings of the 2nd IWDS Conference*, Cardiff, UK.
[3] Freel, M. S. (2000) 'Barriers to innovation in small manufacturing firms', *International Small Business Journal*, Vol. 18, No. 2.
[4] Cooper, R. G. (1998) 'Product Leadership: Creating and Lauching Superior New Products', Perseus Books, USA.
[5] Kahn, K. B., Barczak, G. and Moss, R. (2006) 'Establishing an NPD best practices framework', *Journal of Product Innovation Management*, Vol. 23.
[6] Moultrie, J., Clarkson, P. J. and Probert, D. (2007) 'Development of a design audit tool for SMEs', *Journal of Product Innovation Management*, Vol. 24.

A COMPARISON OF NPD STRATEGIES WITHIN A SMALL COMPANY

The 6th International Conference on Manufacturing Research (ICMR08)
Brunel University, UK, 9-11th September 2008

A KNOWLEDGE-BASED MANUFACTURING PROCESS PLANNING SYSTEM FOR AUTOMOTIVE MOULD MANUFACTURING

K.L. Choy, Y.K. Leung*, C.K. Kwong, T.C. Poon

Department of Industrial and Systems Engineering, The Hong Kong Polytechnic University, Hong Kong   *Corresponding Author

Abstract

Nowadays, it is common for enterprises to work with outside strategic partners in order to minimize operation costs as well as tighten the product life cycle in a competitive market. To fulfill dynamic customer requirements, updated and reliable production information is necessary for manufacturers to formulate a list of process plan. However, formulating a plan is a difficult task, particularly in the environment of Made-to-Order (MTO) production, such as automotive mould manufacturing, in which the production plan of each project or product are different. In addition, production information are always scattered in different partners, making it difficult to obtain essential information for the production of moulds on time. However, this production information among different fields of expertise, which exists as a form of production knowledge, is essential to formulate a MTO type production plan. In this paper, a knowledge-based manufacturing process planning system (KMPS) is proposed to support mould manufacturers for production planning, using technologies of case-based reasoning (CBR) and rule-based reasoning (RBR). By incorporating with radio frequency identification (RFID) and web-based technology, the KMPS is capable to enable manufacturers and its partners to share production information in real-time. In fact, this system not only helps manufacturers formulate fast and reliable production plan, but also creates the collaborative information and knowledge sharing among production partners. The prototype of KMPS is applied in an automotive mould manufacturing company to validate the feasibility in real world practice. As a result, the performance results of production covering planning, manufacturing and the delivery lead time are significantly improved after launching the proposed system.

Keywords: information sharing, make-to-order production, case-based reasoning, rule-based reasoning, radio frequency identification

1.0   Introduction

There are more than 10 thousands of factories in Pearl River Delta. Due to the trend of globalization and shortening product life cycle, manufacturers cooperate with different vendors which specialized in specific working process. A good information sharing strategy is important for manufacturers to maintain a smooth manufacturing supply chain and provide decision-making. The collaboration is exceptionally important for made-to-order production since every single product is different, sufficient information is needed before making decision in manufacturing planning. Mould manufacturing which focusing on automotive is one of the manufacturing industries that mainly operated in made-to-order manners.

The automotive mould manufacturing is an important support process during product development, it serves as an important link between the product designer and manufacturer [7]. The manufacturing process is complicated which include various processes from price quotation, planning, designing and planning, etc as shown in fig. 1. The most important process is the planning which control the production schedule and resources for the manufacturing. During the planning process of automotive mould manufacturing, it is essential for the planners to gathers data from customers, manufacturing shop floor, suppliers and sub-contractors in order to plan for the manufacturing process which can be ran with a smooth manufacturing supply chain. In addition, re-designing of the product due to the changes in customer requirements, re-work of the mould manufacturing process and re-planning of production processes are common in the mould manufacturing [14]. Meanwhile, the automotive mould manufactures also need to react to problem and construct an emergency plan immediately after it's first happened. With regards to the situations and problem, they also face challenges in adopting international standards TS16949 for automotive products to fulfil their customers' needs which make the planning process become more important. However, data for planning is not always readily available when needed. For example, it is not always possible to obtain the production status of a product which is manufacturing at a remote site, or it is difficult to recognize the problems occurred in the production.

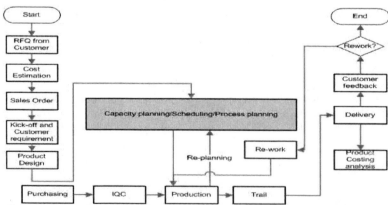

Fig. 1.   The business process for mould manufacturing

In the current process of manufacturing planning, planners gather information from different parties to facilitate their works. For example, sub-contractors would provide products production status of their shop floor while customers would provide product designs of the products. The entire information is necessary for the planners to plan for manufacturing and decision making when there are problems occurred. Meanwhile, different parties would also need to acquire information from the planners for their operation. Planners become a bottle neck in gathering and processing data with a short lead- time. Therefore, a system that helps in gathering data from various parties and enabling decision making for automotive mould manufacturing is said to be valuable. With regard to this, a knowledge-based manufacturing process planning system (KMPS) is proposed to help the automotive mould industry to share information and make decision efficiently and effectively. In this system, Case-Based Reasoning (CBR) is used to provide decision support for manufacturing planning and problem shooting. In order to obtain sufficient information for decision support, an information sharing system and RFID are used to gather production and real-time data.

2.0   Literature Review

2.1   Automotive Mould Manufacturing and Collaborative System

Automotive mould manufacturing process is complicated. The entire process includes costing, prototyping and manufacturing which involve human experience of design knowledge and manufacturing know-how [15]. It is operated in a made-to-order manner and manufactures are necessary to deliver their product in a short period of time due to competition [9]. Mould is very important to the automotive industry. More than thousands of pressed moulds and two hundred automobile fitting moulds are required for producing a finish product in which 80% of moulds will have to replace if the vehicle model is changed. Since automotive mould manufacturers would like to streamline and optimize their process [1], their subcontract some manufacturing process to their partners. Meanwhile, re-design of the product owing to customer requirement changing, re-work of the failure production process and re-plan of production processes are common in the mould industry [14]. Therefore, planning and decision making for each mould product in a short period of time is important for the automotive mould manufacturing industry. However, as there are too much data needed to be processed in a short-lead time, the planner of mould manufacturing cannot manipulate all the related information easily. A decision support system which makes use of Case-based Reasoning is said to be useful in reducing the time in decision making.

2.2   Case-based Reasoning

Case-based reasoning (CBR) is one of the mature and established artificial intelligence [3]. CBR is based on the psychological theory of human reasoning. It simulates the human decision process that comparing the past experience with the new problem facing. The rational of CBR is that new problems are often similar to previously encountered problems and therefore, the solution in the past can be used for future problem solving. In general, CBR can be divided into two modules, a case library which store knowledge of cases and a problem solver which retrieve similar cases and adapts them [6]. CBR is widely used to solve problems which are complex and under unstructured scenarios. It is used in different industry, such as helpdesk [3], Scheduling [11], Manufacturing [6], and planning [13]. It is no doubt that CBR can be used as a decision support with referring to past cases. However, Information is not always readily available for the CBR engine to process. Therefore, some technologies needed to be adopted to collect information for the decision support.

2.3 Technology Used to Obtain Data

In order to obtain information for the decision support system to improve the quality of decisions, two technologies are used to acquire information. They are Radio Frequency identification (RFID) and Web-based information sharing system.

2.3.1 Radio-frequency Identification

Radio Frequency Identification technology uses radio-frequency waves to transfer data between a reader and a movable item to identify, categorize and track different objects. The RFID technology can work well in some challenging conditions that other item tracking technology, such as bar code, work poorly [5]. Due to its fast, reliable nature and does not require physical line of sight communication, it has been widely use in manufacturing and in item tracking. It is used as individual products tracking [12], resource tracking [4] and product status tracking [10]. It is found that RFID is a suitable tool to collect automotive mould information such as production status, production time, location, in the manufacturing shop floor.

2.3.2 Web-based Information Sharing System

As manufacturers have to cope with a numbers of customers' projects at the same time, it is difficult to plan for those projects at once in a short lead-time. Data cannot be gathered efficiently by solely contacting customers and partners one by one. Therefore, a numbers of information sharing system are setup to fulfill the design and planning purpose in manufacturing ([2], [8], [7] and [14]).

3.0 System Architecture

In order to collect manufacturing data and provide decision support efficiently, the proposed knowledge-based manufacturing process planning system (KMPS) is developed. The architecture of KMPS is shown in figure 2. The system can be divided into three parts. The collection of production data module, the decision support module and the system output module. The functions and the details of each module are described below.

3.1 Collection of Production Data Module

This module is used to collect data from various parties which facilitating the quality of decision making in automotive mould manufacturing. The require data can be divided into 3 types: real-time manufacturing data, mould information and manufacturing resource. In the proposed system, there are four types of methods in collecting data, including design software, ERP, collaborative system and RFID. Mould information is mainly obtained from the design software. The original design file is translated into data that can be stored in the database. The mould design, mould structure and mould type can be obtained by this method. Manufacturing resources information is mainly stored in the database of Enterprise Resource Planning (ERP) System. The information includes machine availability, workers availability, due date of the mould product, customer information, supplier information. These are the status information that will not change frequently with time.

An information sharing system which link different parties together is used to collect data from remote site or sub-contractors. The information sharing system is a web based system that enables the ease of access from different parties. Remote site or sub-contractors will provide the shop floor information and production status of different automotive mould by the information sharing system. Meanwhile, customer would also update the product design to the automotive mould manufacturing through the system. Therefore, the collaborative system is used to facilitate information from different parties which enable a better quality of decision making.

RFID readers are strategically location in the shop floor to track the production status of different mould production which is undergoing the production process. The RFID readers are set in the automotive mould manufacturing shop floor, manufacturing shop floor and entrance of remote site and sub-contractors with close relationship. RFID tags are embedded with the mould product which enabling the tracking of their location and status. The real-time data provided by RFID enable the instant alert of problems occurred in the shop floor. For example, the RFID system can provide the production time of mould and alert to the planners if some production processes are delayed. In order to ensure the accuracy of RFID communication, some tests are taken to test for the characteristics and performance of different RFID standard. RFID equipment are set base on the tests.

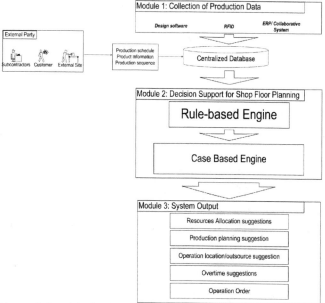

Fig. 2   The architecture for knowledge-based manufacturing process planning system (KMPS)

3.2   Centralized Database

The centralized database use MySQL platfom. MySQL is a free of charge database environment and support query, import and export function. This system is fully adaptable in the prototyping of system and system with relatively small amount of data.

Data collected from various means are synchronized and stored in the centralized database. The data is arranged in various tables according to its nature: (i) Master Data such as Customer Information, Machine Information/Capacity, Staff information/Capacity, etc., (ii) Resources Utilization machine, workers availability and (iii) real-time data such as WIP mould waiting time, production time and Location. It allows efficient data management and data abstraction towards the database.

3.3   Decision Support for Shop Floor Planning

Data from the centralized database are abstracted for the decision support purpose. Some rules are set in the rule-based engine. The rule will sort the data and find out any problems that occurred in the production. An alert is then sent to the user about the problems. Afterward, to CBR is used for decision making in the proposed system. The detailed mechanisms for making decisions by using CBR are as below.

3.3.1   Case Representation

The objective of the system is to help decision making in planning and in manufacturing for the automotive mould industry. Each of the decision is made base on each mould product. Therefore, each of the cases in the CBR is representing a pass case of mould product during the manufacturing process. Each of the case contains a case name which representing the case, attributes which are the parameter set of the case, problem and solution of a case.

3.3.2   Case Categorizing and Indexing

The cases in the CBR are grouped into several clusters by means of their attributes. Since the behavior and handling method of different types of mould are different, it is possible to group cases by their nature.

Step 1 Cases Grouping and indexing
Cases are divided into several groups with the method of *similarity* and *explanation-based* generalization. This method is to group cases into several groups according to its nature which representing different problems. Since problems in automotive mould production can be categorized into several reasons and one case may belong to several groups, this eliminates the problem of missing cases in which the case is not categorized into the right group. The categories of problems are defined by the company according to their needs. For example, delay in time, insufficient in resources, production failure, etc, are the group that cases may be divided. Each of the attributes is defined by the actual value of itself or pre-defined value of different features if the attributes are not in numerical terms.

Step 2 Case Retrieval
When a new problem is entered to the CBR engine, cases with the same problem group will be retrieved. Only the cases that contain the same problem domain will be retrieved for comparison. After the relative cases are

retrieved, Nearest Neighbor is used retrieve the most similar case to the current problem. In this method, weighting are given to every attribute with reference to its importance for decision making. The weighting is pre-determine by the key-user and working staff of the company. The algorithm for calculating nearest neighbor is list as follows:

$$\frac{\sum_{i=1}^{n} Wi sim(fi^I, fi^R)}{\sum_{i=1}^{n} Wi} \qquad (1)$$

Where: W is the importance weighting of a feature i,
sim is the similarity function,
fi is the value for feature i
fr is the feature of retrieved cases

The cases which score high in the retrieval process will be selected for the current case reference. Since the case is categorized and only the case that is relevant to the current case is being calculated by the nearest neighbor method, the time to the CBR process is reduced.

Step 3 Case Reuse and Retain

After the retrieval process, the most highest score cases with be retrieved. The solution of the past case is reused and taken as a reference solution for the current case. A revision of solution is necessary if it is not suitable to the current situation. The entire system provides the real time and external information that cannot be obtained in the current planning process. Meanwhile, the CBR mechanism suggests a case retrieval method that enables shorter retrieval time. A case study will be describes in the following section to illustrate the adaptation of the system by an automotive mould manufacturer.

4.0   Case Study and Validation

In order to validate the concept and the efficiency of the system for providing decision support for mould manufacturing industry, the system is trail run in JCM, an automotive mould manufacturing company located in Hong Kong. The company provides one-stop services include design, production and testing the mould products for their customers. The company has remote production area located in Hong Kong and Pearl River Delta, Mainland China, responsible for different production processes in the manufacturing of various mould components. Meanwhile, the company has a numbers of subcontractors which are responsible for various processes. The planners of the company are responsible for organizing customer projects and scheduling the related production process. These planners need to deal with various subcontractors so that the schedule of the entire production can be run smoothly without any long idling time. Meanwhile, the planners also need to communicate with customers closely so as to obtain customer requirements and update any changes in design immediately after it has been changed. Other internal parties are also required to work together, by means of using the same kind of information to ensure that the project will complete on time. Since the information are scattered in various production sites and there are too much information that planners need to consider, it is difficult for planner to plan and make decision within a short period of time. Hence, KMPS is adopted to help the company make better decisions in a more efficient way. The system is set in the company according to the basic framework of the proposed system. A validation process is also proposed to validate the performance of the system. In the validation process, the result from the CBR engine and the decision generated by the current process are compared under the same operating condition, aiming to determine if the proposed method can generate better result than the current process. Meanwhile, the total time in the decision-making process is used as an efficiency indicator. Another indicator is the percentage of modifying suggested solution to adapt the current situation. This percentage indicates the maturity of the system and will decrease when more case is imported to the case database.

5.0   Results and Discussion

The RCPS help to the automotive mould manufacturing company in facilitating their information flow between parties. The improvement in information flow enhance the decision making process in the mould manufacturing. Meanwhile, a CBR engine is proposed in the system to improve the quality and speed of decision making. Various indicators are used to evaluate the effectiveness of the system which implemented in the testing company and listed in table 1:

Table 1 Indicators for evaluating the effectiveness of KMPS

	Before using KMPS	After using KMPS
Time in decision making	30 mins	5 mins
Time in gathering information for decision making	1 day	5 mins(system process time)
Percentage of modifying solution	-----	81%
Result comparison for using traditional practice and KMPS	74%	
Acceptability of the decision making	80%	81%

Referring to the Table 1, it is found that the time to gather information and make decision is significantly reduced. It shows that the information sharing platform, when combined with the CBR engine, will work together to enhance the quality and efficiency in making a decision. Meanwhile, the result acceptability of using KMPS and traditional practice are similar. However, the acceptability will be improved when the case database becomes bigger after more cases are added.

6.0   Conclusion

Planning and making decision in automotive mould manufacturing is a complicated process. The planner needs to gather different information from different parties in a short period of time so that decision can be made efficiently. Nevertheless, information are scattered in various location in different parties which hinder the obtaining information process in a short lead time. The proposed system provides a decision support system which is supported by a real-time information sharing module is aiming to enhance the decision making process in the automotive mould manufacturing.

The system consists of 3 main modules. The data collection module obtains information from RFID technology, ERP database and design software. Meanwhile, external data is collected to the centralized database through the information sharing system. The system is implemented in JCM to test for its ability in

A KNOWLEDGE-BASED MANUFACTURING PROCESS PLANNING SYSTEM FOR AUTOMOTIVE MOULD MANUFACTURING

decision making. After implementing the system, the time to making decision is shortened. Meanwhile, the qualities of decisions are maintained. Furthermore, a better relationship is maintained between the automotive mould manufacturing with customers and partners.

References

[1] Chan, S.F., Law, C.K., Wong, T.T. (2003), Re-engineering the roto-casting mould making process, Journal of Materials Processing Technology, Vol.139 pp. 527-534.

[2] Chen, Y.J, Chen, Y.M., Chu, H.C (2007), Enabling collaborative product design through distributed engineering knowledge management, Computers in Industry, doi:10.1016 or j.compind.2007.10.001.

[3] Diaz-Agudo, B., Gonzalez-Calero, P., Recio-Garcia, J.A., Sanchez-Ruiz-Granados, A.A. (2007), Building CBR systems with JCOLIBRI, Science of Computer Programming, dio:10.1016/j.scico.2007.02.004.

[4] Huang, G.Q., Zhang, Y.F., Jiang, P.Y. (2007), RFID-based wireless manufacturing for walking-worker assembly islands with fixed-position layouts, Robotics and Computer-Integrated Manufacturing, Vol.23 pp.469-477.

[5] Heinrich, C. (2005), RFID and beyond: growing your business through real world awareness, Wiley Publications, pp.5.

[6] Kim, K.J., Ahn, H., Han, I. (2007), A case-based reasoning system with the two-dimensional reduction technique for customer classification, Expert Systems with Application, Vol.32 pp.1011-1019.

[7] Li, M., Wang, J., Wong, Y.S., Lee, K.S. (2005), A collaborative application portal for the mould industry. International Journal of Production Economics, Vol.96 pp.233-247.

[8] McAdam (2007), Collaborative knowledge sharing in Composite New Product Development: An aerospace study, Technovation, doi:10.1016 or j.technovation.2007.07.003.

[9] Ni, Q, Lu, W.F., Yarlagadda, P.K.D.V., Ming, X., Business information modeling for process integration in mold making industry. Robotics and Computer-Integrated Manufacturing, Vol.25 pp.195-207, 2007

[10] Parlikad, A.K., McFarlane, D (2007), RFID-based product information in end-of-life decision making, Control Engineering Practice, Vol.15 pp.1348-1363.

[11] Priore, P., Fuente, D.D.L., Puente, J., Parreno, J. (2006), A comparison of machine-learning algorithms for dynamic scheduling of flexible manufacturing systems, Engineering Application of Artificial Intelligence, Vol.19 pp.247-255.

[12] Qiu, R.G. (2007), RFID-enabled automation in support of factory integration, Robotics and Computer-Integrated Manufacturing, Vol.23 pp.667-683.

[13] Raphael, B., Domer, B., Saitta, S., Smith, I.F.C. (2007), Incremental development of CBR strategies for computing project cost probabilities, Advanced Engineering Informatics, Vol.21 pp.311-321.

[14] Silva, C., Roque, L., Almeida, A. (2006), MAPP—A Web-based decision support system for the mould industry, Decision Support System, Vol. 42 pp.999-1014

[15] Trappey, A.J.C, Lu, T.H., Fu, L.D (2007), Development of an intelligent agent system for collaborative mould production with RFID technology, Robotics and Computer-Integrated Manufacturing, doi:10.1016/j.rcim.2007.06.002

A KNOWLEDGE-BASED MANUFACTURING PROCESS PLANNING SYSTEM FOR AUTOMOTIVE MOULD MANUFACTURING